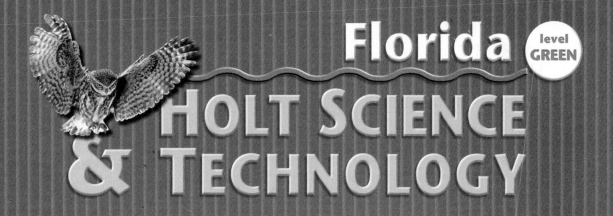

Florida

level GREEN

HOLT SCIENCE & TECHNOLOGY

HOLT, RINEHART AND WINSTON

A Harcourt Education Company

Orlando • **Austin** • New York • San Diego • Toronto • London

Acknowledgments

Contributing Authors

Mario Affatigato, Ph.D.
Professor of Physics
Coe College
Cedar Rapids, Iowa

Katy Z. Allen
Science Writer
Wayland, Massachusetts

Linda Ruth Berg, Ph.D.
*Adjunct Professor of
    Natural Sciences*
St. Petersburg College
St. Petersburg, Florida

Kathleen Meehan Berry
Science Chair
Canon-McMillan School
    District
Canonsburg, Pennsylvania

Steve Feller, Ph.D.
*B.D. Sillman Professor
    of Physics*
Coe College
Cedar Rapids, Iowa

Robert H. Fronk, Ph.D.
*Chair of Science and
    Mathematics Education*
Florida Institute of
    Technology
West Melbourne, Florida

Teresa Greely
*Biological Oceanographer
Director of Education and
    Outreach Programs*
College of Marine Science
University of South Florida
St. Petersburg, Florida

Kathleen Kaska
*Life and Earth Science
    Teacher*
Oak Harbor Middle School
Oak Harbor, Washington

Charles H. Keith, Ph.D.
*Associate Professor of
    Cellular Biology*
University of Georgia
Athens, Georgia

William G. Lamb, Ph.D.
*Winningstad Chair in the
    Physical Sciences*
Oregon Episcopal School
Portland, Oregon

Peter E. Malin, Ph.D.
Professor of Geology
Division of Earth and
    Ocean Sciences
Duke University
Durham, North Carolina

Karen J. Meech, Ph.D.
Associate Astronomer
Institute for Astronomy
University of Hawaii
Honolulu, Hawaii

Terrie Nolinske, Ph.D.
Vice President of Education
Museum of Science and
    Industry
Tampa, Florida

Sten Odenwald, Ph.D.
Astronomer
NASA Goddard Space Flight
    Center
Greenbelt, Maryland

Anthony Pelaez
*Coordinator of Youth and
    Family Programs*
Museum of Science and
    Industry
Tampa, Florida

Robert J. Sager, Ph.D.
*Chair and Professor of
    Earth Sciences*
Pierce College
Lakewood, Washington

Lee Summerlin, Ph.D.
Professor of Chemistry
University of Alabama
Birmingham, Alabama

Florida Teacher Consultants

Susan Biehler
Science Teacher
Kernan Middle School
Jacksonville, Florida

Joe Dexter
*Science Teacher
2004 District Teacher
    of the Year*
Florida State University
    School
Tallahassee, Florida

Trisha Elliot
Science Teacher
Chain of Lakes Middle
    School
Orlando, Florida

Russ Harris
Science Teacher
Addie R. Lewis Middle
    School
Valparaiso, Florida

Victor Hatfield
*Science Teacher and
Department Chair*
Union Park Middle School
Orlando, Florida

Denise Hulette
Science Teacher
Conway Middle School
Orlando, Florida

Janet Keskinen
Science Teacher
Green Cove Springs Middle
    School
Green Cove Springs, Florida

M. R. Penny Kisiah
*Science Teacher and
Department Chair*
Fairview Middle School
Tallahassee, Florida

Rebecca Larsen
Science Teacher
Fernandina Beach Middle
    School
Fernandina Beach, Florida

Anne Malloch
Science Teacher
Morgan Fitzgerald Middle
    School
Largo, Florida

Lynne McDaniel
Science Teacher
Stewart Middle Magnet
    School
Tampa, Florida

Magdalena F. Molledo
Science Department Chair
DeLaura Middle School
Satellite Beach, Florida

Acknowledgments
continued on page 765

ISBN 0-03-036376-4

2 3 4 5 6 7 048 09 08 07 06

Contents in Brief

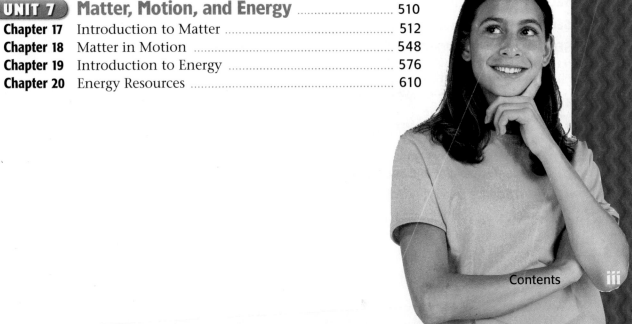

Contents

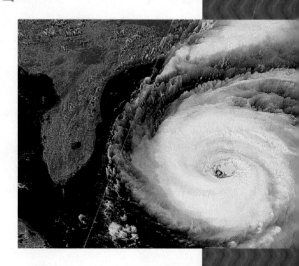

Chapter Labs

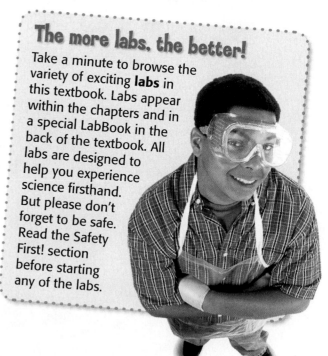

The more labs, the better!

Take a minute to browse the variety of exciting **labs** in this textbook. Labs appear within the chapters and in a special LabBook in the back of the textbook. All labs are designed to help you experience science firsthand. But please don't forget to be safe. Read the Safety First! section before starting any of the labs.

LabBook Labs

Not all laboratory investigations have to be long and involved. The **Quick Labs** found throughout the chapters of this textbook require only a small amount of time and limited equipment. But just because they are quick, don't skimp on safety.

Quick Labs

Pre-Reading Activities

FOLDNOTES

Graphic Organizer

Start your engines with an activity!

Get motivated to learn by doing the two activities at the beginning of each chapter. The **Pre-Reading Activity** helps you organize information as you read the chapter. The **Start-Up Activity** helps you gain scientific understanding of the topic through hands-on experience.

Start-Up Activities

Benchmark Activities

Make sure you really get it!

Mastering the benchmarks of the Florida Sunshine State Standards takes practice! The **Benchmark Activity** found in each chapter will help you understand the content of a particular benchmark through hands-on experience.

Internet Activities

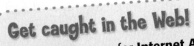

Get caught in the Web!

Go to **go.hrw.com** for **Internet Activities** related to each chapter. To find the Internet Activity for a particular chapter, just type in the keyword listed above.

School to Home

Science brings you closer together!

Bring science into your home by doing **School-to-Home Activities** with a family member or another adult in your household.

Math Practice

Science and math go hand in hand.

The **Math Focus** and **Math Practice** items show you many ways that math applies directly to science and vice versa.

Math Focus

Connection to...

One subject leads to another.

You may not realize it at first, but different subjects are related to each other in many ways. Each **Connection** explores a topic from the viewpoint of another discipline. In this way, all of the subjects you learn about in school merge to improve your understanding of the world around you.

Science In Action

Science moves beyond the classroom!

Read **Science in Action** articles to learn more about science in the real world. These articles will give you an idea of how interesting, strange, helpful, and action-packed science is. At the end of each chapter, you will find three short articles. And if your thirst is still not quenched, go to **go.hrw.com** for in-depth coverage.

How to Use Your Textbook

Your Roadmap for Success with Holt Science and Technology

Get Organized

Do the **Pre-Reading Activity** at the beginning of each chapter to create a **FoldNote** or a **Graphic Organizer,** which are helpful note-taking and study aids.

Read for Meaning

Start your reading with a warm-up. The **Reading Warm-Up** at the beginning of every section provides you with the section's **Objectives.** The Objectives tell you what you'll need to learn. The red benchmark codes indicate which Objectives meet the Florida Sunshine State Standards for science.

The Reading Warm-Up also lists **Terms to Learn** for each section. The blue icons indicate which terms will appear on the FCAT. Each term is highlighted in the text and is defined at point of use and in the margin.

A **Reading Strategy** provides tips to help you organize and remember the information covered in the section.

STUDY TIP Each **Section Review** includes a **Summary.** You can use this summary to preview or review a section.

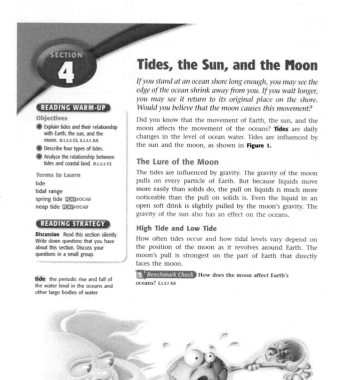

SECTION 4

Tides, the Sun, and the Moon

If you stand at an ocean shore long enough, you may see the edge of the ocean shrink away from you. If you wait longer, you may see it return to its original place on the shore. Would you believe that the moon causes this movement?

Did you know that the movement of Earth, the sun, and the moon affects the movement of the oceans? **Tides** are daily changes in the level of ocean water. Tides are influenced by the sun and the moon, as shown in **Figure 1.**

READING WARM-UP

Objectives
- Explain tides and their relationship with Earth, the sun, and the moon. D.1.3.3 CS, E.1.3.1 AA
- Describe four types of tides.
- Analyze the relationship between tides and coastal land. D.1.3.3 CS

Terms to Learn
tide
tidal range
spring tide *FCAT VOCAB*
neap tide *FCAT VOCAB*

READING STRATEGY

Discussion Read this section silently. Write down questions that you have about this section. Discuss your questions in a small group.

tide the periodic rise and fall of the water level in the oceans and other large bodies of water

The Lure of the Moon

The tides are influenced by gravity. The gravity of the moon pulls on every particle of Earth. But because liquids move more easily than solids do, the pull on liquids is much more noticeable than the pull on solids is. Even the liquid in an open soft drink is slightly pulled by the moon's gravity. The gravity of the sun also has an effect on the oceans.

High Tide and Low Tide

How often tides occur and how tidal levels vary depend on the position of the moon as it revolves around Earth. The moon's pull is strongest on the part of Earth that directly faces the moon.

Benchmark Check How does the moon affect Earth's oceans? E.1.3.1 AA

Figure 1 *Although gravitational forces from both the sun and moon continuously pull on Earth, the moon's gravity is the force that most affects Earth's tides.*

364 Chapter 11 Earth, Sun, and Moon

↗ Be Resourceful—Use the Web

SciLinks boxes in your textbook take you to resources that you can use for science projects, reports, and research papers. Go to **scilinks.org** and type in the **SciLinks code** to find information on a topic.

Visit go.hrw.com
Check out the **Current Science®** magazine articles and other materials that go with your textbook at **go.hrw.com.** Click on the textbook icon and the table of contents to see all of the resources for each chapter.

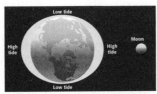

Figure 2 *High tide occurs on the part of Earth that is closest to the moon. At the same time, high tide also occurs on the opposite side of Earth.*

Battle of the Bulge

When a part of the ocean faces the moon, the water there bulges toward the moon. At the same time, water on the opposite side of Earth bulges because of Earth's rotation and the motion of the moon around Earth. These bulges are called *high tides*. **Figure 2** shows how the moon's position causes the water to bulge. High tides draw water away from the area between the high tides and cause *low tides* to form in those areas.

Timing Tides

Tides are determined by Earth's rotation and by the moon's revolution around Earth. The speed at which the moon revolves around Earth is too slow for the moon to always have the same position in relation to Earth. Tides would not alternate between high and low if the moon orbited Earth in one day—fast enough to always have the same position in relation to Earth. As **Figure 3** shows, a spot on Earth that is facing the moon takes longer than a day—24 h 50 min—to rotate and face the moon again.

Figure 3 *Tides [...] Earth too slowly [...]*

CONNECTION TO Language Arts

WRITING SKILL **Mont-St-Michel: Sometimes an Island** Mont-St-Michel is located off the coast of France. Mont-St-Michel experiences extreme tides. The tides are so extreme that Mont-St-Michel is an island during high tide and is connected to the mainland during low tide. Research the history of Mont-St-Michel, and write a short story describing what living there for a day would be like. Include a description of Mont-St-Michel at high tide and at low tide.

Benchmark Activity

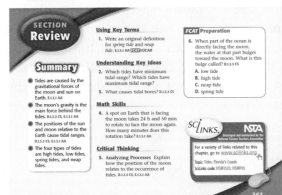

Tides and Topography

After a tidal range has been measured, the times that tides occur can be accurately predicted. This information can be useful for people near the coast, as shown in **Figure 5**. In some coastal areas that have narrow inlets, movements of water called *tidal bores* occur. A tidal bore is a body of water that rushes up through a narrow bay, estuary, or river channel during the rise of high tide and causes a sudden tidal rise.

Figure 5 *It's a good thing that the people on this beach (left) knew when high tide occurred (right). These photos show the Bay of Fundy in New Brunswick, Canada. The Bay of Fundy has the greatest tidal range on Earth.*

Benchmark Check How might tidal bores affect rocks in coastal areas? D.1.3.3 CS

D.1.3.3 CS knows how conditions that exist in one system influence the conditions that exist in other systems.

SECTION Review

Summary

● Tides are caused by the gravitational forces of the moon and sun on Earth. E.1.3.1 AA
● The moon's gravity is the main force behind the tides. D.1.3.3 CS, E.1.3.1 AA
● The positions of the sun and moon relative to the Earth cause tidal ranges. D.1.3.3 CS, E.1.3.1 AA
● The four types of tides are high tides, low tides, spring tides, and neap tides.

Using Key Terms

1. Write an original definition for *spring tide* and *neap tide*. E.1.3.1 AA FCAT VOCAB

Understanding Key Ideas

2. Which tides have minimum tidal range? Which tides have maximum tidal range?

3. What causes tidal bores? D.1.3.3 CS

Math Skills

4. A spot on Earth that is facing the moon takes 24 h and 50 min to rotate to face the moon again. How many minutes does this rotation take? E.1.3.1 AA

Critical Thinking

5. Analyzing Processes Explain how the position of the moon relates to the occurrence of tides. D.1.3.3 CS, E.1.3.1 AA

FCAT Preparation

6. When part of the ocean is directly facing the moon, the water at that part bulges toward the moon. What is this bulge called? D.1.3.3 CS
   A. low tide
   B. high tide
   C. neap tide
   D. spring tide

SCLINKS **NSTA** *Developed and maintained by the National Science Teachers Association*

For a variety of links related to this chapter, go to www.scilinks.org
Topic: Tides; Florida's Coasts
SciLinks code: HSM1525; HSMF05

367

Get Involved

The best way to learn science is to do science. Each chapter has a wide variety of hands-on activities and labs that will help you experience science up close and personal. Activities include **Start-up Activities, School-to-Home Activities,** and **Benchmark Activities.** Labs include **Quick Labs, Chapter Labs,** and additional labs located in the **LabBook** at the back of the book.

Prepare for Exams

It is never too early to start preparing for success. **Reading Checks, Benchmark Checks, Section Reviews,** and **Chapter Reviews** will help you prepare for exams. The **Standardized Test Preparation** located after each Chapter Review will help you practice for the FCAT.

STUDY TIP To make sure you know the material before an exam, take the time to review the Objectives, Terms to Learn, and Summary in each section.

Use the FCAT Study Guide

Your **FCAT Study Guide** contains a variety of resources designed to help you be successful when you take the FCAT. These resources include the **FCAT Glossary, FCAT Science Reference Sheet, Periodic Table,** and **Annually Assessed Benchmark Focus.**

Holt Online Learning

Visit Holt Online Learning

If your teacher gives you a special password to log onto the **Holt Online Learning** site, you'll find your complete textbook on the Web. In addition, you'll find some great learning tools and practice quizzes. You'll be able to see how well you know the material from your textbook.

SAFETY FIRST!

Exploring, inventing, and investigating are essential to the study of science. However, these activities can also be dangerous. To make sure that your experiments and explorations are safe, you must be aware of a variety of safety guidelines. You have probably heard of the saying, "It is better to be safe than sorry." This is particularly true in a science classroom where experiments and explorations are being performed. Being uninformed and careless can result in serious injuries. Don't take chances with your own safety or with anyone else's.

The following pages describe important guidelines for staying safe in the science classroom. Your teacher may also have safety guidelines and tips that are specific to your classroom and laboratory. Take the time to be safe.

Safety Rules!

Start Out Right

Always get your teacher's permission before attempting any laboratory exploration. Read the procedures carefully, and pay particular attention to safety information and caution statements. If you are unsure about what a safety symbol means, look it up or ask your teacher. You cannot be too careful when it comes to safety. If an accident does occur, inform your teacher immediately regardless of how minor you think the accident is.

If you are instructed to note the odor of a substance, wave the fumes toward your nose with your hand. Never put your nose close to the source.

Safety Symbols

All of the experiments and investigations in this book and their related worksheets include important safety symbols to alert you to particular safety concerns. Become familiar with these symbols so that when you see them, you will know what they mean and what to do. It is important that you read this entire safety section to learn about specific dangers in the laboratory.

Eye protection

Clothing protection

Hand safety

Heating safety

Electric safety

Chemical safety

Animal safety

Sharp object

Plant safety

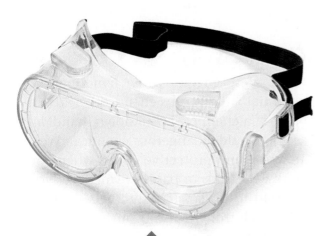

Eye Safety

Wear safety goggles when working around chemicals, acids, bases, or any type of flame or heating device. Wear safety goggles any time there is even the slightest chance that harm could come to your eyes. If any substance gets into your eyes, notify your teacher immediately and flush your eyes with running water for at least 15 minutes. Treat any unknown chemical as if it were a dangerous chemical. Never look directly into the sun. Doing so could cause permanent blindness.

Avoid wearing contact lenses in a laboratory situation. Even if you are wearing safety goggles, chemicals can get between the contact lenses and your eyes. If your doctor requires that you wear contact lenses instead of glasses, wear eye-cup safety goggles in the lab.

Safety Equipment

Know the locations of the nearest fire alarms and any other safety equipment, such as fire blankets and eyewash fountains, as identified by your teacher, and know the procedures for using the equipment.

Neatness

Keep your work area free of all unnecessary books and papers. Tie back long hair, and secure loose sleeves or other loose articles of clothing, such as ties and bows. Remove dangling jewelry. Don't wear open-toed shoes or sandals in the laboratory. Never eat, drink, or apply cosmetics in a laboratory setting. Food, drink, and cosmetics can easily become contaminated with dangerous materials.

Certain hair products (such as aerosol hair spray) are flammable and should not be worn while working near an open flame. Avoid wearing hair spray or hair gel on lab days.

Sharp/Pointed Objects

Use knives and other sharp instruments with extreme care. Never cut objects while holding them in your hands. Place objects on a suitable work surface for cutting.

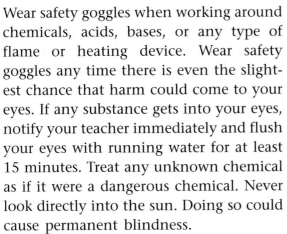

Be extra careful when using any glassware. When adding a heavy object to a graduated cylinder, tilt the cylinder so that the object slides slowly to the bottom.

Heat

Wear safety goggles when using a heating device or a flame. Whenever possible, use an electric hot plate as a heat source instead of using an open flame. When heating materials in a test tube, always angle the test tube away from yourself and others. To avoid burns, wear heat-resistant gloves whenever instructed to do so.

Electricity

Be careful with electrical cords. When using a microscope with a lamp, do not place the cord where it could trip someone. Do not let cords hang over a table edge in a way that could cause equipment to fall if the cord is accidentally pulled. Do not use equipment with damaged cords. Be sure that your hands are dry and that the electrical equipment is in the "off" position before plugging it in. Turn off and unplug electrical equipment when you are finished.

Chemicals

Wear safety goggles when handling any potentially dangerous chemicals, acids, or bases. If a chemical is unknown, handle it as you would a dangerous chemical. Wear an apron and protective gloves when you work with acids or bases or whenever you are told to do so. If a spill gets on your skin or clothing, rinse it off immediately with water for at least 5 minutes while calling to your teacher.

Never mix chemicals unless your teacher tells you to do so. Never taste, touch, or smell chemicals unless you are specifically directed to do so. Before working with a flammable liquid or gas, check for the presence of any source of flame, spark, or heat.

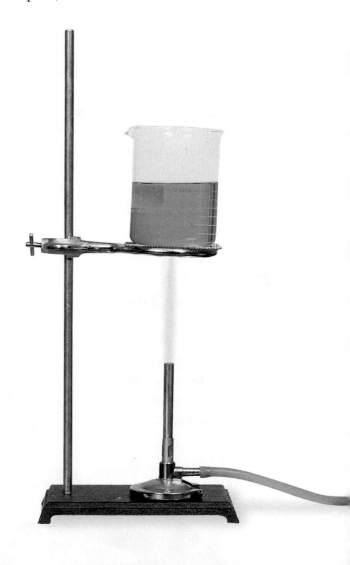

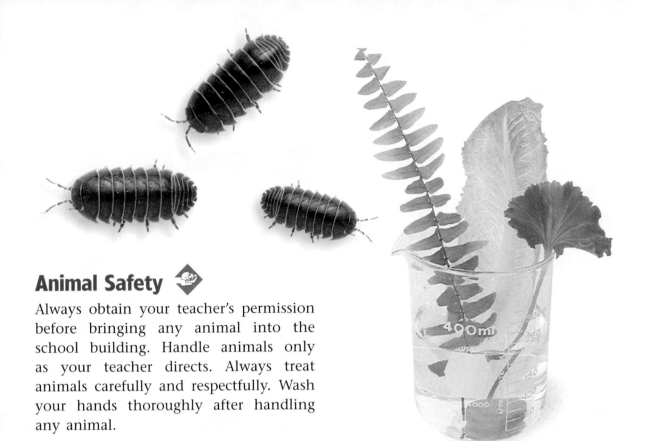

Animal Safety

Always obtain your teacher's permission before bringing any animal into the school building. Handle animals only as your teacher directs. Always treat animals carefully and respectfully. Wash your hands thoroughly after handling any animal.

Plant Safety

Do not eat any part of a plant or plant seed used in the laboratory. Wash your hands thoroughly after handling any part of a plant. When in nature, do not pick any wild plants unless your teacher instructs you to do so.

Glassware

Examine all glassware before use. Be sure that glassware is clean and free of chips and cracks. Report damaged glassware to your teacher. Glass containers used for heating should be made of heat-resistant glass.

UNIT 1

TIMELINE

Science in Our World

What is science? Science is the study of the world around us. There are many types of science, such as life science, Earth science, and physical science. In this unit, you will begin learning about science and the tools and methods that scientists use to learn about the world.

Studying something as small as a cell or as large as Earth is not easy. Yet scientists study these items and more. The timeline shown here identifies a few of the events that have helped shape our understanding of science.

1669

Nicolaus Steno accurately describes the process by which living organisms become fossils.

1904

Roald Amundsen determines the position of the magnetic north pole.

1922

Roy Chapman Andrews discovers fossilized dinosaur eggs in the Gobi Desert. They are the first such eggs to be found.

Fossilized dinosaur eggs from the Gobi Desert

1962

By reaching an altitude of more than 95 km, the *X-15* becomes the first fixed-wing plane to reach space.

1758

Halley's comet makes a reappearance, which confirms Edmond Halley's 1705 prediction. The comet reappeared 16 years after Halley's death.

1799

The Rosetta stone is discovered in Egypt. It enables scholars to decipher Egyptian hieroglyphics.

1896

The first modern Olympic Games are held in Athens, Greece.

1943

The volcano Paricutin grows more than 200 m tall during its first two weeks of eruption.

Paricutín Volcano

1960

The United States launches the first weather satellite, *TIROS I.*

1970

The first Earth Day is celebrated in the United States on April 22.

1990

The *Hubble Space Telescope* is launched into orbit. Three years later, faulty optics are repaired during a space walk.

1994

China begins construction of Three Gorges Dam, the world's largest dam. Designed to control the Yangtze River, the dam will supply an estimated 84 billion kilowatt-hours of hydroelectric power per year.

2002

A new order of insects—Mantophasmatodea—is found preserved in 45 million–year-old amber as well as living in southern Africa.

Hubble Space Telescope

1

The Nature of Science

The Big Idea Scientists use scientific processes to study the patterns of natural events and to solve problems.

About the  PHOTO

What is that man doing? Ricardo Alonso, a geologist in Argentina, is measuring the footprints left by a dinosaur millions of years ago. Taking measurements is just one way that scientists collect data to answer questions and test hypotheses.

PRE-READING ACTIVITY

FOLDNOTES **Key-Term Fold** Before you read the chapter, create the FoldNote entitled "Key-Term Fold" described in the **Study Skills** section of the Appendix. Write a key term from the chapter on each tab of the key-term fold. Under each tab, write the definition of the key term.

START-UP ACTIVITY

Mission Impossible? H.1.3.4 AA

In this activity, you will do some creative thinking to solve what might seem like an impossible problem.

Procedure

1. Examine an **index card.** Your mission is to fit yourself through the card. You can only tear and fold the card. You cannot use tape, glue, or anything else to hold the card together.

2. Brainstorm with a partner ways to complete your mission. Then, record your plan.

3. Test your plan. Did it work? If necessary, get **another index card** and try again. Record your new plan and the results.

4. Share your plans and results with your classmates.

Analysis

1. Why was it helpful to come up with a plan in advance?

2. How did testing your plan help you complete your mission?

3. How did sharing your ideas with your classmates help you complete your mission? What did your classmates do differently?

SECTION 1

Science and Scientists

You are on a hike in the mountains when you see something strange. You pick it up. It looks like a shell. You are curious. How could a shell be up on this mountain?

READING WARM-UP

Objectives

- Describe similarities and differences between science disciplines. H.1.3.3 CS
- Describe three ways to answer questions about science.
- Identify three benefits of science.
- Describe how scientific knowledge may be modified. H.1.3.1 AA
- Describe five jobs that use or contribute to science. H.1.3.6

Terms to Learn

science

READING STRATEGY

Reading Organizer As you read this section, create an outline of the section. Use the headings from the section in your outline.

Congratulations! You just completed the first steps of being a scientist. How did you do it? You observed the world around you. Then, you asked a question about your observations. And that's part of what science is all about.

Starting with a Question

Science is the knowledge gained by observing the natural world. A question is the beginning of science. Asking a question can help you gather knowledge. The world around you is full of amazing things that can lead you to ask questions, such as those in **Figure 1.**

There are many different science disciplines, such as chemistry, astronomy, and biology. These disciplines differ from one another in topic, techniques, and outcomes. But they share a common purpose, philosophy, and enterprise. As you will learn, all scientists carefully gather information in order to answer questions about the natural world.

Benchmark Check **How are science disciplines different? How are they similar? H.1.3.3 CS**

In Your Neighborhood and Beyond

Look around your neighborhood. Often, you take things that you see every day for granted. But one day you might look at something in a new way. That's when a question hits you! You see trees every day. At some point, you may wonder how the leaves change color.

Do you think that you might get tired of asking questions about things in your neighborhood? You could ask questions about deserts, forests, or sandy beaches. But Earth is not the only place to look for questions. You can look to the moon, sun, planets in our solar system, and the rest of the universe! There seem to be enough questions to keep scientists busy for a long time.

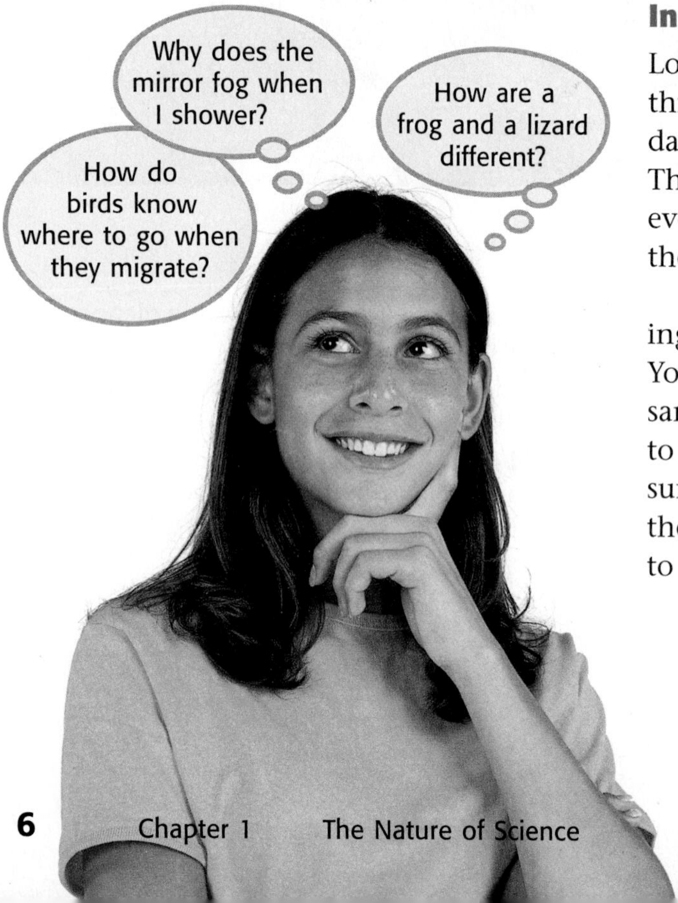
Why does the mirror fog when I shower?
How are a frog and a lizard different?
How do birds know where to go when they migrate?

Figure 1 *Part of science is asking questions about the world around you.*

Investigation: The Search for Answers

Once you ask a question, it's time to look for an answer. But how do you start your investigation? There are several methods that you can use.

Research

You can find answers to some of your questions by doing research, as shown in **Figure 2.** You can ask someone who knows a lot about the subject of your question. You can look up information in textbooks, encyclopedias, and magazines. You could also search on the Internet. You might learn more about your subject if you find the report of an experiment that someone has done. But be sure to think about the source of the information that you find. Scientists use information only from reliable sources.

Observation

You can also find answers to questions by making careful observations. For example, if you want to know which birds live around you, you could go for a walk and look for them. Or you could hang a bird feeder outside your window and observe the birds that use it.

Experimentation

You can even answer some of your questions by doing an experiment, as shown in **Figure 3.** Your research might help you plan your experiment. Of course, you'll need to make careful observations during the experiment. What do you do if your experiment requires materials or conditions that are hard to get? For example, what do you do if you want to see how crystals grow in space? Don't give up! Do more research to see if you can find the results from someone else's experiment!

science the knowledge obtained by observing natural events and conditions in order to discover facts and formulate laws or principles that can be verified or tested

Figure 2 *A library is a good place to begin your search for answers.*

Figure 3 *This student is doing an experiment to find out the hardness of a mineral.*

H.1.3.3 CS knows that science disciplines differ from one another in topic, techniques, and outcomes, but that they share a common purpose, philosophy, and enterprise.

Why Ask Why?

Although people cannot use science to answer every question, many questions can be answered by science. But do any of the answers really matter? Absolutely! Here are just a few ways that science affects our lives.

Saving Lives

Using science, people have answered the question, How can bicycle riding be made safer? Science has helped people develop new materials and designs for safer helmets. Effective helmets help protect a rider's head if it hits the ground. These helmets can prevent injuries that lead to brain damage or even death. Scientific research has led to many life-saving discoveries, such as medicines, weather prediction, and disease prevention.

Using Resources Wisely

Science has also helped answer the question, How can resources be made to last longer? For example, by recycling paper, people can save trees, as shown in **Figure 4.** Recycling helps protect forests and saves fuel and chemicals used to make paper from trees. Also, scientists have learned to plan ahead so that resources are not used up. For example, many areas where trees are cut down are also sites where new trees are planted. Scientists help determine how these trees can remain healthy and grow quickly.

Reading Check What are the benefits of recycling paper?

Figure 4 Resources Saved Through Recycling

Compared with making the paper originally, recycling 1 metric ton (1.1 tons) of paper does the following things.

 produces 30 kg (66 lb) less air pollution

 uses 2.5 m³ (3.3 yd³) less landfill space

 uses 18.7 fewer trees

 uses 4,500 kWh less energy

 uses 29,100 L (7,700 gal) less water

 uses 1,800 L (470 gal) less oil

Healthy Surroundings

Science has helped answer the question, How can we reduce pollution? Pollution can harm our health and the health of other living things. One way that scientists have helped reduce pollution is by finding ways that cars can produce less exhaust. Scientists have developed lightweight materials that can be used to make lighter cars. Lighter cars burn less fuel and therefore make less pollution. Science has also helped people develop new types of cars, such as the one in **Figure 5.**

Figure 5 *This car makes less air pollution than most cars do because it runs on batteries.*

Modifying Scientific Knowledge

Asking questions is also necessary for improving scientific knowledge. As scientists do research, they may find new information that challenges the prevailing theories. This new information can lead to modifications, or changes, in scientific knowledge. Also, asking questions may lead to the development of new theories. These new theories may lead scientists to look at old observations in a new way.

Benchmark Check How does asking questions lead to modifications in scientific knowledge? **H.1.3.1 AA**

Scientists All Around You

Scientists work in many places. Any person who asks questions and looks for answers could be called a scientist! Scientific contributions are made by individuals of diverse backgrounds, interests, talents, and motivations. Keep reading to learn about a few people who use science in their jobs.

H.1.3.1 AA knows that scientific knowledge is subject to modification as new information challenges prevailing theories and as a new theory leads to looking at old observations in a new way.

H.1.3.6 recognizes the scientific contributions that are made by individuals of diverse backgrounds, interests, talents, and motivations.

Environmental Scientists

An *environmental scientist* is a person who studies how humans interact with their environment. Environmental scientists, such as the one shown in **Figure 6,** can find out if humans are damaging the environment. Environmental scientists help people protect the environment, save Earth's resources, and use these resources more wisely.

Figure 6 *These environmental scientists are testing water quality.*

Figure 7 *The Mississippi River helped St. Louis, Missouri, become the large city that it is today. Boats were able to carry supplies and people to and from St. Louis.*

H.1.3.6 recognizes the scientific contributions that are made by individuals of diverse backgrounds, interests, talents, and motivations.

Figure 8 *These zoologists are working to preserve populations of endangered red wolves.*

Cartographers

A *cartographer* (kahr TAHG ruh fuhr) makes maps of the surface of Earth. These maps can be used to plan how cities can grow. Have you ever wondered why cities were built where they are? Often, a city is built in a place because of the features of the land. Many cities, such as the one in **Figure 7,** were built near rivers. Others were built near lakes or oceans. Bodies of water allow the use of boats to move people and goods. Rivers and lakes also provide water for drinking and for raising crops. Maps help people keep track of these natural resources.

Engineers

An *engineer* (EN juh NIR) puts scientific knowledge to practical use. Some engineers design and build the buildings, roads, and bridges that make up cities, such as the city in **Figure 7.** Others design and build electronic devices, such as computers and televisions. Some engineers even design processes and equipment to make chemicals and medicines. Engineers may work for universities, governments, or private companies.

Zoologists

A *zoologist* (zoh AHL uh jist) studies animals. The men shown in **Figure 8** are part of a study on how to protect an endangered species. Some animals are in danger of becoming extinct because of the loss of habitats where the animals live. By learning about animals' needs, zoologists hope to make a plan to help protect many species from dying out.

Science Educators

A *science educator* is a person who teaches others about science. Learning about science can help people understand natural processes. With education, people can be aware of the effects of their actions. As a result, people can act in ways that are healthy for themselves and others around them. Many science educators teach at schools. Others work at zoos, at aquariums, or in national parks, as shown in **Figure 9**.

Benchmark Check Compare the interests and talents of people who use science. H.1.3.6

Figure 9 *Some science educators work as park rangers in national parks.*

SECTION Review

Summary

- Science is the knowledge gained by observing the natural world.
- Science disciplines differ in several ways but share a common purpose, philosophy, and enterprise. **H.1.3.3 CS**
- Scientists answer questions by using research, observation, and experimentation.
- Science can help protect lives, resources, and the environment.
- Asking questions leads to modifications in scientific knowledge as new information is gathered and as new theories are developed. **H.1.3.1 AA**
- Scientific contributions are made by individuals of diverse backgrounds, interests, talents, and motivations. **H.1.3.6**

Understanding Key Ideas

1. How do scientists investigate their questions?

2. Describe the jobs of five people that use or contribute to science. **H.1.3.6**

3. What are three ways that knowledge gained through science can benefit the world around you?

4. Describe two ways that scientific knowledge may be modified. **H.1.3.1 AA**

Critical Thinking

5. **Expressing Opinions** Name a job that interests you that also uses or contributes to science. How would your background, interests, and talents contribute to your success at this job? **H.1.3.6**

6. **Applying Concepts** Imagine that you saw a meteor shower and then wanted to know what causes a shooting star. Name two ways that you could investigate the cause of a shooting star.

7. **Making Comparisons** Compare two science disciplines, such as zoology and environmental science. List three ways that the disciplines differ and three ways that they are similar. **H.1.3.3 CS**

FCAT Preparation

8. One widely accepted theory of why the dinosaurs died off states that a large asteroid hit Earth. The asteroid produced a huge dust cloud that blocked out the sun. Food became scarce, and the dinosaurs died. Predict how scientists may react to a new theory of why dinosaurs died off. **H.1.3.1 AA**

   A. They will ignore the new theory.

   B. They will use the new theory to study old observations.

   C. They will disprove the theory with old observations.

   D. They will disprove the theory with new observations.

SCLINKS®

NSTA
Developed and maintained by the
National Science Teachers Association

For a variety of links related to this chapter, go to www.scilinks.org

Topic: Recycling; Careers in Science
SciLinks code: HSM1277; HSM0225

Scientific Methods and Inquiry

Near a river, several long-necked dinosaurs chew on plants. Through the trees, they see an allosaurus (AL oh SAWR uhs), a common meat-eating dinosaur of the Jurassic period.

This scene is not based only on imagination. Although scientists have never seen a dinosaur, they have been studying dinosaurs for years! How? Scientists gather information about dinosaurs from fossils. Then, they use imagination and scientific methods to re-create what Earth might have been like long ago.

What Are Scientific Methods?

When scientists observe the natural world, they often think of a question or problem. But scientists don't just guess at answers. **Scientific methods** are the ways in which scientists answer questions and solve problems. Studying the methods and events that lead scientists to discoveries can provide information about the inquiry process and its effects.

As scientists look for answers, they often use the same steps. But there is more than one way to use the steps. Look at **Figure 1.** Scientists may use all of the steps or just some of the steps during an investigation. They may even repeat some of the steps or do the steps in a different order. It all depends on what works best to answer their question.

Benchmark Check What knowledge can be gained by studying the events that lead scientists to discoveries? **H.1.3.2 CS**

READING WARM-UP

Objectives

- Describe what can be learned by studying scientific methods and events. **H.1.3.2 CS**
- Identify the steps used in scientific methods.
- Explain how scientific methods are used to answer questions.
- Describe why accurate record keeping, openness, and replication of results are important. **H.1.3.4 AA**
- Explain what happens when similar investigations give different results. **H.1.3.7**

Terms to Learn

scientific methods   hypothesis
observation   data

READING STRATEGY

Reading Organizer As you read this section, make a flowchart of the possible steps in scientific methods.

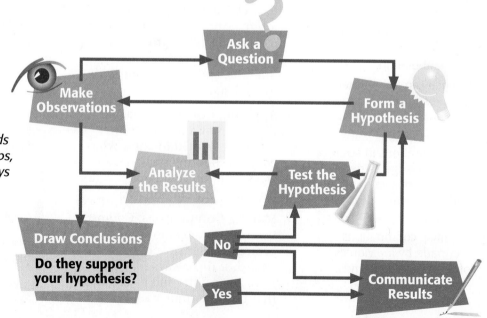

Figure 1 *Scientific methods often involve the same steps, but the steps are not always used in the same order.*

Figure 2 *Bones were found in this part of New Mexico.*

Ask a Question

Asking a question helps focus the purpose of an investigation. Scientists often ask a question after making observations. An **observation** is the act of using the senses to gather information. Observations can be made at any point in an investigation.

There are many kinds of observations. Observations may describe the hardness or softness of a rock. They may describe the color of a substance. Even the patterns in behavior of an animal can be described by observations. Measurements are observations that are made with tools, such as metersticks, stopwatches, and thermometers. Observations lead to answers only when they are accurate and carefully recorded.

A Dinosaur-Sized Question

In 1979, two people on a hike found dinosaur bones in the area of northwestern New Mexico shown in **Figure 2.** Soon after, David D. Gillette, a scientist who studies fossils, went to see the bones. After observing the bones, Gillette may have asked, "What kind of dinosaur did these bones come from?" Gillette would have to use scientific methods to come up with an answer that he could trust.

Reading Check Why do scientists use scientific methods to answer questions?

scientific methods a series of steps followed to solve problems

observation the process of obtaining information by using the senses

H.1.3.2 CS knows that the study of the events that led scientists to discoveries can provide information about the inquiry process and its effects.

Form a Hypothesis

hypothesis an idea or explanation that is based on prior scientific research or observations and that can be tested

When scientists want to investigate a question, they form a hypothesis. A **hypothesis** is a possible explanation or answer to a question. It is sometimes called an *educated guess*. The hypothesis is a scientist's best answer to the question. But a hypothesis can't be just any answer. Someone must be able to test the hypothesis to see if it is true.

From his observations and previous knowledge about dinosaurs, Gillette formed a hypothesis about the bones. He said that the bones, seen in **Figure 3,** came from a kind of dinosaur not yet known to scientists. This hypothesis was Gillette's best testable explanation. To test it, Gillette would have to do a lot of research.

Make Predictions

Before scientists test a hypothesis, they often make predictions. To make a prediction, you say what you think will happen in your experiment or investigation. Predictions are usually stated in an if-then format. For example, Gillette could make the following prediction: *If* the bones are from a dinosaur not yet known to science, *then* at least some of the bones will not match any dinosaur bones that have been studied before. Sometimes, scientists make many predictions about one experiment. After predictions are made, scientists can do experiments to see which predictions, if any, support the hypothesis.

Figure 3 *Gillette and his team had to dig out the bones carefully before studying them.*

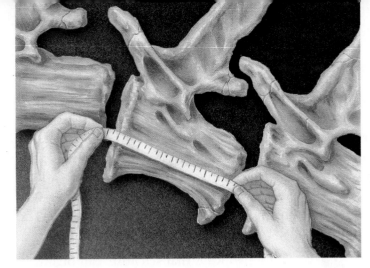

Figure 4 *To test his hypothesis, Gillette took hundreds of measurements of the bones.*

Test the Hypothesis

A hypothesis must be tested for scientists to learn whether an idea can be supported scientifically. Scientists test hypotheses by gathering data. **Data** are any pieces of information gathered through experimentation. The data can help scientists tell if the hypotheses are valid.

To test his hypothesis, Gillette took hundreds of measurements of the bones, as shown in **Figure 4.** He compared his measurements with those of bones from known dinosaurs. He visited museums and talked with other scientists. After gathering all of these data, Gillette was ready for the next step toward answering his question.

Under Control

To test a hypothesis, a scientist may conduct a controlled experiment. A *controlled experiment* tests only one factor at a time. The one factor that is changed in a controlled experiment is called a *variable*. By changing only the variable, scientists can see the results of just that one change.

During experiments, scientists must keep accurate records of everything that they do and observe. Accurate record keeping is essential to maintaining a scientist's credibility with other scientists and society.

 *Benchmark Check* **Why do scientists need to keep accurate records?** **H.1.3.4 AA**

Testing Without Experiments

Not all investigations are made by doing controlled experiments. Sometimes, it is not possible to use a controlled experiment to test something. Also, some scientists depend on observations more than they depend on experiments to test their hypotheses. By observing nature, scientists can often collect large amounts of data about their hypotheses. When large amounts of data support a hypothesis, the hypothesis is probably valid.

data any pieces of information acquired through observation or experimentation

CONNECTION TO Geology

Laguna Colorada In some parts of the world, lake water doesn't look blue. In parts of Bolivia, the lakes may be green, yellow, or red! One Bolivian lake, Laguna Colorada, is a deep-red body of water surrounded by a white stretch of flat land. The land around the lake is white because of the salty minerals in the rock there. Some of the lakes are colored by minerals. Others are colored by the microorganisms that live there. How could you find out why Laguna Colorada is red?

H.1.3.4 AA knows that accurate record keeping, openness, and replication are essential to maintaining an investigator's credibility with other scientists and society.

Analyze the Results

After they finish their tests, scientists must analyze the results. Analyzing the results helps scientists construct reasonable explanations based on the evidence that has been collected. Scientists often make tables and graphs to arrange their data. **Figure 5** shows how Gillette organized his data. When Gillette analyzed his results, he found that the bones of the mystery dinosaur did not match the bones of any known dinosaur. The bones were either too large or too different in shape.

✓ **Reading Check** What are two ways that scientists can organize their data?

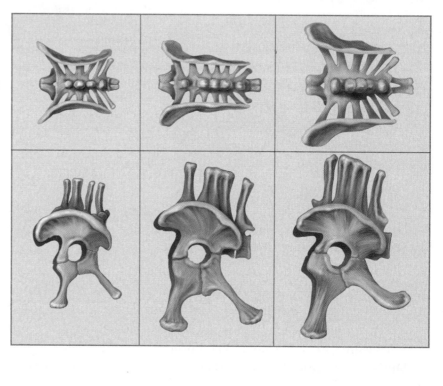

Figure 5 *By organizing his measurements in a chart, Gillette could analyze his results more easily.*

Figure 6 *This model of the skeleton of* Seismosaurus hallorum *is based on Gillette's research. The bones shown in the darker color are the bones that have been found so far.*

2 m

Quick Lab

Mapping a Sphere

1. Examine a **soccer ball,** and notice the patterns on the ball.

2. Place different **stickers** on each pentagon of the ball.

3. Now, try mapping the images from the soccer ball onto a **flat piece of paper.**

4. What problems came up when you tried to represent a sphere on a flat piece of paper?

5. Use your experience to draw a conclusion about why maps of the entire Earth are often represented on a globe. Then, explain why flat maps of the entire Earth are often distorted.

Draw Conclusions

After analyzing the results of their tests, scientists must conclude if the results support the hypothesis. Proving that a hypothesis is not true can be as valuable as proving that it is true. If the hypothesis is not supported, scientists may repeat the investigation to check for mistakes. Or scientists may look at the original question in a new way, ask new questions, and form new hypotheses. New questions and hypotheses can lead to new investigations and discoveries.

From all of his work, Gillette concluded that the bones found in New Mexico, shown in the model in **Figure 6,** were indeed from a yet unknown dinosaur. The dinosaur was about 45 m (148 ft) long and had a mass of almost 100 metric tons. The creature certainly fit the name that Gillette gave it— *Seismosaurus hallorum,* the "earth shaker."

Careers in Earth Science
Investigate an interesting career! Go to **go.hrw.com,** and type in the keyword **HZ5WESW.**

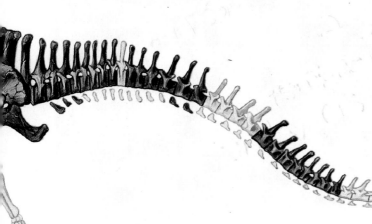

H.1.3.4 AA knows that accurate record keeping, openness, and replication are essential to maintaining an investigator's credibility with other scientists and society.

Communicate Results

After finishing an investigation, scientists communicate their results. By doing so, scientists share what they have learned. Scientists communicate by writing reports and by giving talks. They can also put their results on the Internet.

Science depends on sharing information. Sharing allows other scientists to repeat experiments to see if they get the same results. Openness and replication of experiments maintain a scientist's believability with other scientists and society.

Also, by sharing, scientists can compare hypotheses and form consistent explanations. When sharing information, scientists sometimes learn that similar investigations gave different results. When this happens, scientists must determine whether the differences are significant by doing more studies.

Gillette shared his discovery of *Seismosaurus hallorum* at a press conference at the New Mexico Museum of Natural History and Science. He later sent a report that described his investigation to the *Journal of Vertebrate Paleontology*.

Benchmark Check Name two ways that scientists maintain believability with other scientists and society. **H.1.3.4 AA**

Case Closed?

All of the bones that Gillette found have been dug up from the ground. But as **Figure 7** shows, the fun is not over yet! The work on *Seismosaurus hallorum* continues. The remains of one of the largest dinosaurs ever discovered are still being studied. Like so many other investigations, Gillette's work led to new questions to be answered.

H.1.3.4 AA knows that accurate record keeping, openness, and replication are essential to maintaining an investigator's credibility with other scientists and society.

H.1.3.7 knows that when similar investigations give different results, the scientific challenge is to verify whether the differences are significant by further study.

Figure 7 *David Gillette continues to study the bones of* Seismosaurus hallorum *for new views into the past.*

Summary

- Studying scientific methods and events can provide information about the inquiry process and its effects. **H.1.3.2 CS**

- Scientific methods are the ways in which scientists follow steps to answer questions and solve problems.

- The steps used in scientific methods are to ask a question, form a hypothesis, test the hypothesis, analyze the results, draw conclusions, and communicate results.

- A controlled experiment tests only one factor at a time in order to determine the effects of changes to just that one factor.

- Accurate record keeping, openness, and replication of results are essential to maintaining an investigator's credibility. **H.1.3.4 AA**

- When similar investigations give different results, the scientific challenge is to verify by further study whether the differences are significant. **H.1.3.7**

Understanding Key Ideas

1. Which of the following statements about the steps of scientific methods is true?
   a. Steps must always be used in the same order.
   b. All steps must be used.
   c. Steps are sometimes repeated.
   d. The steps must support the hypothesis.

2. Identify the steps used in scientific methods, and explain how scientific methods are used to answer questions.

3. What can be learned by studying scientific methods and events? **H.1.3.2 CS**

4. Why are accurate record keeping, openness, and replication of results important? **H.1.3.4 AA**

5. What is an observation? Write down one observation about the room that you are in at this moment.

6. What is a controlled experiment?

Critical Thinking

7. **Analyzing Processes** Suppose that two scientists perform the same experiment and find different results. What should the scientists do next? **H.1.3.7**

8. **Applying Concepts** What are two ways that you could analyze data about temperature changes over many years? What are the benefits and limitations of each method?

FCAT Preparation

9. A paleontologist is a scientist who studies fossils. Fossils are the remains, or physical evidence, of an organism preserved by geologic processes. Suppose that a paleontologist has written a scientific article about how she determined which dinosaur a set of fossilized bones came from. What can you learn by reading the article? **H.1.3.2 CS**
   A. how scientists analyze results
   B. how scientists find dinosaur bones
   C. what dinosaurs looked like
   D. how bones become fossilized

10. A scientist claimed to have cloned a dinosaur, but it died before anyone could see it. Many scientists did not believe his claims. How can the scientist convince others of his accomplishment? **H.1.3.4 AA**

SCiLINKS®

NSTA
Developed and maintained by the
National Science Teachers Association

For a variety of links related to this chapter, go to www.scilinks.org

Topic: Scientific Methods
SciLinks code: HSM1359

Tools and Measurement

Would you use a hammer to tighten a bolt on a bicycle? You probably wouldn't. To be successful in many tasks, you need the correct tools.

Tools for Science

Scientists use many tools. A *tool* is anything that helps you do a task. If you observe a jar of pond water, you may see a few insects swimming around. But a microscope can help you see many organisms that you couldn't see before. And a graduated cylinder can help you measure the volume of water in the jar. Different tools help scientists gather specific kinds of data.

Tools for Seeing

Microscopes help you make careful observations of things that are too small to see with just your eyes. The compound light microscope in **Figure 1** is made up of three main parts—a tube that has lenses at each end, a stage, and a light. When you place what you want to see on the stage, light passes through it. The lenses magnify the image.

✓ **Reading Check** Name the three main parts of a compound light microscope.

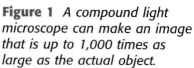

Figure 1 *A compound light microscope can make an image that is up to 1,000 times as large as the actual object.*

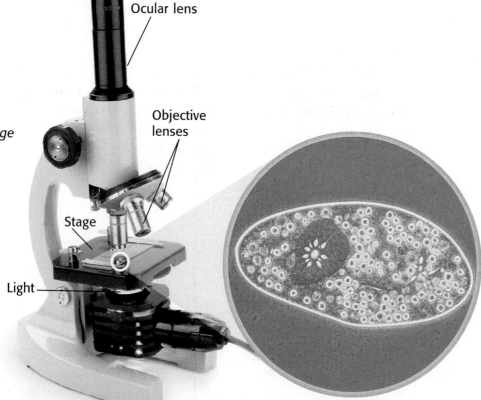

Ocular lens

Objective lenses

Stage

Light

Figure 2 **Measurement Tools**

You can use a **graduated cylinder** to measure volume.

You can use a **stopwatch** to measure time.

You can use a **meterstick** to measure length.

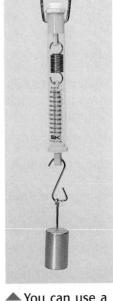

You can use a **spring scale** to measure force.

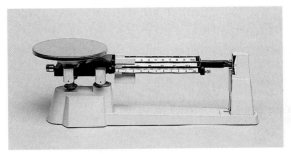

You can use a **balance** to measure mass.

You can use a **thermometer** to measure temperature.

Tools for Measuring

One way to collect data during an experiment is to take measurements. To have the best measurements possible, you need to use the proper tools. Stopwatches, metersticks, and balances are some of the tools you can use to make measurements. Thermometers, spring scales, and graduated cylinders are also helpful tools. **Figure 2** explains what characteristics these tools can be used to measure.

Tools for Analyzing

After you collect data, you need to analyze them. Perhaps you need to find the average of your data. Calculators are handy tools that help you do calculations quickly. Or you might show your data in a graph or a figure. A computer that has the correct software can help you make neat, colorful figures. In fact, computers have become invaluable tools for collecting, storing, and analyzing data. Of course, even a pencil and graph paper are tools that you can use to graph your data.

See for Yourself

1. Use a **metric ruler** to measure the length and width of one of your fingernails. Draw and describe the details of your fingernail.

2. Look at the same fingernail through a **magnifying lens.** Now, draw the details of your fingernail as seen with magnification.

3. How does using a magnifying lens change what details you can see?

Units of Measurement

WRITING SKILL Measure the width of your desk, but do not use a ruler. Pick an object to use as your unit of measurement. It could be a pencil, your hand, or anything else. Find how many units wide your desk is. Compare your measurement with those of your classmates. In your **science journal,** explain why using standard units of measurement is important.

ACTiViTY

Measurement

Hundreds of years ago, different countries used different systems of measurement. At one time in England, the standard for an inch was three grains of barley placed end to end. Other modern standardized units were originally based on parts of the body, such as the foot. Such systems were not very reliable. Their units were based on objects that had different sizes.

The International System of Units

In time, people realized that they needed a simple and reliable measurement system. In the late 1700s, the French Academy of Sciences set out to make that system. Over the next 200 years, the metric system was formed. This system is now called the *International System of Units* (SI).

Today, most scientists and almost all countries use the International System of Units. One advantage of using the SI measurements is that they help all scientists share and compare their observations and results. Another advantage of the SI is that all units are based on the number 10. This feature makes changing from one unit to another easy. **Table 1** shows SI units for length, volume, mass, and temperature.

Table 1 Common SI Units and Conversions

Length		**meter (m)** kilometer (km) decimeter (dm) centimeter (cm) millimeter (mm) micrometer (μm) nanometer (nm)	1 km = 1,000 m 1 dm = 0.1 m 1 cm = 0.01 m 1 mm = 0.001 m 1 μm = 0.000001 m 1 nm = 0.000000001 m
Volume		**cubic meter (m³)** cubic centimeter (cm³) liter (L) milliliter (mL)	1 cm³ = 0.000001 m³ 1 L = 1 dm³ = 0.001 m³ 1 mL = 0.001 L = 1 cm³
Mass		**kilogram (kg)** gram (g) milligram (mg)	1 g = 0.001 kg 1 mg = 0.000001 kg
Temperature		**kelvin (K)** Celsius (°C)	0°C = 273 K 100°C = 373 K

Length

How long is your arm? The student in **Figure 3** could describe the length of her arm by using the **meter** (m), the basic SI unit of length. Remember that SI units are based on the number 10. If you divide 1 m into 100 parts, each part equals 1 cm. In other words, 1 cm is one-hundredth of a meter. To describe the length of microscopic objects, micrometers (μm) or nanometers (nm) are used. To describe the length of larger objects, kilometers (km) are used.

Figure 3 *This student's arm is 0.65 m long.*

Area

How much carpet would it take to cover the floor of your classroom? To answer this question, you must find the area of the floor. **Area** is a measure of how much surface an object has. Area is based on two measurements. For example, to calculate the area of a square or rectangle, you need to measure the length and width. Then, use the following equation for the area of a square or a rectangle:

$$area = length \times width$$

The units for area are square units, such as square meters (m^2), square centimeters (cm^2), and square kilometers (km^2).

✓ **Reading Check** What does area measure?

meter the basic unit of length in the SI (symbol, m)

area a measure of the size of a surface or a region

mass a measure of the amount of matter in an object **FCAT** *VOCAB*

Mass

How many sacks of grain can a mule carry? The answer depends on the strength of the mule and the mass of the sacks of grain. **Mass** is the amount of matter that makes up an object. Scientists often use a balance to measure mass, as shown in **Figure 4.** The kilogram (kg) is the basic unit for mass. The kilogram is used to describe the mass of things such as sacks of grain. Many common objects are not so large, however. The mass of smaller objects, such as an apple, can be described by using grams. One thousand grams equals 1 kg. The mass of large objects, such as an elephant, is given in metric tons. A metric ton equals 1,000 kg.

Figure 4 *This boy is using a balance to measure the mass of an apple.*

Figure 5 *Adding the rock changes the water level from 70 mL to 80 mL. So, the rock displaces 10 mL of water. Because 1 mL = 1 cm³, the volume of the rock is 10 cm³.*

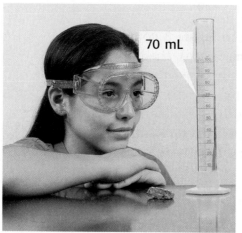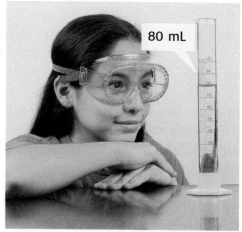

volume a measure of the size of a body or region in three-dimensional space

temperature a measure of how hot (or cold) something is

Volume

Suppose that some hippopotamuses born in a zoo are being moved to Africa. How many hippos will fit into a cage? The answer depends on volume. **Volume** is the amount of space that something occupies or, as in the case of the cage, the amount of space that something contains.

The volume of a large, solid object is given in cubic meters (m³). The volumes of smaller objects can be given in cubic centimeters (cm³) or cubic millimeters (mm³). To calculate the volume of a box-shaped object, multiply the object's length by its width and then by its height. To find the volume of an irregularly shaped object, measure the volume of liquid that the object displaces. This process is shown in **Figure 5.**

The volume of a liquid is often given in liters (L). Liters are based on the meter. A cubic meter (1 m³) is equal to 1,000 L. So, 1,000 L will fit into a box measuring 1 m on each side. A milliliter (mL) will fit into a box measuring 1 cm on each side. So, 1 mL = 1 cm³. Graduated cylinders are used to measure liquid volume in milliliters.

Temperature

How hot is a lava flow? To answer this question, scientists need to measure temperature. **Temperature** is a measure of how hot (or cold) something is. You probably use degrees Fahrenheit (°F) to describe temperature. Scientists often use degrees Celsius (°C). However, the kelvin (K), the SI base unit for temperature, is also used. The thermometer in **Figure 6** shows how two of these units are related.

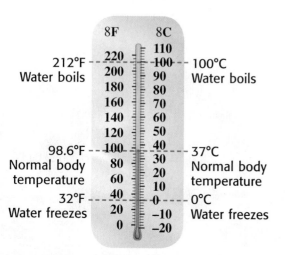

Figure 6 *This thermometer shows the relationship between degrees Fahrenheit and degrees Celsius.*

Measurements and Living Things

When making measurements of living things, scientists must take special precautions. For example, if the research involves animals, the animals must be treated humanely. When research involves human subjects, science ethics require that potential subjects be fully informed about the risks and benefits of the research. People must know what they can gain and what problems might occur. The potential subjects should also have the right to refuse to participate. Science ethics also demand that scientists must not knowingly subject coworkers, students, or the community to health risks or property risks.

Benchmark Check What conditions do science ethics require when making measurements on human subjects? **H.3.3.1 CS, H.3.3.3**

H.3.3.1 CS knows that science ethics demand that scientists must not knowingly subject coworkers, students, the neighborhood, or the community to health or property risks.

H.3.3.3 knows that in research involving human subjects, the ethics of science require that potential subjects be fully informed about the risks and benefits associated with the research and of their right to refuse to participate.

SECTION Review

Summary

- Scientists use tools that help them see, measure, and analyze.
- Scientists use the International System of Units (SI) so that they can share and compare their observations and results.
- Scientists have determined standard ways to measure length, area, mass, volume, and temperature.
- Science ethics demand that scientists must not knowingly subject others to risk. **H.3.3.1 CS**
- Potential human subjects must be informed of the risks and benefits of the research and have the right to refuse to participate. **H.3.3.3**

Understanding Key Ideas

1. SI units are
   a. always based on body parts.
   b. almost always based on the number 10.
   c. used to measure only length.
   d. used only in France.

2. What are three units that are used to measure temperature?

3. Describe ways that you can measure length, area, mass, and volume.

4. Describe three kinds of tools, and give an example of each kind of tool.

5. What special precautions must scientists take when making measurements of living things? **H.3.3.1 CS, H.3.3.3**

Critical Thinking

6. **Making Inferences** Many nations worked together to build the *International Space Station.* Predict what might have happened if they had not used the SI system during construction.

7. **Applying Concepts** Describe two ways that you could determine the volume of a pair of dice.

FCAT Preparation

8. Suppose that a group of doctors has developed a new surgical technique that can be used to treat people who have heart disease. The doctors need volunteers to test the effectiveness of the surgery. What must the doctors tell people who volunteer for the experimental surgery? **H.3.3.1 CS**
   A. the names of other potential volunteers
   B. possible complications of the surgery
   C. the number of people who will have the surgery
   D. unknown side effects of the surgery

SCI LINKS **NSTA**
Developed and maintained by the National Science Teachers Association

For a variety of links related to this chapter, go to www.scilinks.org

Topic: Tools of Life Science; SI Units
SciLinks code: HSM1535; HSM1390

Safety in Science

It's a sunny summer day. You and your best friend are going to ride your bikes to the park. You jump on your bike and start pedaling. But then your friend calls to you, "Wait! You forgot your helmet!"

Always wearing a bike helmet is an important safety rule. Using hand signals, as shown in **Figure 1,** is another rule. Just as you must follow rules to be safe when riding a bike, you must also take special care to be safe when you are learning science.

The Importance of Safety Rules

Bicycle safety rules, like all safety rules, have two purposes. Safety rules help prevent accidents from happening and help prevent injury if an accident does happen.

Preventing Accidents

To be safe while doing science activities, you have to learn some safety rules. Perhaps the most important safety rule is to follow directions. The directions of a science activity are designed to help you avoid accidents. Following directions will also make your work easier, and you will get better results.

Preventing Injury

If an accident happens, you or someone nearby could get hurt. Following safety rules after an accident can help avoid or reduce injuries. For example, you should always wear gloves when cleaning up a spilled chemical. Wearing gloves will prevent the chemical from touching your skin and causing injury.

READING WARM-UP

Objectives
- Explain why safety rules are important.
- Describe five elements of safety.
- Explain how to handle animals used in scientific research. **H.3.3.2**
- Describe what you should do after an accident happens.

Terms to Learn
first aid

READING STRATEGY

Paired Summarizing Read this section silently. In pairs, take turns summarizing the material. Stop to discuss ideas that seem confusing.

Figure 1 *Everyday safety is as important as safety in a science lab.*

Figure 2 Safety Symbols

Eye protection	Clothing protection	Hand safety	Heating safety	Electrical safety
Chemical safety	Animal safety	Sharp object	Plant safety	

Elements of Safety

To provide a safe workplace, you must know what precautions should be taken to prevent accidents. Safety has many parts. To be safe, you need to recognize safety symbols, follow directions, be neat, use safety equipment, and clean up after experiments.

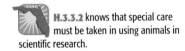 **H.3.3.2** knows that special care must be taken in using animals in scientific research.

Safety Symbols

A red light on a traffic signal has a specific meaning. A red light means that traffic must stop until the light turns green. Signs and symbols with specific meanings are also used in science. Some of these symbols are safety symbols. They tell you what to do to prevent injury or accidents. The safety symbols used in this book are shown in **Figure 2.**

Learn these safety symbols, and learn what they warn you about. For example, you would see the symbol for animal safety when doing an activity such as the one shown in **Figure 3.** The animal safety symbol tells you that special care must be taken when using animals in scientific research. Never squeeze or frighten animals. Follow your teacher's directions on how to pick animals up and how to dispose of animal waste. You should handle only those animals provided by your teacher. And you should always wash your hands with soap and water after touching animals.

Benchmark Check What does the symbol for animal safety tell you? **H.3.3.2**

Figure 3 *Treat living things with respect. When doing an experiment that uses animals or insects, do not do anything that could hurt them.*

Reading and Following Directions

If you wanted to bake cookies, you would use a recipe. The recipe tells you what ingredients to use and the proper procedure to follow. In other words, the recipe includes all of the directions on how to make cookies. When scientists work in a lab, they also follow directions. Likewise, you must follow directions given by your teacher or by the lab procedure.

Read all of the instructions very carefully before doing any science activity. If you do not understand the directions, ask your teacher to explain them. If you can't complete some of the directions, stop your experiment and ask your teacher for help. When you read, understand, and follow directions, you will get better results. And you will reduce the chance of having an accident.

✓ **Reading Check** What should you do if you do not understand the directions in your lab manual?

Neatness

Before starting any experiment, you should also clear your work area of books, backpacks, and other unneeded objects. These objects can get in the way and cause an accident. Long hair and loose clothing can also get in the way and should be tied back. Also, neatly prepare your data tables, and gather needed equipment before starting an activity, as shown in **Figure 4.**

During an experiment, keep your table or desk tidy. Arrange your equipment and materials. You should be able to easily locate and pick up the things you need. Clearly label your materials when instructed to do so. Some lab materials look similar and can be mixed up. As you collect data, record your findings carefully in your data table or notebook. Neatly recorded data are easier to read and analyze.

Figure 4 *Use a straight edge when making data tables.*

Figure 5 *These students are wearing heat-resistant gloves because they are working with hot objects. They are also wearing aprons and goggles to protect themselves from splashes and spills.*

Using Proper Safety Equipment

Safety equipment that you may use in a science lab includes goggles, gloves, and aprons. Some of the safety symbols tell you what safety equipment you need. For example, when you see the symbol for eye protection, you must put on safety goggles. Your goggles should fit comfortably but snugly. Your teacher can help you adjust them for a proper fit.

The chemicals you use are usually not dangerous. But you should always wear aprons and protective gloves when using chemicals. You should also wear protective gloves when handling animals. But if you are handling warm objects, you must wear different gloves. You must wear heat-resistant gloves. The orange gloves in **Figure 5** are heat-resistant gloves.

Reading Check When should you wear protective gloves?

Proper Cleanup Procedures

At the end of a science activity, you must always clean up your work area. Place caps back on bottles, and return everything to its proper place. Wash all of your glassware, and check for chips and cracks. If you find any damaged glassware, give it to your teacher. If you have any extra or waste chemicals, follow your teacher's directions for disposal. Once your table or desk is clear, wipe it with wet paper towels. Finally, wash your hands thoroughly with soap and water.

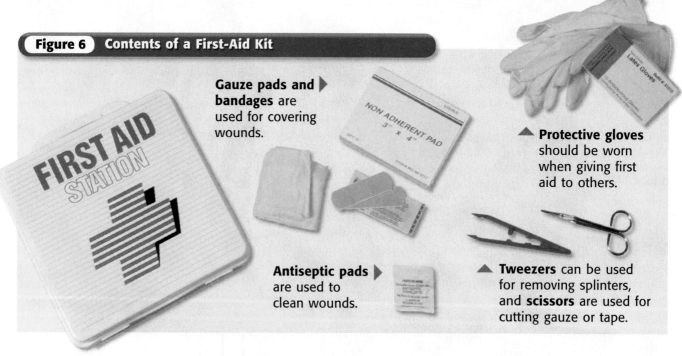

Figure 6 Contents of a First-Aid Kit

Gauze pads and bandages are used for covering wounds.

Protective gloves should be worn when giving first aid to others.

Antiseptic pads are used to clean wounds.

Tweezers can be used for removing splinters, and **scissors** are used for cutting gauze or tape.

Proper Accident Procedures

Sometimes, accidents happen in a lab even if all safety rules are followed. If an accident happens, remain calm. Panicking may make the situation worse. You may be scared, but it is safer for you and those around you if you stay in control.

Report the Accident

Always tell your teacher if an accident happens. Tell your teacher even if the accident is very minor. And tell your teacher even if you are afraid of getting in trouble. You will be in more trouble if you don't report an accident. When you report an accident, describe exactly what happened. Your teacher will need to know details such as what chemicals were spilled or where glassware was broken.

Caring for Injuries

first aid emergency medical care for someone who has been hurt or who is sick

If an accident should result in an injury, your teacher may have to perform first aid. **First aid** is emergency medical care for someone who has been hurt. First aid is only temporary care. But it can keep a victim stable until more complete medical care can be given.

You should not perform first aid unless you have been trained. However, you should know where your classroom's first-aid kit is located. After an accident happens, your teacher may ask you to get your classroom's first-aid kit. You should also be familiar with the contents of the kit and their uses. Your teacher may need your help when giving first aid. **Figure 6** shows some of the items usually found in a first-aid kit.

Reading Check Who should perform first aid if an accident happens in the classroom?

Steps to Follow After an Accident

The steps to follow after an accident are shown in **Figure 7.** Do all the steps in order quickly and carefully. The steps will help to avoid or reduce injury to you and those around you.

Figure 7 What to Do After an Accident

Step 1 Remain calm, and assess what happened.

Step 2 Secure the area. Make sure that no one is in danger.

Step 3 Inform your teacher, or call for help.

Step 4 Assist your teacher with cleanup or first aid.

SECTION Review

Summary

- Following safety rules helps prevent accidents and helps prevent injury when accidents happen.
- Five elements of safety are recognizing safety symbols, following directions, being neat, using safety equipment, and using proper cleanup procedures.
- Animals used in scientific research require special care. **H.3.3.2**
- First aid is emergency medical care for someone who has been hurt.
- When an accident happens, do the four steps to follow after an accident. These steps include reporting the accident and caring for injuries.

Using Key Terms

1. Write an original definition for *first aid.*

Understanding Key Ideas

2. Which of the following items are you likely to find in a first-aid kit?

   a. safety goggles

   b. cold medicine

   c. a fire extinguisher

   d. medical tape

3. Why is it important to follow all safety rules?

4. List and describe five elements of safety.

Critical Thinking

5. **Making Inferences** Imagine that you are recording the changes a tadpole goes through when changing into a frog. Describe how you would care for and handle the tadpole during your experiment. **H.3.3.2**

6. **Applying Concepts** Your lab partner was bitten by a mouse during a science activity. After he was bitten, he dropped the mouse and it ran away. Describe what you would do next.

FCAT Preparation

7. Safe practices must be used when animals are involved in scientific research. Suppose that some scientists are using mice for their research. Which of the following choices describes how the mice should be safely handled? **H.3.3.1 CS**

   A. The scientists should keep all the mice in the same cage.

   B. The scientists should give the mice plenty of food and water.

   C. The scientists should wear protective gloves when handling the mice.

   D. The scientists should throw the mice in the trash after the mice die.

SCILINKS.

NSTA
Developed and maintained by the
National Science Teachers Association

For a variety of links related to this chapter, go to www.scilinks.org

Topic: Safety
SciLinks code: HSM1339

Model-Making Lab

OBJECTIVES

Design a model to demonstrate core sampling.

Create a diagram of a classmate's model by using the core sample method.

MATERIALS

- knife, plastic
- clay, modeling (3 or 4 colors)
- pan or box, opaque
- pencil, unsharpened
- pencils or markers (3 or 4 colors)
- pipe, PVC, 1/2 in. diam.

SAFETY

Using Scientific Methods

Geologists often use a technique called *core sampling* to learn what underground rock layers look like. This technique involves drilling several holes in the ground in different places and taking samples of the underground rock or soil. Geologists then compare the samples from each hole at each depth to construct a diagram that shows the bigger picture.

In this activity, you will model the process that geologists use to diagram underground rock layers. You will first use modeling clay to form a rock-layer model. You will then exchange models with a classmate, take core samples, and draw a diagram of your classmate's rock layers.

- Form a plan for your rock layers. Make a sketch of the layers. Your sketch should include the colors of clay in several layers of varying thicknesses. Note: Do not let the classmates who will be using your model see your plan.

- In the pan or box, mold the clay into the shape of the lowest layer in your sketch.

- Repeat the procedure described in the second bulleted item for each additional layer of clay. Exchange your rock-layer model with a classmate.

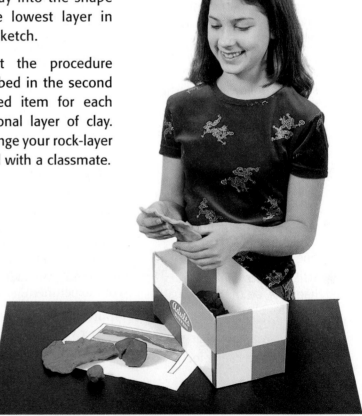

Ask a Question

1 Can unseen features be revealed by sampling parts of the whole?

Form a Hypothesis

2 Form a hypothesis about whether taking core samples from several locations will give a good indication of the entire hidden feature.

Test the Hypothesis

3 Choose three places on the surface of the clay to drill holes. The holes should be far apart and in a straight line. (Do not remove the clay from the pan or box.)

4 Slowly push the PVC pipe through all the layers of clay. Slowly remove the pipe.

5 Gently push the clay out of the pipe with an unsharpened pencil. This clay is a core sample.

6 Draw the core sample, and record your observations. Be sure to use a different color of pencil or marker for each layer.

7 Repeat steps 4–6 for the next two core samples. Make sure your drawings are side by side and in the same order as the samples in the model.

Analyze the Results

1 **Examining Data** Look at the pattern of rock layers in each of your core samples. Think about how the rock layers between the core samples might look. Then, make a diagram of the rock layers.

2 **Organizing Data** Complete your diagram by coloring the rest of each rock layer.

Draw Conclusions

3 **Evaluating Models** Use the plastic knife to cut the clay model along a line connecting the three holes. Remove one side of the model so that you can see the layers. How well does your rock-layer diagram match the model? Explain your answer.

4 **Evaluating Methods** What are some limitations of your diagram as a model of the rock layers?

5 **Drawing Conclusions** Do your conclusions support your hypothesis? Explain your answer.

Applying Your Data

List two ways that the core-sampling method could be improved.

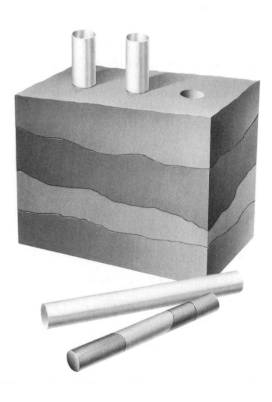

Chapter Review

USING KEY TERMS

Use a term from the chapter to complete each sentence below.

1 The process of gathering knowledge about the natural world is called _____.

2 An explanation that is based on prior scientific research or observations and that can be tested is called a _____.

3 _____ are a series of steps followed to solve problems.

UNDERSTANDING KEY IDEAS

Multiple Choice

4 A good way to investigate answers to scientific questions is to

a. do research only.

b. make observations only.

c. do experiments only.

d. do research, make observations, and do experiments.

5 A pencil measures 14 cm long. How many millimeters long is it?

a. 1.4 mm

b. 140 mm

c. 1,400 mm

d. 1,400,000 mm

6 You are doing a lab in which you use hydrochloric acid. What kind of safety equipment should you wear?

a. goggles

b. goggles and an apron

c. goggles, an apron, and protective gloves

d. goggles, an apron, and heat-resistant gloves

7 Which of the following units is NOT an SI unit?

a. meter   **c.** liter

b. foot   **d.** kelvin

8 Scientists usually take careful notes about what happened during experiments. When the scientists publish their results, they usually include these notes in their report. What is one reason for keeping and publishing detailed notes about experiments? H.1.3.4 AA **FCAT**

a. The notes help other scientists who want to replicate the experiment.

b. The notes allow scientists to publish longer reports.

c. The notes keep the experiments from having to be repeated.

d. The notes prove the scientists' hypotheses.

Short Answer

9 How could a hypothesis that is proven to be false lead to new scientific investigations?

10 Why don't you need to complete the steps of scientific methods in a specific order?

11 What problems could occur if the International System of Units were not used?

12 Which safety symbols would you expect to see for an experiment that requires handling a frog? H.3.3.2

CRITICAL THINKING

Extended Response

13 **Analyzing Ideas** Physicist Dr. Richard Feynman once said, "Science is the belief in the ignorance of experts." How would you interpret Feynman's statement in terms of the way scientific knowledge grows? **H.1.3.1 AA** *FCAT*

14 **Evaluating Conclusions** How could a scientist respond to another scientist who questioned her conclusion?

15 **Identifying Relationships** Science helps us save lives, use resources wisely, and have healthy surroundings. How can healthy surroundings help save lives?

16 **Making Comparisons** Suppose that you are interested in having a job that will help the environment. Explain why you might have trouble deciding between being a science educator or an environmental scientist. **H.1.3.6**

17 **Making Inferences** Often, scientists around the world work on the same problem. For example, scientists in different nations are currently working to find a vaccine or a cure for the AIDS virus. What problems could happen if scientists did not communicate the results of their investigations? **H.1.3.4 AA** *FCAT*

Concept Mapping

18 Use the following terms to create a concept map: *science, scientific methods, hypothesis, problems, experiments, questions,* and *observations.*

INTERPRETING GRAPHICS

Use the graph below to answer the questions that follow.

Atmospheric CO$_2$ (1860–1980)

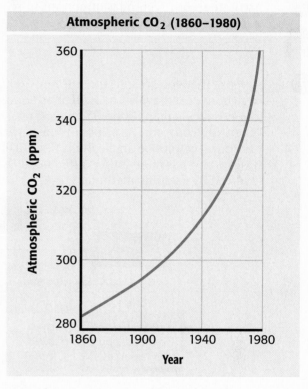

19 Has the amount of CO$_2$ in the atmosphere increased or decreased since 1860?

20 The line on the graph is curved. What does this curve indicate?

21 Was the rate of change in the level of CO$_2$ between 1940 and 1960 higher or lower than it was between 1880 and 1900? How can you tell?

22 What conclusions can you draw from reading this graph?

For the following questions, write your answers on a separate sheet of paper.

1 Accurate record keeping is important in scientific investigations. Give two reasons why this statement is true.

READ
INQUIRE
EXPLAIN

2 Suppose that you are a scientist in the 1600s before the discovery of dinosaurs. You find a large bone. You have seen an elephant once, so you make a hypothesis that the bone you found is an elephant bone. Then, you take the bone to a museum that has elephant bones. When you compare the elephant bones with the bone you found, you realize that the bone you found cannot be an elephant bone. The bone is too large, is too thick, has a different texture, and has many other differences. Examine the diagram below, which shows steps involved in scientific methods.

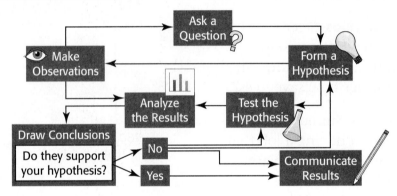

What should you do next?

A. I should discard my hypothesis and put my energy into a different investigation.

B. I should discard my hypothesis, make new observations, and make a new hypothesis that I can test.

C. I should make more observations and stick to my hypothesis so I will not be accused of changing my mind.

D. I should assume that my hypothesis is correct and prepare my observations so that they can be communicated to other scientists.

3 Alli is designing an experiment to see if a connection exists between a person's height and the time that person takes to run 50 meters. Alli wants to use her classmates as test subjects. What do science ethics require Alli to do when designing this experiment?

F. She must not take up too much of the students' time and must inform them about how much time the experiment will take.

G. If she exposes the students to health risks, she must inform the students of the risks and give them the right to refuse to participate.

H. She must not assume that because a person is tall, he or she will be fast. She should give students a second chance to run the 50 meters.

I. She must not subject students to health risks. She should inform the students about any other risks and give them the right to refuse to participate.

4 Luisa ran a controlled experiment. She investigated how dissolving an unknown compound affected the boiling point of water. Using 3 liters of water, she started by determining the boiling point of the water. The water boiled at 100.0°C. Then, she added 100 grams (g) of the unknown compound and brought the mixture to a boil. Then, she tested other amounts of the compound in the same amount of water. Later, she repeated the experiment to verify the effect of the unknown compound on the boiling point of water. The repeated experiment yielded the same results as her first experiment did.

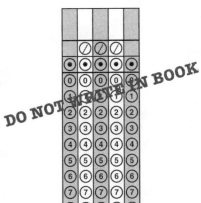

EFFECT OF DIFFERENT AMOUNTS OF AN UNKNOWN SUBSTANCE ON THE BOILING POINT OF WATER

Amount of Substance Added in Grams (g)	Boiling Point of Water in Degrees Celsius (°C) After Substance Added
0.0	100.0
100.0	100.4
200.0	100.8
300.0	101.2

If Luisa dissolved 550 grams of the unknown compound in 3 liters of water, what would be the boiling point of the water?

5 Which of the following statements **best** describes what an environmental scientist, a cartographer, an engineer, a zoologist, and a paleontologist have in common?

A. They are all ethical scientists.

B. They all use scientific methods in their work.

C. They all study organisms and their environments.

D. They all stick to a hypothesis, even if observations do not support it.

6 A scientist publishes results of an investigation in a major scientific journal. Which of the following statements **best** describes what you can assume about those results?

F. that science has solved a problem and the problem needs no more investigation

G. that the case is closed, the results are the truth, and other scientists should accept the results as fact

H. that the results were obtained through poor scientific techniques and more investigation has to be done

I. that the results were obtained through good scientific techniques but they are still subject to more investigation

Science in Action

Science, Technology, and Society

A "Ship" That Flips?

Does your school's laboratory have doors on the floor or tables bolted sideways to the walls? A lab like this exists, and you can find it floating in the ocean. The *Floating Instrument Platform* (FLIP), is a 108 m long ocean research vessel that can tilt 90°. *FLIP* is towed to an area that scientists want to study. Empty chambers within the vessel are filled with water to flip the vessel. *FLIP* begins tilting until almost all of the vessel is underwater. Having most of the vessel below the ocean's surface stabilizes the vessel against wind and waves. Scientists can collect accurate data from the ocean, even during a hurricane!

Social Studies ACTiViTY

Design your own *FLIP*. Make a map on poster board. Draw the layout of a living room, bathroom, and bedroom before your *FLIP* is tilted 90°. Include entrances and walkways to use when *FLIP* is not flipped.

Weird Science

Raining Fish and Frogs

What forms of precipitation have you seen fall from the sky? Rain, snow, hail, sleet, or fish? Wait a minute! Fish? Fish and frogs might not be a form of precipitation, but as early as the second century, they have been reported to fall from the sky during rainstorms. Scientists theorize that tornadoes or waterspouts that pull water into clouds can also pull up unsuspecting fish, frogs, or tadpoles that are near the surface of the water. After being pulled up into the clouds and carried a few miles, these reluctant travelers then rain down from the sky.

Language Arts ACTiViTY

WRITING SKILL You are a reporter for your local newspaper. On a rainy day in spring, while driving to work, you witness a downpour of frogs and fish. You pull off to the side of the road and interview other witnesses. Write an article describing this event for your local newspaper.

Wes Skiles

Diver and Cave Explorer Wes Skiles started diving in his home state of Florida, where he fell in love with the state's hidden underwater caves. These caves were formed by a system of underground rivers that slowly carved their way through the limestone rock. The caves are part of the Floridan Aquifer, one of the largest aquifers in the United States. Skiles travels through these caves like an underwater astronaut. In a diving suit outfitted with space-age gear, he glides through dark worlds that are as silent as outer space.

Skiles is a diver, a cave explorer, and the executive producer of a film and photography company that is based in Florida. Skiles and the other members of his production team have traveled all over the world to take photos and film movies of underwater caves and other natural water systems. Skiles's movies are usually documentaries about cave exploring or about environmental stresses on water systems. His award-winning movies have been shown in IMAX theaters and on television. By watching Skiles's movies, you can learn about the beauty and the life of underwater caves and the importance of preserving these ecosystems.

Math ACTIVITY

The Devil's Eye cave system is located northwest of Gainesville, Florida. The system has 30,000 ft of mapped underwater passageways. How many meters of mapped passageway does the cave system have? (Hint: 1 ft = 0.30 m)

To learn more about these Science in Action topics, visit go.hrw.com and type in the keyword **HT6FSF6F.**

Current Science

Check out Current Science® articles related to this chapter by visiting go.hrw.com. Just type in the keyword **HZ5CS01.**

2

Science and Technology

The Big Idea Science, technology, and society are interwoven and interdependent.

About the PHOTO

This flock of whooping cranes is following an ultralight aircraft piloted by a researcher in a bird suit! The staff of Operation Migration are using technology to teach whooping cranes that were raised in captivity how to migrate between Wisconsin and Florida. Whooping cranes have almost disappeared because of habitat loss. Scientists are helping the species recover by using technology developed specifically for Operation Migration.

PRE-READING ACTIVITY

Table Fold Before you read the chapter, create the FoldNote entitled "Table Fold" described in the **Study Skills** section of the Appendix. Label the columns of the table fold with "Physical models" and "Mathematical models." Label the rows with "Description," "Examples," and "Limitations." As you read the chapter, write examples of each topic under the appropriate column.

START-UP ACTIVITY

What Do Scientists Look Like? H.1.3.6

Do you know any scientists? Maybe you have seen them in movies. What did they look like? What were they doing? What kind of technology did they use? Get out your markers, and draw a scientist in action.

Procedure

1. Form small groups, and brainstorm what scientists look like. Have one group member record your thoughts on a **sheet of paper.**

2. Now, plan the scientist's picture. Remember that you should show the scientist using technology.

3. Use **colored markers** to draw your picture on a **large sheet of paper.**

4. Now, share your pictures with the class, and discuss them.

Analysis

1. In what ways are the pictures similar? In what ways are the pictures different?

2. What does a scientist look like? Where does a scientist work? What tools does a scientist use?

3. What assumptions did your group make about scientists? Were your assumptions correct?

Thinking Like a Scientist

The class party is tomorrow, and you are bringing a gelatin dessert for everyone to eat. As you are mixing the gelatin, you decide to add fresh pineapple chunks. You put the mixture in the refrigerator to set overnight. But in the morning, you find that your dessert is just a pan of yellow liquid with pineapple chunks in it! What happened?

To solve this riddle, you need to think like a scientist. Ask yourself these questions: Did I mix the gelatin enough? Was the water too hot or too cold? Or did the pineapple ruin my dessert? Finally, after some research, you find out that pineapple has an enzyme that prevents gelatin from setting!

Scientific Habits of Mind

Although scientists work in diverse fields, they share certain habits of mind. Scientists are curious, skeptical, open minded, creative, and ethical. And they learn from their mistakes. The inventor Thomas Edison once said that he never failed but that he just found 10,000 ways that did not work.

Curiosity

Scientists are curious about the world around them. For example, **Figure 1** shows a biologist named Jane Goodall. Goodall was very curious about where chimpanzees lived, what they ate, and how they interacted. Curiosity led Goodall to study chimpanzees for more than 30 years. Goodall's questions, research, and writings changed the way that scientists think about chimpanzees and other primates.

Figure 1 *Jane Goodall has studied chimpanzees for more than 30 years. Her curiosity helped her make many discoveries about chimpanzees.*

Skepticism

Skepticism is the practice of questioning accepted ideas or claims. Skepticism helps scientists question the assumptions that influence how we see the world. For example, consider how skepticism helped one scientist uncover a major threat to the environment. Rachel Carson, shown in **Figure 2,** was a biologist in the 1950s. At that time, scientists were developing many new kinds of pesticides to kill insects. Carson was skeptical of the claims made about pesticides by chemical companies. She questioned whether chemicals that killed insects would also harm other living things.

After much research, Carson wrote a book titled *Silent Spring.* The book sparked debates about the use of pesticides in the United States. Some chemical companies threatened to sue Carson and tried to discredit her. But she stood by her findings, and her work led to controls on pesticide use. In particular, *Silent Spring* led to the banning of a chemical called *DDT,* which had threatened bald eagle populations in the United States. By being skeptical and continually asking questions, Carson encouraged others to think about the world around them.

Reading Check Why is skepticism important in science?

Openness to New Ideas

A scientist needs to keep an open mind. This practice is harder than it sounds. Often, people make assumptions about the world based on what they are used to. By keeping an open mind and reporting exactly what you see, you can make sure that you ask the right questions and that your results are accurate.

Figure 2 *Rachel Carson was skeptical of the claims made by pesticide manufacturers. Her research helped bald eagles recover from the effects of pesticides in the environment.*

A Penny for Your Thoughts

1. Predict the number of drops of water that you can place on the head of a penny. Record your prediction.
2. Place a **penny,** with the head facing up, flat on a **table**.
3. Fill an **eyedropper** with **water.**
4. Count the number of drops of water that you can place on the penny. Stop counting when the water runs down the side of the penny.
5. How many drops of water were you able to place on the penny? Was your prediction correct? Explain.

skepticism a habit of mind in which a person questions the validity of accepted ideas

Figure 3 *Creativity helped Andy Michael write "Earthquake Quartet #1." He says that writing the music changed how he thinks about earthquakes.*

Imagination and Creativity

In addition to being curious, skeptical, and open minded, scientists need to be creative and imaginative. Being creative helps scientists think about the world in new or different ways. For example, **Figure 3** shows a scientist who used his imagination to connect earthquakes with music! Andy Michael is a seismologist, a scientist who studies earthquakes. Michael also plays the trombone, and he wrote a piece of music called "Earthquake Quartet #1" for a trombone, a cello, and a vocalist. In the piece, he makes his trombone sound like the tension that builds up inside Earth before an earthquake. He also adds earthquake sounds to the music. He says that writing earthquake music helped him realize that seismologists do not often notice tension building up in Earth's crust because, like the rhythm in a song, the tension is always present.

Intellectual Honesty

Science also depends on honesty. Imagine what would happen if you lied about the results of your experiments and other scientists thought that your results were true. In 1989, two groups of scientists were researching the potential of cold fusion. The goal of *cold fusion* is to join the nuclei of two atoms at low temperatures. If cold fusion were achieved, it would create cheap, limitless energy for the world. One group feared that the other group would publish its results first and become famous. So, members of the first group wrote an article claiming that they had achieved cold fusion even though they had not.

The scientific community was thrilled at first, but no one could repeat the group's results, and the scientists were discredited. To ensure honesty, scientists have their work reviewed by other scientists before it is published. This process, which is called *peer review,* is very important in science. Whether scientists are working in a research lab, for a corporation, or for the government, they must be honest.

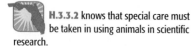 **H.3.3.1 CS** knows that science ethics demand that scientists must not knowingly subject coworkers, students, the neighborhood, or the community to health or property risks.

H.3.3.2 knows that special care must be taken in using animals in scientific research.

H.3.3.3 knows that in research involving human subjects, the ethics of science require that potential subjects be fully informed about the risks and benefits associated with the research and of their right to refuse to participate.

H.3.3.5 understands that contributions to the advancement of science, mathematics, and technology have been made by different kinds of people, in different cultures, at different times, and are an intrinsic part of the development of human culture.

Ethical Responsibility

Scientists must never subject anyone's property or any living thing to unnecessary harm. Ethics help guide scientists as they conduct research. For example, scientists must use compassion when they care for animals used in research. If scientists involve people in research, the scientists must first explain the risks that people may face. This practice is known as *informed consent*. When people are informed of risks, they may refuse to participate. Many organizations monitor ethics in science. The American Association for the Advancement of Science (AAAS), the world's largest scientific and engineering association, creates ethics guidelines for scientific research.

Benchmark Check What is informed consent? **H.3.3.1 CS**

What Does a Scientist Look Like?

What do you think of when someone says the word *scientist*? Do you imagine a man who has crazy white hair and who wears glasses and a white lab coat? There is a great diversity of scientists working to help us understand how the world works. **Figure 4** shows a few of the faces of science.

Figure 4   The Faces of Science

Ⓐ Mae Jemison was a NASA mission specialist. Now, she is adapting space technology to improve the lives of people in West Africa.

Ⓑ David Ho is a researcher who developed new treatments for the virus that causes AIDS.

Ⓒ Stephen Hawking is a theoretical physicist who has changed how we think about the universe.

Figure 5 *You should carefully analyze marketing claims. Advertisers may distort science to convince you to buy their products.*

WRITING SKILL Critiquing the News

With a family member, read a news article, or watch a news broadcast about a current issue in science. In your **science journal,** write your first reactions. Include your thoughts, feelings, and questions. Then, answer these questions:

- Did the report present different sides of the issue?
- Did the report use images or words that made you feel a certain way?
- Did the report provide any facts that helped you form an opinion? Were sources provided for the facts?
- Is there any information that was *not* provided but that might be important?
- When you think more about the issue, does your opinion change?

ACTIVITY

Scientific Literacy

The goal of science education is to improve scientific literacy. **Scientific literacy** is the understanding of the methods of scientific inquiry, the scope of scientific knowledge, and the role of science in society.

Although you may not become a scientist, learning science and becoming scientifically literate give you skills to use in your daily life. Science teaches you how to ask questions and how to find answers. Science helps you make careful observations. Science teaches you to think logically about information and teaches you how to decide whether information is true. Studying science will help you become a better-informed consumer. For example, look at the acne products shown in **Figure 5.** How many of the claims made on the packages can be proven scientifically?

Critical Thinking and Science

All successful scientists have good critical-thinking skills. When you think critically about something, you think clearly, logically, practically, and realistically. You also gather information, ask questions, make inferences, and strive to be objective.

The key to critical thinking is to evaluate the information that you find and to ask yourself if the information makes sense. Ask yourself if the person who presents the information is trying to persuade you. Find out how the information was gathered. Ask yourself if the research was conducted scientifically. Also, find other sources, and find out if they support the claims being made. Finally, analyze how your opinions might influence how you interpret information. Critical thinking is especially important when you are gathering information from the Internet. Many Web sites are designed to make you feel or think a certain way. So, practice your critical-thinking skills when using the Internet.

Reading Check What are three methods to evaluate a source?

Science in Our World

Science is not something that happens only in the laboratory or in the classroom. Science is a process. It is a way of thinking about the world. Every day, ordinary people make important contributions to the advancement of science. People can help scientists in many ways—from discovering comets to helping plant trees. And because science affects everyone, people and communities often speak out on scientific issues that concern them. These issues can include local and global environmental conditions, the research funded by governments, and the ethical questions raised by scientific research. Let's take a closer look at the connections between science and society.

Scientists as Citizens

Scientists play a public role in society, and they use their knowledge and skills to help improve our lives. For example, Mario Molina, shown in **Figure 6,** has worked tirelessly to protect the ozone layer. When he was a graduate student in the 1970s, Molina investigated chemical compounds called *CFCs*. These chemicals were widely used in aerosol sprays and as refrigerants. Molina discovered that these chemicals could damage the ozone layer that protects Earth from the sun's harmful ultraviolet (UV) radiation.

Although Molina warned scientists and others about his discovery, it took a long time for some people to believe him. He worked for many years to educate people about the link between CFCs and ozone destruction. Finally, in the 1990s, the use of CFCs was banned in most of the world. Today, Molina continues his research to help reduce the effects of harmful pollutants in the atmosphere.

scientific literacy the understanding of the methods of scientific inquiry, the scope of scientific knowledge, and the role of science in society

H.3.3.6 knows that no matter who does science and mathematics or invents things, or when or where they do it, the knowledge and technology that result can eventually become available to everyone.

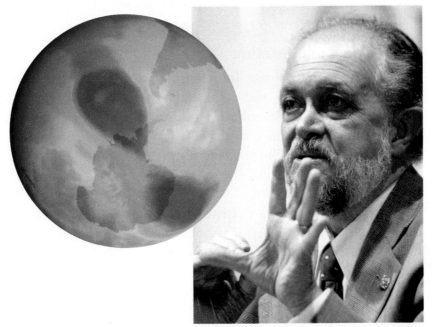

Figure 6 *Mario Molina was awarded the Nobel Prize for his efforts to find the link between CFCs and ozone destruction. In the image of the Earth to the left, the ozone hole is shown in purple.*

Figure 7 *The Oceanography Camp for Girls inspires girls to use chemistry, physics, math, and engineering to study the oceans of the world.*

From the Classroom to the World

In science, the world is your classroom. If you are interested in science, there are many ways to be involved. There are no limits to what you can do. For example, **Figure 7** shows the Oceanography Camp for Girls in Pinellas County. At the camp, high school girls have fun conducting lab experiments, interviewing scientists, and spending a day on a research ship.

Teenagers in Central Florida started a program called *H.O.O.T,* which stands for *Helping Out Owls Together.* The students were concerned about the lack of owl nesting areas in a local park. They researched owls and then worked with scientists to design owl nests. Local businesses donated materials to build the nests. Members of H.O.O.T. are now studying how the owls use their new nests and are designing nests for other owls.

Classroom Collaboration

Your class can participate in science projects that link classrooms around the world. One such project is the JASON Project. Each year, scientists working on the project lead students, teachers, and other scientists on a virtual two-week research trip. You might explore a rain forest, a desert, a volcano, or the ocean. Students chat online with researchers, participate in digital labs, and keep notes in online journals. If your class cannot participate in online projects, you can do a science project at your school. If there is a local science museum, offer to volunteer in the museum's education department or to be an intern. You can rub elbows with scientists, and your volunteer work might even become a paid job!

H.3.3.5 understands that contributions to the advancement of science, mathematics, and technology have been made by different kinds of people, in different cultures, at different times, and are an intrinsic part of the development of human culture.

Summary

- Scientists are curious, creative, skeptical, and open to new ways of thinking about the world.

- It is important that scientists are honest and ethical in their treatment of humans and animals. H.3.3.1 CS, H.3.3.2, H.3.3.3

- People from diverse backgrounds have made many contributions to the advancement of science. H.3.3.5

- Increasing scientific literacy and developing critical-thinking skills are goals of science education.

- Scientists always evaluate the credibility of information that they receive.

- Scientists can have public roles in society. In addition to explaining scientific concepts to the media, scientists work to improve the quality of people's lives. H.3.3.6

- There are many opportunities to participate in science programs in your community.

Using Key Terms

1. Write an original definition for *skepticism* and *scientific literacy*.

Understanding Key Ideas

2. Defend the idea that curiosity, skepticism, and openness to new ideas are important in science.

3. Provide evidence to support why it is important for scientists to follow a code of ethics when conducting research. H.3.3.1 CS, H.3.3.2, H.3.3.3

4. Evaluate two common stereotypes about scientists. H.3.3.5

5. Describe some public roles that scientists have. Describe as many examples as you can of how scientists affect society. H.3.3.6

6. Describe a volunteer science opportunity that interests you.

Critical Thinking

7. **Expressing Opinions** Do you think that scientists should have a different code of ethics for working with animals than for working with people? Explain. H.3.3.2

8. **Evaluating Sources** Explain why scientists must always evaluate sources of information. Why is it important to be particularly skeptical of information found on the Internet?

FCAT Preparation

9. A scientist has developed an experimental drug to treat migraine headaches. She is very excited about the results of lab tests that she conducted using computer models. So, now she is going to test the drug on humans to prove that it works. Which of the following is a reason that this decision could violate a scientific code of ethics? H.3.3.1 CS

   A. She is testing the drug on humans before testing it by computer modeling.

   B. She is testing the drug on humans without identifying an independent variable.

   C. She is testing the drug on humans before determining whether the drug has dangerous side effects.

   D. She is testing the drug on humans before testing it on herself.

SCILINKS®

NSTA

Developed and maintained by the National Science Teachers Association

For a variety of links related to this chapter, go to www.scilinks.org

Topic: Careers in Science
SciLinks code: HSM0225

Models in Science

What do a crash-test dummy, a mathematical equation, and a road map have in common? All of them are models that represent real things.

A **model** is a representation of an object or a process that allows scientists to study something in greater detail. Models also allow scientists to change variables without affecting or harming the subject that they are studying. For example, scientists use crash-test dummies to study the effects of car accidents on people.

Models can represent things that are too small to see, such as atoms. Models can also represent things that are too large to see completely, such as Earth or the solar system. Models can also be used to explain the past and present and to predict the future. Two common types of scientific models are physical models and mathematical models.

Physical Models

Physical models are models that you can touch. Physical models often look like the things they represent. But physical models have limitations. For example, because Earth is round, a globe is the most accurate representation of Earth. But to make a map, you create a flat model of Earth's surface. In the process of making a map, you change the distances between points and the map becomes inaccurate, as shown in **Figure 1.**

✓ **Reading Check** Why are globes more accurate physical models of Earth than maps are?

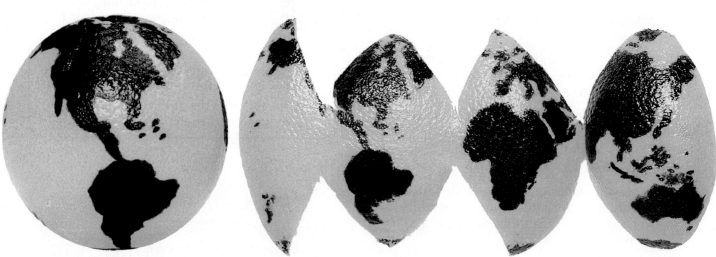

Figure 1 *If you remove and flatten an orange peel, the peel will stretch and tear. Notice how the shapes of the continents change when the orange peel is flattened.*

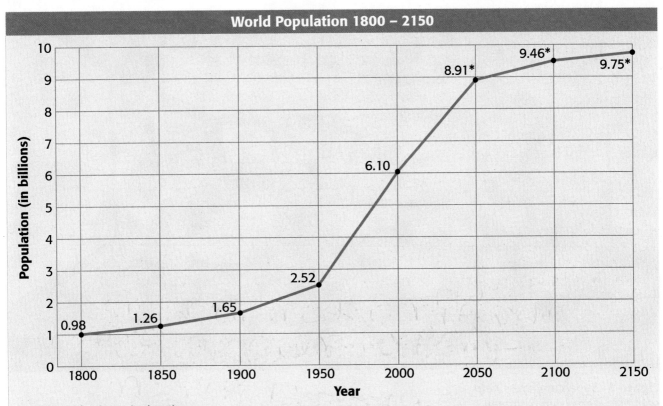

World Population 1800 – 2150

Population (in billions) vs *Year*

0.98 (1800), 1.26 (1850), 1.65 (1900), 2.52 (1950), 6.10 (2000), 8.91* (2050), 9.46* (2100), 9.75* (2150)

* Projected by the United Nations
  Source: Population Division of the Department of Economic and Social Affairs of the United Nations Secretariat.

Mathematical Models

A *mathematical model* is made up of mathematical equations and data. Some mathematical models are simple. These models allow you to calculate things such as how far a car will travel in an hour or how much you would weigh on the moon. Other models are so complex that computers are needed to process them. **Figure 2** shows a graph created by computer models of population growth. Because so many variables affect population changes, scientists use computers to create mathematical models of population growth.

Figure 2 *This graph was the product of mathematical models that were processed by a computer.*

model a pattern, plan, representation, or description designed to show the structure or workings of an object, system, or concept

Graphing To learn more about graphs, refer to **Figure 2** and follow the steps below.

Step 1: The horizontal axis is called the *x-axis*. In this graph, the *x*-axis indicates time. Locate the year 1850 on the *x*-axis.

Step 2: The vertical axis is called the *y-axis*. In this graph, the *y*-axis indicates world population. Find the world population in 1850. *(The world population was 1.26 billion.)*

Now It's Your Turn

1. What is the difference in population between 1800 and 1900? What is the difference in population between 1900 and 2000?

2. If the graph were the same size but showed the world population from 1000 to 2150, what would the graph look like?

3. Why is it important that a graph has a title and that the *x*-axis and the *y*-axis are labeled?

Figure 3 *Supercomputers help scientists create very complex models that predict the results of climate change.*

Computers and Climate Models

You can imagine how hard it is to predict the weather next week, so how can scientists predict Earth's climate 1,000 years from now? Scientists use complex mathematical models to track all of the variables that affect Earth's climate. A climate model is like a complicated recipe that has thousands of ingredients. The amount of each ingredient is constantly changing. To make things worse, when one variable changes, it can affect all of the other variables.

To model climate change, researchers must first identify the variables that they want to include in their model. Climate models include information about land and ocean-water temperatures around Earth. The models also include information about cloud cover, snow and ice cover, ocean currents, and carbon dioxide levels in the atmosphere.

Computers to the Rescue!

You may wonder how a model can be created with so much data. Powerful supercomputers that can make more than 30 trillion calculations every second help scientists process these data. As **Figure 3** shows, supercomputers process climate data from around the world to simulate climate change. These models do not make exact predictions about future climates, but they estimate what might happen if variables change.

 Benchmark Check How do computers extend our ability to predict climate change? **H.3.3.7**

 H.1.3.1 AA knows that scientific knowledge is subject to modification as new information challenges prevailing theories and as a new theory leads to looking at old observations in a new way.

 H.2.3.1 CS recognizes that patterns exist within and across systems.

 H.3.3.7 knows that computers speed up and extend people's ability to collect, sort, and analyze data; prepare research reports; and share data and ideas with others.

Patterns in Nature

It is possible for scientists to make models because events in nature often follow predictable patterns. For example, if you drop a ball from a certain height, you can predict how high it will bounce. Another pattern in nature is yearly migration of some animals. Observing patterns in nature is the basis of science. These observations lead to explanations about the way the world works. Although these explanations are supported by observations, they may not be accurate. For example, **Figure 4** shows that the sun appears to move across the sky. For thousands of years, people observed this pattern and concluded that Earth was the center of the universe.

Theories and Laws

Observing patterns in the natural world can lead to the development of scientific theories and laws. The words *law* and *theory* have special meanings to scientists. In science, a **law** is a statement or equation that reliably predicts events under certain conditions. A theory is not a guess, or hypothesis. A **theory** is a scientific explanation that encompasses many scientific observations and may include many hypotheses and laws.

You might think that scientific theories are less important or less useful than scientific laws. But theories are very powerful explanations of the way the world works. Theories do not eventually become laws if they are proven true. Instead, theories are fully formed scientific explanations that are supported by evidence and data from many scientific disciplines.

law a descriptive statement or equation that reliably predicts events under certain conditions

theory a system of ideas that explains many related observations and is supported by a large body of evidence acquired through scientific investigation

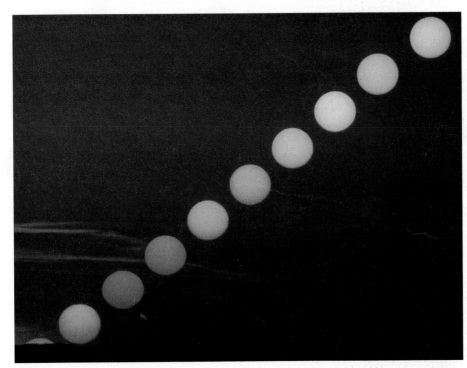

Figure 4 *For thousands of years, people watched the sun appear to move across the sky. From this pattern, they developed a theory that Earth was the center of the universe.*

A Community Solar System
The world's largest solar system model is in Peoria, Illinois. This model shows the distance between the planets and the sun and shows the relative sizes of these bodies. The 11 m–wide dome of a planetarium represents the sun, and the 2.5 cm–wide Pluto is in a furniture store 64 km from the planetarium! With your class, plan a solar system model in your community.

ACTIVITY

Theories Are Supported by Scientific Observations

Like all scientific theories, the theory of an Earth-centered universe was supported by a wealth of scientific evidence. Physics, astronomy, and geography seemed to confirm this idea. But even if a theory is supported by most scientific evidence, the theory may not be correct. After many careful observations, scientists developed a new theory that Earth and all of the other planets travel around the sun, as shown in **Figure 5.** Although this theory is correct, scientists could not explain why the planets travel around the sun. A scientific law helped explain that observation.

Benchmark Check How did the theory of the structure of the solar system change? **H.1.3.1 AA**

Laws Can Support Theories

In science, a law describes things that happen during certain conditions and circumstances. Scientific laws are usually mathematical models. In 1665, Sir Isaac Newton discovered the *law of universal gravitation.* This law states that all objects in the universe, including the sun and planets, attract each other with a force called *gravity.* Gravity holds the planets in their orbit as they travel around the sun. Scientists used this law to explain why the planets travel around the sun. In this way, the theory of a sun-centered solar system was strengthened.

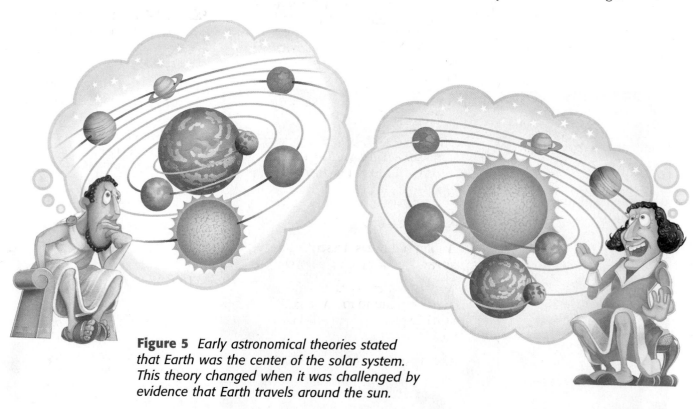

Figure 5 *Early astronomical theories stated that Earth was the center of the solar system. This theory changed when it was challenged by evidence that Earth travels around the sun.*

Limitations of Models

Although models are important scientific tools, all models are limited because they are simplified versions of the systems that they attempt to explain. Simplification makes a model easy to understand and use, but information is left out when a model is created. You should also remember that all models can change. Models can change if a scientist finds new data or comes up with a new way to think about things. Scientists work to continually improve the models that we use to understand the world. Sometimes, new technology challenges existing models. Other times, technology helps create new models that allow us to understand the world in a different way.

INTERNET ACTIVITY

Maps of the Future

How is technology changing maps? Go to **go.hrw.com**, and type in the keyword **HZ5MAPW** to find out!

H.1.3.1 AA knows that scientific knowledge is subject to modification as new information challenges prevailing theories and as a new theory leads to looking at old observations in a new way.

SECTION Review

Summary

- Physical models and mathematical models are common scientific models.

- Scientists must choose the right type of model to study a topic.

- Climate models have so many variables that supercomputers are needed to process the data. **H.3.3.7**

- Events in nature usually follow patterns. Scientists develop theories and laws by observing these patterns. **H.2.3.1 CS**

- Theories and laws are models that describe how the universe works. Theories and laws can change as new information becomes available. **H.1.3.1 AA**

Using Key Terms

1. Write an original definition for *law* and *theory*.

Understanding Key Ideas

2. Why do scientists use models?

3. Describe how computers have helped scientists develop more-accurate climate models. **H.3.3.7**

4. Explain which type of model you would use to study the flight of birds.

5. Give examples of physical and mathematical models.

6. Give one example of how a law or a theory changed when new information became available. **H.1.3.1 AA**

Critical Thinking

7. **Analyzing Ideas** Describe one advantage of physical models.

8. **Applying Concepts** Do all events in nature follow a pattern? Explain why or why not. **H.2.3.1 CS**

9. **Applying Concepts** What is the difference between theories and laws? Are laws better than theories? Explain your answer.

FCAT Preparation

10. Copernicus's theory of a sun-centered solar system was developed based on the observations of many astronomers that came before him. Copernicus used this data to develop his theories.

PART A What role did the observations of early astronomers play in the development of Copernicus's theory?

PART B Describe how technology such as a telescope would have helped early astronomers develop more-accurate models of the solar system. **H.1.3.1 AA**

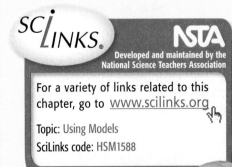

SCILINKS

NSTA

Developed and maintained by the National Science Teachers Association

For a variety of links related to this chapter, go to www.scilinks.org

Topic: Using Models
SciLinks code: HSM1588

READING WARM-UP

Objectives

- Describe the roles of engineering and science in the development of technology.
- Describe three constraints that could affect technological design. H.3.3.4 CS
- Explain the relationship between science, technology, and society. H.3.3.6
- Explain how technology presents risks and benefits. H.3.3.1 CS
- Describe three technological tools used by scientists and science students. H.3.3.7

Terms to Learn

technology   engineering

READING STRATEGY

Paired Summarizing Read this section silently. In pairs, take turns summarizing the material. Stop to discuss ideas that seem confusing.

technology the use of tools, machines, materials, and processes to meet human needs

Technology

Your digital alarm clock wakes you up, and you take a hot shower while listening to your waterproof MP3 player. As you microwave your breakfast, you send a text message to a friend in another state. You continue the conversation as you head out the door to catch the bus.

It is not difficult to find examples of technology in your life. Even if your morning routine is simply to roll out of bed and run out the door, you use technology.

What Is Technology?

When you think about technology, you might think about electronic gadgets that beep and blink. But even the door you close when you leave your house is an example of technology. In fact, technology does not even have to be a thing. Simply put, **technology** is the development and application of tools, materials, and processes to help meet human needs. Technology is often adapted and changed for different uses. For example, Aborigines, Australia's first peoples, invented the boomerang as a hunting tool more than 25,000 years ago. Over time, boomerang design changed, and the ancient hunting tool began to be used as a toy, as shown in **Figure 1.**

Figure 1 *The boomerang is an example of technology that was developed to meet the basic human need for food. Today, it is used as a toy.*

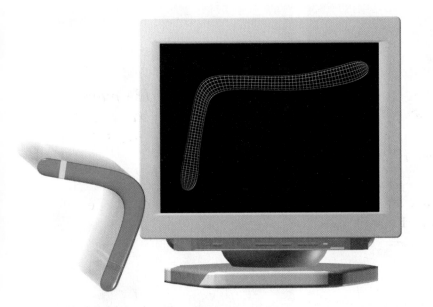

Figure 2 *Dimantchev's boomerang was developed by using computer models. The final design is made of fiberglass, carbon fiber, and resin.*

How Constraints Affect Technological Design

If you draw a plan for an invention on a napkin, you are limited only by your imagination. You can imagine that the rules of physics have changed—that gravity does not exist, for example. However, when scientists develop technology, they must consider a variety of constraints that could affect their design. A scientist might consider the following questions when developing technology: What scientific laws influence my design? What are the properties of the materials that I can use? Is my design too expensive for people to use? Do politics influence my design? Is my design safe? Finally, is my design attractive? One key principle of technological design is that there is usually more than one solution for a problem.

Benchmark Check Give an example of how constraints such as natural laws and values can influence technological design. **H.3.3.4 CS**

Building a Better Boomerang

Inventor Georgi Dimantchev wanted to develop a boomerang that could stay aloft for as long as possible. As **Figure 2** shows, he used the principles of engineering to reinvent this 25,000-year-old tool. **Engineering** is the use of science and mathematics to solve real-life problems. Engineers work with energy sources and the properties of matter to meet human needs.

To engineer his boomerang, Dimantchev used a mathematical model of the dynamics of boomerang flight. To develop the final design for his boomerang, he used computer-modeling software to determine the boomerang's shape. He selected high-tech materials to make the boomerang as light and stiff as possible. All of this hard work was worthwhile—the boomerang that he created can stay in the air for more than 10 minutes!

engineering the application of science and mathematics to solve real-life problems

H.3.3.4 CS knows that technological design should require taking into account constraints such as natural laws, the properties of the materials used, and economic, political, social, ethical, and aesthetic values.

Figure 3 *A system of bar codes and lasers was developed by NASA to track rocket parts. Protective clothing for fire-fighters also uses technology from space programs.*

How Does Technology Relate to Science?

Science and technology are not the same. Science is a process of studying the natural world. Technology is the development of solutions to meet human needs. However, science and technology support each other. A new scientific finding might influence the development of technology. New technology can also give scientists better tools to study the world. For example, the first telescopes were probably invented for military purposes, not for astronomy. But in 1609, Galileo Galilei adapted the telescope to study the stars and planets. Galileo used his telescope to discover Jupiter's moons and Saturn's rings. These findings led to a new understanding of the solar system.

Spinoffs

Technology is often used to meet needs that are very different from the needs for which it was developed. For example, technology developed by governments or for militaries often becomes available to everyone. These technologies are known as *spinoffs*. Some well-known spinoffs from military technologies include radar, satellite tracking systems, mass production, and nuclear power. Space programs have also generated a long list of spinoffs that have benefited daily life. Spinoffs from space programs include smoke detectors, artificial hearts, cordless power tools, and surgical lasers, as well as the examples shown in **Figure 3.**

Benchmark Check List three examples of military and space technologies that have become available to everyone. H.3.3.6

H.3.3.1 CS knows that science ethics demand that scientists must not knowingly subject coworkers, students, the neighborhood, or the community to health or property risks.

H.3.3.6 knows that no matter who does science and mathematics or invents things, or when or where they do it, the knowledge and technology that result can eventually become available to everyone.

Risks and Benefits of Technology

Technological advances have brought many benefits to today's society. Technology has helped people live longer, healthier lives. It has also allowed people to communicate and to share more information than they could before. However, technology also introduces risks and challenges. People must be aware of the risks and benefits of technology so that they can make informed decisions. How people evaluate the risks and benefits of technology is influenced by the values that they consider important. To explore this idea further, consider the debate over the use of a chemical technology called *DDT*.

Evaluating Risks and Benefits

DDT is a pesticide that was widely used in the 1950s and 1960s to kill the mosquito that carries the disease malaria. The pesticide was highly effective, and in some countries, it virtually eliminated malaria. According to the World Health Organization, DDT prevented 5 million deaths in the first eight years of its use.

Eventually, scientists discovered that DDT was killing fish and harming bird populations. So, DDT was banned in the United States and in many other countries. But malaria is still a serious problem in many parts of the world. As shown in **Figure 4,** some countries have begun to use DDT again because many people think that the danger of malaria outweighs the environmental risks of DDT. The debate over the use of DDT will continue as scientists search for alternatives.

CONNECTION TO Social Studies

Malaria and DDT Debate
Malaria is the second leading cause of death in Africa. Chemicals such as DDT are very effective in killing the mosquitoes that carry the disease, but using DDT poses environmental risks. Form two groups, and research the use of DDT. Then, have a class debate about the risks and benefits of using this chemical technology. One group should defend the use of DDT. The other group should argue for alternative ways to control malaria.

ACTIVITY

Figure 4 *Spraying DDT in South Africa has greatly reduced malaria outbreaks. In neighboring Mozambique, where DDT is not used, malaria is the leading cause of death.*

Technology in Science

Although scientific tools can be highly specialized for a particular field, some kinds of technology are used in a wide variety of scientific fields. Let's take a closer look at some of the tools that scientists commonly use today.

Computers

Computers have changed how scientists research, conduct experiments, analyze data, and communicate results. Computers can quickly manipulate and analyze vast amounts of data. This ability makes them useful for modeling complex systems and physical structures. For example, engineers can use computer models to test the performance of aircraft designs in extreme weather. Computer models help engineers develop new designs without building the aircraft or testing a model in wind tunnels. As computers become more powerful, scientists can answer increasingly complex questions about the world.

Benchmark Check Why are computers useful in science? **H.3.3.7**

The Global Positioning System

H.3.3.7 knows that computers speed up and extend people's ability to collect, sort, and analyze data; prepare research reports; and share data and ideas with others.

The global positioning system (GPS) is a network of satellites that orbit Earth. The GPS is shown in **Figure 5.** These satellites broadcast microwave signals that are picked up by GPS receivers on Earth. A GPS receiver uses the signals to determine its location with great accuracy. Scientists use the GPS in many ways, including in tracking wildlife, recording the location of fossil discoveries, and gathering data to create maps.

Figure 5 How GPS Works

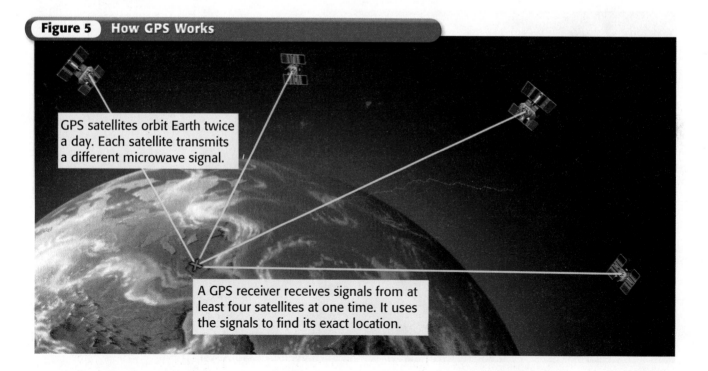

GPS satellites orbit Earth twice a day. Each satellite transmits a different microwave signal.

A GPS receiver receives signals from at least four satellites at one time. It uses the signals to find its exact location.

Geographic Information Systems

Geographic information systems (GIS) are computerized systems that visually present information about an area. GIS organizes information in overlapping layers. Scientists can compare the layers to answer questions. **Figure 6** shows how GIS helped plan conservation areas for Florida black bears near Ocala National Forest.

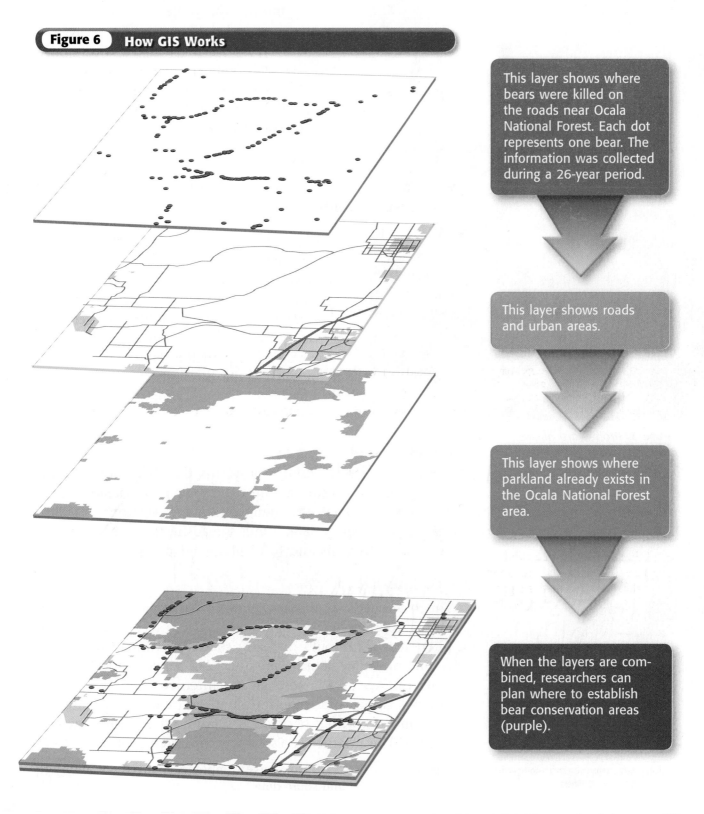

Figure 6 How GIS Works

This layer shows where bears were killed on the roads near Ocala National Forest. Each dot represents one bear. The information was collected during a 26-year period.

This layer shows roads and urban areas.

This layer shows where parkland already exists in the Ocala National Forest area.

When the layers are combined, researchers can plan where to establish bear conservation areas (purple).

Technology in the Classroom

Ask an adult to describe his or her middle school science classes. There were probably desks and chairs, but the technology used might be different from the technology that you use. In many classrooms, marker boards, multimedia projectors, and computers have replaced chalkboards, film projectors, and slide rules. Although new technology has changed science classrooms, the basic methods of scientific research are unchanged. Let's explore some technological tools in the modern classroom.

Probeware

Probeware is a system of probes, hardware, and software that are used to gather and display data for analysis. Probeware is a powerful scientific tool because it allows you to gather data in the field, as shown in **Figure 7.** Probeware also allows you to take very accurate measurements. By using probeware, you can measure temperature, dissolved oxygen, pH, pressure, motion, and many other variables. After you have gathered data, you can share them with other students. These data can then be graphed by a computer or a graphing calculator.

Figure 7 *Probeware allows science students to collect accurate data in the field.*

Spreadsheets

Spreadsheets are computer programs that help organize and display data. By using a spreadsheet, you can organize large amounts of data quickly. Then, you can create graphs and tables that clearly display data. Using spreadsheets is a good way to develop math skills and to display your project data.

The Internet

The Internet is a military spinoff that may be one of the most important technological advances in recent history. The Internet is a computer network that allows interactive global communication. Because anyone who has a connected computer can access the Internet, the Internet has revolutionized how we gather and share information. By using the Internet, you can work with other students around the world to explore science. The Internet is also a great research tool.

H.3.3.7 knows that computers speed up and extend people's ability to collect, sort, and analyze data; prepare research reports; and share data and ideas with others.

Benchmark Check How have computers changed our ability to collect, organize, and share data? **H.3.3.7**

Summary

- Technology is the development and application of tools, materials, and processes to meet human needs.

- Engineering is the use of science and mathematics to solve real-world problems.

- Engineers and scientists must consider natural laws, the properties of materials, and a variety of values in the planning and creation of a final product. **H.3.3.4 CS**

- Science and technology support each other. Society benefits from the contributions made by science. **H.3.3.5, H.3.3.6**

- To make informed decisions, people must be aware of the risks and benefits of technology. **H.3.3.1 CS**

- Computers, the GPS, and GIS are important technology used by scientists. Probeware, spreadsheets, and the Internet are often used in the science classroom. **H.3.3.7**

Using Key Terms

1. Write an original definition for *technology*.

Understanding Key Ideas

2. Describe three examples of spinoffs. **H.3.3.6**

3. Analyze the risks and benefits of car air bags.

4. Distinguish between the GPS and a GIS.

5. Describe how probeware, spreadsheets, and the Internet are used in science. **H.3.3.7**

6. Describe the role of engineering in the development of technology. **H.3.3.4 CS**

7. Describe three constraints that affect technological design. **H.3.3.4 CS**

Critical Thinking

8. **Making Inferences** Describe three ways an engineer might improve the design of a bicycle.

9. **Applying Concepts** Describe the relationship between science, technology, and society. **H.3.3.5 CS**

10. **Evaluating Assumptions** Evaluate the idea that modern technology has improved the quality of human life. Then, write a balanced essay describing two viewpoints on this idea.

11. **Making Comparisons** Imagine the kinds of technology that could be available to science students in 20 years. Illustrate the science classroom of the future.

FCAT Preparation

12. A scientist is developing an experimental airplane that can fly in the upper atmosphere. The airplane could fly very fast because it would bounce on the upper layer of the stratosphere. Which of the following is an example of a natural law that could affect the design of the aircraft? **H.3.3.4 CS**

   A. The surface area and shape of the wing generate a certain amount of lift.

   B. A scientist in another country is also working to develop a similar airplane.

   C. The plane could travel at a speed fast enough to endanger the passengers.

   D. The airplane is so expensive to produce that the plane will likely never be used for commercial flights.

SCiLINKS®

NSTA
Developed and maintained by the
National Science Teachers Association

For a variety of links related to this chapter, go to www.scilinks.org

Topic: Science and Technology of Florida
SciLinks code: HSMF14

Skills Practice Lab

Caught in Their Tracks

Help! Art thieves have stolen Jasper Rothkenberg's most famous artwork! The criminals stole the painting in broad daylight, and all they left behind were footprints. Can you help solve this mystery and catch the art thieves? To nab the robbers, you need to use forensic print analysis, which is a forensic science that examines shoe prints. In this activity, you will learn how forensic investigators collect information from shoe prints.

Procedure

1. Answer the following questions in your **science journal:** What information can you obtain from a shoe print? How can this information be used in forensic science?

2. Look at your shoes. If someone could see only your shoe prints, what would they say about you?

3. Your group will obtain a shoe box with a shoe print from your teacher. Examine the shoe print closely, but DO NOT touch the shoe print.

4. Discuss what you can learn about the person that made the shoe print. Record your ideas.

5 Examine the shoe print very closely by using a hand lens or magnifying glass. Record your observations.

6 Measure the shoe print by using a metric ruler. What shoe size do you think the shoe is? Do you think that a man or a woman left the shoe print? Record your observations.

7 Draw a very careful sketch of the print. Make sure that you record every detail that you observe. When you are finished, write a detailed description of the shoe print.

8 Look at some of the other shoe prints in the room. Were any of them made by the same person? How do you know?

9 Now, see if you can practice your shoe-print matching skills. Look at the shoe print left at a crime scene (Exhibit A). Compare it to the shoe prints of the suspects (Exhibit B).

10 Try to find and circle five marks, cuts, or flaws that one of the suspect's shoe prints has in common with the shoe print left at the crime scene. In a court case, 12 matches are needed for shoe-print evidence to be accepted.

11 Decide which suspect left the shoe print at the crime scene.

Analyze the Results

1 **Explaining Events** Describe how flaws on the bottom of a shoe can lead to the identification of suspects.

2 **Analyzing Data** What other information can you tell about the suspect from the shoe print?

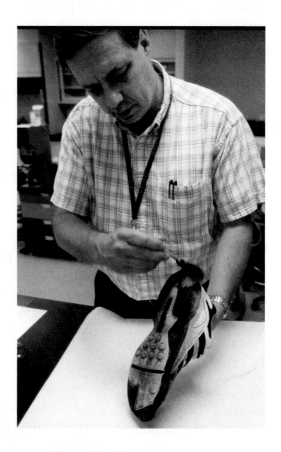

Draw Conclusions

3 **Evaluating Methods** Detectives cannot keep a shoe print forever. What are some ways of cataloging shoe-print evidence?

4 **Evaluating Ideas** Is a shoe print enough evidence to convict the art thieves? What other kinds of evidence would you look for?

Chapter Review

USING KEY TERMS

For each pair of terms, explain how the meanings of the terms differ.

1 *skepticism* and *scientific literacy*

2 *engineering* and *technology*

3 *law* and *theory*

UNDERSTANDING KEY IDEAS

Multiple Choice

4 Scientists must not knowingly subject people to health risks. Which of the following is a health risk that could result from the scientific research of a new drug? **H.3.3.1 CS** *FCAT*

a. The side effects of the drug could harm people.

b. The drug could be too expensive for people to buy.

c. The drug might not treat the disease.

d. The drug test could be inconclusive.

5 To determine the weight of supplies that you could carry in a space shuttle, you would use a

a. visual model.

b. physical model.

c. mathematical model.

d. All of the above

6 Which of the following is a limitation of models?

a. They are too small to see.

b. They are visual.

c. They are too large to see.

d. They are a simplified version of what they represent.

7 A geographic information system

a. uses satellites that broadcast microwave signals to locations around the world.

b. is a visual presentation of scientific information about an area.

c. is a type of climate model.

d. is a system of probes, software, and hardware.

8 Scientific theories are

a. scientific hypotheses.

b. scientific estimates.

c. scientific explanations supported by laws and observations.

d. scientific guesses.

9 People observe the pattern of the sun rising and setting every day. Which of the following is the best explanation for that pattern? **H.2.3.1 CS** *FCAT*

a. The sun orbits Earth, which is at the center of the solar system.

b. Earth orbits the sun, which is at the center of the solar system.

c. The sun moves across the sky every day.

d. Earth moves across the sky every day.

10 Many different kinds of values can influence technological design. Which of the following is a value that affects technological design? **H.3.3.4 CS** *FCAT*

a. the properties of materials

b. natural laws

c. technology

d. ethics

11 Scientific knowledge is subject to change as new information becomes available. Which of the following is an example of how scientific knowledge changes? **H.1.3.1 AA FCAT**

  a. A scientist has her work reviewed by peers before she publishes it.

  b. A scientist conducts an experiment that proves his theories are correct.

  c. A scientist communicates her results in a scientific journal.

  d. A scientist revises his theories after a new discovery is made.

Short Answer

12 Describe three technology spinoffs, and explain the purpose for which they were originally developed. **H.3.3.4**

13 What is the meaning of the term *technology*? Describe five examples of technologies that affect your life.

14 Why is it useful for computers to be able to manipulate large amounts of data? **H.3.3.7**

CRITICAL THINKING

Extended Response

15 Evaluating Sources Why is evaluating sources important in science? Give at least one example of how you have had to evaluate sources when completing a class project.

16 Evaluating Assumptions Is scientific literacy important? How does being scientifically literate help you in your life?

17 Applying Concepts Why is it important for people to be informed of the risks and benefits of technology? Describe one example in which people should be informed of the risks and benefits of technology. **H.3.3.1 CS**

Concept Mapping

18 Use the following terms to create a concept map: *patterns*, *observations*, *theories*, *laws*, and *models*.

INTERPRETING GRAPHICS

Use the graph below to answer the questions that follow.

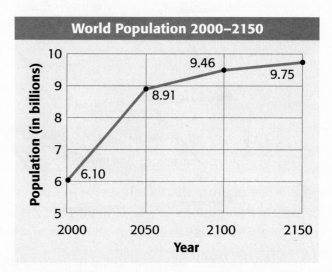

World Population 2000–2150

19 What are the titles on the *x*-axis and *y*-axis of the graph?

20 What is the range of values for the population between 2000 and 2150?

21 During which 50-year period is the projected population increase the greatest? What is the population increase during that period?

For the following questions, write your answers on a separate sheet of paper.

1 Computers and computer technology are used to create geographic information system (GIS) images like the one shown below. That image was used to answer the question: "Where are the best places near Ocala National Forest to create conservation areas for Florida black bears?"

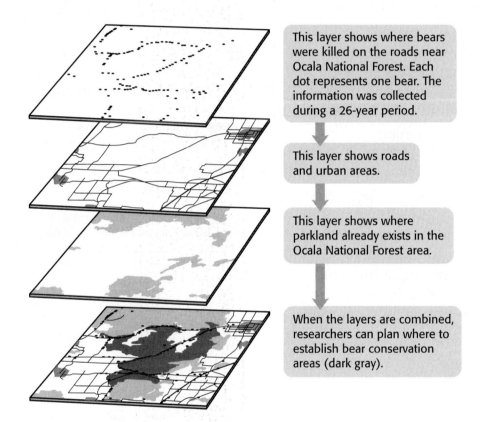

This layer shows where bears were killed on the roads near Ocala National Forest. Each dot represents one bear. The information was collected during a 26-year period.

This layer shows roads and urban areas.

This layer shows where parkland already exists in the Ocala National Forest area.

When the layers are combined, researchers can plan where to establish bear conservation areas (dark gray).

Why is a GIS image more useful than an ordinary map in this situation?

A. because a GIS image is more portable than a map

B. because a GIS image only shows one type of information about an area

C. because a GIS image compares many different types of information about an area

D. because a GIS image includes a composite map that shows the same information as an ordinary map

2 Why is it possible for scientists to make models?

    F.   Events in nature often follow predictable patterns.

    G.   Models are useful in representing patterns in nature.

    H.   Models explain inconsistencies in patterns in nature.

    I.   They need a way to explain unpredictable patterns in nature.

3 Science is a process in which ordinary people can participate. You can make a contribution to science and technology without being a scientist. Which one of the following lists some ways you could do this?

    A.   visiting national parks

    B.   searching for comets and speaking out on scientific issues such as the ethical questions raised by scientific research

    C.   searching the Internet to find out about new scientific and technological developments that affect society

    D.   volunteering to participate in marketing research programs that test new products before they are made available to the public

4 Scientists have an ethical responsibility to avoid subjecting any living thing to unnecessary harm. When scientists use human subjects in their research, they must inform the people of any risks involved and give them the option of not participating in the research. What is this called?

    F.   implied consent

    G.   informed consent

    H.   advise and consent

    I.   consent of the governed

5 During the 1950s, scientists developed new kinds of pesticides to kill insects. People thought that these pesticides could be used to improve the environment and agriculture without harming other living things. A scientist named Rachel Carson thought that pesticides could harm organisms in the environment. She was skeptical of the claims made by pesticide manufacturers and carefully researched and documented the effects of pesticides on the environment.

Part A   Describe how Rachel Carson was skeptical of the claims made by pesticide manufacturers.

Part B   What was the result of Rachel Carson's work?

Science in Action

Science, Technology, and Society

Geocaching

Wouldn't it be exciting to go on a hunt for buried treasure? Thousands of people around the world participate in geocaching, which is an adventure game for GPS users. In this adventure game, individuals and groups of people put caches, or hidden treasures, in places all over the world. Once the cache is hidden, the coordinates of the cache's location are posted on the Internet. Then, geocaching teams compete to find the cache. Geocaching should be attempted only with parental supervision.

Language Arts ACTiViTY

Why was the word *geocaching* chosen for this adventure game? Use the Internet or another source to find the origin and meaning of the word *geocaching*.

Weird Science

Artificial Reefs

Coral-reef ecosystems are some of the most endangered habitats in the world. When coral dies, it can take a very long time to grow back. So, to help restore coral-reef habitat, people have begun making artificial reefs by sinking warships, barges, airplanes, oil rigs, and school buses in the ocean! After a while, coral attaches to these sunken objects and begins to grow. Fish and other coral-reef organisms soon move in. Like natural reefs, artificial reefs provide a home for animals and protect them from predators. Artificial reefs are just one more example of how technology is developed for one purpose and ends up being used for another purpose!

Social Studies ACTiViTY

Research one of the world's major reef systems. Then, create a computer presentation about the coral-reef system. Include information about the importance of the reef system to human communities that live near it.

Carlos Lemos

Geologist If you could take an X ray of the Earth, what would you see? Carlos Lemos, CEO of Ambient Technologies in St. Petersburg, Florida, knows. Lemos is a geologist—a scientist who studies the Earth. Instead of using X-ray machines, Lemos and his employees use tools such as ground-penetrating radar, high-tech drilling equipment, and seismic imaging technology to map the world beneath our feet.

When people want to build anything from a huge shopping mall to a house, they need to know what is beneath the surface, and geologists such as Lemos can help them find out. Lemos can also help when there is an environmental problem underground. From the surface, it is hard to know if the rock and soil are polluted because you cannot see the pollution. For example, it is difficult to know if an old gas station has leaking underground fuel tanks until there is a serious environmental problem. That is where Lemos comes in. His training in geology and geophysics helps him study underground pollution and map the path of pollutants from their source. By drilling beneath the surface, Lemos and his employees take samples of soil, rock, and water. By studying these samples, Lemos can determine how far the pollution has spread, where it is headed, and what it will take to stop the problem.

Math ACTIVITY

An underground storage tank contains 500 L of fuel, and it is leaking fuel at a rate of 7.2 L per year. How many years will it take for the tank to leak all of its fuel?

To learn more about these Science in Action topics, visit **go.hrw.com** and type in the keyword **HT6FTF6F.**

Current Science

Check out Current Science® articles related to this chapter by visiting go.hrw.com. Just type in the keyword HP5CS19.

UNIT 2

TIMELINE

The Atmosphere, Climate, and Oceans

In this unit, you will learn about Earth's atmosphere, weather and climate, and the oceans. Each of these characteristics of Earth has an impact on our lives. The atmosphere protects Earth and helps keep Earth warm. Weather and climate may determine where people can safely live. The oceans supply food. But human activity can also affect the atmosphere and oceans. This timeline shows some of the events that have occurred as scientists have studied the atmosphere, weather and climate, and oceans.

1281

A sudden typhoon destroys a fleet of Mongolian ships about to reach Japan. This "divine wind," or *kamikaze* in Japanese, saves the country from invasion and conquest.

1778

Carl Scheele concludes that air is made mostly of nitrogen and oxygen.

1838

John James Audubon publishes *The Birds of America.*

1974

Chlorofluorocarbons (CFCs) are recognized as being harmful to the ozone layer.

1982

Weather information becomes available 24 hours a day, 7 days a week, on commercial TV.

1655

Saturn's rings are recognized as rings. Galileo Galilei had seen them in 1610, but his telescope was not strong enough to show that they were rings.

1718

Gabriel Fahrenheit builds the first mercury thermometer.

1749

Benjamin Franklin explains that updrafts of air are due to the sun heating the local atmosphere.

1920

Milutin Milankovitch, a Serbian scientist, determines that over tens of thousands of years, changes in Earth's motion through space have profound effects on climate.

1945

The first atmospheric test of an atomic bomb takes place near Alamogordo, New Mexico.

1985

Scientists discover an ozone hole over Antarctica.

1986

The world's worst nuclear accident takes place at Chernobyl, Ukraine, and spreads radiation through the atmosphere as far as the western United States.

1999

The first nonstop balloon trip around the world is successfully completed when Brian Jones and Bertrand Piccard land in Egypt.

2003

During one week in May, a record 393 tornadoes are observed in the United States.

The Breitling Orbiter 3 lands in Egypt on March 21, 1999.

This image shows the path of radioactive material released from Chernobyl.

3

The Atmosphere

The Big Idea Processes on Earth's surface and in the atmosphere interact.

About the PHOTO

This photograph taken from space shows Hurricane Frances moving northwest across the Florida Peninsula on September 5, 2004. The storm made landfall near Palm Beach and had maximum sustained winds of close to 180 km/h. The computer-generated outlines of Florida and nearby states clearly show the size of the giant hurricane.

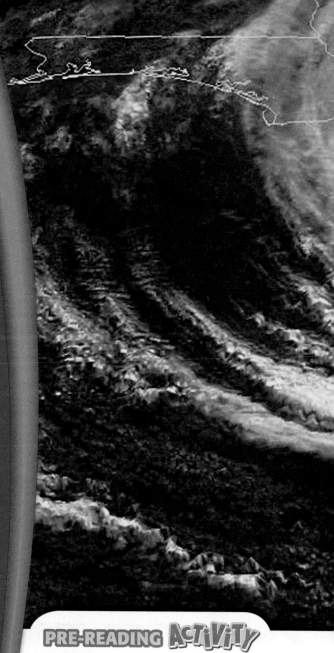

PRE-READING ACTIVITY

FOLDNOTES **Booklet** Before you read the chapter, create the FoldNote entitled "Booklet" described in the **Study Skills** section of the Appendix. Label each page of the booklet with a main idea from the chapter. As you read the chapter, write what you learn about each main idea on the appropriate page of the booklet.

START-UP ACTIVITY

Does Air Have Mass? A.1.3.1 AA

In this activity, you will compare an inflated balloon with a deflated balloon to find out if air has mass.

Procedure

1. In a **notebook,** answer the following questions: Does air have mass? Will an inflated balloon weigh more than a deflated balloon?

2. Inflate **two large balloons,** and tie the balloons closed. Attach each balloon to opposite ends of a **meterstick** using identical **pushpins.** Balance the meterstick on a **pencil** held by a volunteer. Check that the meterstick is perfectly balanced.

3. Predict what will happen when you pop one balloon. Record your predictions.

4. Put on **safety goggles,** and carefully pop one of the balloons with a **pushpin.**

5. Record your observations.

Analysis

1. Explain your observations. Was your prediction correct?

2. Based on your results, does air have mass? If air has mass, is the atmosphere affected by Earth's gravity? Explain your answers.

The Atmosphere   **75**

Characteristics of the Atmosphere

If you were lost in the desert, you could survive for a few days without food and water. But you wouldn't last more than five minutes without the atmosphere.

The **atmosphere** is a mixture of gases that surrounds Earth. In addition to containing the oxygen you need to breathe, the atmosphere protects you from the sun's damaging rays. The atmosphere is always changing. Every breath you take, every tree that is planted, and every vehicle you ride in affects the atmosphere's composition.

The Composition of the Atmosphere

As you can see in **Figure 1,** the atmosphere is made up mostly of nitrogen gas. The oxygen you breathe makes up a little more than 20% of the atmosphere. In addition to containing nitrogen and oxygen, the atmosphere contains small particles, such as dust, volcanic ash, sea salt, and smoke. The next time you turn off the lights at night, shine a flashlight, and you will see some of these tiny particles floating in the air.

Water is also found in the atmosphere. Liquid water (water droplets) and solid water (snow and ice crystals) are found in clouds. But most water in the atmosphere exists as an invisible gas called *water vapor*. When atmospheric conditions change, water vapor can change into solid or liquid water, and rain or snow might fall from the sky.

✓ **Reading Check** Describe the three physical states of water in the atmosphere.

READING WARM-UP

Objectives

● Describe the composition of Earth's atmosphere.

● Explain why air pressure changes as altitude changes.

● Explain how air temperature changes with atmospheric composition.

● Describe the layers of the atmosphere.

Terms to Learn

atmosphere	stratosphere
air pressure	mesosphere
troposphere	thermosphere

READING STRATEGY

Mnemonics As you read this section, create a mnemonic device to help you remember the layers of the Earth's atmosphere.

Figure 1 Composition of the Atmosphere

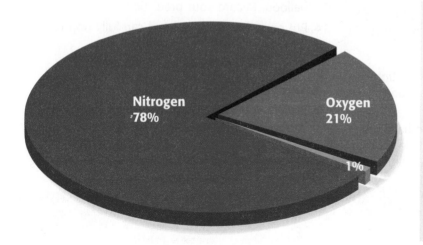

Nitrogen 78%

Oxygen 21%

1%

Nitrogen, the most common atmospheric gas, is released when dead plants and dead animals break down and when volcanoes erupt.

Oxygen, the second most common atmospheric gas, is made by phytoplankton and plants.

The **remaining 1%** of the atmosphere is made up of argon, carbon dioxide, water vapor, and other gases.

Atmospheric Pressure and Temperature

You may be surprised to learn that you carry a 500 km column of air every day. Although air is not heavy, at sea level, a square inch of surface area is under almost 15 lb of air.

As Altitude Increases, Air Pressure Decreases

The atmosphere is held around Earth by gravity. Gravity acts to move gas molecules in the atmosphere toward Earth's center. The force of gravity is balanced by air pressure. **Air pressure** is the measure of the force with which air molecules push on a surface. Air pressure is strongest at Earth's surface because more air is above you. As you move farther away from Earth's surface, fewer gas molecules are above you. So, as altitude (distance from sea level) increases, air pressure decreases. Think of the forces of air pressure and gravity as a human pyramid, as shown in **Figure 2**. The people at the bottom of the pyramid can feel all the weight of the people on top. The people at the bottom push up to balance the weight of the people above them. In a similar way, air pressure and gravity exist near a state of balance or equilibrium.

Atmospheric Composition Affects Air Temperature

Air temperature also changes as altitude increases. The temperature differences result mainly from the way solar energy is absorbed as it moves through the atmosphere. Some parts of the atmosphere are warmer because they contain a high percentage of gases that absorb solar energy. Other parts of the atmosphere contain less of these gases and are cooler.

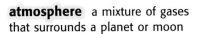

CONNECTION TO Physics

Air-Pressure Experiment
Does air pressure push only downward? Try this experiment to find out. Fill a plastic cup to the brim with water. Firmly hold a piece of cardboard over the mouth of the cup. Quickly invert the glass over a sink, and observe what happens. How do the effects of air pressure explain your observations?

ACTIVITY

atmosphere a mixture of gases that surrounds a planet or moon

air pressure the measure of the force with which air molecules push on a surface

Lower pressure

Higher pressure

Figure 2 *As in a human pyramid, air pressure increases closer to Earth's surface.*

C.2.3.3 knows that if more than one force acts on an object, then the forces can reinforce or cancel each other, depending on their direction and magnitude.

Modeling the Atmosphere
In teams, use a metric ruler to create an illustrated scale model of the atmosphere similar to the one shown on this page. Assume that the atmosphere is about 500 km high. If you reduced the height of the atmosphere by a factor of 100,000, your scale model would be 5 m long, and the troposphere would be 11.5 cm long. Think of a creative way to display your model. You could use sidewalk chalk, stakes and string, poster board, or other materials approved by your teacher. Do some research to add interesting information about each layer.

ACTIVITY

Layers of the Atmosphere

Based on temperature changes, Earth's atmosphere is divided into four layers, as shown in **Figure 3.** These layers are the *troposphere, stratosphere, mesosphere,* and *thermosphere.* Although these words might sound complicated, the name of each layer gives you clues about its features.

For example, *-sphere* means "ball," which suggests that each layer of the atmosphere surrounds Earth like a hollow ball. *Tropo-* means "turning" or "change," and the troposphere is the layer where gases turn and mix. *Strato-* means "layer," and the stratosphere is the layer where gases are layered and do not mix very much. *Meso-* means "middle," and the mesosphere is the middle layer. Finally, *thermo-* means "heat," and the thermosphere is the layer where temperatures are highest.

✓ **Reading Check** What does the name of each atmospheric layer mean?

Figure 3 *The layers of the atmosphere are defined by changes in temperature.*

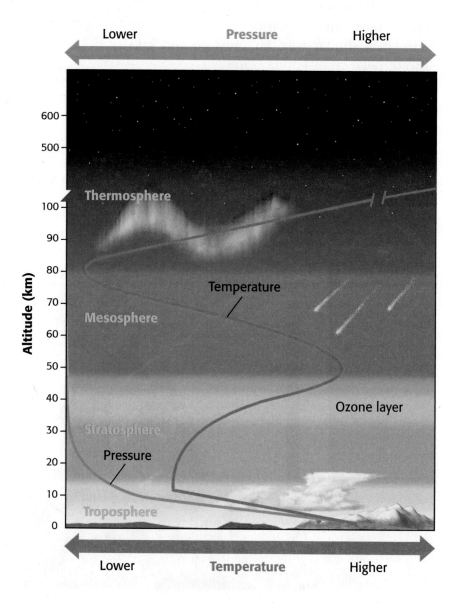

The Troposphere: The Layer in Which We Live

The lowest layer of the atmosphere, which lies next to Earth's surface, is called the **troposphere.** The troposphere is also the densest atmospheric layer. It contains almost 90% of the atmosphere's total mass! Almost all of Earth's carbon dioxide, water vapor, clouds, air pollution, weather, and life-forms are in the troposphere. As shown in **Figure 4,** temperatures vary greatly in the troposphere. Differences in air temperature and density cause gases in the troposphere to mix continuously.

The Stratosphere: Home of the Ozone Layer

The atmospheric layer above the troposphere is called the **stratosphere. Figure 5** shows the boundary between the stratosphere and the troposphere. Gases in the stratosphere are layered and do not mix as much as gases in the troposphere. The air is also very thin in the stratosphere and contains little moisture. The lower stratosphere is extremely cold. Its temperature averages –60°C. But temperature rises as altitude increases in the stratosphere. This rise happens because ozone in the stratosphere absorbs ultraviolet radiation from the sun, which warms the air. Almost all of the ozone in the stratosphere is contained in the ozone layer. The *ozone layer* protects life on Earth by absorbing harmful ultraviolet radiation.

The Mesosphere: The Middle Layer

Above the stratosphere is the mesosphere. The **mesosphere** is the middle layer of the atmosphere. It is also the coldest layer. As in the troposphere, the temperature decreases as altitude increases in the mesosphere. Temperatures can be as low as –93°C at the top of the mesosphere.

Figure 4 *As altitude increases in the troposphere, temperature decreases. Snow remains all year on this mountaintop.*

troposphere the lowest layer of the atmosphere, in which temperature decreases at a constant rate as altitude increases

stratosphere the layer of the atmosphere that is above the troposphere and in which temperature increases as altitude increases

mesosphere the layer of the atmosphere between the stratosphere and the thermosphere and in which temperature decreases as altitude increases

Figure 5 *This photograph of Earth's atmosphere was taken from space. The troposphere is the yellow layer; the stratosphere is the white layer.*

thermosphere the uppermost layer of the atmosphere, in which temperature increases as altitude increases

Test Pilot! Use your new flying machine to explore the atmosphere! Go to **go.hrw.com,** and type in the keyword **HZ5ATMW.**

The Thermosphere: The Edge of the Atmosphere

The uppermost atmospheric layer is called the **thermosphere.** In the thermosphere, temperature again increases with altitude. Atoms of nitrogen and oxygen absorb high-energy solar radiation and release thermal energy, which causes temperatures in the thermosphere to be 1,000°C or higher.

When you think of an area that has high temperatures, you probably think of a place that is very hot. Although the thermosphere has very high temperatures, it does not feel hot. Temperature is different from heat. Temperature is a measure of the average energy of particles in motion. The high temperature of the thermosphere means that particles in that layer are moving very fast. Heat, however, is the transfer of thermal energy between objects of different temperatures. Particles must touch one another to transfer thermal energy. The space between particles in the thermosphere is so great that particles do not transfer much energy. In other words, the density of the thermosphere is so low that particles do not often collide and transfer energy. **Figure 6** shows how air density affects the heating of the troposphere and the thermosphere.

Reading Check Explain why the thermosphere does not feel hot.

Figure 6 **Temperature in the Troposphere and the Thermosphere**

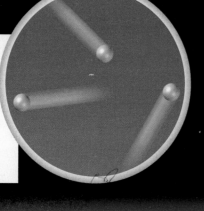

The **thermosphere** is less dense than the troposphere. So, although particles are moving very fast, they do not transfer much thermal energy.

The **troposphere** is denser than the thermosphere. So, although particles in the troposphere are moving much slower than particles in the thermosphere, they can transfer much more thermal energy.

The Ionosphere: Home of the Auroras

In the upper mesosphere and the lower thermosphere, nitrogen and oxygen atoms absorb harmful solar energy. As a result, the thermosphere's temperature rises, and gas particles become electrically charged. Electrically charged particles are called *ions*. Therefore, this part of the thermosphere is called the *ionosphere*. As shown in **Figure 7,** in polar regions these ions radiate energy as shimmering lights called *auroras*. The ionosphere also reflects AM radio waves. When conditions are right, an AM radio wave can travel around the world by reflecting off the ionosphere. These radio signals bounce off the ionosphere and are sent back to Earth.

Figure 7 *Charged particles in the ionosphere cause auroras, or northern and southern lights.*

SECTION Review

Summary

- Nitrogen and oxygen make up most of Earth's atmosphere.
- Air pressure decreases as altitude increases.
- The composition of atmospheric layers affects their temperature.
- The troposphere is the lowest atmospheric layer. It is the layer in which we live.
- The stratosphere contains the ozone layer, which protects us from harmful UV radiation.
- The mesosphere is the coldest atmospheric layer.
- The thermosphere has very high temperatures but does not feel hot.

Using Key Terms

1. Use *atmosphere, troposphere, stratosphere, mesosphere,* and *thermosphere* in the same sentence.

Understanding Key Ideas

2. Why does air pressure decrease as altitude increases?

3. How can the thermosphere have high temperatures but not feel hot?

4. What determines the temperature of atmospheric layers?

5. What two gases make up most of the atmosphere?

Critical Thinking

6. **Applying Concepts** Apply what you know about the relationship between altitude and air pressure to explain why rescue helicopters have a difficult time flying at altitudes above 6,000 m.

7. **Making Inferences** If the upper atmosphere is very thin, why do space vehicles heat up as they enter the atmosphere?

FCAT Preparation

8. Ozone (O_3) is a molecule that contains three oxygen atoms. Almost all of the ozone in Earth's atmosphere is confined to a layer in the stratosphere— the ozone layer. The ozone layer is very important because it protects life on Earth. How would Earth be affected if pollutants created by humans decreased ozone levels in the stratosphere? **G.2.3.4 AA**

A. Less ultraviolet radiation would reach Earth.

B. More ultraviolet radiation would reach Earth.

C. Earth's temperature would become colder.

D. Ozone levels would increase near Earth's surface.

SCi LINKS.

NSTA
Developed and maintained by the
National Science Teachers Association

For a variety of links related to this chapter, go to www.scilinks.org
Topic: Composition of the Atmosphere
SciLinks code: HSM0328

Atmospheric Heating

You are lying in a park. Your eyes are closed, and you feel the warmth of the sun on your face. You may have done this before, but have you ever stopped to think that it takes a little more than eight minutes for the energy that warms your face to travel from a star that is 149,000,000 km away?

READING WARM-UP

Objectives

● Describe what happens to solar energy that reaches Earth.
  B.1.3.1 AA, B.1.3.3

● Summarize energy transfer in the atmosphere by radiation, conduction, and convection. **B.1.3.1 AA**

● Explain the relationship between the greenhouse effect and global warming. **D.2.3.2, G.2.3.4 AA**

Terms to Learn

radiation **FCAT** *VOCAB*
conduction **FCAT** *VOCAB*
convection **FCAT** *VOCAB*
greenhouse effect
global warming

READING STRATEGY

Reading Organizer As you read this section, make a table comparing radiation, conduction, and convection.

Energy in the Atmosphere

In the scenario above, your face was warmed by energy from the sun. Earth and its atmosphere are also warmed by energy from the sun. In this section, you will find out what happens to solar energy as it enters the atmosphere.

Radiation: Energy Transfer by Waves

Earth receives energy from the sun by radiation. **Radiation** is the transfer of energy as electromagnetic waves. Although the sun radiates a huge amount of energy, Earth receives only a very small fraction of this energy. But this small fraction of energy is enough to drive the weather cycle and make Earth habitable. **Figure 1** shows what happens to solar energy once it enters the atmosphere.

Figure 1 *Energy from the sun is absorbed by the atmosphere, land, and water and is changed into thermal energy.*

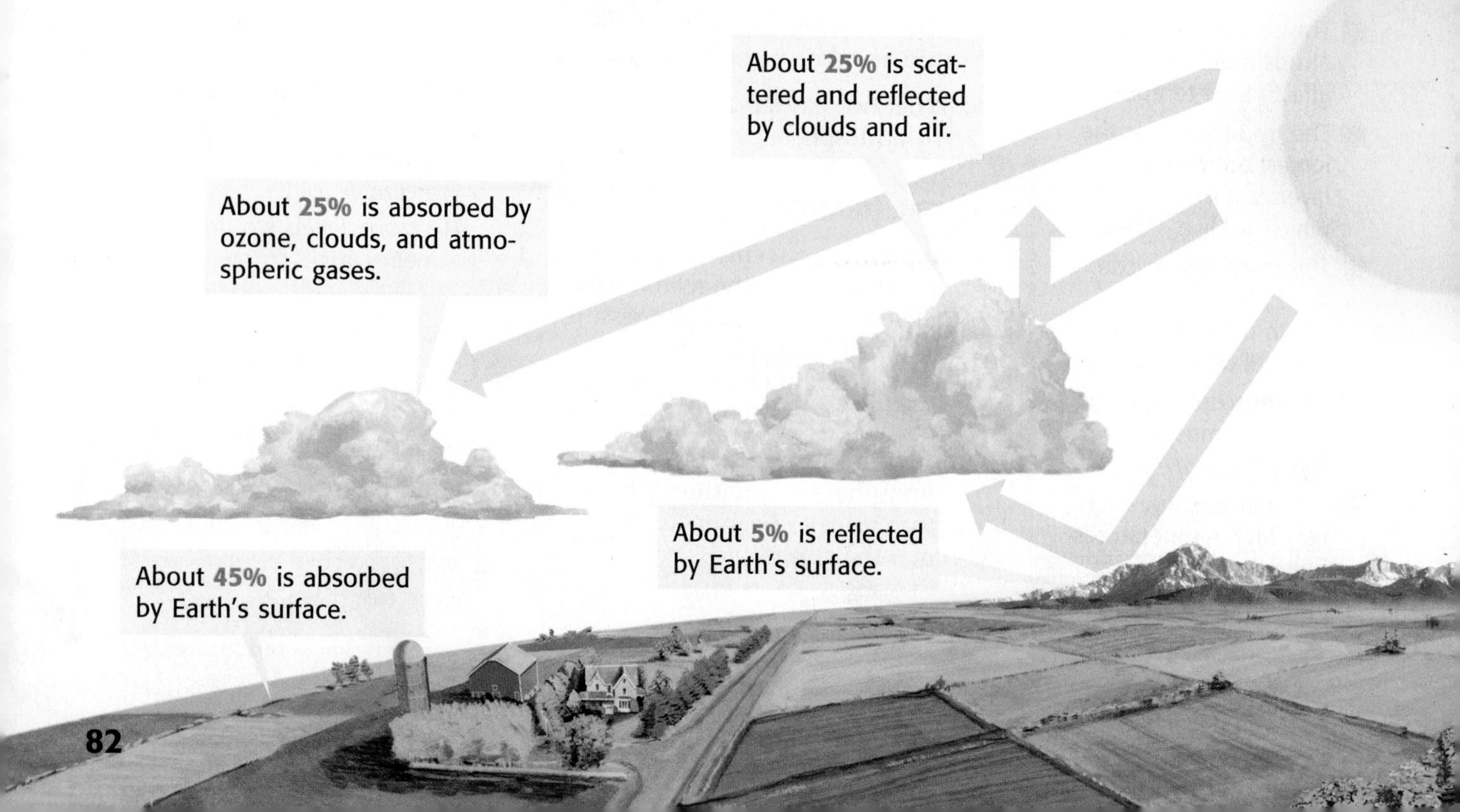

About **25%** is scattered and reflected by clouds and air.

About **25%** is absorbed by ozone, clouds, and atmospheric gases.

About **5%** is reflected by Earth's surface.

About **45%** is absorbed by Earth's surface.

Conduction: Energy Transfer by Contact

If you have ever touched something hot, you have experienced the process of conduction. **Conduction** is the transfer of thermal energy through a material. Thermal energy is always transferred from warm to cold areas. When air molecules come into direct contact with the warm surface of Earth, thermal energy is transferred to the atmosphere.

Convection: Energy Transfer by Circulation

If you have ever watched water boil in a pot, you have observed convection. **Convection** is the transfer of thermal energy by the circulation or movement of a liquid or gas. Most thermal energy in the atmosphere is transferred by convection. For example, as air is heated, it becomes less dense and rises. Cool air is denser, so it sinks. As the cool air sinks, it pushes the warm air up. The cool air is eventually heated by Earth's surface and begins to rise again. This cycle of warm air rising and cool air sinking causes a circular movement of air, called a *convection current*, as shown in **Figure 2.**

Benchmark Check Describe three ways energy is transferred in the atmosphere. **B.1.3.1 AA**

radiation the transfer of energy as electromagnetic waves *FCAT VOCAB*

conduction the transfer of energy as heat through a material *FCAT VOCAB*

convection the transfer of thermal energy by the circulation or movement of a liquid or gas *FCAT VOCAB*

B.1.3.1 AA identifies forms of energy and explains that they can be measured and compared.

B.1.3.3 knows the various forms in which energy comes to Earth from the sun (e.g., visible light, infrared, and microwave).

B.1.3.5 CS knows the processes by which thermal energy tends to flow from a system of higher temperature to a system of lower temperature.

Figure 2 *The processes of radiation, conduction, and convection heat Earth and its atmosphere.*

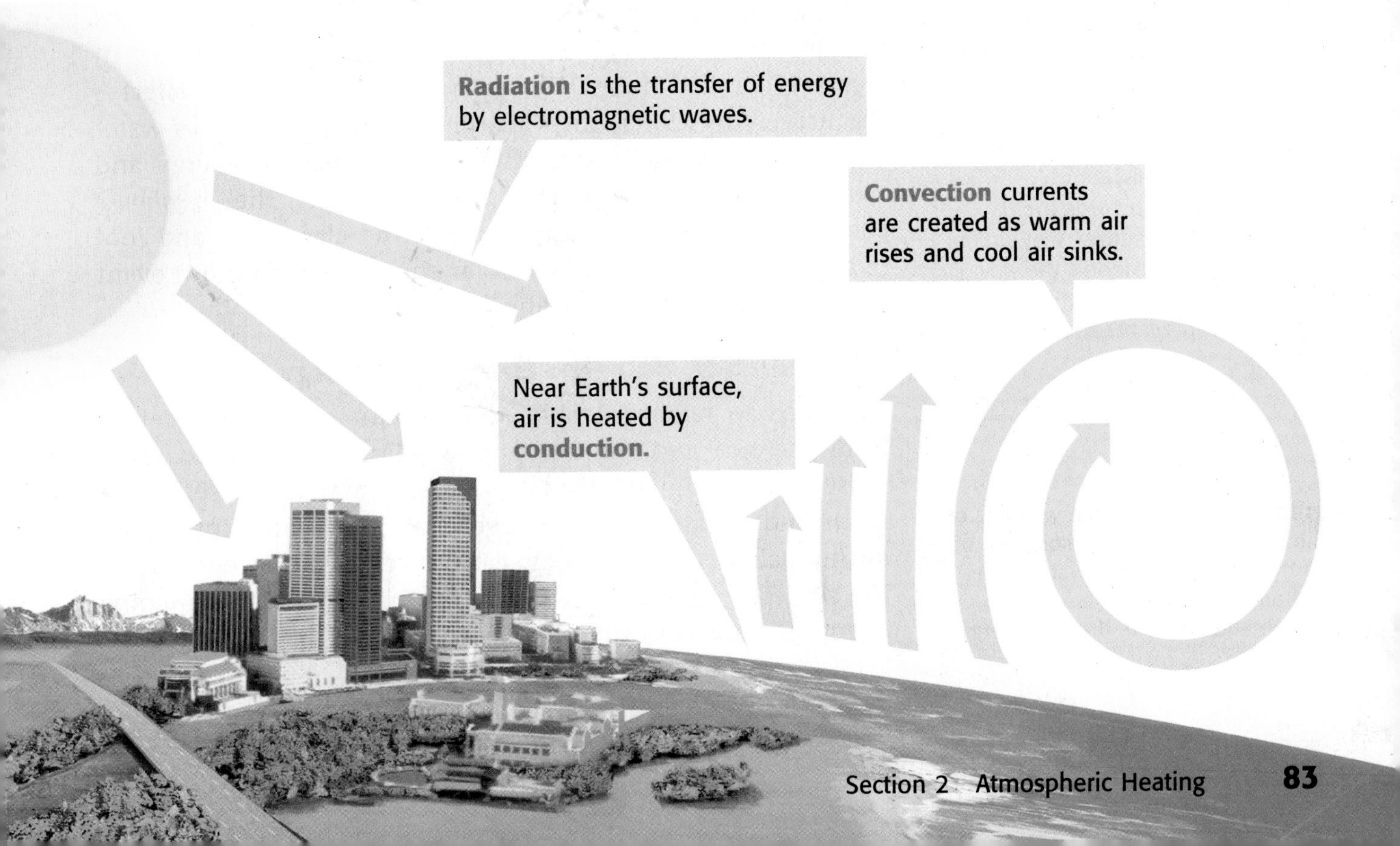

Radiation is the transfer of energy by electromagnetic waves.

Convection currents are created as warm air rises and cool air sinks.

Near Earth's surface, air is heated by **conduction**.

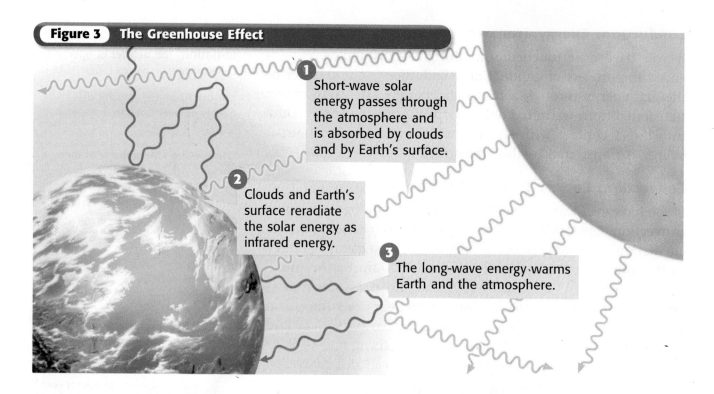

Figure 3 The Greenhouse Effect

1. Short-wave solar energy passes through the atmosphere and is absorbed by clouds and by Earth's surface.

2. Clouds and Earth's surface reradiate the solar energy as infrared energy.

3. The long-wave energy warms Earth and the atmosphere.

greenhouse effect the warming of the surface and lower atmosphere of Earth that occurs when water vapor, carbon dioxide, and other gases absorb and reradiate thermal energy

The Greenhouse Effect and Life on Earth

As you have learned, about 70% of the radiation that enters Earth's atmosphere is absorbed by clouds and by Earth's surface. This energy is converted into thermal energy that warms the planet. In other words, short-wave visible light is absorbed and reradiated into the atmosphere as infrared energy. So, why doesn't this thermal energy escape back into space? Most of it does, but the atmosphere is like a warm blanket that traps enough energy to make Earth livable. This process, shown in **Figure 3,** is called the *greenhouse effect*. The **greenhouse effect** is the process by which gases in the atmosphere, such as water vapor and carbon dioxide, CO_2, absorb thermal energy and radiate it back to Earth. This process is called the *greenhouse effect* because the gases function like the glass walls and roof of a greenhouse, which allow solar energy to enter but prevent thermal energy from escaping.

The Radiation Balance: Energy In, Energy Out

For Earth to remain livable, the amount of energy received from the sun and the amount of energy returned to space must be approximately equal. Solar energy that is absorbed by Earth and its atmosphere is eventually reradiated into space as thermal energy. Every day, Earth receives more energy from the sun. The balance between incoming energy and outgoing energy is known as the *radiation balance*.

Greenhouse Gases and Global Warming

Many scientists have become concerned about data that show that average global temperatures have increased in the past 100 years. Such an increase in average global temperatures is called **global warming.** Some scientists have hypothesized that an increase of greenhouse gases in the atmosphere may be the cause of this warming trend. Greenhouse gases are gases that absorb thermal energy in the atmosphere.

Human activity, such as the burning of fossil fuels and deforestation, may be increasing levels of greenhouse gases, such as carbon dioxide, in the atmosphere. Increasing levels of greenhouse gases may in turn cause average global temperatures to continue to rise. If global warming continues, global climate patterns could be disrupted. Plants and animals that are adapted to live in specific climates would be affected. However, climate models are extremely complex, and scientists continue to debate whether the global warming trend is the result of an increase in greenhouse gases.

Benchmark Check Explain how humans may be contributing to global warming. **D.2.3.2, G.2.3.4 AA**

global warming a gradual increase in average global temperature

B.1.3.3 knows the various forms in which energy comes to Earth from the sun (e.g. visible light, infrared, and microwave).

B.1.3.5 CS knows the processes by which thermal energy tends to flow from a system of higher temperature to a system of lower temperature.

D.2.3.2 knows the positive and negative consequences of human action on the Earth's systems.

G.2.3.4 AA understands that humans are a part of an ecosystem and their activities may deliberately or inadvertently alter the equilibrium in ecosystems.

SECTION
Review

Summary

- Energy from the sun is transferred in the atmosphere by radiation, conduction, and convection. **B.1.3.1 AA, B.1.3.3**

- Radiation is energy transfer by electromagnetic waves. Conduction is energy transfer by direct contact. Convection is energy transfer by circulation. **B.1.3.5 CS**

- The greenhouse effect is Earth's natural heating process. Increasing levels of greenhouse gases could cause global warming. **D.2.3.2, G.2.3.4 AA**

Using Key Terms

1. Use *radiation* and *convection* in separate sentences. **FCAT VOCAB**

Understanding Key Ideas

2. Describe what happens to solar energy that reaches Earth.

3. Describe three ways that energy is transferred in the atmosphere. **B.1.3.5 CS**

4. What is the relationship between the greenhouse effect and global warming? **D.2.3.2**

Critical Thinking

5. **Making Predictions** How might global warming affect life on Earth? **G.2.3.4 AA**

6. **Applying Concepts** Describe global warming in terms of the radiation balance.

FCAT Preparation

7. In Earth's atmosphere, thermal energy is transferred by different processes. How is thermal energy in Earth's atmosphere transferred by conduction? **B.1.3.1 AA**

A. by electromagnetic waves

B. by rising and sinking air

C. by direct contact with Earth's surface

D. by reradiation from Earth's surface

SCILINKS
NSTA
Developed and maintained by the National Science Teachers Association

For a variety of links related to this chapter, go to www.scilinks.org

Topic: Energy in the Atmosphere
SciLinks code: HSM0512

Global Winds and Local Winds

If you open the valve on a bicycle tube, the air rushes out. Why? The air inside the tube is at a higher pressure than the air is outside the tube. In effect, letting air out of the tube created a wind.

wind the movement of air caused by differences in air pressure

Why Air Moves

The movement of air caused by differences in air pressure is called **wind.** The greater the pressure difference, the faster the wind moves. The devastation shown in **Figure 1** was caused by winds that resulted from extreme differences in air pressure.

Movement of Air at the Equator and at the Poles

Differences in air pressure are generally caused by the unequal heating of Earth. The equator receives more direct solar energy than other latitudes, so air at the equator is warmer and less dense than the surrounding air. Warm, less dense air rises and creates an area of low pressure. This warm, rising air flows toward the poles. At the poles, the air is colder and denser than the surrounding air, so it sinks. As the cold air sinks, it creates areas of high pressure around the poles. This cold polar air then flows toward the equator.

Figure 1 *In 1992, Hurricane Andrew became the most destructive hurricane in U.S. history. The winds from the hurricane reached 264 km/h.*

 H.2.3.1 CS recognizes that patterns exist within and across systems.

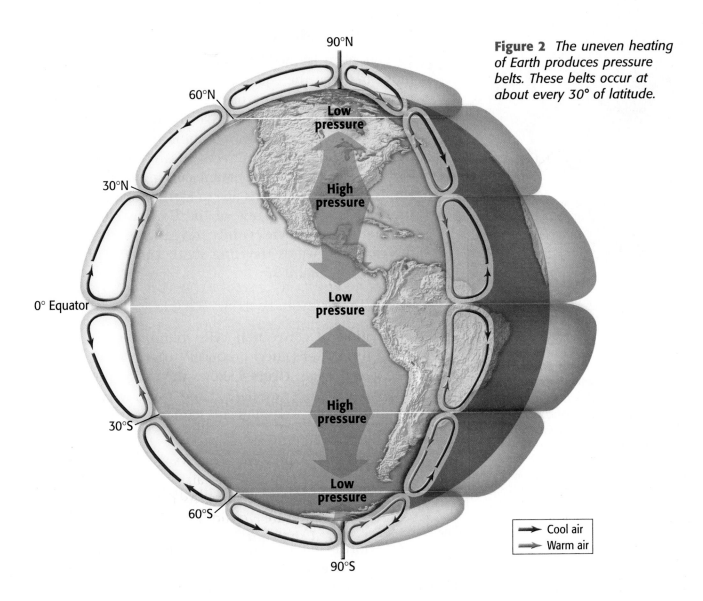

90°N

60°N

30°N

0° Equator

30°S

60°S

90°S

Low pressure

High pressure

Low pressure

High pressure

Low pressure

→ Cool air
→ Warm air

Pressure Belts

You may imagine that wind moves in one huge, circular pattern from the poles to the equator. In fact, air travels in many large, circular patterns called *convection cells*. Convection cells are separated by *pressure belts,* bands of high pressure and low pressure found about every 30° of latitude, as shown in **Figure 2.** As warm air rises over the equator and moves toward the poles, the air begins to cool. At about 30° north and 30° south latitude, some of the cool air begins to sink. Cool, sinking air causes high pressure belts near 30° north and 30° south latitude. This cool air flows back to the equator, where the air warms and rises again. At the poles, cold air sinks and moves toward the equator. Air warms as it moves away from the poles. Around 60° north and 60° south latitude, the warmer air rises, which creates a low pressure belt. This air flows back to the poles.

Benchmark Check Explain what causes convection cells to form in the atmosphere. H.2.3.1 CS

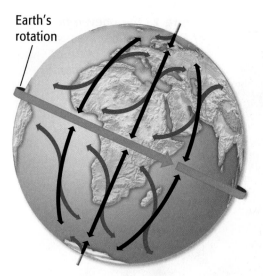

Earth's rotation

| Path of wind without Coriolis effect |
| Approximate path of wind |

Figure 3 *The Coriolis effect in the Northern Hemisphere causes winds traveling north to appear to curve to the east and winds traveling south to appear to curve to the west.*

Coriolis effect the apparent curving of the path of a moving object from an otherwise straight path due to the Earth's rotation

polar easterlies prevailing winds that blow from east to west between 60° and 90° latitude in both hemispheres

westerlies prevailing winds that blow from west to east between 30° and 60° latitude in both hemispheres

trade winds prevailing winds that blow east to west from 30° latitude to the equator in both hemispheres

The Coriolis Effect

As you have learned, pressure differences cause air to move between the equator and the poles. But try spinning a globe and using a piece of chalk to trace a straight line from the equator to the North Pole. The chalk line curves because the globe was spinning. Like the chalk line, winds do not travel directly north or south, because Earth is rotating. The apparent curving of the path of winds and ocean currents due to Earth's rotation is called the **Coriolis effect.** Because of the Coriolis effect in the Northern Hemisphere, winds traveling north curve to the east, and winds traveling south curve to the west, as shown in **Figure 3.**

Global Winds

The combination of convection cells found at every 30° of latitude and the Coriolis effect produces patterns of air circulation called *global winds.* **Figure 4** shows the major global wind systems: polar easterlies, westerlies, and trade winds. Winds such as easterlies and westerlies are named for the direction from which they blow.

Polar Easterlies

The wind belts that extend from the poles to 60° latitude in both hemispheres are called the **polar easterlies.** The polar easterlies are formed as cold, sinking air moves from the poles toward 60° north and 60° south latitude. In the Northern Hemisphere, polar easterlies can carry cold arctic air over the United States, producing snow and freezing weather.

Westerlies

The wind belts found between 30° and 60° latitude in both hemispheres are called the **westerlies.** The westerlies flow toward the poles from west to east. The westerlies can carry moist air over the United States, producing rain and snow.

Trade Winds

In both hemispheres, the winds that blow from 30° latitude almost to the equator are called **trade winds.** The Coriolis effect causes the trade winds to curve to the west in both hemispheres. Early traders used the trade winds to sail from Europe to the Americas. As a result, the winds became known as "trade winds."

Benchmark Check) Explain why the trade winds curve to the west in both the Northern and Southern Hemispheres. **H.2.3.1 CS**

The Doldrums

The trade winds of the Northern and Southern Hemispheres meet in an area around the equator called the *doldrums*. In the doldrums, there is very little wind because the warm, rising air creates an area of low pressure. The name *doldrums* means "dull" or "sluggish."

The Horse Latitudes

At about 30° north and 30° south latitude, sinking air creates an area of high pressure. The winds at these locations are weak. These areas are called the *horse latitudes*. According to legend, this name was given to these areas when sailing ships carried horses from Europe to the Americas. When the ships were stuck in this windless area, horses were sometimes thrown overboard to save drinking water for the sailors. Most of the world's deserts are located in the horse latitudes because the sinking air is very dry.

H.2.3.1 CS recognizes that patterns exist within and across systems.

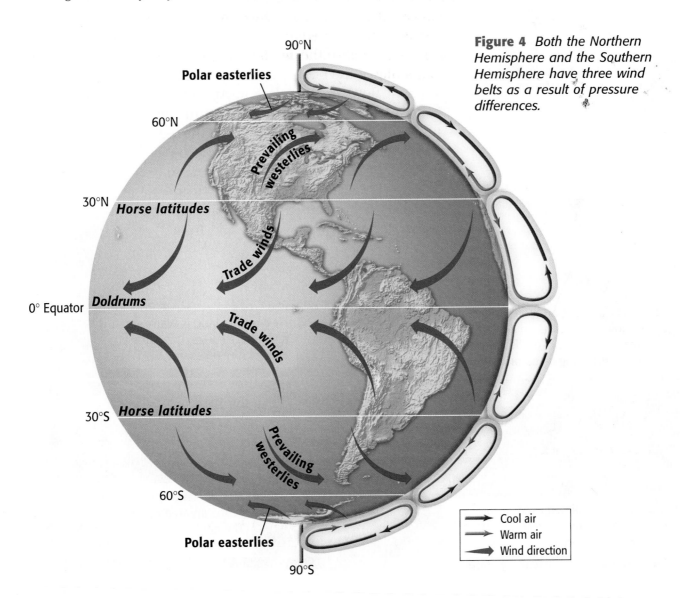

Figure 4 *Both the Northern Hemisphere and the Southern Hemisphere have three wind belts as a result of pressure differences.*

Figure 5 *The jet stream forms this band of clouds as it flows above Earth.*

jet stream a narrow belt of strong winds that blow in the upper troposphere

B.1.3.5 CS knows the processes by which thermal energy tends to flow from a system of higher temperature to a system of lower temperature.

Jet Streams: Atmospheric Conveyor Belts

The flight from Seattle to Boston can be 30 minutes faster than the flight from Boston to Seattle. Why? Pilots take advantage of a jet stream similar to the one shown in **Figure 5.** The **jet streams** are narrow belts of high-speed winds that blow in the upper troposphere and lower stratosphere. These winds can reach maximum speeds of 400 km/h. Unlike other global winds, the jet streams do not follow regular paths around Earth. Knowing the path of a jet stream is important not only to pilots but also to meteorologists. Because jet streams affect the movement of storms, meteorologists can track a storm if they know the location of a jet stream.

Local Winds

Local winds generally move short distances and can blow from any direction. Local geographic features, such as a shoreline or a mountain, can produce temperature differences that cause local winds. For example, the formation of sea and land breezes is shown in **Figure 6.** During the day, the land heats up faster than the water, so the air above the land becomes warmer than the air above the ocean. The warm land air rises, and the cold ocean air flows in to replace it. At night, the land cools faster than water, so the wind blows toward the ocean.

Figure 6 **Sea and Land Breezes**

During the day, air over the ocean is cooler and forms an area of high pressure. The cool air flows to the land, producing a sea breeze.

Air over the land is warmer. As warm air rises, it creates an area of low pressure.

At night, air over the ocean is warmer. As the warm air rises, it forms an area of low pressure.

Air over land is cooler and forms an area of high pressure. The cool air moves toward the ocean, producing a land breeze.

Mountain Breezes and Valley Breezes

Mountain and valley breezes are other examples of local winds caused by an area's geography. Campers in mountainous areas may feel a warm afternoon quickly change into a cold night soon after the sun sets. During the day, the sun warms the air along the mountain slopes. This warm air rises up the mountain slopes, creating a valley breeze. At nightfall, the air along the mountain slopes cools. This cool air moves down the slopes into the valley, producing a mountain breeze.

Benchmark Check Explain why wind tends to rise up mountain slopes during the day. **B.1.3.5 CS**

CONNECTION TO Social Studies

Local Breezes The chinook, the shamal, the sirocco, and the Santa Ana are all local winds. Find out about an interesting local wind, and create a poster-board display that shows how the wind forms and how it affects human cultures.

ACTiViTY

SECTION Review

Summary

- Winds blow from areas of high pressure to areas of low pressure.
- Pressure belts are found approximately every 30° of latitude. **H.2.3.1 CS**
- The Coriolis effect causes wind to appear to curve as it moves across Earth's surface. **H.2.3.1 CS**
- Global winds include the polar easterlies, the westerlies, and the trade winds. **H.2.3.1 CS**
- Local winds include sea and land breezes and mountain and valley breezes. **B.1.3.5 CS, H.2.3.1 CS**

Using Key Terms

1. Write an original definition for *polar easterlies, westerlies,* and *trade winds.*

Understanding Key Ideas

2. What are pressure belts?

3. What causes winds?

4. How does the Coriolis effect affect wind movement? **H.2.3.1 CS**

5. How are sea and land breezes similar to mountain and valley breezes? **B.1.3.5 CS, H.2.3.1 CS**

Critical Thinking

6. **Applying Concepts** Would winds exist if Earth's surface was a uniform temperature? Explain your answer. **H.2.3.1 CS**

7. **Making Inferences** In the Northern Hemisphere, why do westerlies flow from the west while trade winds flow from the east? **H.2.3.1 CS**

8. **Applying Concepts** Imagine that you are near an ocean in the daytime. You want to go to the ocean, but you do not know how to get there. How might a local wind help you find the ocean? **H.2.3.1 CS**

FCAT Preparation

9. Local winds generally move short distances and can blow from any direction. Local geographic features, such as a shoreline or a mountain, can produce temperature differences that cause local winds. Different local winds include sea breezes, land breezes, mountain breezes, and valley breezes. Which of the following flow patterns causes a mountain breeze? **B.1.3.5 CS**

   A. warm air flows down a mountain

   B. warm air rises up a mountain

   C. cool air rises up a mountain

   D. cool air flows down a mountain

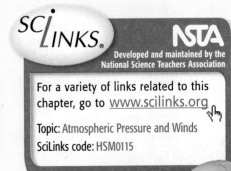

SciLINKS.

NSTA
Developed and maintained by the National Science Teachers Association

For a variety of links related to this chapter, go to www.scilinks.org

Topic: Atmospheric Pressure and Winds
SciLinks code: HSM0115

Air Pollution

In December 1952, one of London's dreaded "pea souper" fogs settled on the city. But this was no ordinary fog—it was thick with coal smoke and air pollution. It burned people's lungs, and the sky grew so dark that people could not see their hands in front of their faces. When the fog lifted four days later, thousands of people were dead!

READING WARM-UP

Objectives

- Compare primary and secondary air pollutants. D.2.3.2, G.2.3.4 AA
- Identify sources of air pollution caused by point-source and nonpoint-source pollution. D.2.3.2, G.2.3.4 AA
- Identify sources of human-caused air pollution. D.2.3.2, G.2.3.4 AA
- Describe how acid precipitation affects the environment. D.1.3.3 CS, D.2.3.2, G.2.3.4 AA

Terms to Learn

air pollution
acid precipitation

READING STRATEGY

Reading Organizer As you read this section, make a table that identifies major sources of air pollution and the effects of each.

air pollution the contamination of the atmosphere by the introduction of pollutants from human and natural sources

London's killer fog shocked the world and caused major changes in England's air-pollution laws. People began to think that air pollution was not simply a part of urban life that had to be endured. Air pollution had to be reduced. Although this event is an extreme example, air pollution is common in many parts of the world. However, nations are taking major steps to reduce air pollution. But what is air pollution? **Air pollution** is the contamination of the atmosphere by the introduction of pollutants from human and natural sources. Air pollutants are classified according to their source as either primary pollutants or secondary pollutants.

Primary Pollutants

Pollutants that are put directly into the air by human or natural activity are *primary pollutants*. Primary pollutants from natural sources include dust, sea salt, volcanic gases and ash, smoke from forest fires, and pollen. Primary pollutants from human sources include carbon monoxide, dust, smoke, and chemicals from paint and other substances. In urban areas, vehicle exhaust is a common source of primary pollutants. Examples of primary pollutants are shown in **Figure 1.**

Benchmark Check Identify three primary pollutants that are created by human activity. D.2.3.2

| **Figure 1** | **Examples of Primary Pollutants** |

Industrial emissions

Vehicle exhaust

Volcanic ash

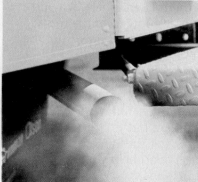

Secondary Pollutants

Pollutants that form when primary pollutants react with other primary pollutants or with naturally occurring substances are *secondary pollutants*. Ozone and smog are examples of secondary pollutants. Ozone is formed when sunlight reacts with vehicle exhaust and air. You may have heard of "Ozone Action Day" warnings in your community. When such a warning is issued, people are discouraged from outdoor physical activity because ozone can damage their lungs. In the stratosphere, ozone forms a protective layer that absorbs harmful radiation from the sun. Near Earth's surface, however, ozone is a dangerous pollutant that negatively affects the health of organisms. **Figure 2** shows how smog is formed.

Point- and Nonpoint-Source Pollutants

All sources of pollutants can be classified as either point-source pollutants or nonpoint-source pollutants. *Point-source pollutants* are pollutants that are released from a single source. Examples of point-source pollutants are smoke from burning brush, chemical wastes and gases from agricultural industries as shown in **Figure 3,** and particulate matter. Particulate matter is any small particle of dust, dirt, or soot in the air. *Nonpoint-source pollutants* are pollutants that come from many different sources and are often difficult to identify. Examples of nonpoint-source pollutants include ozone and haze. Ozone forms when emissions from industries and motor vehicles react with air and sunlight. Haze forms when emissions from power plants react with air.

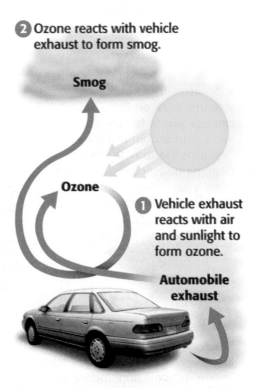

2 Ozone reacts with vehicle exhaust to form smog.

Smog

Ozone

1 Vehicle exhaust reacts with air and sunlight to form ozone.

Automobile exhaust

Figure 2 *Smog forms when sunlight reacts with ozone and vehicle exhaust.*

Figure 3 *Chemicals, such as methane from animal waste, are considered point-source pollutants.*

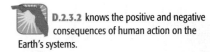

D.2.3.2 knows the positive and negative consequences of human action on the Earth's systems.

G.2.3.4 AA understands that humans are a part of an ecosystem and their activities may deliberately or inadvertently alter the equilibrium in ecosystems.

CONNECTION TO Biology

Cleaning the Air with Plants Did you know that common houseplants can help fight indoor air pollution? Some houseplants are so effective at removing air pollutants that NASA might use them as part of the life-support system in future space stations. Back on Earth, you can use plants to clean the air in your school or home. Research the top 10 air-cleaning houseplants, and find out if you can grow any of them in your classroom or home.

ACTIVITY

Sources of Human-Caused Air Pollution

Human-caused air pollution comes from a variety of sources. Cars contribute about 10% to 20% of the human-caused air pollution in the United States. Vehicle exhaust contains nitrogen oxide, which contributes to smog formation and acid precipitation. However, pollution controls and cleaner gasoline have greatly reduced air pollution from vehicles.

Industrial Air Pollution

Many industrial plants and electric power plants burn fossil fuels, such as coal, to produce energy. Burning some types of coal without pollution controls can release large amounts of air pollutants. Some industries also produce chemicals that can pollute the air. Oil refineries, chemical manufacturing plants, dry-cleaning businesses, furniture refinishers, and auto body shops are all potential sources of air pollution.

Indoor Air Pollution

Sometimes, the air inside a building can be more polluted than the air outside. Some sources of indoor air pollution are shown in **Figure 4.** *Ventilation,* or the mixing of indoor air with outdoor air, can reduce indoor air pollution. Another way to reduce indoor air pollution is to limit the use of chemical solvents and cleaners.

Figure 4 *There are many sources of indoor air pollution. Indoor air pollution can be difficult to detect because it is often invisible.*

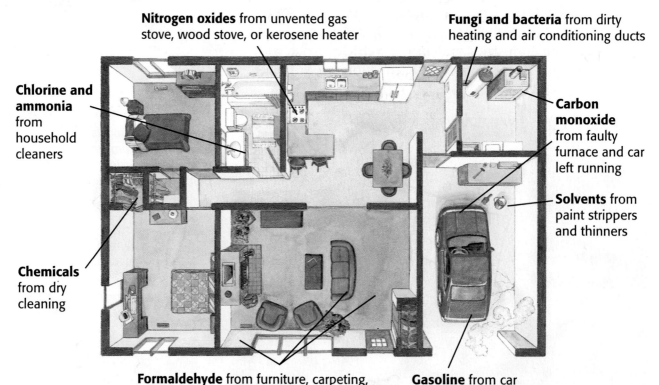

Nitrogen oxides from unvented gas stove, wood stove, or kerosene heater

Fungi and bacteria from dirty heating and air conditioning ducts

Chlorine and ammonia from household cleaners

Carbon monoxide from faulty furnace and car left running

Solvents from paint strippers and thinners

Chemicals from dry cleaning

Formaldehyde from furniture, carpeting, particleboard, and foam insulation

Gasoline from car and lawn mower

Acid Precipitation

When fossil fuels are burned, they can release sulfur dioxide and nitrogen oxide into the atmosphere. When these pollutants combine with water in the atmosphere, they form sulfuric acid and nitric acid. Precipitation such as rain, sleet, or snow that contains these acids from air pollution is called **acid precipitation.** Precipitation is naturally acidic, but sulfuric acid and nitric acid can make it so acidic that it can negatively affect the environment. In most areas of the world, pollution controls have helped reduce acid precipitation.

Acid Precipitation and Plants

Plant communities have adapted over long periods of time to the natural acidity of the soil in which they grow. Acid precipitation can cause the acidity of soil to increase. This process, called *acidification*, changes the balance of a soil's chemistry in several ways. When the acidity of soil increases, some nutrients are broken down. Nutrients that plants need for growth get washed away by acidic rainwater. Increased acidity also releases aluminum and other toxic metals from the soil. Some of these toxic metals are absorbed by the roots of plants.

Benchmark Check Explain how acid precipitation can negatively affect plant communities. **D.1.3.3 CS, D.2.3.2, G.2.3.4 AA**

The Effects of Acid Precipitation on Forests

Forest ecology is complex. Scientists are still trying to fully understand the long-term effects of acid precipitation on groups of plants and their habitats. In some areas of the world, however, acid precipitation has damaged large areas of forest. The effects of acid precipitation are most noticeable in Eastern Europe, as shown in **Figure 5.** Forests in the northeastern United States and in eastern Canada have also been affected by acid precipitation.

acid precipitation rain, sleet, or snow that contains a high concentration of acids

Testing for Particulates

1. Particulates are pollutants such as dust that are extremely small. In this lab, you will measure the amount of particulates in the air. Begin by covering **10 5 in. × 7 in. index cards** with a thin coat of **petroleum jelly.**

2. Hang the cards in various locations inside and outside your school.

3. One day later, use a **magnifying lens** to count the number of particles on the cards. Which location had the fewest number of particulates? Which location had the highest number of particulates? Hypothesize why.

D.1.3.3 CS knows how conditions that exist in one system influence the conditions that exist in other systems.

D.2.3.2 knows the positive and negative consequences of human action on the Earth's systems.

G.2.3.4 AA understands that humans are a part of an ecosystem and their activities may deliberately or inadvertently alter the equilibrium in ecosystems.

Figure 5 *This forest in Poland has been damaged by acid precipitation.*

Acid Precipitation and Aquatic Ecosystems

Aquatic organisms have adapted to live in water that has a particular range of acidity. If acid precipitation increases the acidity of a lake or stream, aquatic plants, fish, and other aquatic organisms living in the lake or stream may die.

The effects of acid precipitation are worst in the spring, when the acidic snow that built up in the winter melts and acidic water flows into lakes and rivers. A rapid change in a body of water's acidity is called *acid shock*. Acid shock can cause large numbers of fish in a population to die, as shown in **Figure 6.** Acid shock can affect how fish absorb oxygen and nutrients. To reduce the effects of acid precipitation on aquatic ecosystems, some communities add powdered limestone (calcium carbonate) to acidified lakes in the spring. Limestone neutralizes acids in the lakes. Unfortunately, limestone cannot prevent all acid damage to lakes.

Benchmark Check Explain how acid precipitation can damage an aquatic ecosystem.
D.1.3.3 CS, D.2.3.2, G.2.3.4 AA

Acid Precipitation and Humans

Acid precipitation can also affect humans. An increase in soil acidity can cause toxic metals, such as aluminum and mercury, to be released from the soil. These toxic metals can find their way into crops, water, fish, and then eventually into the human body. Studies have also shown that acid precipitation may harm the respiratory health of children.

Figure 6 *Acid shock, which is a rapid change in a body of water's acidity, can prevent fish from absorbing oxygen and nutrients. Acid shock can cause populations of fish to die.*

D.1.3.3 CS knows how conditions that exist in one system influence the conditions that exist in other systems.

D.2.3.1 understands that quality of life is relevant to personal experience.

D.2.3.2 knows the positive and negative consequences of human action on the Earth's systems.

G.2.3.4 AA understands that humans are a part of an ecosystem and their activities may deliberately or inadvertently alter the equilibrium in ecosystems.

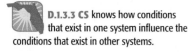

Neutralizing Acid Precipitation

1. Pour 1/2 tbsp of **vinegar** into one cup of **distilled water,** and stir the mixture well. Check the pH of the mixture by using **pH paper.** The pH should be about 4.

2. Crush one stick of **blackboard chalk** into powder. Pour the powder into the vinegar and water mixture. Check the pH of the mixture.

3. Did the vinegar and water mixture become more or less acidic after the powdered chalk was poured in?

International Cooperation

Controlling acid precipitation is complicated. Pollutants that are released in one area may later fall to the ground as acid precipitation in an area hundreds of kilometers away. Sometimes, pollution from one country results in acid precipitation in another country. For example, almost half of the acid precipitation that falls in southeastern Canada results from pollution produced in the United States. In the spirit of cooperation, the governments of Canada and the United States signed the Canada–U.S. Air Quality Agreement in 1991. Both countries agreed to reduce acidic emissions that flowed across the Canada–U.S. boundary. More of these international agreements may be necessary to control acid precipitation.

CONNECTION TO Chemistry

Acidity of Precipitation
Acidity is measured by using a pH scale, the units of which range from 0 to 14. Solutions that have a pH of less than 7 are acidic. Research recorded pH levels of acid rain in your area. Then, compare these pH levels with the pH levels of other common acids, such as lemon juice and acetic acid.

SECTION Review

Summary

- Primary pollutants are pollutants that are put directly into the air by human or natural activity. **D.2.3.2**

- Secondary pollutants form when primary pollutants react with other primary pollutants or with naturally occurring substances. **D.2.3.2, G.2.3.4 AA**

- Transportation, industry, and natural sources are the main sources of air pollution. **D.2.3.2, G.2.3.4 AA**

- Acid precipitation can have harmful effects on plants, animals, and humans. **D.1.3.3 CS**

Using Key Terms

Correct each statement by replacing the underlined term.

1. Air pollution is a sudden change in the acidity of a stream or lake.

2. Smog is rain, sleet, or snow that has a high concentration of acid.

Understanding Key Ideas

3. Compare primary and secondary air pollutants. **D.2.3.2, G.2.3.4 AA**

4. Identify air pollution caused by point-source pollution and air pollution caused by nonpoint-source pollution. **D.2.3.2, G.2.3.4 AA**

5. Identify sources of human-caused air pollution. **D.2.3.2, G.2.3.4 AA**

6. How can acid precipitation affect the environment? **D.1.3.3 CS, D.2.3.2, G.2.3.4 AA**

Critical Thinking

7. **Expressing Opinions** How do you think that nations should resolve air-pollution problems that cross national boundaries? **D.2.3.2**

FCAT Preparation

8. Pollutants are either point- or nonpoint-source pollutants. Which of the following pollutants is a nonpoint-source pollutant? **G.2.3.4 AA**

A. smog

B. volcanic ash

C. burning brush

D. a chemical spill

9. Air pollution can negatively effect Earth's organisms. Which of the following pollutants has the most direct effect on plant communities and aquatic ecosystems? **D.1.3.3 CS**

F. smog

G. ozone

H. haze

I. acid precipitation

SCiLINKS

NSTA
Developed and maintained by the National Science Teachers Association

For a variety of links related to this chapter, go to www.scilinks.org

Topic: Acid Precipitation
SciLinks code: HSM1690

Maintaining Air Quality

Have you ever seen or heard a weather forecaster report the day's air quality? Have you ever had to stay indoors because the air outside was unhealthy?

The air quality in your area affects your health and your everyday life. It is important to learn about the air quality in your area and to know the short-term and long-term effects of air pollution on your health.

READING WARM-UP

Objectives

- Identify three effects of air pollution on the human body. D.1.3.3 CS, D.2.3.1
- Describe how air quality is monitored and measured.
- Describe how air quality is communicated to the public. D.2.3.1
- Identify ways to reduce air pollution. D.2.3.1, D.2.3.2

READING STRATEGY

Reading Organizer As you read this section, create an outline of the section. Use the headings from the section in your outline.

Air Pollution and Human Health

Daily exposure to small amounts of air pollution can cause serious health problems. Children, elderly people, and people who have asthma, allergies, lung problems, and heart problems are especially vulnerable to the effects of air pollution.

Short-Term and Long-Term Effects

Many of the effects of air pollution on the human body are short-term effects and are immediately noticeable. Coughing, headaches, irritation to the eyes, nose, and throat, and an increase in asthma-related problems are only a few of the short-term effects of air pollution. One good way to avoid experiencing any short-term effects of air pollution is to stay indoors on days when the air quality is poor in your area. People who cannot stay indoors because of their jobs, such as the police officer in **Figure 1,** can wear masks and other gear to protect themselves from air pollution.

The damaging long-term effects of air pollution include lung cancer and heart disease. Long-term health effects may not be noticed until many years after an individual has been exposed to pollutants.

Benchmark Check Identify three short-term effects and two long-term effects of air pollution on human health. D.1.3.3 CS, D.2.3.1

Figure 1 *This police officer wears a mask to protect him from harmful pollutants as he directs traffic in Bangkok, Thailand.*

Monitoring Air Quality

In 1970, the United States Congress passed the Clean Air Act. The Clean Air Act is a law that gives the Environmental Protection Agency (EPA) the authority to regulate the amount of air pollutants that can be released into the atmosphere from any source, such as cars and factories.

Air-Quality Standards

The EPA sets air-quality standards for each state to follow. There are specific standards regarding levels of pollutants, such as carbon monoxide, lead, and ozone. These standards restrict how much of each pollutant can be released into the air. The EPA works to improve air quality in areas where air quality is poor and to prevent air pollution in areas where air quality is healthy. There are two types of standards—primary and secondary. Primary standards protect against the effects of air pollution on human health. Secondary standards protect against the effects of air pollution on crops, vegetation, and buildings. If air quality worsens, the EPA can set stricter standards. The Clean Air Act was strengthened in 1990.

Air Quality Index

The EPA and local governments are responsible for setting and enforcing air-quality standards, as well as for reporting the air quality to the public. The Air Quality Index (AQI), shown in **Table 1,** is used to provide the public with daily air-quality information. The AQI measures the air quality of an area with a value from 0 to 500. The AQI is determined after air pollution monitors record the concentrations of the major pollutants in an area. The higher the AQI, the higher the level of air pollution, and the higher the health risk. Once the AQI value is determined for a certain area, a level of health concern and color is also given.

Benchmark Check Explain how the AQI is used to report air quality to people in the United States. D.2.3.1

CONNECTION TO
Environmental Science

WRITING SKILL **The Ozone Hole** In 1985, scientists reported an alarming discovery about Earth's protective ozone layer. Over the Antarctic, the ozone layer was thinning. Chemicals called *CFCs* were causing ozone to break down into oxygen, which does not block the sun's harmful ultraviolet (UV) rays. The thinning of the ozone layer was creating an ozone hole, which was allowing more UV radiation to reach Earth's surface. UV radiation is dangerous to organisms because it damages genes and can cause skin cancer. Using the Internet or library resources, research the current state of the ozone layer. Also, find out if *CFCs* are still being used today. Report your findings in a short essay. D.2.3.2

Table 1 Air Quality Index

Air Quality Index (AQI) Values	Levels of Health Concern	Colors
0 to 50	good	green
51 to 100	moderate	yellow
101 to 150	unhealthy for sensitive groups	orange
151 to 200	unhealthy	red
201 to 300	very unhealthy	purple
301 to 500	hazardous	maroon

 D.1.3.3 CS knows how conditions that exist in one system influence the conditions that exist in other systems.

 D.2.3.1 understands that quality of life is relevant to personal experience.

 D.2.3.2 knows the positive and negative consequences of human action on the Earth's systems.

Figure 2 *This power plant in Florida is leading the way in clean-coal technology. The plant turns coal into a gas before it is burned, so fewer pollutants are released.*

D.2.3.1 understands that quality of life is relevant to personal experience.

D.2.3.2 knows the positive and negative consequences of human action on the Earth's systems.

Figure 3 *Many states require cars to get emissions tests. Regulating the amount of emissions that vehicles release helps reduce air pollution.*

Reducing Air Pollution

Much progress has been made in reducing air pollution. The Clean Air Act, stricter air-quality standards, advancements in pollution-control technology, and lifestyle changes all help reduce air pollution.

Controlling Air Pollution from Industry

The Clean Air Act requires many industries to use pollution-control devices such as scrubbers. A *scrubber* is a device that is used to remove some pollutants before they are released by smokestacks. Scrubbers in coal-burning power plants remove particles such as ash from the smoke. Other industrial plants, such as the power plant shown in **Figure 2,** focus on burning fuel more efficiently so that fewer pollutants are released.

Reducing Motor Vehicle Emissions

A large percentage of air pollution in the United States comes from the vehicles we drive. To reduce air pollution from vehicles, the EPA requires car makers to meet a certain standard for vehicle exhaust. Devices such as catalytic converters remove many pollutants from exhaust and help cars meet this standard. To make sure that cars continue to meet this standard, some states require vehicles to pass an emissions inspection, as shown in **Figure 3.**

Cleaner fuels and more-efficient engines have also helped reduce air pollution from vehicles. Car makers are also designing cars that run on fuels other than gasoline. Some of these cars run on hydrogen or natural gas. Hybrid cars, which are becoming more common, use gasoline and electric power to reduce emissions.

Ways To Reduce Air Pollution

People can make choices that can help reduce air pollution. For example, you can reduce air pollution by carpooling, using public transportation, walking, or biking to your destination, as shown in **Figure 4.** Planning ahead to combine trips or errands instead of making multiple trips also helps reduce pollution. Keeping cars and other gas-powered machines in good condition helps reduce the amount of fuel the engine consumes, and therefore reduces the amount of emissions the engine releases.

Conserving electricity also helps reduce air pollution. Turning off lights and other electrical appliances when they are not in use can reduce the amount of air pollution that is created when electricity is generated. You can also learn more about reducing air pollution by talking to your state environmental agency or by joining a group that is working to reduce air pollution in your area.

Benchmark Check Describe one way that you can help reduce air pollution. **D.2.3.1, D.2.3.2**

Figure 4 *In Copenhagen, Denmark, companies lend free bicycles in exchange for publicity. The program helps reduce air pollution and auto traffic.*

SECTION Review

Summary

- Coughing, headaches, and an increase in asthma-related problems are three effects of air pollution on the human body. **D.1.3.3 CS, D.2.3.1**

- The EPA and local governments set and enforce air-quality standards, and inform the public about air quality. **D.2.3.1, D.2.3.2**

- Air pollution can be reduced by legislation, by pollution-control technology, and by changes in lifestyle. **D.2.3.1, D.2.3.2**

Understanding Key Ideas

1. Describe the Clean Air Act. When was the Clean Air Act passed by Congress? **D.2.3.2**

2. Explain how the EPA ensures that areas maintain healthy air quality. **D.2.3.2**

3. What do the EPA's primary and secondary air-quality standards protect? **D.2.3.1, D.2.3.2**

4. Describe three effects of air pollution on human health. **D.2.3.1**

5. How can industries help reduce the air pollution they release? **D.2.3.2**

6. What is the Air Quality Index? **D.2.3.1**

Critical Thinking

7. **Identifying Relationships** How can advancements in technology help reduce motor vehicle emissions? **D.2.3.2**

FCAT Preparation

8. Air pollution can have both long-term and short-term effects on human health. Which of the following is a long-term health effect of air pollution on humans? **D.1.3.3 CS**

   A. allergies

   B. headaches

   C. asthma

   D. lung cancer

SCiLINKS. **NSTA** Developed and maintained by the National Science Teachers Association

For a variety of links related to this chapter, go to www.scilinks.org

Topic: Air Pollution
SciLinks code: HSM0033

Skills Practice Lab

Under Pressure!

Imagine that you are planning a picnic with your friends, so you look in the newspaper for the weather forecast. The temperature this afternoon should be in the low 80s. This temperature sounds quite comfortable! But you notice that the newspaper's forecast also includes the barometer reading. What's a barometer? And what does the reading tell you? In this activity, you will build your own barometer and will discover what this tool can tell you.

OBJECTIVES

Predict how changes in air pressure affect a barometer.

Build a barometer to test your hypothesis.

MATERIALS

- balloon
- can, coffee, large, empty, 10 cm in diameter
- card, index
- scissors
- straw, drinking
- tape, masking, or rubber band

SAFETY

Ask a Question

1. How can I use a barometer to detect changes in air pressure?

Form a Hypothesis

2. Write a few sentences that answer the question above.

Test the Hypothesis

3. Stretch the balloon a few times. Then, blow up the balloon, and let the air out. This step will make your barometer more sensitive to changes in atmospheric pressure.

4. Cut off the open end of the balloon. Next, stretch the balloon over the open end of the coffee can. Then, attach the balloon to the can with masking tape or a rubber band.

5. Cut one end of the straw at an angle to make a pointer.

6. Place the straw on the stretched balloon so that the pointer is directed away from the center of the balloon. Five centimeters of the end of the straw should hang over the edge of the can. Tape the straw to the balloon as shown in the illustration at right.

7. Tape the index card to the side of the can as shown in the illustration at right. Congratulations! You have just made a barometer!

8. Now, use your barometer to collect and record information about air pressure. Place the barometer outside for 3 or 4 days. On each day, mark on the index card where the tip of the straw points.

Analyze the Results

1. **Explaining Events** What atmospheric factors affect how your barometer works? Explain your answer.

2. **Recognizing Patterns** What does it mean when the straw moves up?

3. **Recognizing Patterns** What does it mean when the straw moves down?

Draw Conclusions

4. **Applying Conclusions** Compare your results with the barometric pressures listed in your local newspaper. What kind of weather is associated with high pressure? What kind of weather is associated with low pressure?

5. **Evaluating Results** Does the barometer you built support your hypothesis? Explain your answer.

Applying Your Data

Now, you can use your barometer to measure the actual air pressure! Get the weather section from your local newspaper for the same 3 or 4 days that you were testing your barometer. Find the barometer reading in the newspaper for each day, and record the reading beside that day's mark on your index card. Use these markings on your card to create a scale with marks at regular intervals. Transfer this scale to a new card, and attach it to your barometer.

Chapter Review

USING KEY TERMS

For each pair of terms, explain how the meanings of the terms differ.

1. *air pressure* and *wind*

2. *troposphere* and *thermosphere*

3. *greenhouse effect* and *global warming*

4. *convection* and *conduction* **FCAT VOCAB**

5. *global wind* and *local wind*

6. *stratosphere* and *mesosphere*

UNDERSTANDING KEY IDEAS

Multiple Choice

7. What is the most abundant gas in the atmosphere?

   a. oxygen　　　c. nitrogen
   b. water vapor　d. carbon dioxide

8. The space between particles in motion can be so great that particles do not collide often and transfer much transfer thermal energy. In which atmospheric layer do particles move rapidly but not collide often or transfer thermal energy? **B.1.3.5 CS** **FCAT**

   a. stratosphere　c. thermosphere
   b. troposphere　d. mesosphere

9. The bottom layer of the atmosphere, where almost all weather occurs, is the

   a. stratosphere.　c. thermosphere.
   b. troposphere.　d. mesosphere.

10. What percentage of the solar energy that reaches the outer atmosphere is absorbed at Earth's surface? **B.1.3.3**

    a. 20%　　　c. 45%
    b. 25%　　　d. 70%

11. The ozone layer is located in the

    a. stratosphere.　c. thermosphere.
    b. troposphere.　d. mesosphere.

12. By which method does most thermal energy in the atmosphere circulate? **B.1.3.5 CS**

    a. conduction
    b. convection
    c. the greenhouse effect
    d. radiation

13. Most of the United States is located between 30°N latitude and 60°S latitude. In which wind belt is most of the United States located? **H.2.3.1 CS** **FCAT**

    a. doldrums　　c. trade winds
    b. polar easterlies　d. westerlies

14. Which of the following pollutants is NOT a primary pollutant? **D.2.3.2**

    a. car exhaust
    b. acid precipitation
    c. smoke from a factory
    d. fumes from burning plastic

15. The Clean Air Act

    a. controls the amount of air pollutants that can be released from many sources.
    b. requires cars to run on fuels other than gasoline.
    c. requires many industries to use scrubbers.
    d. Both (a) and (c)

Short Answer

16 Why does the atmosphere become less dense as altitude increases? C.2.3.3

17 Explain why air rises when it is heated.

18 What is the main cause of temperature changes in the atmosphere?

19 What are secondary pollutants, and how do they form? Give an example of a secondary pollutant. D.2.3.2

20 Give one example of a point-source pollutant and one example of a nonpoint-source pollutant. D.2.3.2

21 Describe two sources of air pollution caused by humans, and describe what can be done to reduce the air pollution each source creates. D.2.3.1, D.2.3.2

22 What do the primary and secondary air-quality standards protect? D.2.3.1, D.2.3.2

23 How is air quality information communicated to the public? Explain why this information is important to the public. D.2.3.1

CRITICAL THINKING

Extended Response

24 **Identifying Relationships** What is the relationship between the greenhouse effect and global warming?

25 **Applying Concepts** How does acid precipitation affect plants, animals, and humans? What can be done to reduce acid precipitation? D.1.3.3 CS, D.2.3.1, G.2.3.4 AA

26 **Making Inferences** The atmosphere of Venus has a very high level of carbon dioxide. How might this fact influence the greenhouse effect on Venus?

Concept Mapping

27 Use the following terms to create a concept map: *layer, temperature, troposphere, mesosphere, stratosphere,* and *atmosphere.*

INTERPRETING GRAPHICS

The diagram shows two boats traveling. Assume that ocean currents do not affect the path of the boats. Use the diagram below to answer the questions that follow.

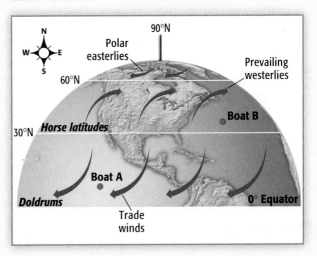

28 If Boat A traveled to 50°N, from which direction would the prevailing winds blow? H.2.3.1 CS

29 If Boat B sailed with the prevailing westerlies in the Northern Hemisphere, in which direction would the boat be traveling? H.2.3.1 CS

Standardized Test Preparation

For the following questions, write your answers on a separate sheet of paper.

1 The chart below shows some of the properties of the different layers of the atmosphere.

PROPERTIES OF THE ATMOSPHERE

Layer of the Atmosphere	Temperature in Celsius (°C)	Altitude in Kilometers (km)	Amount of Heat Energy
Troposphere	Varies greatly	10	High levels
Stratosphere	–60	40	Moderate levels
Mesosphere	–93	65	Low levels
Thermosphere	1000	100	Very low levels

Which of the four layers of Earth's atmosphere has the highest temperature but also has very little transfer of heat energy?

A. the mesosphere
B. the stratosphere
C. the thermosphere
D. the troposphere

2 Which of the following answers is an example of conduction that we can commonly experience in our own homes?

F. a microwave
G. a fire in the fireplace
H. an electrical space heater
I. a hot spoon in a pot on the stove

3 Dwayne is trying to explain the difference between heat and temperature to his lab partner. Which of the following statements is true and could help him explain the difference between the two?

A. Temperature describes how fast particles are moving.
B. Heat is the density of an element at a specific pressure.
C. Heat is the space between particles at the same altitude.
D. Temperature is the difference in pressure of various molecules.

4   As Carlotta was walking home from school, she noticed that the air was hotter above the concrete road than it was above the grass. By what process is thermal energy transferred from the concrete to the air?

F.   conduction
G.   convection
H.   diffusion
I.   radiation

5   When Josh and his family went to the beach, they were amazed by how much cooler the air was at the seashore than the air was a few miles inland. Which of the following statements explains why there is usually a cool breeze at the seashore?

A.   The air coming from land is cooler during the daytime.
B.   The warm air from the land creates a high pressure system.
C.   The warm air from the ocean creates a low pressure system.
D.   The air coming from the ocean is cooler during the daytime.

6   The map below shows the locations of low- and high-pressure belts across North America and South America.

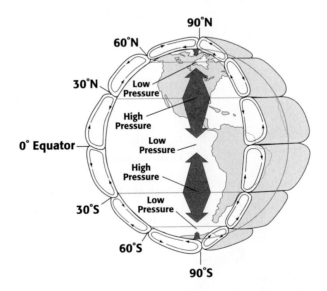

What causes the formation of high-pressure belts?
F.   the rising and warming of cool air
G.   the rising and cooling of warm air
H.   the sinking and warming of cool air
I.   the sinking and cooling of warm air

Science in Action

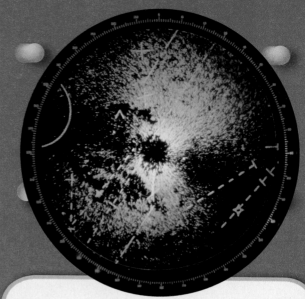

FOCUS ON FLORIDA

Science, Technology, and Society

Mercury in the Everglades

In the 1980s, scientists measuring pollutants in Florida lakes and streams made a scary discovery. Concentrations of the toxic element mercury were rising in wildlife throughout the state. And in the Everglades, mercury levels were skyrocketing! But where was the mercury coming from? Scientists found that mercury was released into the atmosphere when garbage was burned in incinerators. This atmospheric mercury entered the Everglades through rain. Pollution controls placed on incinerators decreased mercury emissions to almost nothing after 10 years. Another 10 years later, mercury levels in fish dropped by 60%.

Math ACTIVITY

Before pollution controls were put in place, incinerators in South Florida burned a maximum of 9,000 tons of garbage per day. What was the maximum amount of garbage that these incinerators burned in 1 year?

WARNING
HEALTH HAZARD
DO NOT EAT BASS CAUGHT BEYOND THIS POINT DUE TO HIGH MERCURY CONTENT
NPS-EVER

Weird Science

Radar Zoology

"For tonight's forecast, expect a light shower of mayflies. A wave of warblers will approach from the south. Tomorrow will be cloudy, and a band of free-tailed bats will move to the south in the early evening." Such a forecast may not make the evening news, but it is a familiar scenario for radar zoologists. Radar zoologists use a type of radar called *NEXRAD* to track migrating birds, bands of bats, and swarms of insects. NEXRAD tracks animals in the atmosphere in the same way that it tracks storms. The system sends out a microwave signal. If the signal hits an object, some of the energy reflects back to a receiver. NEXRAD has been especially useful to scientists who study bird migration. Birds tend to migrate at night, when the atmosphere is more stable, so until now, nighttime bird migration has been difficult to observe. NEXRAD has also helped identify important bird migration routes and critical stopovers. For example, scientists have discovered that many birds migrate over instead of around the Gulf of Mexico.

Social Studies ACTIVITY

Geography plays an important role in bird migration. Many birds ride the "thermals" produced by mountain ranges. Find out what thermals are, and create a map of bird migration routes over North America.

Ellen Paneok

Bush Pilot For Ellen Paneok, understanding weather patterns is a matter of life and death. As a bush pilot, she flies mail, supplies, and people to remote villages in Alaska that can be reached only by plane. Bad weather is one of the most serious challenges Paneok faces. "It's beautiful up here," she says, "but it can also be harsh." One dangerous situation is landing a plane in mountainous regions. "On top of a mountain you can't tell which way the wind is blowing," Paneok says. In this case, she flies in a rectangular pattern to determine the wind direction. Landing a plane on the frozen Arctic Ocean is also dangerous. In white-out conditions, the horizon can't be seen because the sky and the ground are the same color. "It's like flying in a milk bottle full of milk," Paneok says. In these conditions, she fills black plastic garbage bags and drops them from the plane to help guide her landing.

Paneok had to overcome many challenges to become a pilot. As a child, she lived in seven foster homes before being placed in an all-girls' home at the age of 14. In the girls' home, she read a magazine about careers in aviation and decided then and there that she wanted to become a pilot. At first, she faced a lot of opposition from people telling her that she wouldn't be able to become a pilot. Now, she encourages young people to pursue their goals. "If you decide you want to go for it, go for it. There may be obstacles in your way, but you've just got to find a way to go over them, get around them, or dig under them," she says.

Language Arts ACTiViTY

Beryl Markham lived an exciting life as a bush pilot delivering mail and supplies to remote areas of Africa. Read about her life or the life of Bessie Coleman, one of the most famous African American women in the history of flying.

Ellen Paneok is shown at right with two of her Inupiat passengers.

go.hrw.com
To learn more about these Science in Action topics, visit go.hrw.com and type in the keyword HT6FAMFF.

Current Science
Check out Current Science® articles related to this chapter by visiting go.hrw.com. Just type in the keyword HZ5CS15.

4

Climate and Weather

The Big Idea Weather and climate are dependent systems that occur in consistent patterns.

About the PHOTO

Flamingos in the bathroom? This may look like someone's idea of a practical joke, but in fact, it's a practical idea! These flamingos reside at the Miami-Metro Zoo in Florida. They were put in the bathroom for protection against the incredibly dangerous winds of Hurricane Floyd in September of 1999.

PRE-READING ACTIVITY

 **Layered Book** Before you read the chapter, create the FoldNote entitled "Layered Book" described in the **Study Skills** section of the Appendix. Label the tabs of the layered book with "Climate," "Water in the air," "Air masses and fronts," "Severe weather," and "Forecasting the weather." As you read the chapter, write information you learn about each category under the appropriate tab.

START-UP ACTIVITY

Meeting of the Masses

In this activity, you will model what happens when two air masses that have different temperature characteristics meet.

Procedure

1. Pour **500 mL of water** into a **beaker.** Pour **500 mL of cooking oil** into a **second beaker.** The water represents a dense cold air mass. The cooking oil represents a less dense warm air mass.

2. Predict what would happen to the two liquids if you tried to mix them.

3. Pour the contents of both beakers into a **clear, plastic, rectangular container** at the same time from opposite ends of the container.

4. Observe the interaction of the oil and water.

Analysis

1. What happens when the liquids meet?

2. Does the prediction that you made in step 2 of the Procedure match your results?

3. Using your results, hypothesize what would happen if a cold air mass met a warm air mass.

What Is Climate?

Suppose you receive a call from a friend who is coming to visit you tomorrow. To decide what clothing to bring, he asks about the current weather in your area.

You step outside to see if rain clouds are in the sky and to check the temperature. But what would you do if your friend asked you about the climate in your area? What is the difference between weather and climate?

Climate Vs. Weather

The main difference between weather and climate is the length of time over which both are measured. **Weather** is the condition of the atmosphere at a particular time. Weather conditions vary from day to day and include temperature, humidity, precipitation, wind, and visibility. **Climate,** on the other hand, is the average weather condition in an area over a long period of time. Climate is mostly determined by two factors—temperature and precipitation. Different parts of the world can have different climates, as shown in **Figure 1.** But why are climates so different? The answer is complicated. It includes factors in addition to temperature and precipitation, such as latitude, wind patterns, mountains, large bodies of water, and ocean currents.

✓ **Reading Check** How is climate different from weather?

Figure 1 *How does the climate in northern Africa differ from the climate where you live?*

North America

South America

Africa

Latitude

Think of the last time you looked at a globe. Do you recall the thin, horizontal lines that circle the globe? Those lines are called lines of latitude. **Latitude** is the distance north or south, measured in degrees, from the equator. In general, the temperature of an area depends on its latitude. The higher the latitude is, the colder the climate tends to be. One of the coldest places on Earth, the North Pole, is 90° north of the equator. However, the equator, at latitude 0°, is usually hot.

As shown in **Figure 2,** if you were to take a trip to different latitudes in the United States, you would experience different climates. For example, the climate in Washington, D.C., which is at a higher latitude, is different from the climate in Texas.

Solar Energy and Latitude

Solar energy, which is energy from the sun, heats Earth. The amount of direct solar energy a particular area receives is determined by latitude. **Figure 3** shows how the curve of Earth affects the amount of direct solar energy at different latitudes. Notice that the sun's rays hit the equator directly, at almost a 90° angle. At this angle, a small area of Earth's surface receives more direct solar energy than at a lesser angle. As a result, that area has high temperatures. However, the sun's rays strike the poles at a lesser angle than they do the equator. At this angle, the same amount of direct solar energy that hits the area at the equator is spread over a larger area at the poles. The result is lower temperatures at the poles.

Figure 2 *Winter in south Texas (top) is different from winter in Washington D.C. (bottom).*

weather the short-term state of the atmosphere, including temperature, humidity, precipitation, wind, and visibility

climate the average weather condition in an area over a long period of time

latitude the distance north or south from the equator; expressed in degrees

Figure 3 The sun's rays strike Earth's surface at different angles because the surface is curved.

Sun's rays

Equator

Seasons and Latitude

In most places in the United States, the year consists of four seasons. But there are places in the world that do not have such seasonal changes. For example, areas near the equator have approximately the same temperatures and same amount of daylight year-round. Seasons happen because Earth is tilted on its axis at a 23.5° angle. This tilt affects how much solar energy an area receives as Earth moves around the sun. **Figure 4** shows how latitude and the tilt of Earth determine the seasons and the length of the day in a particular area.

 Benchmark Check How does Earth's tilt affect the seasons as Earth travels around the sun? **D.1.3.3 CS, H.2.3.1 CS**

D.1.3.3 CS knows how conditions that exist in one system influence the conditions that exist in other systems.

H.2.3.1 CS recognizes that patterns exist within and across systems.

Figure 4 **The Seasons**

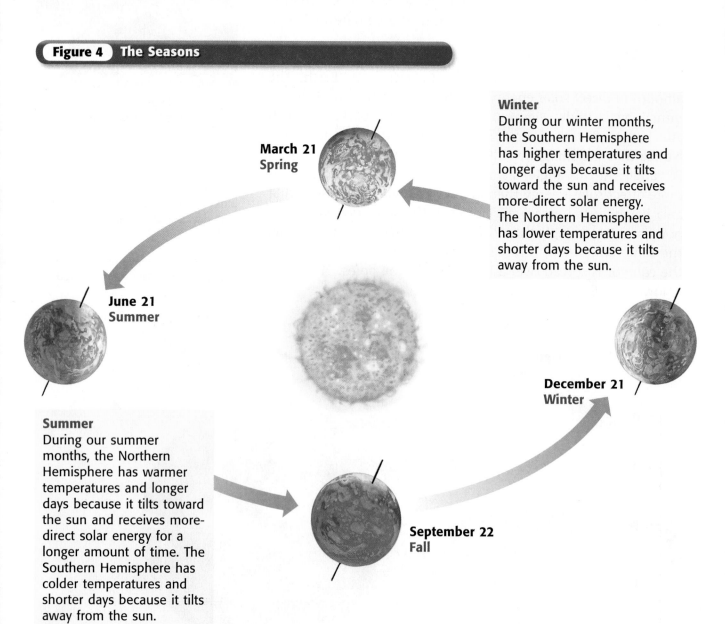

March 21
Spring

Winter
During our winter months, the Southern Hemisphere has higher temperatures and longer days because it tilts toward the sun and receives more-direct solar energy. The Northern Hemisphere has lower temperatures and shorter days because it tilts away from the sun.

June 21
Summer

December 21
Winter

Summer
During our summer months, the Northern Hemisphere has warmer temperatures and longer days because it tilts toward the sun and receives more-direct solar energy for a longer amount of time. The Southern Hemisphere has colder temperatures and shorter days because it tilts away from the sun.

September 22
Fall

Figure 5 The Circulation of Warm Air and Cold Air

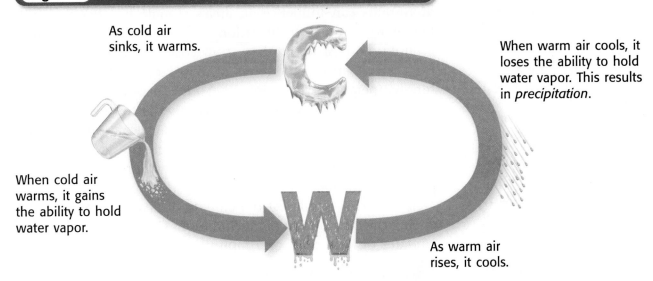

As cold air sinks, it warms.

When warm air cools, it loses the ability to hold water vapor. This results in *precipitation*.

When cold air warms, it gains the ability to hold water vapor.

As warm air rises, it cools.

Prevailing Winds

Winds that blow mainly from one direction are **prevailing winds.** Before you learn how the prevailing winds affect climate, take a look at **Figure 5** to learn about some of the basic properties of air.

Prevailing winds affect the amount of precipitation that a region receives. If the prevailing winds form from warm air, they may carry moisture. If the prevailing winds form from cold air, they will probably be dry.

The amount of moisture in prevailing winds is also affected by whether the winds blow across land or across a large body of water. Winds that travel across large bodies of water absorb moisture. Winds that travel across land tend to be dry. Even if a region borders the ocean, the area might be dry. **Figure 6** shows an example of how dry prevailing winds can cause the land to be dry though the land is near an ocean.

prevailing winds winds that blow mainly from one direction during a given period

A Cool Breeze

1. Hold a **thermometer** next to the top edge of a **cup** of **water** containing two **ice cubes.** Record the temperature next to the cup.

2. Have your lab partner fan the surface of the cup with a **paper fan.** Record the temperature again. Has the temperature changed? Why or why not?

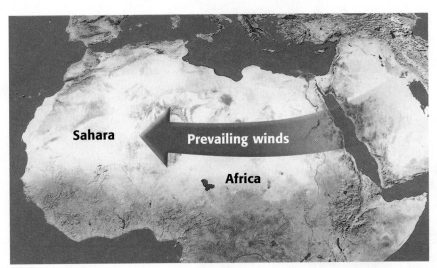

Figure 6 *The Sahara, in northern Africa, is extremely dry because of the dry prevailing winds that blow across the continent.*

Mountains

Mountains can influence an area's climate by affecting both temperature and precipitation. Kilimanjaro is the tallest mountain in Africa. It has snow-covered peaks year-round, even though it is only about 3° (320 km) south of the equator. Temperatures on Kilimanjaro and in other mountainous areas are affected by elevation. **Elevation** is the height of surface landforms above sea level. As the elevation increases, the ability of air to transfer energy from the ground to the atmosphere decreases. Therefore, as elevation increases, temperature decreases.

Mountains also affect the climate of nearby areas by influencing the distribution of precipitation. **Figure 7** shows how the climates on two sides of a mountain can be very different.

Benchmark Check Why does the atmosphere become cooler at higher elevations? **D.1.3.3 CS, H.2.3.1 CS**

Figure 7 How Mountains Affect Climate

The Wet Side
Mountains force air to rise. The air cools as it rises, releasing moisture as snow or rain. The land on the windward side of the mountain is usually green and lush because the wind releases its moisture.

The Dry Side
After dry air crosses the mountain, the air begins to sink. As the air sinks, it is warmed and absorbs moisture. The dry conditions created by the sinking, warm air usually produce a desert. This side of the mountain is in a *rain shadow*.

Large Bodies of Water

Large bodies of water can influence an area's climate. Water absorbs and releases heat slower than land does. Because of this quality, water helps to moderate the temperatures of the land around it. So, sudden or extreme temperature changes rarely take place on land near large bodies of water. For example, the state of Michigan, which is surrounded by the Great Lakes, has more-moderate temperatures than other places at the same latitude. The lakes also increase the moisture content of the air, which leads to heavy snowfall in the winter. This "lake effect" can cause 350 inches of snow to drop in one year!

Ocean Currents

The circulation of ocean surface currents has a large effect on an area's climate. **Surface currents** are streamlike movements of water that occur at or near the surface of the ocean. **Figure 8** shows the pattern of the major ocean surface currents.

As surface currents move, they carry warm or cool water to different locations. The surface temperature of the water affects the temperature of the air above it. Warm currents heat the surrounding air and cause warmer temperatures. Cool currents cool the surrounding air and cause cooler temperatures. The Gulf Stream current carries warm water northward off the east coast of North America and past Iceland. Iceland is an island country located just below the Arctic Circle. The warm water from the Gulf Stream heats the surrounding air and creates warmer temperatures in southern Iceland. Iceland experiences milder temperatures than Greenland, its neighboring island. Greenland's climate is cooler because Greenland is not influenced by the Gulf Stream.

 Benchmark Check Why does Iceland experience milder temperatures than Greenland? **D.1.3.3 CS, H.2.3.1 CS**

INTERNET ACTIVITY

A Century Later Predict how the climate of your hometown may change over the next 100 years. Go to **go.hrw.com,** and type in the keyword **HZ5CLMW.**

elevation the height of an object above sea level

surface current a horizontal movement of ocean water that is caused by wind and that occurs at or near the ocean's surface

D.1.3.3 CS knows how conditions that exist in one system influence the conditions that exist in other systems.

H.2.3.1 CS recognizes that patterns exist within and across systems.

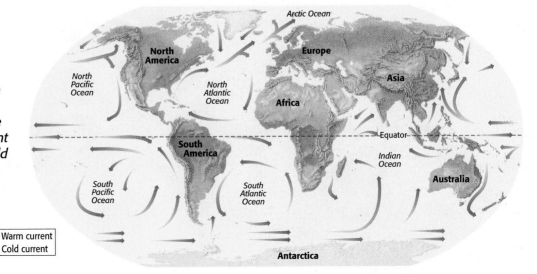

Figure 8 *The red arrows represent the movement of warm surface currents. The blue arrows represent the movement of cold surface currents.*

Warm current
Cold current

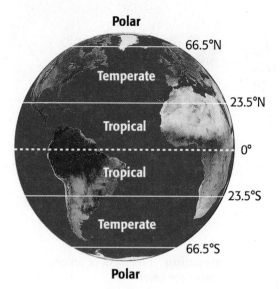

Figure 9 *The three major climate zones are determined by latitude.*

biome a large region characterized by a specific type of climate and certain types of plant and animal communities

Climates of the World

Have you seen any polar bears in your neighborhood lately? You probably have not. That's because polar bears live only in very cold arctic regions. Why are the animals in one part of the world so different from the animals in other parts? One of the differences has to do with climate. Plants and animals that have adapted to one climate may not be able to live in another climate. For example, frogs would not be able to survive at the North Pole.

Climate Zones

Earth's three major climate zones—tropical, temperate, and polar—are shown in **Figure 9.** Each zone has a temperature range that relates to its latitude. However, in each of these zones, there are several types of climates because of differences in the geography and the amount of precipitation. Because of the various climates in each zone, there are different biomes in each zone. A **biome** is a large region characterized by a specific type of climate and certain types of plant and animal communities. **Figure 10** shows the distribution of Earth's land biomes. In which biome do you live?

✔ *Reading Check* What factors distinguish one biome from another biome?

Figure 10   The Earth's Land Biomes

- Tundra
- Taiga
- Temperate forest
- Tropical rain forest
- Temperate grassland
- Tropical savanna
- Temperate desert
- Tropical desert
- Chaparral
- Mountains

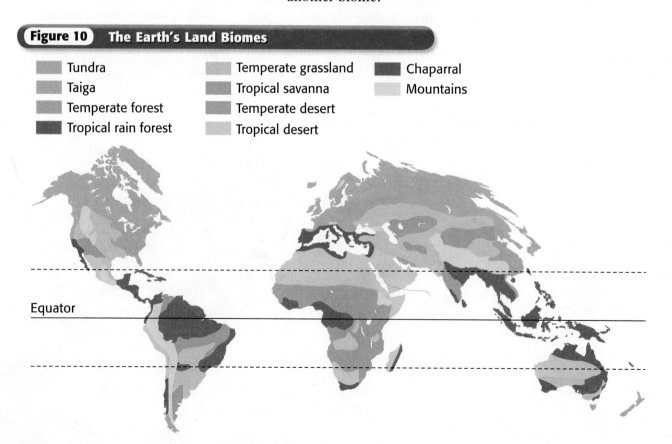

Equator

Summary

- Climate systems affect the weather in different regions. **D.1.3.3 CS, H.2.3.1 CS**
- Climate is the average weather condition in an area over a long period of time. **D.1.3.3 CS, H.2.3.1 CS**
- The higher the latitude, the cooler the climate. **D.1.3.3 CS, H.2.3.1 CS**
- Prevailing winds affect the climate of an area by the amount of moisture they carry. **D.1.3.3 CS, H.2.3.1 CS**

- Mountains influence an area's climate by affecting both temperature and precipitation. **D.1.3.3 CS, H.2.3.1 CS**
- Large bodies of water and ocean currents influence the climate of an area by affecting the temperature of the air over the water. **D.1.3.3 CS, H.2.3.1 CS**
- The three climate zones of the world are the tropical zone, the temperate zone, and the polar zone.

Using Key Terms

1. Write an original definition for *weather, climate, latitude, prevailing winds, elevation, surface currents,* and *biome.*

Understanding Key Ideas

2. Which of the following affects climate by causing the air to rise? **D.1.3.3 CS, H.2.3.1 CS**

   a. mountains

   b. ocean currents

   c. large bodies of water

   d. latitude

3. Differentiate between weather systems and climate systems. **D.1.3.3 CS, H.2.3.1 CS**

4. Identify five factors that determine climates. **D.1.3.3 CS, H.2.3.1 CS**

5. Explain why there is a difference in climate between areas at 0° latitude and areas at 45° latitude.

6. Identify the three climate zones of the world.

Critical Thinking

7. **Analyzing Relationships** Hypothesize how the seasons would be different if Earth did not tilt on its axis. **D.1.3.3 CS, H.2.3.1 CS**

8. **Applying Concepts** During what months does Australia have summer? Explain.

FCAT Preparation

9. Ocean currents affect the temperature of air currents. If air blows over a cold ocean current, it will cool and could loose water. If air blows over a warm current, it could warm and gain water. Which of the following describes the relationship between ocean currents and air currents? **D.1.3.3 CS, H.2.3.1 CS**

   A. Ocean currents cause air to loose water.

   B. Ocean currents cause air to gain water.

   C. Ocean currents affect the temperature and amount of moisture of air currents.

   D. Ocean currents and air currents are not related.

10. Carla placed cotton balls of equal mass in two jars. Then, she moistened each cotton ball with the same amount of water. She sealed the jars and placed one in a sunny spot and the other in a shaded spot. After 30 min, she weighed the cotton balls. What was the variable in the experiment? **H.1.3.5 AA**

For a variety of links related to this chapter, go to www.scilinks.org

Topic: What Is Climate?
SciLinks code: HSM1659

SECTION 2

Water in the Air

What will the weather be this weekend? Depending on what you have planned, knowing the answer to this question could be important. A picnic in the rain can be a mess!

READING WARM-UP

Objectives

- Explain how water moves through the water cycle.
- Describe how relative humidity is affected by temperature and levels of water vapor.
- Describe the relationship between dew point and condensation.
- Identify three types of cloud formations.
- Identify four kinds of precipitation.

Terms to Learn

humidity
relative humidity
condensation
cloud
precipitation

READING STRATEGY

Paired Summarizing Read this section silently. In pairs, take turns summarizing the material. Stop to discuss ideas that seem confusing.

As you learned earlier, *weather* is the condition of the atmosphere at a certain time and place. The condition of the atmosphere is affected by the amount of water in the air. So, to understand weather, you need to understand how water cycles through Earth's atmosphere.

The Water Cycle

Water in liquid, solid, and gaseous states is constantly being recycled through the water cycle. The *water cycle* is the continuous movement of water from sources on Earth's surface—such as lakes, oceans, and plants—into the air, onto and over land, into the ground, and back to the surface. The movement of water through the water cycle is shown in **Figure 1.**

Reading Check What is the water cycle?

Figure 1 **The Water Cycle**

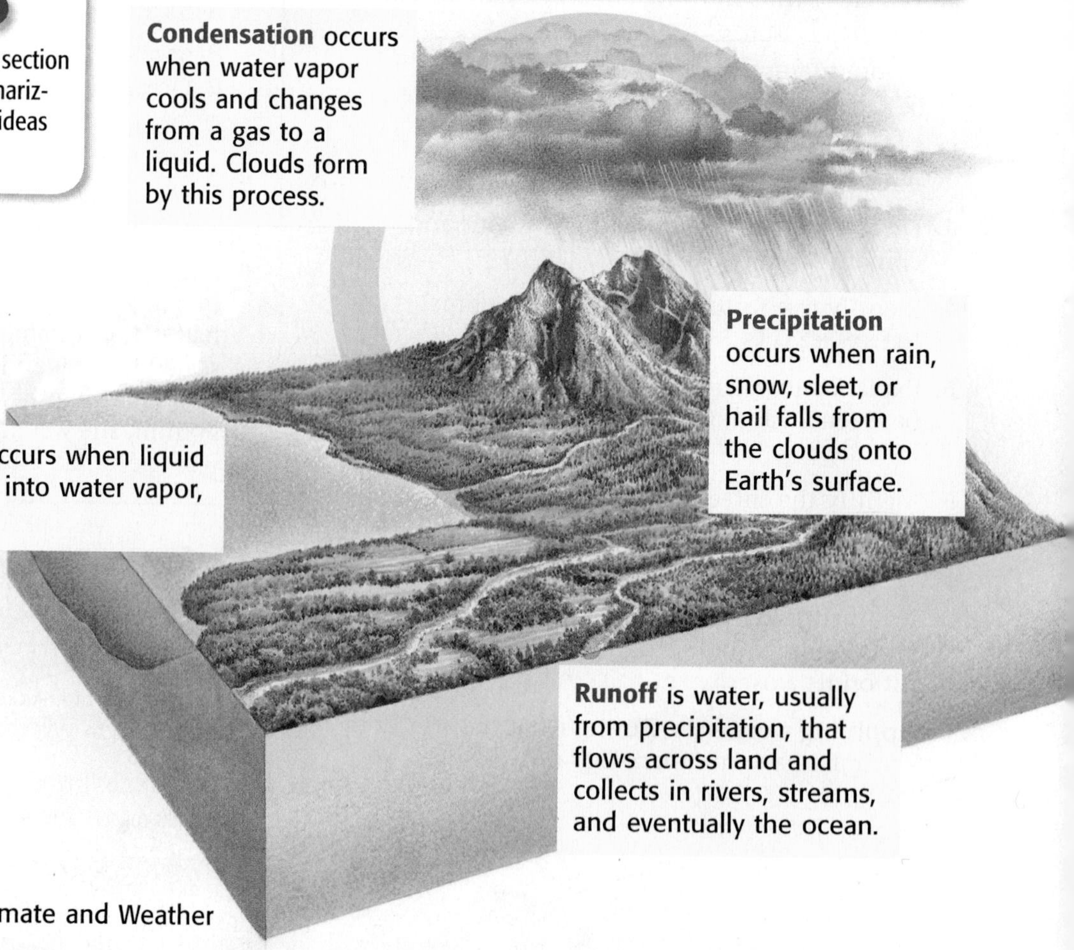
Condensation occurs when water vapor cools and changes from a gas to a liquid. Clouds form by this process.
Precipitation occurs when rain, snow, sleet, or hail falls from the clouds onto Earth's surface.
Evaporation occurs when liquid water changes into water vapor, which is a gas.
Runoff is water, usually from precipitation, that flows across land and collects in rivers, streams, and eventually the ocean.

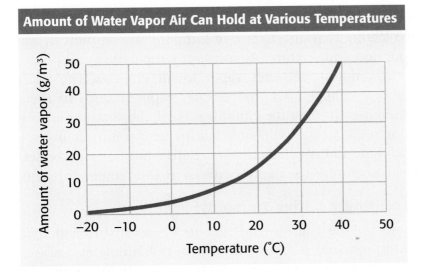

Amount of Water Vapor Air Can Hold at Various Temperatures

Figure 2 *This graph shows that as air gets warmer, the amount of water vapor that the air can hold increases.*

Humidity

As water evaporates from lakes, oceans, and plants, it becomes *water vapor,* or moisture in the air. Water vapor is invisible. The amount of water vapor in the air is called **humidity.** As water evaporates and becomes water vapor, the humidity of the air increases. The air's ability to hold water vapor changes as the temperature of the air changes. **Figure 2** shows that as the temperature of the air increases, the air's ability to hold water vapor also increases.

humidity the amount of water vapor in the air

relative humidity the ratio of the amount of water vapor in the air to the amount of water vapor needed to reach saturation at a given temperature

Relative Humidity

One way to express humidity is through relative humidity. **Relative humidity** is the amount of water vapor in the air compared with the maximum amount of water vapor that would saturate the air at a certain temperature. So, relative humidity is given as a percentage. When air holds all of the water that it can at a given temperature, it is said to be *saturated.* Saturated air has a relative humidity of 100%. But how do you find the relative humidity of air that is not saturated? If you know the maximum amount of water vapor that air can hold at a given temperature and the actual amount of water vapor in the air, you can calculate the relative humidity.

Suppose that 1 m³ of air at a certain temperature can hold 24 g of water vapor. However, you know that the air actually contains 18 g of water vapor. You can calculate the relative humidity by using the following formula:

Relative Humidity

Assume that 1 m³ of air at 25°C contains 11 g of water vapor. At this temperature, the air can hold 24 g/m³ of water vapor. Calculate the relative humidity of the air.

$$\frac{actual\ water\ vapor\ content\ (g/m^3)}{saturation\ water\ vapor\ content\ (g/m^3)} \times 100 = relative\ humidity\ (\%)$$

$$\frac{18\ g/m^3}{24\ g/m^3} = 75\%$$

Factors Affecting Relative Humidity

Two factors that affect relative humidity are amount of water vapor and temperature. At constant temperature and pressure, as the amount of water vapor in air changes, the relative humidity changes. The more water vapor there is in the air, the higher the relative humidity is. If the amount of water vapor in the air stays the same but the temperature changes, the relative humidity changes. The relative humidity decreases as the temperature rises and increases as the temperature drops.

Measuring Relative Humidity

A *psychrometer* (sie KRAHM uht uhr) is an instrument that is used to measure relative humidity. A psychrometer consists of two thermometers, one of which is a wet-bulb thermometer. The bulb of a wet-bulb thermometer is covered with a damp cloth. The other thermometer is a dry-bulb thermometer.

The difference in temperature readings between the thermometers indicates the amount of water vapor in the air. The larger the difference between the two readings is, the less water vapor the air contains and thus the lower the humidity is. **Figure 3** shows how to use a table of differences between wet-bulb and dry-bulb readings to determine relative humidity.

✓ **Reading Check** What tool is used to measure relative humidity?

Figure 3 Determining Relative Humidity

Find the relative humidity by locating the column head that is equal to the difference between the wet-bulb and dry-bulb readings. Then, locate the row head that equals the temperature reading on the dry-bulb thermometer. The value that lies where the column and row intersect equals the relative humidity. You can see a psychrometer below.

Relative Humidity (%)								
Dry-bulb reading (°C)	Difference between wet-bulb reading and dry-bulb reading (°C)							
	1	2	3	4	5	6	7	8
0	81	64	46	29	13			
2	84	68	52	37	22			
4	85	71	57	43	29	16		
6	86	73	60	48	35	24	11	
8	87	75	63	51	40	29	19	
10	88	77	66	55	44	34	24	15
12	89	78	68	58	48	39	29	21
14	90	79	70	60	51	42	34	26
16	90	81	71	63	54	46	38	30
18	91	82	73	65	57	49	41	34
20	91	83	74	66	59	51	44	37

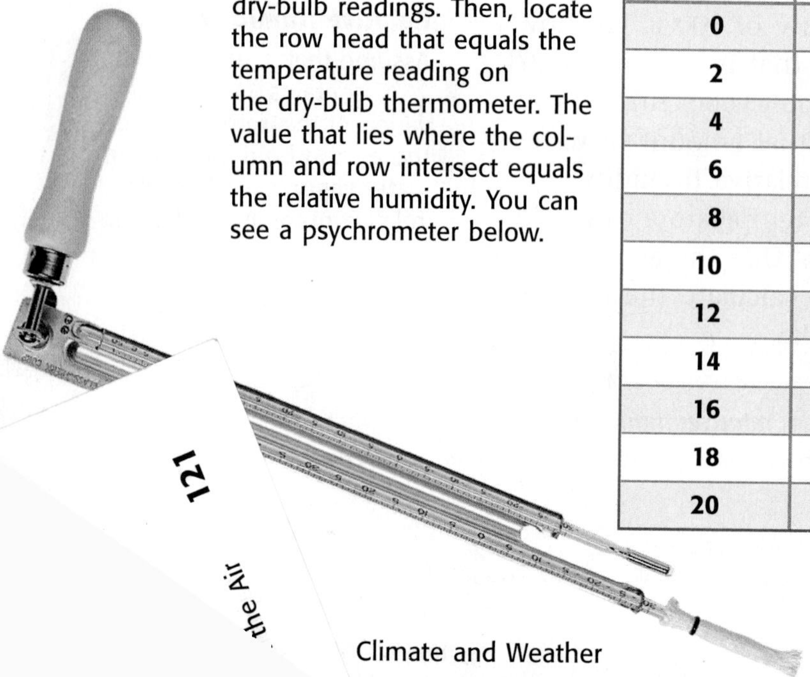

the Air

Climate and Weather

How a Wet-Bulb Thermometer Works

A wet-bulb thermometer works differently than a dry-bulb thermometer, which measures only air temperature. As air passes over the wet-bulb thermometer, the water in the cloth evaporates. As the water evaporates, the cloth cools. If the humidity is low, the water will evaporate more quickly and the temperature reading on the wet-bulb thermometer will drop. If the humidity is high, only a small amount of water will evaporate from the cloth of the wet-bulb thermometer and the change in temperature will be small.

✓ Reading Check Explain how a wet-bulb thermometer works.

Condensation

You have probably seen water droplets form on the outside of a glass of ice water, as shown in **Figure 4.** Where did those water drops come from? The water came from the surrounding air, and droplets formed as a result of condensation. **Condensation** is the process by which a gas, such as water vapor, becomes a liquid. Before condensation can occur, the air must be saturated, which means that the air must have a relative humidity of 100%. Condensation occurs when saturated air cools.

Figure 4 *Condensation occurred when the air surrounding the glass cooled to its dew point.*

condensation the change of state from a gas to a liquid

Dew Point

Air can become saturated when water vapor is added to the air through evaporation. Air can also become saturated when it cools to its dew point. The *dew point* is the temperature at which a gas condenses into a liquid. At its dew point, air is saturated. The ice in the glass of water causes the air surrounding the glass to cool to its dew point.

Before water vapor can condense, though, it must have a surface to condense on. In the case of the glass of ice water, water vapor condenses on the outside of the glass.

Out of Thin Air

1. Pour **room-temperature water** into a **plastic container,** such as a drinking cup, until the water level is near the top of the cup.
2. Observe the outside of the container, and record your observations.
3. Add **one or two ice cubes** to the container of water.
4. Watch the outside of the container for any changes.
5. What happened to the outside of the container?
6. What is the liquid on the container?
7. Where did the liquid come from? Explain your answer.

Figure 5 Three Forms of Clouds

Cumulus clouds look like piles of cotton balls.

Stratus clouds are not as tall as cumulus clouds, but they cover more area.

Cirrus clouds are made of ice crystals.

cloud a collection of small water droplets or ice crystals suspended in the air, which forms when the air is cooled and condensation occurs

CONNECTION TO Language Arts

Cloud Clues Did you know that the name of a cloud actually describes the characteristics of the cloud? For example, the word *cumulus* comes from the Latin word meaning "heap." A cumulus cloud is a puffy, white cloud, which could be described as a "heap" of clouds. Use a dictionary or the Internet to find the word origins of the names of the other cloud types you learn about in this section.

Clouds

Have you ever wondered what clouds are and how they form? A **cloud** is a collection of millions of tiny water droplets or ice crystals. Clouds form as warm air rises and cools. As the rising air cools, it becomes saturated. When the air is saturated, the water vapor changes to a liquid or a solid, depending on the air temperature. At temperatures above freezing, water vapor condenses on small particles in the air and forms tiny water droplets. At temperatures below freezing, water vapor changes to a solid to form ice crystals. Clouds are classified by form, as shown in **Figure 5,** and by altitude.

Cumulus Clouds

Puffy, white clouds that tend to have flat bottoms are called *cumulus clouds* (KYOO myoo luhs KLOWDZ). Cumulus clouds form when warm air rises. These clouds generally indicate fair weather. However, when these clouds get larger, they produce thunderstorms. Thunderstorms come from a kind of cumulus cloud called a *cumulonimbus cloud* (KYOO myoo loh NIM buhs KLOWD). Clouds that have names that include *-nimbus* or *nimbo-* are likely to produce precipitation.

Stratus Clouds

Clouds called *stratus clouds* (STRAYT uhs KLOWDZ) are clouds that form in layers. Stratus clouds cover large areas of the sky and often block out the sun. These clouds can be caused by a gentle lifting of a large body of air into the atmosphere. *Nimbostratus clouds* (NIM boh STRAYT uhs KLOWDZ) are dark stratus clouds that usually produce light to heavy, continuous rain. *Fog* is a stratus cloud that has formed near the ground.

Cirrus Clouds

As you can see in **Figure 5,** *cirrus clouds* (SIR uhs KLOWDZ) are thin, feathery, white clouds found at high altitudes. Cirrus clouds form when the wind is strong. If they get thicker, cirrus clouds indicate that a change in the weather is coming.

Clouds and Altitude

Clouds are also classified by the altitude at which they form. **Figure 6** shows two altitude groups used to describe clouds and the altitudes at which they form in the middle latitudes. The prefix *cirro-* is used to describe clouds that form at high altitudes. For example, a cumulus cloud that forms high in the atmosphere is called a *cirrocumulus cloud*. The prefix *alto-* describes clouds that form at middle altitudes. Clouds that form at low altitudes do not have a specific prefix to describe them.

Reading Check At what altitude does an altostratus cloud form?

Figure 6 Cloud Types Based on Form and Altitude

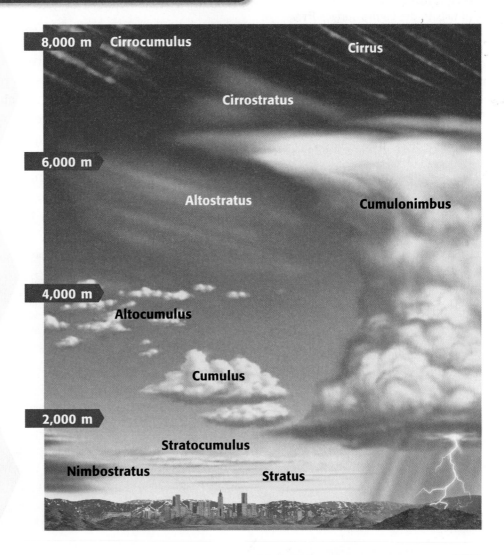

High Clouds Because of the cold temperatures at high altitude, high clouds are made up of ice crystals. The prefix *cirro-* is used to describe high clouds.

Middle Clouds Middle clouds can be made up of both water drops and ice crystals. The prefix *alto-* is used to describe middle clouds.

Low Clouds Low clouds are made up of water drops. There is no specific prefix to describe low clouds.

8,000 m Cirrocumulus

Cirrus

Cirrostratus

6,000 m

Altostratus

Cumulonimbus

4,000 m

Altocumulus

Cumulus

2,000 m

Stratocumulus

Nimbostratus

Stratus

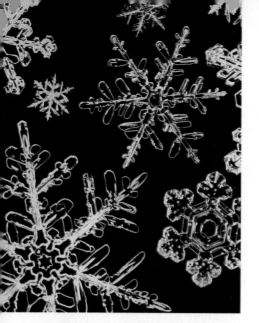

Figure 7 *Snowflakes are six-sided ice crystals that can be several millimeters to several centimeters in size.*

precipitation any form of water that falls to the Earth's surface from the clouds

Precipitation

When water from the air returns to Earth's surface, it returns as precipitation. **Precipitation** is water, in solid or liquid form, that falls from the air to Earth. There are four major forms of precipitation—rain, snow, sleet, and hail.

Rain

The most common form of precipitation is *rain*. A cloud produces rain when the water drops in the cloud become large enough to fall. A water drop in a cloud begins as a droplet that is smaller than the period at the end of this sentence. Before such a water drop falls as rain, it must become about 100 times its original size.

Sleet and Snow

Sleet forms when rain falls through a layer of freezing air. The rain freezes in the air, which produces falling ice. *Snow* forms when temperatures are so cold that water vapor changes directly to a solid. Snow can fall as single ice crystals or can join to form snowflakes, as shown in **Figure 7.**

Hail

Balls or lumps of ice that fall from clouds are called *hail*. Hail forms in cumulonimbus clouds. When updrafts of air in the clouds carry raindrops high in the clouds, the raindrops freeze and hail forms. As hail falls, water drops coat it. Another updraft of air can send the hail up again. Here, the water drops collected on the hail freeze to form another layer of ice on the hail. This process can happen many times. Eventually, the hail becomes too heavy to be carried by the updrafts and so falls to Earth's surface, as shown in **Figure 8.**

Figure 8 *The impact of large hailstones can damage property and crops. The inset photograph shows layers inside of a hailstone, which reveal how it formed.*

Summary

- Weather is affected by the amount of water vapor in the air.
- The water cycle describes the movement of water above, on, and below Earth's surface.
- Humidity describes the amount of water vapor in the air. Relative humidity is a way to express humidity.

- When the temperature of the air cools to its dew point, the air has reached saturation and condensation occurs.
- Clouds form as air cools to its dew point. Clouds are classified by form and by the altitude at which they form.
- Precipitation occurs when the water vapor that condenses in the atmosphere falls back to Earth in solid or liquid form.

Using Key Terms

1. Write an original definition for the terms *relative humidity, condensation, cloud,* and *precipitation.*

Understanding Key Ideas

2. Which of the following clouds is most likely to produce light to heavy, continuous rain?
   a. a cumulus cloud
   b. a cumulonimbus cloud
   c. a nimbostratus cloud
   d. a cirrus cloud

3. Explain how relative humidity is affected by the amount of water vapor in the air.

4. What does a relative humidity of 75% mean?

5. Describe the path of water through the water cycle.

6. Identify four types of precipitation.

Critical Thinking

7. **Applying Concepts** Hypothesize why some clouds are formed from water droplets, while others are made up of ice crystals.

8. **Applying Concepts** Explain how rain and hail can fall from the same cumulonimbus cloud.

9. **Identifying Relationships** What happens to relative humidity as the air temperature drops below the dew point?

FCAT Preparation

10. Janice made a psychrometer to measure relative humidity. She tested the psychrometer in the morning, and the temperature difference between the dry bulb and the wet bulb was 2° C. Later that afternoon, the difference was 6° C. Identify which variable changed during her investigation. **H.1.3.5 AA**
    A. the temperature difference between the thermometer bulbs
    B. the amount of moisture the pyschrometer absorbed from the air
    C. the size of the pyschrometer
    D. the relational humidity

11. Most natural events occur in patterns. Which of the following events is most likely to occur in a daily pattern? **H.2.3.1 CS**
    F. a severe thunderstorm in the evening
    G. a hailstorm in the morning
    H. dew formation in the early morning
    I. precipitation at noon

SCI**LINKS**®

NSTA
Developed and maintained by the
National Science Teachers Association

For a variety of links related to this chapter, go to www.scilinks.org
Topic: The Water Cycle
SciLinks code: HSM1626

Air Masses and Fronts

Have you ever wondered how the weather can change so quickly? For example, the weather may be warm and sunny in the morning and cold and rainy by afternoon.

Changes in weather are caused by the movement and interaction of air masses. An **air mass** is a large body of air where temperature and moisture content are similar throughout. In this section, you will learn about air masses and their effect on weather.

Air Masses

Air masses are characterized by their moisture content and temperature. The moisture content and temperature of an air mass are determined by the area over which the air mass forms. These areas are called *source regions*. An example of a source region is the Gulf of Mexico. An air mass that forms over the Gulf of Mexico is warm and wet because this area is warm and has a lot of water that evaporates. There are many types of air masses, each of which is associated with a particular source region. The characteristics of these air masses are represented on maps by a two-letter symbol, as shown in **Figure 1.** The first letter indicates the moisture content that is characteristic of the air mass. The second letter represents the temperature that is characteristic of the air mass.

READING WARM-UP

Objectives

- Identify the four kinds of air masses that influence weather in the United States.
- Describe the four major types of fronts.
- Explain how fronts cause weather changes.
- Explain how cyclones and anticyclones affect the weather.

Terms to Learn

air mass   cyclone
front   anticyclone

READING STRATEGY

Reading Organizer As you read this section, make a table comparing cold, warm, occluded, and stationary fronts.

Figure 1 Air Masses That Affect Weather in North America

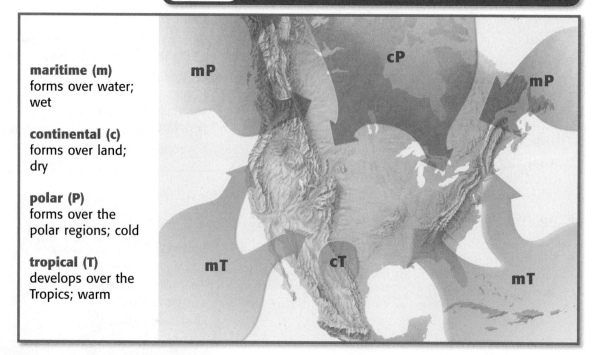

maritime (m)
forms over water; wet

continental (c)
forms over land; dry

polar (P)
forms over the polar regions; cold

tropical (T)
develops over the Tropics; warm

Figure 2 *Cold air masses that form over the North Atlantic Ocean can bring severe weather, such as blizzards, in the winter.*

Cold Air Masses

Most of the cold winter weather in the United States is influenced by three polar air masses. A continental polar (cP) air mass forms over northern Canada, which brings extremely cold winter weather to the United States. In the summer, a cP air mass generally brings cool, dry weather.

A maritime polar (mP) air mass that forms over the North Pacific Ocean is cool and very wet. This air mass brings rain and snow to the Pacific Coast in the winter and cool, foggy weather in the summer.

A maritime polar air mass that forms over the North Atlantic Ocean brings cool, cloudy weather and precipitation to New England in the winter, as shown in **Figure 2.** In the summer, the air mass brings cool weather and fog.

air mass a large body of air throughout which temperature and moisture content are similar

Warm Air Masses

Four warm air masses influence the weather in the United States. A maritime tropical (mT) air mass that develops over warm areas in the Pacific Ocean is milder than the maritime polar air mass that forms over the Pacific Ocean.

Other maritime tropical air masses develop over the warm waters of the Gulf of Mexico and the Atlantic Ocean. These air masses move north across the East Coast and into the Midwest. In the summer, they bring hot and humid weather, hurricanes, and thunderstorms, as shown in **Figure 3.** In the winter, they bring mild, often cloudy weather.

A continental tropical (cT) air mass forms over the deserts of northern Mexico and the southwestern United States. This air mass moves northward and brings clear, dry, and hot weather in the summer.

Reading Check What type of air mass contributes to the hot and humid summer weather in the midwestern United States?

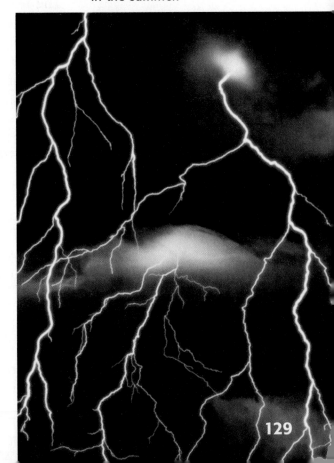

Figure 3 *Warm air masses that develop over the Gulf of Mexico bring thunderstorms in the summer.*

Figure 4 **Fronts That Affect Weather in North America**

Cold Front

Warm Front

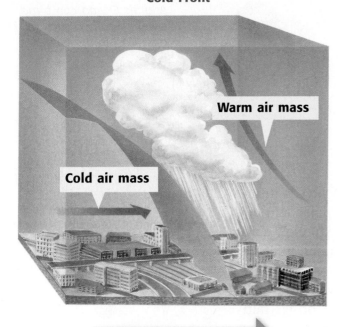

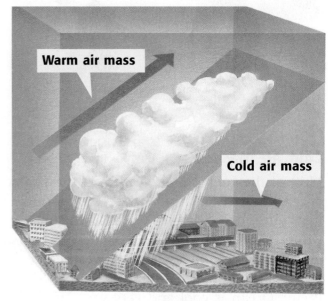

Warm air mass

Cold air mass

Warm air mass

Cold air mass

Direction of front

Direction of front

Fronts

Air masses that form from different areas often do not mix. The reason is that the air masses have different densities. For example, warm air is less dense than cold air. So, when two types of air masses meet, warm air generally rises. The area in which two types of air masses meet is called a **front.** The four kinds of fronts—cold fronts, warm fronts, occluded fronts, and stationary fronts—are shown in **Figure 4.** Fronts are associated with weather in the middle latitudes.

front the boundary between air masses of different densities and usually different temperatures

Cold Front

A cold front forms where cold air moves under warm air, which is less dense, and pushes the warm air up. Cold fronts can move quickly and bring thunderstorms, heavy rain, or snow. Cooler weather usually follows a cold front because the air mass behind the cold front is cooler and drier than the air mass that it is replacing.

Warm Front

A warm front forms where warm air moves over cold, denser air. In a warm front, the warm air gradually replaces the cold air. Warm fronts generally bring drizzly rain and are followed by clear and warm weather.

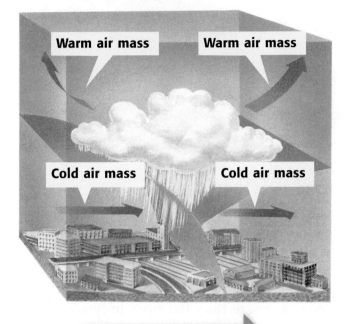

Occluded Front

Stationary Front

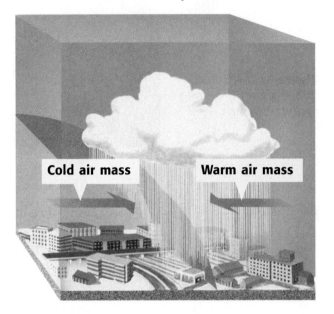

Warm air mass

Warm air mass

Cold air mass

Cold air mass

Direction of front

Cold air mass

Warm air mass

Occluded Front

An occluded front forms when a warm air mass is caught between two colder air masses. The coldest air mass moves under and pushes up the warm air mass. The coldest air mass then moves forward until it meets a cold air mass that is warmer and less dense. The colder of these two air masses moves under and pushes up the warmer air mass. Sometimes, though, the two colder air masses mix. An occluded front has cool temperatures and large amounts of rain and snow.

✔ *Reading Check* **What type of weather would you expect an occluded front to produce?**

Stationary Front

A stationary front forms when a cold air mass meets a warm air mass. In this case, however, both air masses do not have enough force to lift the warm air mass over the cold air mass. So, the two air masses remain separated. This may happen because there is not enough wind to keep the air masses pushing against each other. A stationary front often brings many days of cloudy, wet weather.

CONNECTION TO Environmental Science

Air Pollution Scientific research suggests that air pollution may decrease the amount of precipitation an area receives. Scientists use weather satellite photos to determine if a cloud is polluted or not. A polluted cloud will reveal pollution tracks or trails of the type of pollution it contains. Pollution in low clouds is usually caused by urban and industrial sources, such as power plants and oil refineries. Scientists also use weather satellites to determine how much precipitation a cloud produces. But how can air pollution prevent precipitation? Using the Internet or library sources, find out how air pollution can affect the amount of precipitation a cloud produces.

Figure 5 *This satellite image shows a cyclone system forming.*

Air Pressure and Weather

You may have heard a weather reporter on TV or radio talking about areas of low pressure and high pressure. These areas of different pressure affect the weather.

Cyclones

cyclone an area in the atmosphere that has lower pressure than the surrounding areas and has winds that spiral toward the center

Areas that have lower pressure than the surrounding areas do are called **cyclones.** Cyclones are areas where air masses come together, or converge, and rise. **Figure 5** shows a satellite image of the formation of a cyclone system.

Anticyclones

anticyclone the rotation of air around a high-pressure center in the direction opposite to Earth's rotation

Areas that have high pressure are called **anticyclones.** Anti-cyclones are areas where air moves apart, or diverges, and sinks. The sinking air is denser than the surrounding air, and the pressure is higher. Cooler, denser air moves out of the center of these high-pressure areas toward areas of lower pressure. **Figure 6** shows how wind can spiral out of an anticyclone and into a cyclone.

Figure 6 *As the colder, denser air spirals out of the anticyclone, it moves towards areas of low pressure, which sometimes forms a cyclone.*

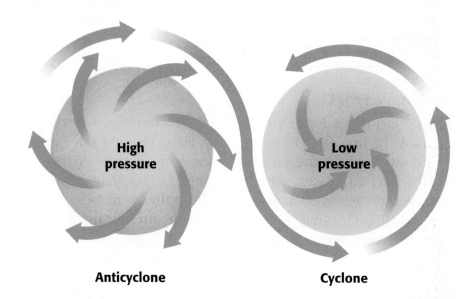

High pressure

Low pressure

Anticyclone

Cyclone

Cyclones, Anticyclones, and Weather

You have learned what cyclones and anticyclones are. So, now you might be wondering how do cyclones and anticyclones affect the weather? As the air in the center of a cyclone rises, it cools and forms clouds and rain. The rising air in a cyclone causes stormy weather. In an anticyclone, the air sinks. As the air sinks, it gets warmer and absorbs moisture. The sinking air in an anticyclone brings dry, clear weather. By keeping track of cyclones and anticyclones, meteorologists can predict the weather.

✓ **Reading Check** Describe the different types of weather that a cyclone and an anticyclone can produce.

CONNECTION TO Astronomy

Storms on Jupiter Cyclones and anticyclones occur on Jupiter! Usually, cyclones on Jupiter appear as dark ovals, and anticyclones are bright ovals. Jupiter's Great Red Spot is an anticyclone that has existed for centuries. Research the weather on a planet other than Earth, and write a weather report for the planet.

SECTION Review

Summary

- Air masses are characterized by moisture content and temperature.
- A front occurs where two air masses meet.
- Four major types of fronts are cold, warm, occluded, and stationary fronts.
- Differences in air pressure cause cyclones, which bring stormy weather, and anticyclones, which bring dry, clear weather.

Understanding Key Ideas

1. Identify the four major air masses that influence the weather in the United States.

2. What is one source region of a maritime polar air mass?

3. What are the characteristics of an air mass whose two-letter symbol is cP?

4. Describe the four major types of fronts.

5. Explain how fronts cause weather changes.

6. Explain how cyclones and anticyclones affect the weather.

Critical Thinking

7. **Applying Concepts** Explain how air masses that form over the land and ocean affect weather in the United States.

8. **Identifying Relationships** Hypothesize why the Pacific Coast has cool, wet winters and warm, dry summers.

9. **Applying Concepts** Which air masses influence the weather where you live? Explain.

FCAT Preparation

10. Meteorologists use Doppler radar to determine the location and movement of air masses. Doppler radar emits microwave signals that are reflected by air masses. The reflected signals are analyzed by computers to track the air masses. In what way does this technology benefit society? **H.3.3.4 CS**

   A. Doppler radar stops air masses.

   B. Doppler radar helps change weather patterns.

   C. Doppler radar does not help society.

   D. Doppler radar provides information that allows people to plan for weather conditions.

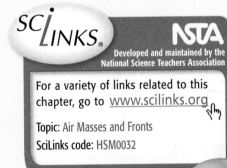

SCiLINKS®

NSTA

Developed and maintained by the National Science Teachers Association

For a variety of links related to this chapter, go to www.scilinks.org

Topic: Air Masses and Fronts
SciLinks code: HSM0032

Severe Weather

CRAAAACK! BOOM! What made that noise? You didn't expect it, and it sure made you jump.

A big boom of thunder has probably surprised you at one time or another. And the thunder was probably followed by a thunderstorm. A thunderstorm is an example of severe weather. *Severe weather* is weather that can cause property damage and sometimes death.

Thunderstorms

A **thunderstorm,** such as the one shown in **Figure 1,** is a small, intense weather system that produces strong winds, heavy rain, lightning, and thunder. Thunderstorms can occur along cold fronts. But thunderstorms can develop in other places, too. There are only two atmospheric conditions required to produce thunderstorms: warm and moist air near Earth's surface and an unstable atmosphere. The atmosphere is unstable when the surrounding air is colder than the rising air mass. The air mass will continue to rise as long as the surrounding air is colder than the air mass.

When the rising warm air reaches its dew point, the water vapor in the air condenses and forms cumulus clouds. If the atmosphere is extremely unstable, the warm air will continue to rise, which causes the cloud to grow into a dark, cumulonimbus cloud.

Benchmark Check **What weather conditions lead to the formation of a thunderstorm?** D.1.3.3 CS

thunderstorm a usually brief, heavy storm that consists of rain, strong winds, lightning, and thunder

Figure 1 *A typical thunderstorm, such as this one over Dallas, Texas, generates an enormous amount of electrical energy.*

D.1.3.3 CS knows how conditions that exist in one system influence the conditions that exist in other systems.

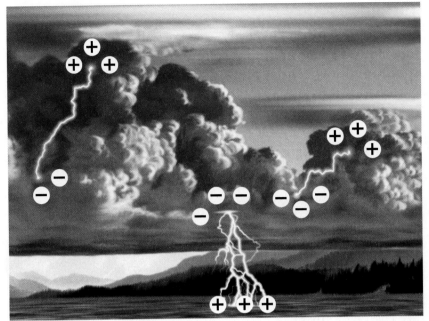

Figure 2 *The upper part of a cloud usually carries a positive electric charge, while the lower part of the cloud carries mainly negative charges.*

Lightning

Thunderstorms are very active electrically. **Lightning** is an electric discharge that occurs between a positively charged area and a negatively charged area, as shown in **Figure 2.** Lightning can happen between two clouds, between Earth and a cloud, or even between two parts of the same cloud. Have you ever touched someone after scuffing your feet on the carpet and received a mild shock? If so, you have experienced how lightning forms. While you walk around, friction between the floor and your shoes builds up an electric charge in your body. When you touch someone else, the charge is released.

When lightning strikes, energy is released. This energy is transferred to the air and causes the air to expand rapidly and send out sound waves. **Thunder** is the sound that results from the rapid expansion of air along the lightning strike.

Severe Thunderstorms

Severe thunderstorms can produce one or more of the following conditions: high winds, hail, flash floods, and tornadoes. Hailstorms damage crops, dent the metal on cars, and break windows. Flash flooding that results from heavy rains causes millions of dollars in property damage annually. And every year, flash flooding is a leading cause of weather-related deaths.

Lightning, as shown in **Figure 3,** happens during all thunderstorms and is very powerful. Lightning is responsible for starting thousands of forest fires each year and for killing or injuring hundreds of people a year in the United States.

lightning an electric discharge that takes place between two oppositely charged surfaces, such as between a cloud and the ground, between two clouds, or between two parts of the same cloud

thunder the sound caused by the rapid expansion of air along an electrical strike

Figure 3 *Lightning often strikes the tallest object in an area, such as the Eiffel Tower in Paris, France.*

Tornadoes

tornado a destructive, rotating column of air that has very high wind speeds, is visible as a funnel-shaped cloud, and touches the ground

Tornadoes happen in only 1% of all thunderstorms. A **tornado** is a small, spinning column of air that has high wind speeds and low central pressure and that touches the ground. A tornado starts out as a funnel cloud that pokes through the bottom of a cumulonimbus cloud and hangs in the air. The funnel cloud becomes a tornado when it makes contact with Earth's surface. **Figure 4** shows how a tornado forms.

Figure 4   **How a Tornado Forms**

❶ Wind moving in two directions causes a layer of air in the middle to begin to spin like a roll of toilet paper.

❷ The spinning column of air is turned to a vertical position by strong updrafts of air in the cumulonimbus cloud. The updrafts of air also begin to spin.

❸ The spinning column of air moves to the bottom of the cumulonimbus cloud and forms a funnel cloud.

❹ The funnel cloud becomes a tornado when it touches the ground.

Figure 5 *The tornado that hit Kissimmee, Florida, in 1998 had wind speeds of up to 416 km/h.*

Damage Caused by Tornadoes

About 75% of the world's tornadoes occur in the United States. Most of these tornadoes happen in the spring and early summer when cold, dry air from Canada meets warm, moist air from the Tropics. The size of a tornado's path of destruction is usually about 8 km long and 10 to 60 m wide. Although most tornadoes last only a few minutes, they can cause a lot of damage. Their ability to cause damage is due to their strong spinning winds. The average tornado has wind speeds between 120 and 180 km/h, but rarer, more violent tornadoes can have spinning winds of up to 500 km/h. The winds of tornadoes can uproot trees and destroy buildings, as shown in **Figure 5.** Tornadoes are capable of picking up heavy objects, such as mobile homes and cars, and hurling them through the air.

D.1.3.3 CS knows how conditions that exist in one system influence the conditions that exist in other systems.

hurricane a severe storm that develops over tropical oceans and whose strong winds of more than 120 km/h spiral in toward the intensely low-pressure storm center

Benchmark Check What weather conditions lead to the formation of tornadoes? **D.1.3.3 CS**

Hurricanes

A large, rotating tropical weather system that has wind speeds of at least 120 km/h is called a **hurricane,** as shown in **Figure 6.** Hurricanes are the most powerful storms on Earth. Hurricanes have different names in different parts of the world. In the western Pacific Ocean, hurricanes are called *typhoons*. Hurricanes that form over the Indian Ocean are called *cyclones*.

Most hurricanes form in the areas between 5° and 20° north latitude and between 5° and 20° south latitude over warm, tropical oceans. At higher latitudes, the water is too cold for hurricanes to form. Hurricanes vary in size from 160 to 1,500 km in diameter and can travel for thousands of kilometers.

Figure 6 *This photograph of Hurricane Fran was taken from space.*

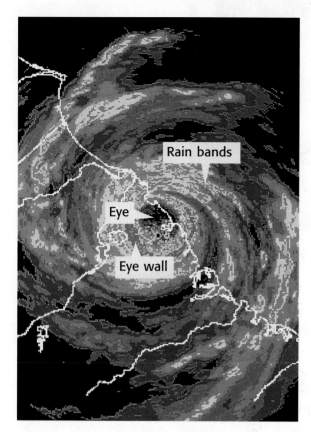

Figure 7 *This photo shows a bird's-eye view of a hurricane.*

How a Hurricane Forms

A hurricane begins as a group of thunderstorms moving over tropical ocean waters. Winds traveling in two different directions meet and cause the storm to spin. Because of the Coriolis effect, the storm turns counterclockwise in the Northern Hemisphere and clockwise in the Southern Hemisphere.

A hurricane gets its energy from the condensation of water vapor. Once formed, the hurricane is fueled through contact with the warm ocean water. Moisture is added to the warm air by evaporation from the ocean. As the warm, moist air rises, the water vapor condenses and releases large amounts of energy. The hurricane continues to grow as long as it is over its source of warm, moist air. When the hurricane moves into colder waters or over land, it begins to die because it has lost its source of energy. **Figure 7** and **Figure 8** show two views of a hurricane.

Benchmark Check How do weather patterns relate to hurricane formation? **D.1.3.3 CS, H.2.3.1 CS**

Figure 8 **Cross Section of a Hurricane**

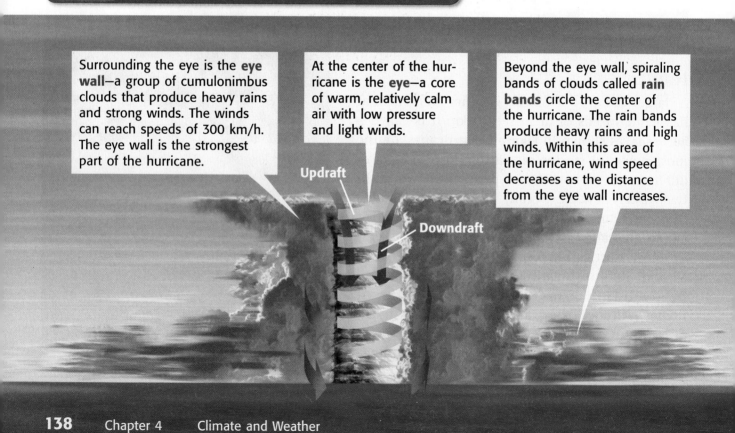

Surrounding the eye is the **eye wall**—a group of cumulonimbus clouds that produce heavy rains and strong winds. The winds can reach speeds of 300 km/h. The eye wall is the strongest part of the hurricane.

At the center of the hurricane is the **eye**—a core of warm, relatively calm air with low pressure and light winds.

Beyond the eye wall, spiraling bands of clouds called **rain bands** circle the center of the hurricane. The rain bands produce heavy rains and high winds. Within this area of the hurricane, wind speed decreases as the distance from the eye wall increases.

Updraft

Downdraft

Figure 9 *A hurricane's storm surge can cause severe damage to homes near the shoreline.*

Damage Caused by Hurricanes

Hurricanes can cause a lot of damage when they move near or onto land. Wind speeds of most hurricanes range from 120 to 150 km/h. Some can reach speeds as high as 300 km/h. Hurricane winds can knock down trees and telephone poles and can damage and destroy buildings and homes.

While high winds cause a large amount of damage, most hurricane damage is caused by flooding associated with heavy rains and storm surges. A *storm surge* is a wall of water that builds up over the ocean because of the strong winds and low atmospheric pressure. The wall of water becomes larger as it nears the shore, and the water reaches its greatest height when it crashes on the shore. Depending on the hurricane's strength, a storm surge can be 1 to 8 m high and 65 to 160 km long. Flooding causes major damage to property and can endanger lives when a storm surge occurs, as shown in **Figure 9.**

Severe Weather Safety

Severe weather can be very dangerous, so it is important to keep yourself safe. One way to stay safe is to turn on the radio or TV during a storm. Your local radio and TV stations will let you know if a storm is becoming more severe.

Thunderstorm Safety

Lightning is one of the most dangerous parts of a thunderstorm. Lightning is attracted to tall objects. If you are outside, stay away from trees, which can be struck down. If you are in the open, crouch down. Otherwise, you will be the tallest object in the area! Stay away from bodies of water. If lightning hits water while you are in it, you could be hurt or could even die.

Benchmark Activity

Hurricane Damage
Hurricane winds and storm surges can cause major changes to Earth's surface. Investigate how a hurricane affected landforms, ecosystems, and human communities in Florida. Then, create a small newspaper with stories and pictures of the hurricane's effects. **D.1.3.3 CS**

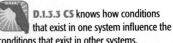

D.1.3.3 CS knows how conditions that exist in one system influence the conditions that exist in other systems.

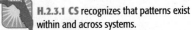

H.2.3.1 CS recognizes that patterns exist within and across systems.

Figure 10 *During a tornado warning, it is best to protect yourself by crouching against a wall and covering the back of your head and neck with your hands or a book.*

Tornado Safety

Weather forecasters use watches and warnings to let people know about tornadoes. A *watch* is a weather alert that lets people know that a tornado may happen. A *warning* is a weather alert that lets people know that a tornado has been spotted.

If there is a tornado warning for your area, find shelter quickly. The best place to go is a basement or a ground-level floor. Or you can go to a windowless room in the center of the building, such as a bathroom, closet, or hallway, as **Figure 10** shows. If you are outside, lie in a large field or a deep ditch.

Flood Safety

An area can receive so much rain that the area is flooded. So, like tornadoes, floods have watches and warnings. However, floodwaters rise so quickly that warnings are often late. A flash flood is a flood that rises and falls very suddenly. The best thing to do during a flood is to find a high place to wait out the flood. You should always stay out of floodwaters. Even shallow water can be dangerous if it is moving fast.

Figure 11 *These store owners are boarding up their windows to protect the windows from strong winds during a hurricane.*

Hurricane Safety

If a hurricane is headed to you area, your local TV or radio station will keep you updated on its condition. People living near the ocean may be asked to evacuate the area. If you live in an area where hurricanes strike, your family should have a disaster supply kit that includes enough water and food to last several days. To protect the windows in your home, you should cover them with plywood, as shown in **Figure 11.** The most important thing to remember is that you must stay indoors during the storm.

Summary

- Thunderstorms are weather systems that produce strong winds, heavy rain, lightning, and thunder. **D.1.3.3 CS, H.2.3.1 CS**

- Lightning is a large electric discharge that occurs between two oppositely charged surfaces. Lightning releases a great deal of energy and can be very dangerous.

- Tornadoes are small, rotating columns of air that touch the ground and can cause severe damage. **D.1.3.3 CS, H.2.3.1 CS**

- Hurricanes form when groups of thunderstorms travel over tropical ocean waters. Winds traveling in two different directions meet and cause the storm to spin. **D.1.3.3 CS, H.2.3.1 CS**

- In the event of severe weather, it is important to stay safe. Listening to your local TV or radio station for updates and remaining indoors and away from windows are good rules to follow.

Using Key Terms

Use a term from the section to complete each sentence below.

1. Thunderstorms often cause ___.

2. A ___ forms when a funnel cloud pokes through the bottom of a cumulonimbus cloud and makes contact with the ground.

Understanding Key Ideas

3. The safest thing to do if you are outdoors during a tornado is to
   a. stay near buildings and roads.
   b. head for an open area.
   c. seek shelter near a large tree.
   d. None of the above

4. Describe how tornadoes form. **D.1.3.3 CS, H.2.3.1 CS**

5. Which weather patterns lead to the formation of hurricanes? **D.1.3.3 CS, H.2.3.1 CS**

6. What is lightning? What happens when lightning strikes?

Critical Thinking

7. **Applying Concepts** Predict what items you would need in a disaster kit. Explain your choices.

8. **Identifying Relationships** Explain what happens to a hurricane as it moves over land. **D.1.3.3 CS, H.2.3.1 CS**

FCAT Preparation

9. Conditions that exist in one system can influence the conditions in another system. The relationship between hurricanes and weather patterns is an example of this idea. Which of the following statements best explains the relationship between weather conditions and hurricanes? **D.1.3.3 CS, H.2.3.1 CS**

   A. Hurricanes form when cool air masses travel over ocean waters. If the air masses collide, they begin to spin.

   B. Hurricanes form when a group of thunderstorms moves over tropical waters. Winds traveling in different directions meet and cause the storm to spin.

   C. A hurricane is a large, rotating tropical weather system that can cause severe property damage.

   D. Hurricanes often lead to the formation of storm surges.

SCiLINKS®

NSTA
Developed and maintained by the
National Science Teachers Association

For a variety of links related to this chapter, go to www.scilinks.org

Topic: Severe Weather
SciLinks code: HSM1383

Forecasting the Weather

You watch the weather forecast on the evening news. The news is good—there's no rain in sight. But how can the weather forecasters tell that it won't rain?

Weather affects how you dress and how you plan your day, so it is important to get accurate weather forecasts. But where do weather reporters get their information? And how do they predict the weather? A *weather forecast* is a prediction of weather conditions over the next 3 to 5 days. A *meteorologist* is a person who observes and collects data on atmospheric conditions to make weather predictions. In this section, you will learn how weather data are collected and shown.

Weather-Forecasting Technology

To accurately forecast the weather, meteorologists need to measure various atmospheric conditions, such as air pressure, humidity, precipitation, temperature, wind speed, and wind direction. Meteorologists use special instruments to collect data on weather conditions both near and far above Earth's surface.

High in the Sky

Weather balloons carry electronic equipment that can measure weather conditions as high as 30 km above Earth's surface. Weather balloons, such as the one in **Figure 1,** carry equipment that measures temperature, air pressure, and relative humidity. By tracking the balloons, meteorologists can also measure wind speed and direction.

✓ Reading Check How do meteorologists gather data on atmospheric conditions above Earth's surface?

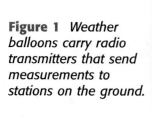

Figure 1 *Weather balloons carry radio transmitters that send measurements to stations on the ground.*

Windsock

Figure 2 *Meteorologists use these tools to collect atmospheric data.*

Thermometer

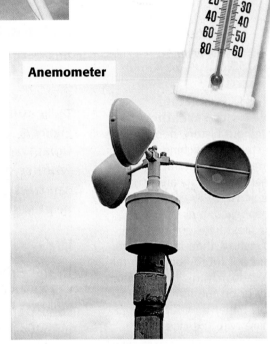

Anemometer

Measuring Air Temperature and Pressure

A tool used to measure air temperature is called a **thermometer.** Most thermometers use a liquid sealed in a narrow glass tube, as shown in **Figure 2.** When air temperature increases, the liquid expands and moves up the glass tube. As air temperature decreases, the liquid shrinks and moves down the tube.

A **barometer** is an instrument used to measure air pressure. A mercurial barometer consists of a glass tube that is sealed at one end and placed in a container full of mercury. As the air pressure pushes on the mercury inside the container, the mercury moves up the glass tube. The greater the air pressure is, the higher the mercury will rise.

Measuring Wind Direction

Wind direction can be measured by using a windsock or a wind vane. A windsock, shown in **Figure 2,** is a cone-shaped cloth bag open at both ends. The wind enters through the wide end and leaves through the narrow end. Therefore, the wide end points into the wind. A wind vane is shaped like an arrow with a large tail and is attached to a pole. As the wind pushes the tail of the wind vane, the wind vane spins on the pole until the arrow points into the wind.

Measuring Wind Speed

An instrument used to measure wind speed is called an **anemometer.** An anemometer, as shown in **Figure 2,** consists of three or four cups connected by spokes to a pole. The wind pushes on the hollow sides of the cups and causes the cups to rotate on the pole. The motion sends a weak electric current that is measured and displayed on a dial.

thermometer an instrument that measures and indicates temperature

barometer an instrument that measures atmospheric pressure

anemometer an instrument used to measure wind speed

Figure 3 *Using Doppler radar, meteorologists can predict a tornado up to 20 minutes before it touches the ground.*

Radar and Satellites

Radar is used to find the location, movement, and amount of precipitation. It can also detect what form of precipitation a weather system is carrying. You might have seen a kind of radar called *Doppler radar* used in a local TV weather report. **Figure 3** shows how Doppler radar is used to track precipitation. *Weather satellites* that orbit Earth provide the images of weather systems that you see on TV weather reports. Satellites can track storms and measure wind speeds, humidity, and temperatures at different altitudes.

Weather Maps

In the United States, the National Weather Service (NWS) and the National Oceanic and Atmospheric Administration (NOAA) collect and analyze weather data. The NWS produces weather maps based on information gathered from about 1,000 weather stations across the United States. On these maps, each station is represented by a station model. A *station model* is a small circle that shows the location of the weather station. As shown in **Figure 4,** surrounding the small circle is a set of symbols and numbers, which represent the weather data.

Figure 4 **A Station Model**

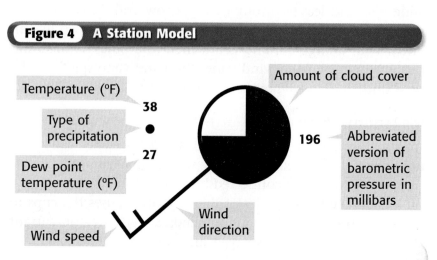

Temperature (°F)

Type of precipitation

Dew point temperature (°F)

Wind speed

38

27

Amount of cloud cover

196

Abbreviated version of barometric pressure in millibars

Wind direction

Reading a Weather Map

Weather maps that you see on TV include lines called *isobars*. Isobars are lines that connect points of equal air pressure. Isobars that form closed circles represent areas of high or low pressure. These areas are usually marked on a map with a capital *H* or *L*. Fronts are also labeled on weather maps, as you can see on the weather map in **Figure 5.**

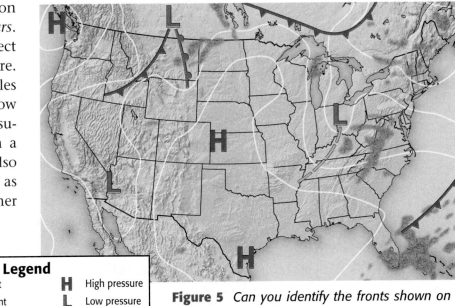

Legend

Symbol		Symbol	
	Cold front	**H**	High pressure
	Warm front	**L**	Low pressure
	Low pressure trough		Rain
	Isobar		Fog

Figure 5 *Can you identify the fronts shown on the weather map?*

SECTION Review

Summary

● Meteorologists use several instruments, such as weather balloons, thermometers, barometers, anemometers, windsocks, weather vanes, radar, and weather satellites, to forecast the weather.

● Station models show the weather conditions at various points across the United States.

● Weather maps show areas of high and low pressure as well as the location of fronts.

Using Key Terms

1. Write an original definition for *barometer* and *anemometer*.

Understanding Key Ideas

2. Describe the tools that scientists use to predict the weather.

3. Explain how radar and weather satellites help meteorologists forecast the weather.

Critical Thinking

4. **Applying Concepts** Hypothesize why a meteorologist would compare a new weather map with one that is 24 h old.

5. **Making Inferences** In the United States, why are weather data gathered from a large number of station models?

6. **Making Inferences** Hypothesize why station models from different regions plotted on a map may help a meteorologist.

FCAT Preparation

7. You notice that the mirror in your bathroom is fogged after you take a hot shower. But after you take a cold shower you notice that the mirror is not fogged. Describe two variables that you would need to control if you developed an experiment to determine why the mirror was fogged. **H.1.3.5 AA**

SCi LINKS®

NSTA
Developed and maintained by the National Science Teachers Association

For a variety of links related to this chapter, go to www.scilinks.org

Topic: Forecasting the Weather
SciLinks code: HSM0606

Inquiry Lab

OBJECTIVES

Construct a device that uses water to measure temperature.

Calibrate the new device by using a mercury thermometer.

MATERIALS

- bottle, plastic
- can, aluminum soda
- card, index, 3 in. × 5 in.
- clay, modeling (1 lb)
- container, yogurt, with lid
- cup, plastic-foam, large (2)
- film canister
- food coloring, red (1 bottle)
- funnel, plastic or paper cone
- gloves, heat-resistant
- hot plate
- ice, cube (5 or 6)
- pan, aluminum pie
- pitcher
- plastic tubing, 5 mm diameter, 30 cm long
- ruler, metric
- straw, plastic, inflexible, clear (1)
- tape, transparent (1 roll)
- thermometer, Celsius
- water, tap

SAFETY

Boiling Over!

Safety Industries, Inc., would like to produce and sell thermometers that are safer than mercury thermometers. The company would like your team of inventors to design a thermometer that uses water instead of mercury. The company will offer a contract to the team that creates the best design of a water thermometer. Good luck!

Ask a Question

1 What causes the liquid in a thermometer to rise? How can I use this information to make a thermometer?

Form a Hypothesis

2 Brainstorm with a classmate to design a thermometer that uses only water to measure temperature. Sketch your design. Write a one-sentence hypothesis that describes how your thermometer will work.

Test the Hypothesis

3 Following your design, build a thermometer by using only materials from the materials list. Like a mercury thermometer, your thermometer needs a bulb and a tube. However, the liquid in your thermometer will be water.

4 To test your design, place the aluminum pie pan on a hot plate. Use the pitcher to carefully pour water into the pan until the pan is half full. Turn on the hot plate, and heat the water.

5 Put on your safety goggles and heat-resistant gloves, and carefully place the "bulb" of your thermometer in the hot water. Observe the water level in the tube. Does the water level rise?

6 If the water level does not rise, change your design as necessary and repeat steps 3–5. When the water level in your thermometer does rise, sketch the design of this thermometer as your final design.

7 After you decide on your final design, you must calibrate your thermometer by using a laboratory thermometer. Tape an index card to your thermometer's tube so that the part of the tube that sticks out from the "bulb" of your thermometer touches the card.

8 Place the plastic funnel or the cone-shaped paper funnel into a plastic-foam cup. Carefully pour hot water from the pie pan into the funnel. Be sure that no water splashes or spills.

9 Place your thermometer and a laboratory thermometer in the hot water. As your thermometer's water level rises, mark the level on the index card. At the same time, observe and record the temperature of the laboratory thermometer, and write this value beside your mark on the card.

10 Repeat steps 8–9 using warm tap water.

11 Repeat steps 8–9 using ice water.

12 Draw evenly spaced scale markings between your temperature markings on the index card. Write the temperatures that correspond to the scale marks on the index card.

Analyze the Results

1 **Analyzing Results** How well does your thermometer measure temperature?

Draw Conclusions

2 **Drawing Conclusions** Compare your thermometer design with other students' designs. How would you change your design to make your thermometer measure temperature better?

3 **Applying Conclusions** Take a class vote to see which design should be used by Safety Industries. Why was this thermometer design chosen? How did it differ from other designs in the class?

Chapter Review

USING KEY TERMS

For each pair of terms, explain how the meanings of the terms differ.

1. *relative humidity* and *dew point*

2. *condensation* and *precipitation*

3. *air mass* and *front*

4. *weather* and *climate*

5. *tornado* and *hurricane*

6. *barometer* and *anemometer*

UNDERSTANDING KEY IDEAS

Multiple Choice

7. Systems interact and affect each other in many ways. Climate systems are affected by other Earth systems such as the atmosphere. Which of the following is a factor that affects a climate system? **D.1.3.3 CS** *FCAT*

    a. snow

    b. hurricanes

    c. ocean currents

    d. lightning

8. Which of the following is NOT a type of condensation?

    a. fog   c. snow

    b. cloud   d. dew

9. Natural events often occur in consistent patterns. Which of the following occurs in a consistent pattern? **H.2.3.1 CS** *FCAT*

    a. the water cycle   c. a hail storm

    b. a station model   d. water vapor

10. Strong updrafts within a thunderhead can produce **D.1.3.3 CS**

    a. snow.   c. sleet.

    b. rain.   d. hail.

11. A maritime tropical air mass contains

    a. warm, wet air.   c. warm, dry air.

    b. cold, moist air. d. cold, dry air.

12. Fronts that form when a warm air mass is trapped between cold air masses and is forced to rise are **D.1.3.3 CS**

    a. snow fronts.   c. occluded fronts.

    b. warm fronts.   d. cold fronts.

13. A severe storm that forms from a rapidly rotating funnel cloud is a

    a. hurricane.   c. typhoon.

    b. tornado.   d. thunderstorm.

14. The lines connecting points of equal air pressure on a weather map are called

    a. contour lines.   c. isobars.

    b. highs.   d. lows.

Short Answer

15 Explain the relationship between condensation and dew point.

16 Describe the conditions along a stationary front.

17 Explain how a hurricane develops. D.1.3.3 CS, H.2.3.1 CS

18 Describe the water cycle, and explain how it affects weather. D.1.3.3 CS

19 Identify the major similarities and differences between hurricanes and tornadoes. D.1.3.3 CS

20 Explain how prevailing winds can influence precipitation. D.1.3.3 CS, H.2.3.1 CS

21 Describe an interaction between a weather system and an ocean system. D.1.3.3 CS, H.2.3.1 CS

22 What is a station model? What types of information do station models provide?

23 What type of technology is used to locate and measure the amount of precipitation in an area?

24 Identify two ways to keep yourself informed during severe weather.

CRITICAL THINKING

Extended Response

25 **Making Inferences** If both the air temperature and the amount of water vapor in the air change, is it possible for the relative humidity to stay the same? Explain.

26 **Applying Concepts** What assumption can you make about the amount of water vapor in the air if there is no difference between the wet- and dry-bulb readings of a psychrometer?

27 **Identifying Relationships** Explain the relationship between the tilt of the Earth's axis and seasonal changes in different latitudes. D.1.3.3 CS

Concept Mapping

28 Use the following terms to create a concept map: *evaporation, relative humidity, water vapor, dew, psychrometer, cloud,* and *fog.*

INTERPRETING GRAPHICS

Use the weather map below to answer the questions that follow.

29 Where are thunderstorms most likely to occur? Explain your answer.

30 What are the weather conditions in Tulsa, Oklahoma? Explain your answer.

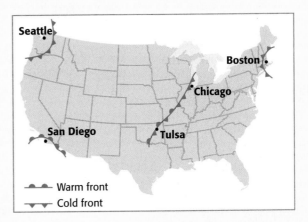

For the following questions, write your answers on a separate sheet of paper.

1 A severe thunderstorm is in the area. A meteorologist says that a cold air mass has moved in. This cold air mass has forced a warm air mass upward. As the warm air cools, it releases energy in the form of severe weather. What is the name for this type of front?

A. cold front
B. warm front
C. occluded front
D. stationary front

2 The diagram below shows the different components of a hurricane.

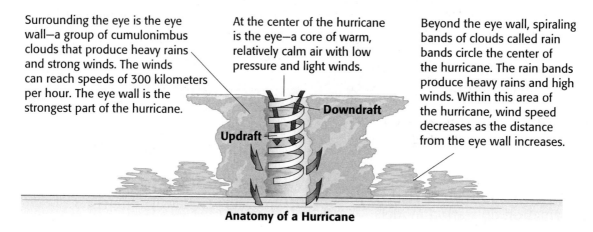

Surrounding the eye is the eye wall—a group of cumulonimbus clouds that produce heavy rains and strong winds. The winds can reach speeds of 300 kilometers per hour. The eye wall is the strongest part of the hurricane.

At the center of the hurricane is the eye—a core of warm, relatively calm air with low pressure and light winds.

Beyond the eye wall, spiraling bands of clouds called rain bands circle the center of the hurricane. The rain bands produce heavy rains and high winds. Within this area of the hurricane, wind speed decreases as the distance from the eye wall increases.

Updraft

Downdraft

Anatomy of a Hurricane

In which area of the hurricane is the **greatest** release of energy occurring?

F. eye
G. eye wall
H. rain bands
I. storm surge

3 The amount of rainfall that an area receives each year depends on a few major factors, such as geographical features. Look at the map below. It shows the geography of California. Barstow, California, is a city in the Mojave Desert.

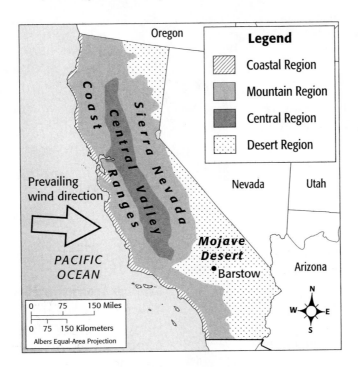

Based on the map, which of the following factors has the **greatest** influence on the amount of annual precipitation in Barstow?

A. prevailing westerly winds

B. latitude north of the equator

C. location near a mountain range

D. location near a large body of water

Science in Action

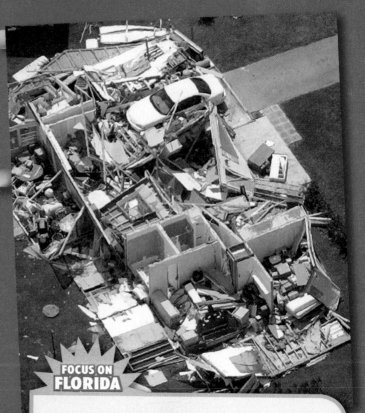

Science Fiction

"All Summer in a Day" by Ray Bradbury

It is raining, just as it has been for seven long years. For the people who live on Venus, constant rain is a fact of life. But today is a special day—a day when the rain stops and the sun shines. This day comes once every seven years. At school, the students have been looking forward to this day for weeks. But Margot longs to see the sun even more than the others do. The reason for her longing makes the other kids jealous, and jealous kids can be cruel. What happens to Margot? Find out by reading Ray Bradbury's "All Summer in a Day" in the *Holt Anthology of Science Fiction.*

Weird Science

Shelter from the Storm

The researchers at WHIRL, the Wind and Hurricane Impact Research Laboratory, are using high-tech tools to help design buildings that can withstand the impact of hurricanes, tornadoes, thunderstorms, and storm surges. The WHIRL is part of the Florida Institute of Technology in Melbourne, Florida. The WHIRL scientists have developed new technology to help them measure the effects of hurricane-force winds on houses. The scientists place sensors on houses in the path of hurricanes. Then, when a hurricane threatens Florida, they are ready to gather real-time data about the effect of the storm. These data will help the scientists design homes that really are shelters from the storm.

Language Arts ACTIVITY

WRITING SKILL What would living in a place where it rained all day and every day for seven years be like? Write a short story describing what your life would be like if you lived in such a place. In your story, describe what you and your friends would do for fun after school.

HOLT ANTHOLOGY OF
Science Fiction

HOLT, RINEHART AND WINSTON

Math ACTIVITY

The WHIRL wind tunnel can create winds as fast as 112 mi/h. But hurricane winds can travel 160 mi/h! How much faster are hurricane winds than the winds in the wind tunnel? Express the answer as a percentage.

Careers

Mercedes Pascual

Ecologist Mercedes Pascual is a theoretical ecologist at the University of Michigan. Pascual has been able to help the people of Bangladesh save lives by using information about climate changes to predict outbreaks of the disease cholera. Cholera can be a deadly disease that people usually contract by drinking contaminated water. Pascual knew that in Bangladesh, outbreaks of cholera peak every 3.7 years. She noticed that this period matches the frequency of the El Niño Southern Oscillations, which is a weather event that occurs in the Pacific Ocean. El Niño affects weather patterns in many regions of the world, including Bangladesh. El Niño increases the temperatures of the sea off the coast of Bangladesh. Pascual found that increased sea temperatures led to higher numbers of the bacteria that cause cholera. In turn, more people contract cholera. But because of the research conducted by Pascual and other scientists, the people of Bangladesh can better predict and prepare for outbreaks of cholera.

Social Studies ACTIVITY

Research the effects of El Niño. Write a **WRITING SKILL** report describing El Niño and its affects on a country other than Bangladesh.

go.hrw.com

To learn more about these Science in Action topics, visit go.hrw.com and type in the keyword **HT6FCLFF.**

Current Science

Check out Current Science® articles related to this chapter by visiting go.hrw.com. Just type in the keyword **HZ5CS16.**

Exploring the Oceans

The Big Idea Oceans contain natural resources that require protection.

About the PHOTO

What weighs as much as a pick up truck, looks like a giant pancake with fins, and lives off the coast of Florida? The answer is a *Mola mola* fish, of course! *Mola mola* fish are the largest bony fish in the world. They weigh as much as 1,300 kg! And while these huge fish may look intimidating, they are harmless to humans. Instead, *Mola mola* fish feed on squid, jellyfish, and sponges.

PRE-READING ACTIVITY

FOLDNOTES **Layered Book** Before you read the chapter, create the FoldNote entitled "Layered Book" described in the **Study Skills** section of the Appendix. Label the tabs of the layered book with "Characteristics of ocean water," "The ocean floor," "Ocean zones," and "Resources from the ocean." As you read the chapter, write information you learn about each category under the appropriate tab.

START-UP ACTIVITY

Exit Only?

To study what life underwater would be like, scientists sometimes live in underwater laboratories. How do these scientists enter and leave these labs? Believe it or not, the simplest way is through a hole in the lab's floor. You might think water would come in through the hole, but it doesn't. How is this possible? Do the following activity to find out.

Procedure

1. Fill a **large bowl** about two-thirds full of **water.**

2. Turn a **clear plastic cup** upside down.

3. Slowly guide the cup straight down into the water. Be careful not to guide the cup all the way to the bottom of the bowl. Also, be careful not to tip the cup.

4. Record your observations.

Analysis

1. How does the air inside the cup affect the water below the cup?

2. How do your findings relate to the hole in the bottom of an underwater research lab?

Earth's Oceans

What makes Earth so different from Mars? What does Earth have that Mercury doesn't?

Earth stands out from the other planets in our solar system primarily for one reason—71% of Earth's surface is covered with water. Most of Earth's water is found in the global ocean. The global ocean is divided by the continents into four main oceans. The divisions of the global ocean are shown in **Figure 1.**

Divisions of the Global Ocean

The largest ocean is the *Pacific Ocean.* It flows between Asia and the Americas. The volume of the *Atlantic Ocean,* the second-largest ocean, is about half the volume of the Pacific. The *Indian Ocean* is the third-largest ocean. The *Arctic Ocean* is the smallest ocean. This ocean is unique because much of its surface is covered by ice. Therefore, the Arctic Ocean has not been fully explored.

READING WARM-UP

Objectives

- List the major divisions of the global ocean.
- Describe the history of Earth's oceans.
- Identify the properties of ocean water. A.1.3.1 AA
- Describe how conditions in the oceans affect air temperatures on Earth. D.1.3.3 CS

Terms to Learn

salinity
water cycle

READING STRATEGY

Discussion Read this section silently. Write down questions that you have about this section. Discuss your questions in a small group.

Figure 1 *The global ocean is divided by the continents into four main oceans.*

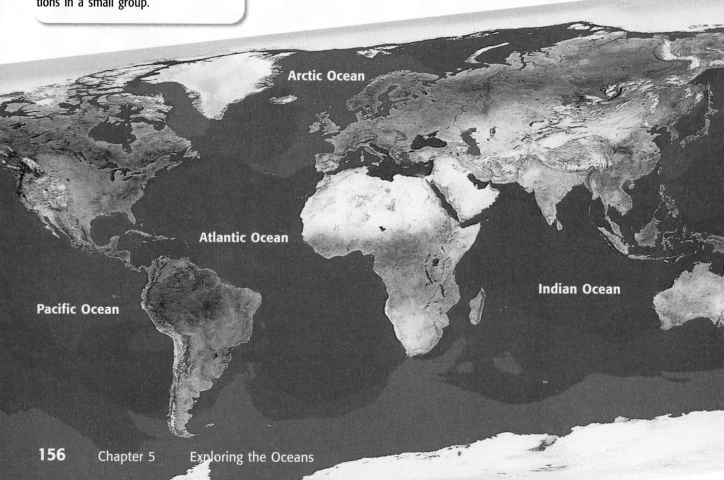

Arctic Ocean

Atlantic Ocean

Indian Ocean

Pacific Ocean

Figure 2 The History of Earth's Oceans

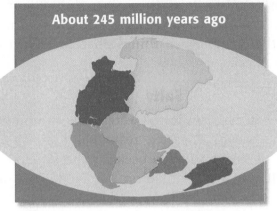

About 245 million years ago

The continents were one giant landmass called Pangaea. The oceans were one giant body of water called Panthalassa.

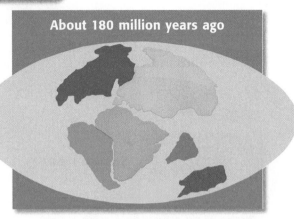

About 180 million years ago

As Pangaea broke apart, the North Atlantic Ocean and the Indian Ocean began to form.

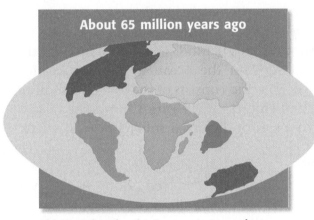

About 65 million years ago

The South Atlantic Ocean was much smaller than it is today.

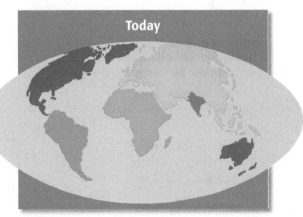

Today

The continents continue to move at a rate of 1 to 10 cm per year. The Pacific Ocean is getting smaller. However, the other oceans are growing.

How Did the Oceans Form?

About 4.5 billion years ago, Earth was a very different place. There were no oceans. Volcanoes spewed lava, ash, and gases all over the planet. The volcanic gases began to form Earth's atmosphere. Meanwhile, Earth was cooling. Sometime before 4 billion years ago, Earth cooled enough for water vapor to condense. This water began to fall as rain. The rain filled the deeper levels of Earth's surface, and the first oceans began to form.

The shape of the Earth's oceans has changed a lot over time. Much has been learned about the oceans' history. Some of this history is shown in **Figure 2.**

✔ Reading Check How did the first oceans begin to form on Earth?

Characteristics of Ocean Water

You know that ocean water is different from the water that flows from your sink at home. For one thing, ocean water is not safe to drink. But there are other things that make ocean water special.

Ocean Water Is Salty

Have you ever swallowed water while swimming in the ocean? It tasted really salty, didn't it? Most of the salt in the ocean is the same kind of salt that we sprinkle on our food. This salt is called *sodium chloride.*

Salts have been added to the ocean for billions of years. As rivers and streams flow toward the oceans, they dissolve various minerals on land. The running water carries these dissolved minerals to the ocean. At the same time, water is *evaporating* from the ocean and is leaving the dissolved solids behind. The most abundant dissolved solid in the ocean is sodium chloride. This compound consists of the elements sodium, Na, and chlorine, Cl. **Figure 3** shows the relative percentages of dissolved solids in ocean water.

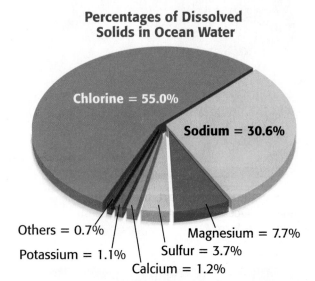

Percentages of Dissolved Solids in Ocean Water

Chlorine = 55.0%
Sodium = 30.6%
Others = 0.7%
Potassium = 1.1%
Sulfur = 3.7%
Calcium = 1.2%
Magnesium = 7.7%

Figure 3 *This pie graph shows the composition of dissolved solids in ocean water by percentage mass.*

salinity a measure of the amount of dissolved salts in a given amount of liquid

Chock-Full of Solids

A measure of the amount of dissolved solids in a given amount of liquid is called **salinity.** Salinity is usually measured as grams of dissolved solids per kilogram of water. Think of it this way: 1 kg (1,000 g) of ocean water can be evaporated to 35 g of dissolved solids, on average. Therefore, if you evaporated 1 kg of ocean water, 965 g of fresh water would be removed and 35 g of solids would remain.

Climate Affects Salinity

Some parts of the ocean are saltier than others. Coastal water in places with hotter, drier climates typically has a higher salinity. Coastal water in cooler, more humid places typically has a lower salinity. One reason for this difference is that heat increases the evaporation rate. Evaporation removes water but leaves salts and other dissolved solids behind. Salinity levels are also lower in coastal areas that have a cooler, more humid climate because more fresh water from streams and rivers runs into the ocean in these areas.

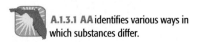

A.1.3.1 AA identifies various ways in which substances differ.

Benchmark Check What is the difference between ocean water and freshwater? A.1.3.1 AA

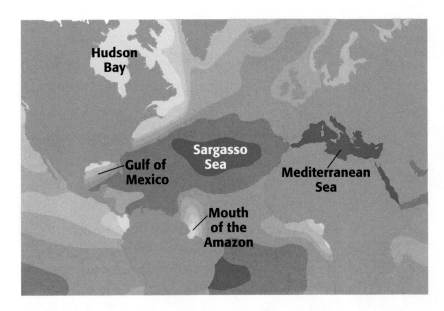

Figure 4 *Salinity varies in different parts of the ocean because of variations in evaporation, circulation, and freshwater inflow.*

Proportion of salt per 1,000 parts of sea water

	32 or less
	33
	34
	35
	36
	37
	38 or more

Water Movement Affects Salinity

Another factor that affects ocean salinity is water movement. Some parts of the ocean, such as bays, gulfs, and seas, move less than other parts. Parts of the open ocean that do not have currents running through them can also be slow moving. Slower-moving areas of water develop higher salinity. **Figure 4** shows salinity differences in different parts of the ocean.

Temperature Zones

The temperature of ocean water decreases as depth increases. However, this temperature change does not happen gradually from the ocean's surface to its bottom. Water in the ocean can be divided into three layers by temperature. As **Figure 5** shows, the temperature at the surface is much warmer than the average temperature of ocean water.

Figure 5 Temperature Zones in the Ocean

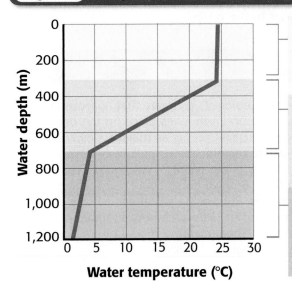

Surface zone The *surface zone* is the warm, top layer of ocean water. It can extend to 300 m below sea level. Sunlight heats the top 100 m of the surface zone. Surface currents mix the heated water with cooler water below.

Thermocline The *thermocline* is the second layer of ocean water. It can extend from 300 m below sea level to about 700 m below sea level. In the thermocline, temperature drops with increased depth faster than it does in the other two zones.

Deep zone The *deep zone* is the bottom layer that extends from the base of the thermocline to the bottom of the ocean. The temperature in this zone can range from 1°C to 3°C.

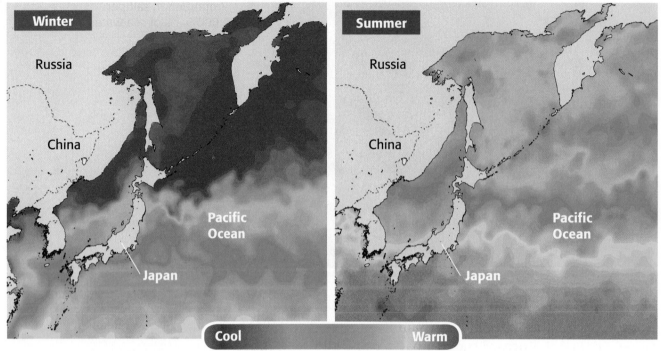

Winter
Russia
China
Japan
Pacific
Ocean

Summer
Russia
China
Japan
Pacific
Ocean

Cool   Warm

Figure 6 *These satellite images show that the surface temperatures in the northern Pacific Ocean change with the seasons.*

Surface Temperature Changes

If you live near the coast, you may know how different a swim in the ocean feels in December than it feels in July. Temperatures in the surface zone vary with latitude and the time of year. Surface temperatures range from 1°C near the poles to about 24°C near the equator. Parts of the ocean along the equator are warmer because they receive more direct sunlight per year than areas closer to the poles. However, both hemispheres receive more direct sunlight during their summer seasons. Therefore, the surface zone is heated more in the summer. **Figure 6** shows how surface-zone temperatures vary depending on the time of year.

✓ *Reading Check* Why are parts of the ocean along the equator warmer than those closer to the poles?

CONNECTION TO Geology

Submarine Volcanoes Geologists estimate that approximately 80% of the volcanic activity on Earth takes place on the ocean floor. Most of the volcanic activity occurs as magma slowly flows onto the ocean floor where tectonic plates pull away from each other. Other volcanic activity is the result of volcanoes that are located on the ocean floor. Both of these types of volcanoes are called *submarine volcanoes*. Submarine volcanoes behave differently than volcanoes on land do. Research how submarine volcanoes behave underwater. Then, create a model of a submarine volcano based on the information you find.

ACTIVITY

The Ocean and the Water Cycle

The Earth system is made up of three basic components—water, land, and air. All three are part of a process called the water cycle, as shown in **Figure 7.** The **water cycle** is the continuous movement of water from the ocean to the atmosphere to the land and back to the ocean. The ocean is an important part of the water cycle because nearly all of Earth's water is in the ocean.

Benchmark Check How is the ocean influenced by the water cycle? **D.1.3.3 CS**

water cycle the continuous movement of water from the ocean to the atmosphere to the land and back to the ocean

D.1.3.3 CS knows how conditions that exist in one system influence the conditions that exist in other systems.

Figure 7 The Water Cycle

Condensation As water vapor rises into the atmosphere, it cools and interacts with dust particles. Eventually, the water vapor turns to liquid water. This change from a gas to a liquid is called *condensation.*

Evaporation The sun heats liquid water, causing it to rise into the atmosphere as water vapor. This physical change from a liquid to a gas is called *evaporation.* Water evaporates directly from oceans, lakes, rivers, falling rain, plants, animals, and other sources.

Precipitation When water droplets become heavy enough, they fall back to Earth's surface as precipitation. *Precipitation* is solid or liquid water that falls to Earth. Most precipitation falls directly back into the ocean.

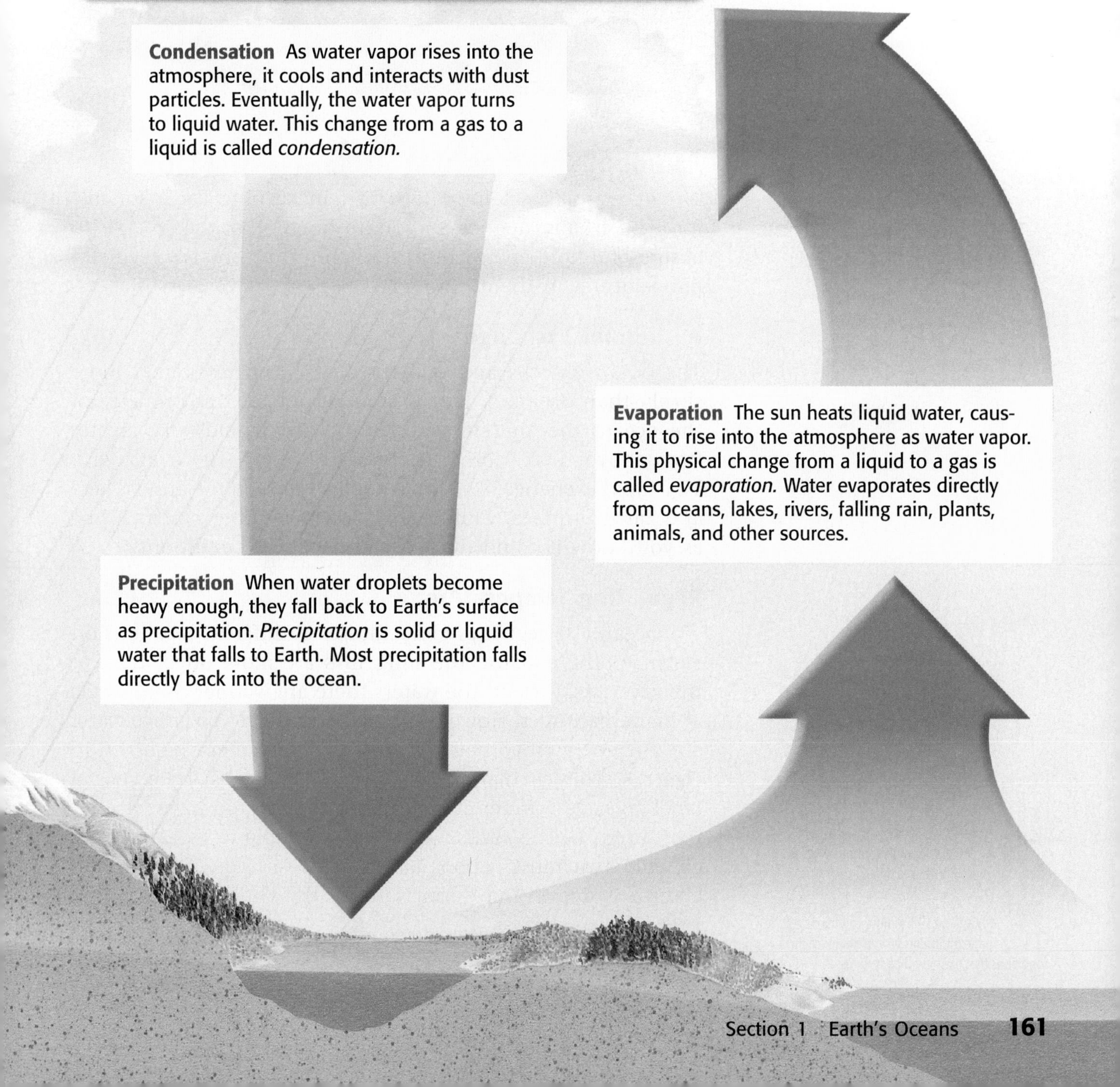

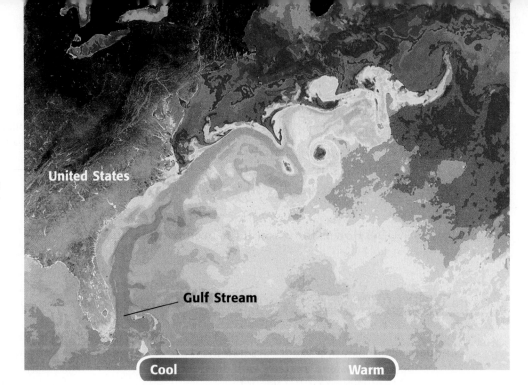

Figure 8 *This infrared satellite image shows the Gulf Stream moving warm water from lower latitudes to higher latitudes.*

United States

Gulf Stream

Cool   Warm

A Global Thermostat

The ocean plays an important part in keeping Earth suitable for life. Perhaps the most important function of the ocean is to absorb and hold energy from sunlight. This function regulates temperatures in the atmosphere.

A Thermal Exchange

The ocean absorbs and releases thermal energy much more slowly than dry land does. If it were not for this property of the ocean, the air temperature on Earth could vary greatly from above 100°C during the day to below −100°C at night. This rapid exchange of thermal energy between the atmosphere and Earth's surface would cause violent weather patterns. Life as you know it could not exist under these conditions.

Regulating Temperature

The ocean also regulates temperatures at different locations on Earth. At the equator, the sun's rays are more direct than at the poles. As a result, the waters there are warmer than waters at higher latitudes. However, currents in the ocean move water and the energy it contains. Part of this movement is shown in **Figure 8.** This circulation of warm water causes some coastal lands to have warmer climates than they would have without the currents. The British Isles, for example, have a warmer climate than most regions at the same latitude. This warmer climate is due to the warm water of the Gulf Stream.

 A.1.3.1 AA identifies various ways in which substances differ.

 D.1.3.3 CS knows how conditions that exist in one system influence the conditions that exist in other systems.

Benchmark Check How do conditions in the oceans affect temperatures around the world? **D.1.3.3 CS**

Summary

- The global ocean is divided by the continents into four main oceans: Pacific Ocean, Atlantic Ocean, Indian Ocean, and Arctic Ocean.

- The four oceans as we know them today formed within the last 300 million years.

- Salts have been added to the ocean for billions of years. Salinity is a measure of the amount of dissolved salts in a given weight or mass of liquid. **A.1.3.1 AA**

- The three temperature zones of ocean water are the surface zone, the thermocline, and the deep zone.

- The water cycle is the continuous movement of water from the ocean to the atmosphere to the land and back to the ocean. Ocean conditions play the largest role in the water cycle. **D.1.3.3 CS**

- The ocean stabilizes Earth's weather conditions by absorbing and holding thermal energy. **A.1.3.1 AA, D.1.3.3 CS**

Using Key Terms

1. Write an original definition for *salinity* and *water cycle*.

Understanding Key Ideas

2. Name the major divisions of the global ocean.

3. Explain how Earth's first oceans formed.

4. Why is the ocean an important part of the water cycle?

5. Between which two steps of the water cycle does the ocean fit? **D.1.3.3 CS**

6. How would the air temperature on land be different if the ocean did not release thermal energy so slowly?

7. What is the difference between how the ocean and the land absorb and release thermal energy? **A.1.3.1 AA**

Critical Thinking

8. **Making Inferences** Describe the role that the ocean plays in stabilizing Earth's weather conditions. **D.1.3.3 CS**

9. **Identifying Relationships** List one factor that affects salinity in the ocean and one factor that affects ocean temperatures. Explain how each factor affects salinity or temperature.

FCAT Preparation

10. Earth's atmosphere is influenced by many environmental conditions. How is the atmosphere influenced by the surface temperature of the ocean? **D.1.3.3 CS**

   A. As the ocean's surface cools, gases in the atmosphere heat it.

   B. As the ocean's surface cools, less atmospheric gas is absorbed by the water.

   C. As the ocean's surface is heated, more water evaporates and enters the atmosphere.

   D. As the ocean's surface is heated, the air in the atmosphere cools.

SCINKS.

NSTA

Developed and maintained by the
National Science Teachers Association

For a variety of links related to this chapter, go to www.scilinks.org

Topic: Exploring Earth's Oceans
SciLinks code: HSM0557

The Ocean Floor

What lies at the bottom of the ocean? How deep is the ocean at its deepest point?

These questions were once unanswerable. By using new technology, scientists have learned a lot about the ocean floor. Scientists have discovered landforms on the ocean floor and have measured depths for almost the entire ocean floor.

Studying the Ocean Floor

Sending people into deep water to study the ocean floor can be risky. Fortunately, there are other ways to study the deep ocean. These ways include surveying from the ocean surface and from high above in space.

Seeing by Sonar

Sonar stands for *sound navigation and ranging*. This technology is based on the echo-ranging behavior of bats. Scientists use sonar to determine the ocean's depth by sending sound pulses from a ship down into the ocean. The sound moves through the water, bounces off the ocean floor, and returns to the ship. The deeper the water is, the longer the round trip takes. Scientists then calculate the depth by multiplying half the travel time by the speed of sound in water (about 1,500 m/s). This process is shown in **Figure 1.**

READING WARM-UP

Objectives

● Describe technologies for studying the ocean floor.

● Identify the two major regions of the ocean floor.

● Classify subdivisions and features of the two major regions of the ocean floor.

Terms to Learn

continental shelf	rift valley
continental slope	seamount
continental rise	ocean trench
abyssal plain	
mid-ocean ridge	
ocean basin *FCAT VOCAB*	

READING STRATEGY

Reading Organizer As you read this section, create an outline of the section. Use the headings from the section in your outline.

Figure 1 Ocean Floor Mapping with Sonar

3 Scientists use sonar signals to make a *bathymetric profile,* which is a map of the ocean floor that shows the ocean's depth.

Oceanography via Satellite

In the 1970s, scientists began studying Earth from satellites in orbit around Earth. In 1978, scientists launched the satellite *Seasat.* This satellite focused on the ocean by sending images back to Earth that allowed scientists to measure the direction and speed of ocean currents.

Studying the Ocean with *Geosat*

Geosat, once a top-secret military satellite, has been used to measure slight changes in the height of the ocean's surface. Different underwater features, such as mountains and trenches, affect the height of the water above them. Scientists measure the different heights of the ocean surface and use the measurements to make detailed maps of the ocean floor. Maps made using satellite measurements, such as the map in **Figure 2,** can cover much more territory than maps made using ship-based sonar readings.

✓ **Reading Check** How do scientists use satellites to make detailed maps of the ocean floor?

Figure 2 *This map was generated by satellite measurements of different heights of the ocean surface.*

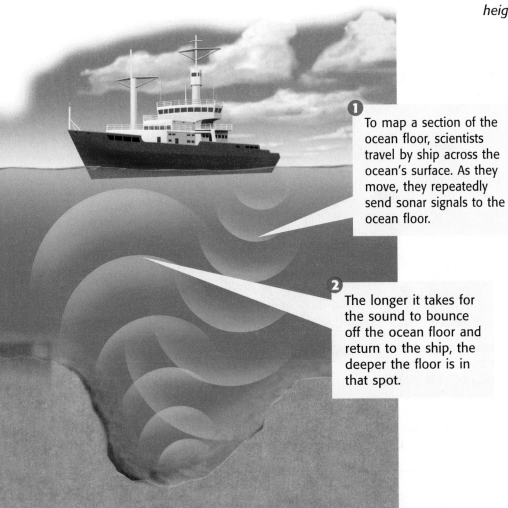

① To map a section of the ocean floor, scientists travel by ship across the ocean's surface. As they move, they repeatedly send sonar signals to the ocean floor.

② The longer it takes for the sound to bounce off the ocean floor and return to the ship, the deeper the floor is in that spot.

Revealing the Ocean Floor

continental shelf the gently sloping section of the continental margin located between the shoreline and the continental slope

continental slope the steeply inclined section of the continental margin located between the continental rise and the continental shelf

continental rise the gently sloping section of the continental margin located between the continental slope and the abyssal plain

abyssal plain a large, flat, almost level area of the deep-ocean basin

Can you imagine being an explorer assigned to map uncharted areas on the planet? You might think that there are not many uncharted areas left because most of the land has already been explored. But what about the bottom of the ocean?

The ocean floor is not a flat surface. If you could go to the bottom of the ocean, you would see a number of impressive features. You would see the world's longest mountain chain, which is about 64,000 km (40,000 mi) long as well as canyons deeper than the Grand Canyon. And because it is underwater and some areas are so deep, much of the ocean floor is still not completely explored.

Reading Check How long is the longest mountain chain in the world? Where is it located?

Figure 3 The Ocean Floor

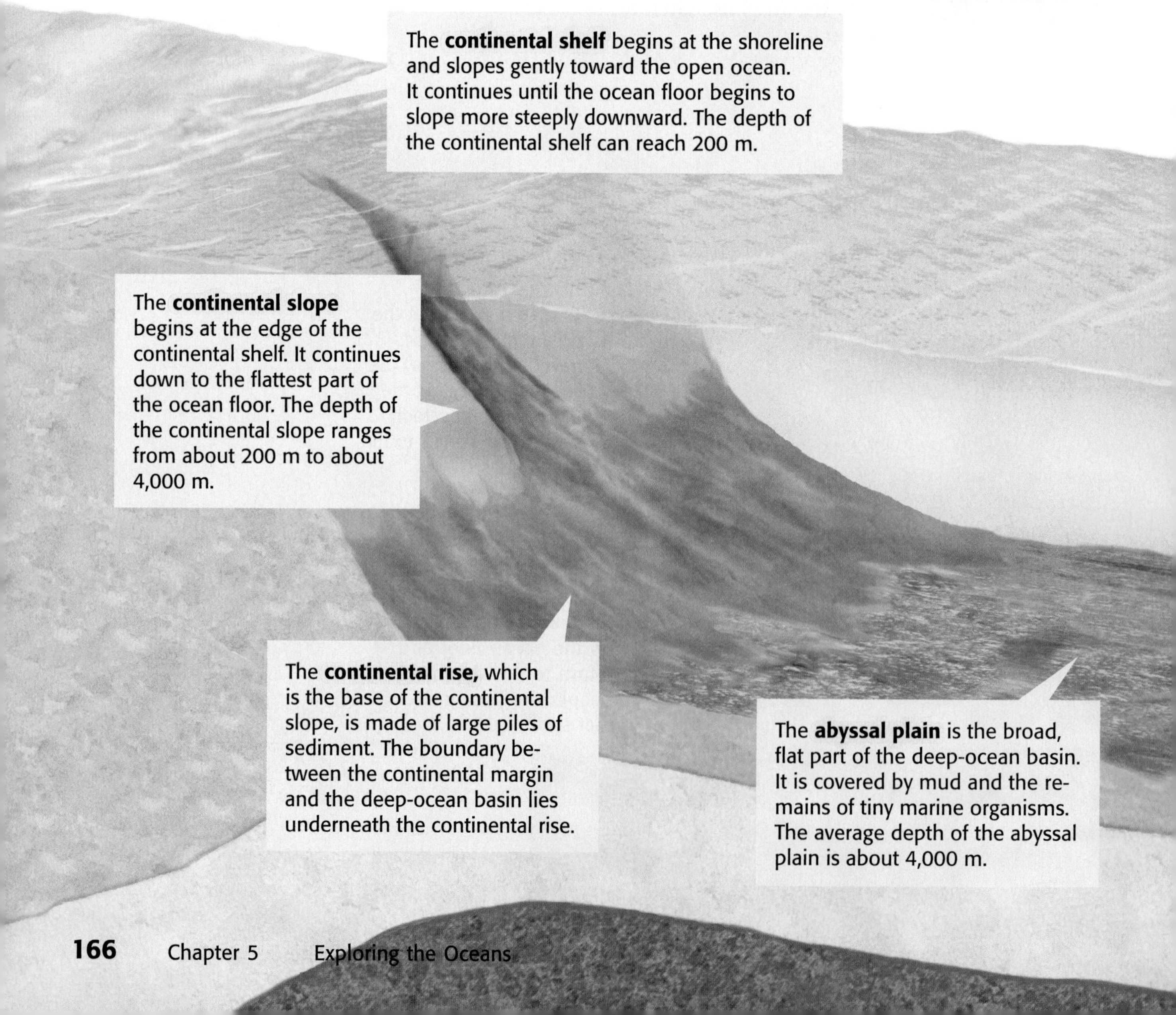

The **continental shelf** begins at the shoreline and slopes gently toward the open ocean. It continues until the ocean floor begins to slope more steeply downward. The depth of the continental shelf can reach 200 m.

The **continental slope** begins at the edge of the continental shelf. It continues down to the flattest part of the ocean floor. The depth of the continental slope ranges from about 200 m to about 4,000 m.

The **continental rise,** which is the base of the continental slope, is made of large piles of sediment. The boundary between the continental margin and the deep-ocean basin lies underneath the continental rise.

The **abyssal plain** is the broad, flat part of the deep-ocean basin. It is covered by mud and the remains of tiny marine organisms. The average depth of the abyssal plain is about 4,000 m.

Regions of the Ocean Floor

The ocean floor, also known as the **ocean basin,** is the area of Earth that is covered by ocean water. The ocean basin is composed of the continental margin and the deep ocean basin. The *continental margin* is made of continental crust, and the *deep ocean basin* is made of oceanic crust. Imagine that the ocean is a giant swimming pool. The continental margin is the shallow end of the pool, and the deep-ocean basin is the deep end of the pool. The figure below shows how these two regions are subdivided.

Underwater Real Estate

As you can see in **Figure 3** below, the continental margin is subdivided into the continental shelf, the continental slope, and the continental rise. These divisions are based on depth and changes in slope. The deep-ocean basin consists of the abyssal (uh BIS uhl) plain, mid-ocean ridges, rift valleys, and ocean trenches. All of these features form near the boundaries of Earth's *tectonic plates*. On parts of the deep-ocean basin that are not near plate boundaries, there are thousands of seamounts. Seamounts are submerged volcanic mountains on the ocean floor.

mid-ocean ridge a long, undersea mountain chain that forms along the floor of the major oceans

rift valley a long, narrow valley that forms as tectonic plates separate

seamount a submerged mountain on the ocean floor that is at least 1,000 m high and that has a volcanic origin

ocean trench a steep, long depression in the deep-sea floor that runs parallel to a chain of volcanic islands or a continental margin

ocean basin the area of Earth that is covered by oceans **FCAT** VOCAB

Mid-ocean ridges are mountain chains that form where tectonic plates pull apart. This pulling motion creates cracks in the ocean floor called *rift zones*. As rifts form, magma rises to fill the spaces. Heat from the magma causes the crust on either side of the rifts to expand, which forms the ridges.

As mountains build up, a **rift valley** forms between them in the rift zone.

Seamounts are individual mountains of volcanic material. They form where magma pushes its way through or between tectonic plates. If a seamount builds up above sea level, it becomes a volcanic island.

Ocean trenches are huge cracks in the deep-ocean basin. Ocean trenches form where one oceanic plate is pushed beneath a continental plate or another oceanic plate.

Exploring the Ocean with Underwater Vessels

Just as astronauts explore space with rockets, scientists explore the oceans with underwater vessels. These vessels contain the air that the explorers need to breathe and all of the scientific instruments that the explorers need to study the oceans.

Piloted Vessels: *Alvin* and *Deep Flight*

One research vessel used to travel to the deep ocean is called *Alvin*. *Alvin* is 7 m long and can reach some of the deepest parts of the ocean. Scientists have used *Alvin* for many underwater missions, including searches for sunken ships, the recovery of a lost hydrogen bomb, and explorations of the sea floor. In 1977, scientists aboard *Alvin* discovered an oasis of life around hydrothermal vents near the Galápagos Islands. Ecosystems near hydrothermal vents are unique because some organisms living around the vent do not rely on photosynthesis for energy. Instead, these organisms rely on chemicals in the water as their source of energy.

Another modern vessel that scientists use to explore the deep ocean is an underwater airplane called *Deep Flight*. This vessel, shown in **Figure 4,** moves through the water in much the same way that an airplane moves through the air. Future models of *Deep Flight* will be designed to transport pilots to the deepest parts of the ocean, which are more than 11,000 m deep.

✔ **Reading Check** Why is the ecosystem discovered by *Alvin* unique?

CONNECTION TO
Social Studies

The JASON Project The JASON project, started by oceanographer Dr. Robert Ballard, allows students and teachers to take part in virtual field trips to some of the most exotic locations on Earth. Using satellite links and the Internet, students around the world have participated in scientific expeditions to places such as the Galápagos Islands, the Sea of Cortez, and deep-sea hydrothermal vents. Using the Internet, research where the JASON project is headed to next!

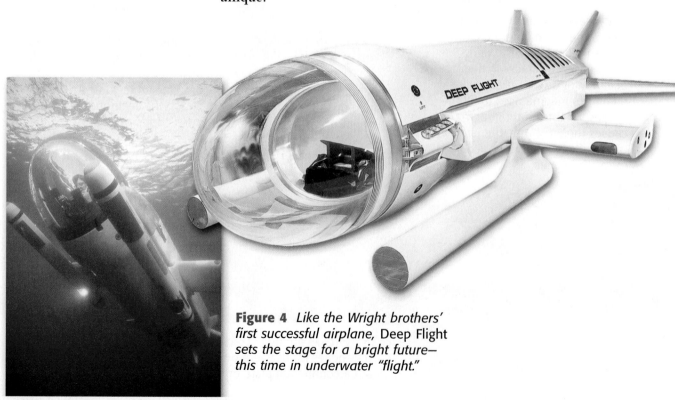

Figure 4 *Like the Wright brothers' first successful airplane, Deep Flight sets the stage for a bright future—this time in underwater "flight."*

Robotic Vessels: *JASON II* and *Medea*

Exploring the deep ocean by using piloted vessels is expensive and can be very dangerous. For these reasons, scientists often use robotic vessels to explore the ocean. One interesting robot team consists of *JASON II* and *Medea*. These robots are designed to withstand pressures much greater than those found in the deepest parts of the ocean. *JASON II* is "flown" by a pilot at the surface and is used to explore the ocean floor. *Medea* is attached to *JASON II* with a tether and explores above the sea floor. In the future, unpiloted "drone" robots shaped like fish may be used. Another robot under development uses the ocean's thermal energy for power. These robots could explore the ocean for years and send data to scientists at the surface.

H.3.3.7 knows that computers speed up and extend people's ability to collect, sort, and analyze data; and share data and ideas with others.

SECTION Review

Summary

- Scientists study the ocean floor from the surface using sonar and satellites.

- The ocean floor is divided into two regions—the continental margin and the deep-ocean basin.

- The continental margin consists of the continental shelf, the continental slope, and the continental rise.

- The deep-ocean basin consists of the abyssal plain, mid-ocean ridges, rift valleys, seamounts, and ocean trenches.

- Scientists explore the ocean from below the surface by using piloted vessels and robotic vessels.

Using Key Terms

For each pair of terms, explain how the meanings of the terms differ.

1. *continental shelf* and *ocean basin* **FCAT VOCAB**

2. *abyssal plain* and *ocean trench*

3. *mid-ocean ridge* and *seamount*

Understanding Key Ideas

4. Describe the subdivisions of the continental margin.

5. List three technologies used for studying the ocean floor, and explain how they are used.

6. List three underwater missions for which *Alvin* has been used.

7. Explain how *Jason II* and *Medea* are used to explore the ocean.

8. Describe how a bathymetric profile is made.

Critical Thinking

9. **Making Comparisons** How is exploring the oceans similar to exploring space?

10. **Applying Concepts** Is the ocean floor a flat surface? Explain your answer.

FCAT Preparation

11. Deep-sea robots travel far below the ocean's surface to explore the ocean floor. The technological design of a deep-sea robot must take into account which of the following constraints? **H.3.3.4 CS**

    A. air temperature

    B. oxygen levels

    C. water pressure

    D. water salinity

12. An engineer is studying penguins to design a boat that can move through water at the same speed as a penguin does. Why is it important for the engineer to keep accurate notes about his research? **H.1.3.4 AA**

SCI LINKS

Developed and maintained by the National Science Teachers Association

For a variety of links related to this chapter, go to www.scilinks.org

Topic: The Ocean Floor; Science and Technology in Florida

SciLinks code: HSM1062; HSMF14

Life in the Ocean

In which part of the ocean does an octopus live? And where do dolphins spend most of their time?

Just as armadillos and birds occupy very different places on Earth, octopuses and dolphins live in very different parts of the ocean. Trying to study life in the oceans can be a challenge for scientists. The oceans are so large that many forms of marine life have not been discovered, and there are many more organisms that scientists know little about. To make things easier, scientists classify marine organisms into three main groups.

The Three Groups of Marine Life

The three main groups of marine life, as shown in **Figure 1,** are plankton, nekton, and benthos. Marine organisms are placed into one of these three groups according to where they live and how they move.

Organisms that float or drift freely near the ocean's surface are called **plankton**. Most plankton are microscopic. Plankton are divided into two groups—those that are plant-like (*phytoplankton*) and those that are animal-like (*zooplankton*). Organisms that swim actively in the open ocean are called **nekton.** Types of nekton include mammals, such as whales, dolphins, and sea lions, as well as many varieties of fish. **Benthos** are organisms that live on or in the ocean floor. There are many types of benthos, such as crabs, starfish, worms, coral, sponges, seaweed, and clams.

Figure 1
Plankton, nekton, and benthos are the three groups of organisms that live in the ocean.

Zooplankton

Nekton

Phytoplankton

Benthos

The Benthic Environment

In addition to being divided into zones based on depth, the ocean floor is divided into ecological zones based on where different types of benthos live. These zones are grouped into one major marine environment—the benthic environment. The **benthic environment,** or bottom environment, is the region near the ocean floor and all the organisms that live on or in it.

Figure 2 *Organisms such as sea anemones and starfish attach themselves to rocks and reefs. These organisms must be able to survive both wet and dry conditions.*

The Intertidal Zone

The shallowest benthic zone, called the *intertidal zone,* is located between the low-tide and high-tide limits. Twice a day, the intertidal zone changes. As the tide flows in, the zone is covered with ocean water. Then, as the tide flows out, the intertidal zone is exposed to the air and sun.

Because of the change in tides, intertidal organisms must be able to live both underwater and on exposed land. Some organisms, such as the sea anemones and starfish shown in **Figure 2,** attach themselves to rocks and reefs to avoid being washed out to sea during low tide. Other organisms, such as clams, oysters, barnacles, and crabs, have tough shells that give them protection against strong waves during high tide and against harsh sunlight during low tide. Some animals can burrow in sand or between rocks to avoid harsh conditions. Plants also protect themselves from being washed away by strong waves. Plants such as seaweed have strong *holdfasts* (rootlike structures) that allow them to grow in this zone.

plankton the mass of mostly microscopic organisms that float or drift freely in freshwater and marine environments

nekton all organisms that swim actively in open water, independent of currents

benthos the organisms that live at the bottom of the sea or ocean

benthic environment the region near the bottom of a pond, lake, or ocean

Benchmark Check What behavior do starfish and sea anemones exhibit in response to their environment? **F.1.3.7 CS**

F.1.3.7 CS (partial) knows that behavior is a response to the environment and influences growth, development, maintenance, and reproduction.

Figure 3 *Corals, like many other types of organisms, can live in both the sublittoral zone and the intertidal zone. However, they are more common in the sublittoral zone.*

Sublittoral zone

The Sublittoral Zone

The *sublittoral zone* begins where the intertidal zone ends, at the low-tide limit, and extends to the edge of the continental shelf. This zone of the benthic environment is more stable than the intertidal zone. The temperature, water pressure, and amount of sunlight remain fairly constant in the sublittoral zone. Sublittoral organisms, such as corals, shown in **Figure 3,** do not have to cope with as much change as intertidal organisms do. Although the sublittoral zone extends down 200 m below sea level, plants and most animals stay in the upper 100 m, where small amounts of sunlight reaches the ocean floor.

The Bathyal Zone

The *bathyal* (BATH ee uhl) *zone* extends from the edge of the continental shelf to the abyssal plain. The depth of this zone ranges from 200 m to 4,000 m below sea level. Because of the lack of sunlight at these depths, plant life is scarce in this part of the benthic environment. Animals in this zone include sponges, brachiopods, sea stars, echinoids, and octopuses, such as the one shown in **Figure 4.**

Figure 4 *Octopuses are one of the animals common to the bathyal zone.*

Bathyal zone

Figure 5 *Tube worms can tolerate higher temperatures than most other organisms can. These animals survive in water as hot as 81°C.*

Abyssal zone

The Abyssal Zone

No plants and very few animals live in the *abyssal zone,* which is on the abyssal plain. The abyssal zone is the largest ecological zone of the ocean and can reach 4,000 m in depth. Animals such as crabs, sponges, worms, and sea cucumbers live within the abyssal zone. Many of these organisms, such as the tube worms shown in **Figure 5,** live around hot-water vents called *black smokers.* Scientists know very little about this benthic environment because it is so deep and dark.

✓ Reading Check What types of animals live in the abyssal zone?

The Hadal Zone

The deepest benthic zone is the *hadal* (HAYD'l) *zone.* This zone consists of the floor of the ocean trenches and any organisms found there. The hadal zone can reach from 6,000 m to 7,000 m in depth. Scientists know even less about the hadal zone than they do about the abyssal zone. So far, scientists have discovered life forms such as sponges and worms. Scientists have also found clams such as those shown in **Figure 6.**

INTERNET ACTIVITY

Life Under the Waves
Describe your life as a sea creature. Go to **go.hrw.com** and type in the keyword **HZ5OCEW.**

Hadal zone

Figure 6 *These clams are one of the few types of organisms known to live in the hadal zone.*

Neritic zone

Figure 7 *Many marine animals, such as these dolphins, live in the neritic zone.*

pelagic environment in the ocean, the zone near the surface or at middle depths, beyond the sublittoral zone and above the abyssal zone

The Pelagic Environment

The zone near the ocean's surface and at the middle depths of the ocean is called the **pelagic environment**. It is beyond the sublittoral zone and above the abyssal zone. There are two major zones in the pelagic environment—the neritic zone and the oceanic zone.

The Neritic Zone

The *neritic zone* covers the continental shelf. This warm, shallow zone contains the largest concentration of marine life. Fish, plankton, and marine mammals, such as the dolphins in **Figure 7**, are just a few of the animal groups found in this zone. The neritic zone contains diverse marine life because it receives more sunlight than the other zones in the ocean. Sunlight allows plankton, which are food for other marine organisms, to grow. The many animals in the benthic zone below the neritic zone also serve as a food supply.

Benchmark Check **Why does the neritic zone contain the largest concentration of marine life in the ocean?** G.1.3.4 AA

> **CONNECTION TO**
> **Language Arts**
>
> **WRITING SKILL** **Water, Water, Everywhere** Samuel Taylor Coleridge wrote "The Rime of the Ancient Mariner" in 1798. The following is an excerpt from the poem:
>
> Water, water, everywhere, / And all the boards did shrink / Water, water, everywhere, / Nor any drop to drink . . . / And every tongue through utter drought, / Was withered at the root; / We could not speak, no more than if / We had been choked with soot.
>
> What do you think this excerpt means? Write a short essay describing the meaning of this passage.

G.1.3.4 AA (partial) knows that the interactions of organisms with each other and the non-living parts of their environment result in the flow of energy and the cycling of matter throughout the system.

The Oceanic Zone

The *oceanic zone* includes the volume of water that covers the entire sea floor except for the continental shelf. In the deeper parts of the oceanic zone, the water temperature is colder and the pressure is much greater than in the neritic zone. Also, organisms are more spread out in the oceanic zone than in the neritic zone. Although many of the same organisms that live in the neritic zone are found throughout the upper regions, some strange animals lurk in the darker depths, as shown in **Figure 8.** Other animals in the deeper parts of this zone include giant squids and some whale species.

Oceanic zone

Figure 8 *The angler fish is a predator that uses a wormlike lure attached to its head to attract prey.*

SECTION Review

Summary

- The three main groups of marine life are plankton, nekton, and benthos.

- Plants and animals are uniquely adapted to live in the benthic and pelagic environments. **F.1.3.7 CS**

- The ecological zones of the benthic environment include the intertidal zone, sublittoral zone, bathyal zone, abyssal zone, and hadal zone. **G.1.3.4 AA**

- The ecological zones of the pelagic environment include the neritic zone and the oceanic zone. **G.1.3.4 AA**

Understanding Key Ideas

1. List and briefly describe the three main groups of marine organisms.

2. Name the two ocean environments. In your own words, describe where they are located in the ocean.

Critical Thinking

3. **Making Inferences** Describe why organisms in the intertidal zone must be able to live underwater and on exposed land.

4. **Applying Concepts** How would the ocean's ecological zones change if sea level dropped 300 m?

Interpreting Graphics

5. Look at the diagram below. Identify the names of the ecological zones of the benthic environment shown.

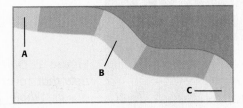

FCAT Preparation

6. Many kinds of shellfish, such as muscles and clams, live in intertidal zones. How does a clam respond to its environment when the tide is low? **F.1.3.7 CS**

   A. The clam moves to the oceanic zone.

   B. The clam opens its shell to dry out.

   C. The clam does not respond to its environment.

   D. The clam tightly closes its shell to hold in stored water.

7. Plankton are at the base of almost all marine food chains. What is the source of energy on which photosynthetic plankton rely? **G.1.3.4 AA**

Developed and maintained by the
National Science Teachers Association

For a variety of links related to this chapter, go to www.scilinks.org
Topic: Life in the Oceans; Aquariums and Museums of Florida
SciLinks code: HSM0874; HSMF01

SECTION 4

Resources from the Ocean

The next time you enjoy your favorite ice cream, remember that without seaweed, it would be a runny mess!

READING WARM-UP

Objectives

- Describe two positive and two negative consequences of harvesting the ocean's living resources. D.2.3.2., G.2.3.4 AA
- Identify three nonliving resources in the ocean. G.2.3.1 CS
- Describe the ocean's energy resources. G.2.3.1 CS

Terms to Learn

desalination

READING STRATEGY

Paired Summarizing Read this section silently. In pairs, take turns summarizing the material. Stop to discuss ideas that seem confusing.

G.2.3.4 AA (partial) understands that humans are a part of an ecosystem and their activities may deliberately or inadvertently alter the equilibrium in ecosystems.

The ocean offers a vast supply of resources. These resources are put to a number of uses. For example, a seaweed called *kelp* is used as a thickener for many food products, including ice cream. Food, raw materials, energy, and drinkable water are all harvested from the ocean. As human populations have grown, however, the demand for these resources has increased, while the availability has decreased.

Living Resources

People have been harvesting plants and animals from the ocean for thousands of years. Many civilizations formed in coastal regions where the ocean offered plenty of food for a growing population. Today, harvesting food from the ocean is a multi-billion-dollar industry.

Fishing the Ocean

Of all the marine organisms, fish are the largest group of organisms that are taken from the ocean. Almost 75 million tons of fish are harvested each year. With improved technology, such as drift nets, fishers have become better at taking fish from the ocean. **Figure 1** shows the large number of fish that can be caught using a drift net. In recent years, many people have become concerned that we are overfishing the ocean, or taking more fish than can be naturally replaced. Also, animals other than fish, especially dolphins and turtles, can be accidentally caught in drift nets. Today, the fishing industry is making efforts to prevent overfishing and damage to other wildlife from drift nets.

Benchmark Check **How do human activities alter the equilibrium of ocean ecosystems?** G.2.3.4 AA

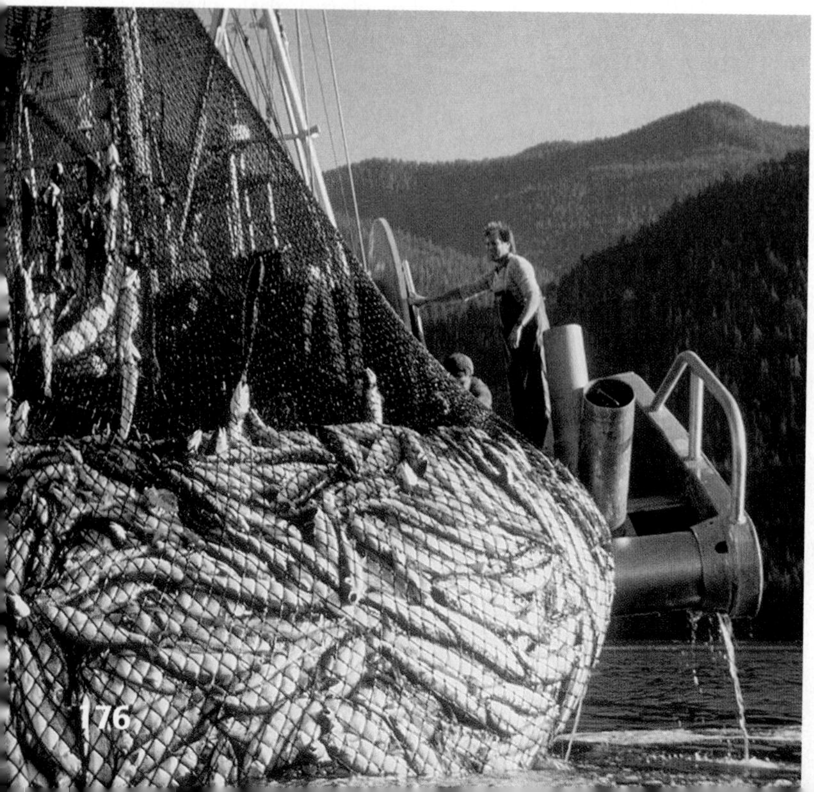

Figure 1 *Drift nets are fishing nets that cover kilometers of ocean. Whole schools of fish can be caught with a single drift net.*

Farming the Ocean

Overfishing reduces fish populations. Recently, laws regulating fishing have become stricter. As a result, it is becoming more difficult to supply our demand for fish. Many people have begun to raise ocean fish in fish farms to help meet the demand. Fish farming requires several holding ponds. Each pond contains fish at a certain level of development. **Figure 2** shows a holding pond in a fish farm. When the fish are old enough, they are harvested and packaged for shipping.

Fish are not the only seafood harvested in a farmlike setting. Shrimp, oysters, crabs, and mussels are raised in enclosed areas near the shore. Mussels and oysters are grown attached to ropes. Huge nets line the nursery area, preventing the animals from being eaten by their natural predators.

Benchmark Check What are the negative consequences of overfishing? What are the possible positive consequences of fish farming? **D.2.3.2**

Figure 2 *Eating fish raised in a fish farm helps lower the number of fish harvested from the ocean.*

Savory Seaweed

Many types of seaweed, which are species of alga, are harvested from the ocean. For example, kelp, shown in **Figure 3,** is a seaweed that grows as much as 33 cm a day. Kelp is harvested and used as a thickener in jellies, ice cream, and similar products. Seaweed is rich in protein. In fact, several species of seaweed are staples of the Japanese diet. For example, some kinds of sushi, a Japanese dish, are wrapped in seaweed.

D.2.3.2 knows the positive and negative consequences of human action on the Earth's systems.

Figure 3 *Kelp, a type of alga, can grow up to 33 cm a day. It is harvested and used in a number of products, including ice cream.*

Nonliving Resources

Humans also harvest many nonliving resources from the ocean. These resources provide raw materials, drinkable water, and energy for our growing population. Some resources are easy to get, while others are very difficult to harvest.

Oil and Natural Gas

Modern civilization continues to be very dependent on oil and natural gas for energy. Oil and natural gas are *nonrenewable resources*. They are used up faster than they can be replenished naturally. Both oil and natural gas are found under layers of impermeable rock. Petroleum engineers must drill through this rock in order to reach these resources.

Benchmark Check What are nonrenewable resources? Give an example of a nonrenewable resource. G.2.3.1 CS

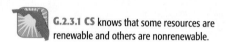

G.2.3.1 CS knows that some resources are renewable and others are nonrenewable.

Searching for Oil

How do engineers know where to drill for oil and natural gas? They use seismic equipment. Special devices send powerful pulses of sound to the ocean floor. The pulses move through the water and penetrate the rocks and sediment below. The pulses are then reflected back toward the ship, where they are recorded by electronic equipment and analyzed by a computer. The computer readings indicate how rock layers are arranged below the ocean floor. Petroleum workers, such as the one in **Figure 4,** use these readings to locate a promising area to drill.

Figure 4 *Petroleum workers, such as the one below, drill for oil and gas in the ocean floor. By using seismic equipment, workers can decide which spot will be best for drilling.*

Fresh Water and Desalination

In parts of the world where fresh water is limited, people desalinate ocean water. **Desalination** (DEE SAL uh NAY shuhn) is the process of removing salt from sea water. After the salt is removed, the fresh water is then collected for human use. But desalination is not as simple as it sounds, and it is very expensive. Countries with enough annual rainfall rely on the fresh water provided by precipitation and do not need costly desalination plants. Some countries located in drier parts of the world, such as Saudi Arabia and Kuwait, use desalination plants to produce fresh water. Kuwait stores fresh water in the towers shown in **Figure 5.**

desalination a process of removing salt from ocean water

Reading Check Explain where desalination plants are most likely to be built.

The Desalination Plant

1. Measure **1,000 mL of warm water** in a **graduated cylinder.** Pour the water in a **large pot.**

2. Carefully, add **35 g of table salt.** Stir the water until all of the salt is dissolved.

3. Place the pot on a **hot plate,** and allow all of the water to boil away.

4. Using a **wooden spoon,** scrape the salt residue from the bottom of the pot.

5. Measure the mass of the salt that was left in the bottom of the pot. How much salt did you separate from the water?

6. How does this activity model what happens in a desalination plant? What would be done differently in a desalination plant?

Figure 6 *Manganese nodules are difficult to mine because they are located on the deep ocean floor.*

Sea-Floor Minerals

Mining companies are interested in mineral nodules that are lying on the ocean floor. These nodules are made mostly of manganese, which can be used to make certain types of steel. They also contain iron, copper, nickel, cobalt, and phosphates. Phosphates are used to make fertilizer.

Nodules are formed from dissolved substances in sea water that stick to solid objects, such as pebbles. As more substances stick to the pebble, a nodule begins to grow. Manganese nodules can be as small as a marble or as large as a soccer ball. **Figure 6** shows a number of nodules on the ocean floor. Scientists estimate that 15% of the ocean floor is covered with these nodules. However, these nodules are located in the deeper parts of the ocean. Mining them is costly and difficult.

Tidal Energy

The ocean generates a great deal of energy simply because of its constant movement. The gravitational pulls of the sun and moon cause the ocean to rise and fall as tides. *Tidal energy* is energy generated from the movement of tides. Tidal energy can be an excellent source of power. If the water during high tide can be rushed through a narrow coastal passageway, the water's force can be powerful enough to generate electrical energy. **Figure 7** shows how this process works. Tidal energy is a clean, inexpensive, and renewable resource. A *renewable resource* can be replenished, in time, after being used. Unfortunately, tidal energy is practical only in a few parts of the world. These areas must have a coastline with shallow, narrow channels. For example, the coastline at Cook Inlet, in Alaska, is ideal for generating electrical energy.

 G.2.3.1 CS knows that some resources are renewable and others are nonrenewable.

Benchmark Check List three examples of a renewable resource. **G.2.3.1 CS**

Figure 7 | Using Tides to Generate Electrical Energy

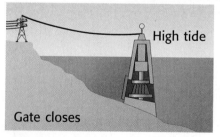

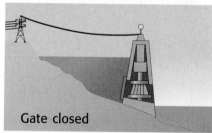

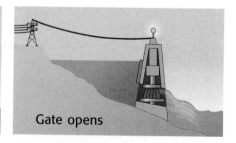

1 As the tide rises, water enters a bay behind a dam. The gate then closes at high tide.

2 The gate remains closed as the tide lowers.

3 At low tide, the gate opens, and the water rushes through the dam and moves the turbines, which, in turn, generate electrical energy.

Wave Energy

Have you ever stood on the beach and watched as waves crashed on the shore? This constant motion is an energy resource. Wave energy, like tidal energy, is a clean, renewable resource. Recently, computer programs have been developed to analyze wave energy. Researchers have found certain areas of the world where wave energy can generate enough electrical energy to make building power plants worthwhile. Wave energy in the North Sea is strong enough to produce power for parts of Scotland and England.

✓ Reading Check Why would wave energy be a good alternative energy resource?

SECTION Review

Summary

- Humans depend on the ocean for living and non-living resources. **G.2.3.1 CS**

- Fish and other marine life are being raised in ocean farms to help feed growing human populations. **D.2.3.2**

- Nonliving ocean resources include oil and natural gas, water, minerals, and tidal and wave energy. **G.2.3.1 CS**

Understanding Key Ideas

1. List two ways of harvesting the ocean's living resources.

2. Name four nonliving resources in the ocean.

3. Explain how fish farms help meet the demand for fish.

4. Explain how engineers decide where to drill for oil and natural gas in the ocean.

Critical Thinking

5. **Analyzing Processes** Explain why tidal energy and wave energy are considered renewable resources. **G.2.3.1 CS**

6. **Predicting Consequences** Define the term *overfishing* in your own words. What would happen to the population of fish in the ocean if laws did not regulate fishing? Without these laws, what would happen to the ocean ecosystem? **G.2.3.4 AA**

7. **Analyzing Ideas** What is one benefit and one consequence of building a desalination plant? Would a desalination plant be beneficial to your local area? Explain why or why not. **D.2.3.2**

FCAT Preparation

8. Nonrenewable resources are natural resources that cannot easily be replaced. Which of the following is a nonrenewable resource? **G.2.3.1 CS**

   A. kelp
   B. natural gas
   C. ocean water
   D. wave energy

9. Humans burn oil products for things such as making electricity and powering cars. There are many positive and negative consequences of using oil. Describe three consequences of using oil. **G.2.3.4 AA**

SCI LINKS®

NSTA
Developed and maintained by the
National Science Teachers Association

For a variety of links related to this chapter, go to www.scilinks.org

Topic: Ocean Resources; Florida's Coasts
SciLinks code: HSM1065, HSMF05

Ocean Pollution

It's a hot summer day at the beach. You can hardly wait to swim in the ocean. You run to the surf only to be met by piles of trash washed up on the shore. Where did all that trash come from?

Humans have thrown their trash in the ocean for hundreds, if not thousands, of years. This trash has harmed the plants and animals that live in the oceans, as well as the people and animals that depend on them. Fortunately, we are becoming more aware of ocean pollution, and we are learning from our mistakes.

Nonpoint-Source Pollution

There are many sources of ocean pollution. Some of these sources are easily identified, but others are more difficult to pinpoint. **Nonpoint-source pollution** is pollution that comes from many sources rather than just from a single site. Some common sources of nonpoint-source pollutants are shown in **Figure 1.** Most ocean pollution is nonpoint-source pollution. Human activities on land can pollute streams and rivers, which then flow into the ocean and bring the pollutants they carry with them. Because nonpoint-source pollutants can enter bodies of water in many different ways, they are very hard to regulate and control. Nonpoint-source pollution can be reduced by using less lawn chemicals and disposing of used motor oil properly.

READING WARM-UP

Objectives

- Explain the difference between point-source pollution and nonpoint-source pollution.
- Identify three different types of point-source ocean pollution. **G.2.3.4 AA, D.2.3.2**
- Describe what is being done to control ocean pollution and how this affects people's quality of life. **D.2.3.1, G.2.3.4 AA, D.2.3.2**

Terms to Learn

nonpoint-source pollution
point-source pollution

READING STRATEGY

Reading Organizer As you read this section, create an outline of the section. Use the headings from the section in your outline.

Figure 1 **Examples of Nonpoint-Source Pollution**

Oil and gasoline that have leaked from cars onto streets can wash into storm sewers and then drain into waterways.

Boats and personal watercraft can leak gasoline and oil directly into bodies of water.

Pesticides, herbicides, and fertilizer from residential lawns, golf courses, and farmland can wash into waterways.

Figure 2 *This barge is headed out to the open ocean, where it will dump the trash it carries.*

Point-Source Pollution

Water pollution caused by a leaking oil tanker, a factory, or a wastewater treatment plant is one type of point-source pollution. **Point-source pollution** is pollution that comes from a specific site. Even when the source of pollution is known, cleanup of the pollution is difficult.

nonpoint-source pollution pollution that comes from many sources rather than from a single, specific site

point-source pollution pollution that comes from a specific site

Trash Dumping

People dump trash in many places, including the ocean. In the 1980s, scientists became alarmed by the kinds of trash that were washing up on beaches. Bandages, vials of blood, and syringes (needles) were found among the waste. Some of the blood in the vials even contained the AIDS virus. The Environmental Protection Agency (EPA) began an investigation and discovered that hospitals in the United States produce an average of 3 million tons of medical waste each year. Because of stricter laws, much of this medical waste is now buried in sanitary landfills. However, dumping trash in the deeper part of the ocean is still a common practice in many countries. The barge in **Figure 2** will dump the trash it carries into the open ocean.

D.2.3.2 knows the positive and negative consequences of human action on the Earth's systems.

G.2.3.4 AA understands that humans are a part of an ecosystem and their activities may deliberately or inadvertently alter the equilibrium in ecosystems.

Figure 3 *Marine animals can be strangled by plastic trash or can choke if they mistake the plastic for food.*

Effects of Trash Dumping

Trash thrown into the ocean can affect the organisms that live in the ocean and those organisms that depend on the ocean for food. Trash such as plastic can be particularly harmful to ocean organisms. This is because most plastic materials do not break down for thousands of years. Marine animals can mistake plastic materials for food and choke or become strangled. The sea gull in **Figure 3** is tangled up in a piece of plastic trash.

Benchmark Check **What is one effect of trash dumping?** D.2.3.2, G.2.3.4 AA

Sludge Dumping

By 1990, the United States alone had discharged 38 trillion liters of treated sludge into the waters along its coasts. Sludge is part of raw sewage. *Raw sewage* is all the liquid and solid wastes that are flushed down toilets and poured down drains. After collecting in sewer drains, raw sewage is sent through a treatment plant, where it undergoes a cleaning process that removes solid waste. The solid waste is called *sludge*, as shown in **Figure 4.** In many areas, people dump sludge into the ocean several kilometers offshore, intending for it to settle and stay on the ocean floor. Unfortunately, currents can stir the sludge up and move it closer to shore. This sludge can pollute beaches and kill marine life. Many countries have banned sludge dumping, but it continues to occur in many areas of the world.

Figure 4 *Sludge is the solid part of waste matter and often carries bacteria. Sludge makes beaches dirty and kills marine animals.*

Oil Spills

Because oil is in such high demand across the world, large tankers must transport billions of barrels of it across the oceans. If not handled properly, these transports can turn disastrous and cause oil spills. **Figure 5** shows some of the major oil spills that have occurred off the coast of North America.

Figure 5 *This map shows some of the major oil spills that have occurred off the coast of North America in the last 30 years.*

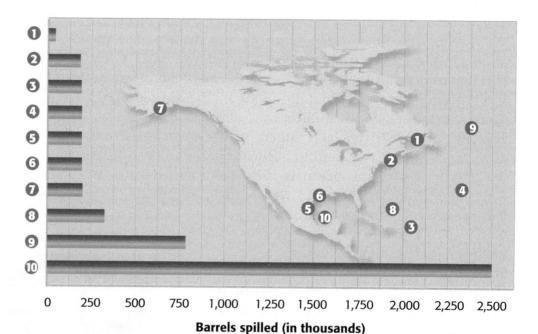

Barrels spilled (in thousands)

❶ *Kurdistan* Gulf of St. Lawrence, Canada, 1979

❷ *Argo Merchant* Nantucket, MA, 1976

❸ Storage Tank Benuelan, Puerto Rico, 1978

❹ *Athenian Venture* Atlantic Ocean, 1988

❺ Unnamed Tanker Tuxpan, Mexico, 1996

❻ *Burmah Agate* Galveston Bay, TX, 1979

❼ *Exxon Valdez* Prince William Sound, AK, 1989

❽ *Epic Colocotronis* Caribbean Sea, 1975

❾ *Odyessey* North Atlantic Ocian, 1988

❿ Exploratory Well Bay of Campeche, 1979

Effects of Oil Spills

One of the oil spills shown on the map in **Figure 5** occurred in Prince William Sound, Alaska, in 1989. The supertanker *Exxon Valdez* struck a reef and spilled more than 260,000 barrels of crude oil along the shorelines of Alaska. The amount of spilled oil is roughly equivalent to 125 olympic-sized swimming pools.

Although some animals were saved, such as the bird in **Figure 6,** many plants and animals died as a result of the spill. Alaskans who made their living from fishing lost their businesses. The Exxon Oil Company spent $2.1 billion to try to clean up the mess. But Alaska's wildlife and economy will continue to suffer for decades.

While oil spills can harm plants, animals, and people, oils spills are responsible for only about 5% of oil pollution in the oceans. Most of the oil that pollutes the oceans is caused by nonpoint-source pollution on land from cities and towns.

Figure 6 *Many oil-covered animals were rescued and cleaned after the* Exxon Valdez *spill.*

Preventing Oil Spills

Today, many oil companies are using new technology to safeguard against oil spills. Tankers are now being built with two hulls instead of one. The inner hull prevents oil from spilling into the ocean if the outer hull of the ship is damaged. **Figure 7** shows the design of a double-hulled tanker.

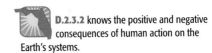 **Benchmark Check** How can two hulls on an oil tanker help prevent an oil spill? **D.2.3.2, G.2.3.4 AA**

D.2.3.2 knows the positive and negative consequences of human action on the Earth's systems.

G.2.3.4 AA understands that humans are a part of an ecosystem and their activities may deliberately or inadvertently alter the equilibrium in ecosystems.

Figure 7 *If the outer hull of a double-hulled tanker is punctured, the oil will still be contained within the inner hull.*

Saving Our Ocean Resources

Humans have done much to harm the ocean's resources, but we have also begun to do more to save them. From international treaties to volunteer cleanups, efforts to conserve the ocean's resources are making an impact around the world.

Nations Taking Notice

When ocean pollution reached an all-time high, many countries recognized the need to work together to solve the problem. In 1989, a treaty was passed by 64 countries that prohibits the dumping of certain metals, plastics, oil, and radioactive wastes into the ocean. Even though many other international agreements and laws restricting ocean pollution have been made, waste dumping and oil spills still occur. Therefore, waste continues to wash ashore, as shown in **Figure 8.**

Citizens Taking Charge

Citizens of many countries have demanded that their governments do more to solve the growing problem of ocean pollution. Because of public outcry, the United States now spends more than $130 million each year to protect the oceans and beaches. United States citizens have also begun to take the matter into their own hands. In the early 1980s, citizens began organizing beach cleanups. One of the largest cleanups is the semiannual Adopt-a-Beach program, shown in **Figure 8,** which originated with the Texas Coastal Cleanup campaign. Millions of tons of trash have been gathered from the beaches, and people are being educated about the hazards of ocean dumping.

Benchmark Check How can cleaning up a beach improve a person's quality of life? D.2.3.1

Figure 8 *Making an effort to pick up trash on a beach can help make the beach safer for plants, animals, and people.*

Action in the United States

The United States, like many other countries, has taken additional measures to control local pollution. For example, in 1972, Congress passed the Clean Water Act, which put the Environmental Protection Agency in charge of issuing permits for any dumping of trash into the ocean. Later that year, a stricter law—the U.S. Marine Protection, Research, and Sanctuaries Act—was passed. This act prohibits the dumping of any material that would affect human health or welfare, the marine environment or ecosystems, or businesses that depend on the ocean.

Benchmark Check What are some likely positive consequences of the U.S. Marine Protection, Research, and Sanctuaries Act? **D.2.3.2**

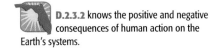 **D.2.3.2** knows the positive and negative consequences of human action on the Earth's systems.

SECTION Review

Summary

● The two main types of ocean pollution are non-point-source pollution and point-source pollution. **G.2.3.4 AA, D.2.3.2**

● Types of nonpoint-source pollution include oil and gasoline from cars, trucks, and watercraft, as well as the use of pesticides, herbicides, and fertilizers. **G.2.3.4 AA, D.2.3.2**

● Types of point-source ocean pollution include trash dumping, sludge dumping, and oil spills.

● Efforts to save ocean resources include laws, international treaties, and volunteer clean-ups. **D.2.3.2**

Using Key Terms

1. Use *point-source pollution* and *non-point-source pollution* in the same sentence.

Understanding Key Ideas

2. List three types of ocean pollution. How can each of these types be prevented or minimized?

3. Which part of raw sewage is a type of ocean pollution?

Math Skills

4. Only 3% of Earth's water is drinkable. What percentage of Earth's water is not drinkable?

Critical Thinking

5. **Identifying Relationships** List and describe three measures that governments have taken to control ocean pollution. **D.2.3.2**

6. **Evaluating Data** What were two effects of the *Exxon Valdez* oil spill? Describe two ways to prevent oil spills. **D.2.3.2**

7. **Predicting Consequences** How can trash dumping and sludge dumping affect food chains in the ocean? **G.2.3.4 AA**

FCAT Preparation

8. Human activities on land can pollute streams and rivers. For example, chemicals sprayed on crops to kill insects can be washed off by rain and can pollute rivers and streams. What is one negative consequence of pollution in rivers and streams? **G.2.3.4 AA**

A. The streams and rivers grow wider and flood the land.

B. The streams and rivers carry the pollutants to the ocean.

C. The streams and rivers absorb the pollutants, so the pollutants are harmless.

D. The streams and rivers carry the pollutants far away from humans.

SCiLINKS®

NSTA
Developed and maintained by the National Science Teachers Association

For a variety of links related to this chapter, go to www.scilinks.org

Topic: Ocean Pollution
SciLinks code: HSM1063

Model-Making Lab

OBJECTIVES

Model a method of mapping the ocean floor.

Construct a map of an ocean-floor model.

MATERIALS

- clay, modeling (1 lb)
- pencil, unsharpened (8 of equal length)
- ruler, metric
- scissors
- shoe box with lid

SAFETY

Probing the Depths

In the 1870s, the crew of the ship the HMS *Challenger* used a wire and a weight to discover and map some of the deepest places in the world's oceans. The crew members tied a wire to a weight and dropped the weight overboard. When the weight reached the bottom of the ocean, they hauled the weight back up to the surface and measured the length of the wet wire. In this way, they were eventually able to map the ocean floor. In this activity, you will model this method of mapping by making a map of an ocean-floor model.

Procedure

1. Use the clay to make a model ocean floor in the shoe box. The model ocean floor should have some mountains and valleys.

2. Cut eight holes in a line along the center of the lid. The holes should be just big enough for a pencil to slide through. Place the lid on the box.

3. Exchange boxes with another student or group of students. Do not look into the box.

4. Copy the table shown on the facing page onto a piece of paper. Also, copy the graph shown on the facing page.

5. Measure the length of the probe (pencil) in centimeters. Record the length in your data table.

6. Gently insert the probe into the first hole position in the box until the probe touches the model ocean floor. Do not push the probe down. Pushing the probe down could affect your reading.

7. Make sure that the probe is straight up and down, and measure the length of probe showing above the lid. Record your data in the data table.

8. Use the formula below to calculate the depth in centimeters.

$$\text{length of probe} - \text{length of probe showing (cm)} = \text{depth (cm)}$$

Ocean Depth Table				
Hole position	Length of probe	Length of probe showing (cm)	Depth (cm)	Depth (m) scale of 1cm = 200m
1				
2				
3				
4				
5				
6				
7				
8				

DO NOT WRITE IN BOOK

9 To better represent real ocean depths, use the scale 1 cm = 200 m to convert the depth in centimeters to depth in meters. Add the data to your table.

10 Plot the depth in meters for hole position 1 on your graph.

11 Repeat steps 6–10 for the other hole positions.

12 After plotting the data for the eight hole positions, connect the plotted points with a smooth curve.

13 Put a pencil in each of the holes in the shoe box. Compare the rise and fall of the eight pencils with the shape of your graph.

Analyze the Results

1 **Describing Events** How deep was the deepest point of your ocean-floor model? How deep was the shallowest point of your ocean-floor model?

2 **Explaining Events** Did your graph resemble the ocean-floor model, as shown by the pencils in step 13? If not, why not?

Draw Conclusions

3 **Applying Conclusions** Why is measuring the real ocean floor difficult? Explain your answer.

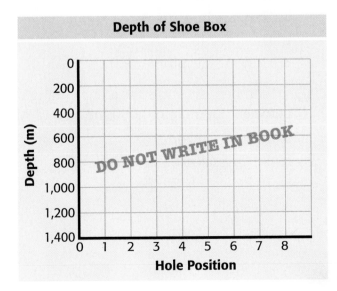

Depth of Shoe Box

DO NOT WRITE IN BOOK

Depth (m)

Hole Position

Chapter Review

USING KEY TERMS

Complete each of the following sentences by choosing the correct term from the chapter.

1 The region of the ocean floor that is closest to the shoreline is the ___.

2 ___ is the process of removing salt from sea water.

3 ___ is a measure of the amount of dissolved salts in a liquid.

4 The ___ is the broad, flat part of the deep-ocean basin.

5 The area of Earth that is covered by ocean water is called the ___. **FCAT VOCAB**

6 Pollution that comes from many sources rather than from a single, specific source is called ___.

UNDERSTANDING KEY IDEAS

Multiple Choice

7 A large amount of water constantly evaporates from the oceans. How does this affect the atmosphere over the ocean? **D.1.3.3 CS FCAT**

a. This leads to fewer clouds.

b. This increases the air temperature.

c. This increases the moisture in the air.

d. This does not affect the atmosphere.

8 Which of the following affects the ocean's salinity?

a. fresh water added by rivers

b. currents

c. evaporation

d. All of the above

9 Most precipitation falls

a. on land.

b. into lakes and rivers.

c. into the ocean.

d. in rain forests.

10 Which of the following is a non-renewable resource in the ocean? **G.2.3.1 CS**

a. fish

b. tidal energy

c. oil

d. All of the above

11 Many types of clams live in intertidal zones. Sometimes, they bury themselves in sand. What causes them to do this? **F.1.3.7 CS FCAT**

a. The tide moves out.

b. They are hunting.

c. The tide moves in.

d. They are sleeping.

12 Which benthic zone has a depth range between 200 m and 4,000 m?

a. the bathyal zone

b. the abyssal zone

c. the hadal zone

d. the sublittoral zone

13 The ocean floor and all of the organisms that live on or in it is the

a. benthic environment.

b. pelagic environment.

c. neritic zone.

d. oceanic zone.

Short Answer

14 Why does coastal water in areas that have hot, dry climates typically have a higher salinity than coastal water in cool, humid areas does?

15 Describe two technologies used for studying the ocean floor.

16 Identify the two major regions of the ocean floor, and describe how the continental shelf, the continental slope, and the continental rise are related.

17 List two living resources and two non-living resources that are harvested from the ocean.

18 Explain why overfishing disrupts the equilibrium of ocean ecosystems. G.2.3.4 AA *FCAT*

CRITICAL THINKING

Extended Response

19 **Making Inferences** What benefit other than being able to obtain fresh water from salt water comes from desalination?

20 **Analyzing Ideas** Explain why almost all marine life is dependent upon a continuous input of energy from the sun. G.1.3.4 AA *FCAT*

21 **Applying Concepts** In your own words, define *nonpoint-source pollution* and *point-source pollution*. Give an example of each. What is being done to control ocean pollution? D.2.3.2, G.2.3.4 AA *FCAT*

Concept Mapping

22 Use the following terms to create a concept map: *water cycle, evaporation, condensation, precipitation, atmosphere,* and *ocean*.

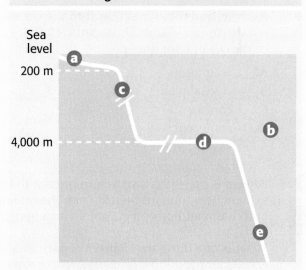

INTERPRETING GRAPHICS

The graph below shows the ecological zones of the ocean. Use the graph to answer the questions that follow.

Ecological Zones of the Ocean

23 At which point would you most likely find an anglerfish?

24 Which ecological zone is shown at point c? Which depth zone is shown at point c?

25 Name an organism that you might find at point e.

Standardized Test Preparation

FCAT

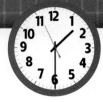

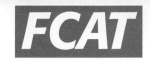

For the following questions, write your answers on a separate sheet of paper.

1 The ocean water off the coast of Maine in the United States is not as salty as the ocean water off the coast of Africa. Which of the following factors could be responsible for this difference in salinity?

A. climate
B. marine life
C. ocean pollution
D. underground formations

2 Jared learned that rain showers can form from water in the ocean. Which of the following processes in the water cycle **best** describes how ocean water becomes available for rain clouds?

F. circulation
G. condensation
H. evaporation
I. precipitation

3 As rivers and tributaries flow into the oceans, they carry particles of rocks and other sediments from land. These particles and sediments settle on the ocean floor. On which area of the ocean floor does **most** of this material settle?

A. seamounts
B. abyssal plain
C. continental rise
D. continental slope

4 READ INQUIRE EXPLAIN

Rajeem is preparing a speech to present to his class about ocean resources. He wants to explain how humans benefit from the ocean. He also wants to explain how humans can both harm and protect ocean environments.

What is one thing that Rajeem can list as a way that humans benefit from the ocean? What is an example of how humans harm ocean environments? How do humans protect ocean environments?

5 The chart below shows the relationship between ocean water temperature in degrees Celsius (°C) and ocean depth in meters (m).

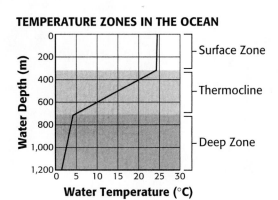

TEMPERATURE ZONES IN THE OCEAN

What is the greatest difference in water temperature between the surface zone and the deep zone?

F. 2°C

G. 20°C

H. 21°C

I. 23°C

 6 The timeline below shows processes that occurred billions of years ago during the formation of the oceans.

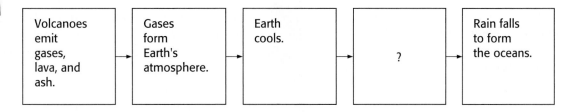

What should go in the missing entry on the timeline? How did this event result in the rain that created the oceans?

FCAT Preparation

Science in Action

FOCUS ON FLORIDA

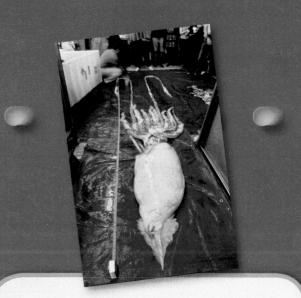

Science, Technology, and Society

Aquarius Underwater Research Lab

The Aquarius Underwater Research Lab is the world's only permanent underwater research station. Aquarius is 60 ft below the surf in the coral reef system of the Florida Keys. Scientists can live and work in Aquarius for up to 10 days. When they live in Aquarius, scientists can study coral reefs any time—even at night! In addition, Aquarius has a sophisticated laboratory with high-tech computer equipment for researchers to use. More than 200 scientists have stayed on Aquarius, and their research is changing the way we understand coral reef ecosystems.

Social Studies ACTiViTY

WRITING SKILL The Aquarius Underwater Research Lab is not used only by scientists studying coral reefs. Astronauts also use the lab to train for missions to the *International Space Station.* Research the history of the *International Space Station.* Write a brief report about the space station, including what countries sponsor it and what kind of work is done on the space station.

Scientific Discoveries

In Search of the Giant Squid

You might think that giant squids exist only in science fiction novels. You aren't alone, because many people have never seen a giant squid or do not know that giant squids exist. Scientists have not been able to study giant squids in the ocean. They have been able to study only dead or dying squids that have washed ashore or that have been trapped in fishing nets. As the largest of all invertebrates, giant squids range from 8 to 25 m long and have a mass of as much as 2,000 kg. Giant squids are very similar to smaller squids. But a giant squid's body parts are much larger. For example, a giant squid's eye may be as large as a volleyball! Because of the size of giant squids, you may think that they don't have any enemies in the ocean, but they do. They are usually eaten by sperm whales that can weigh 20 tons!

Math ACTiViTY

A giant squid that washed ashore has a mass of 900 kg. A deep-sea squid that washed ashore has a mass that is 93% smaller than the mass of the giant squid. What is the mass in kilograms of the deep-sea squid?

Jacques Cousteau

Ocean Explorer Jacques Cousteau was born in France in 1910. Cousteau performed his first underwater diving mission at age 10 and became very fascinated with the possibilities of seeing and breathing underwater. As a result, in 1943, Cousteau and Emile Gagnan developed the first aqualung, a self-contained breathing system for underwater exploration. Using the aqualung and other underwater equipment that he developed, Cousteau began making underwater films. In 1950, Cousteau transformed the *Calypso*, a retired minesweeper boat, into an oceanographic vessel and laboratory. For the next 40 years, Cousteau sailed with the *Calypso* around the world to explore and film the world's oceans. Cousteau produced more than 115 films, many of which have won awards.

Jacques Cousteau opened the eyes of countless people to the sea. During his long life, Cousteau explored Earth's oceans and documented the amazing variety of life that they contain. He was an environmentalist, inventor, and teacher who inspired millions with his joy and wonder of the ocean. Cousteau was an outspoken defender of the environment. He campaigned vigorously to protect the oceans and environment. Cousteau died in 1997 at age 87. Before his death, he dedicated the *Calypso II*, a new research vessel, to the children of the world.

Language Arts ACTiViTY

WRITING SKILL Ocean pollution and overfishing are subjects of intense debate. Think about these issues, and discuss them with your classmates. Take notes on what you discuss with your classmates. Then, write an essay in which you try to convince readers of your point of view.

Cousteau sailed his ship, the Calypso, around the world exploring and filming the world's oceans.

To learn more about these Science in Action topics, visit go.hrw.com and type in the keyword **HT6FOCFF**.

Current Science

Check out Current Science® articles related to this chapter by visiting go.hrw.com. Just type in the keyword **HZ5CS13**.

TIMELINE

Shaping the Earth

In this unit, you will learn about rocks, weathering, and how land on Earth changes over time. You likely see rocks of various sizes every day. These rocks may have been worn smooth by wind or water, or they may have been broken down into small particles to form soil.

Earth's land surfaces also continuously change. As landmasses slowly move around Earth's surface, mountain ranges or volcanoes may form. Sometimes, earthquakes result from these movements. This timeline shows some of the events that have occurred as scientists have studied how Earth's surface changes.

1864

Jules Verne's *A Journey to the Center of the Earth* is published. In this fictional story, the heroes enter and exit Earth through volcanoes.

1912

Alfred Wegener proposes his theory of continental drift.

1979

Volcanoes are discovered on Io, one of Jupiter's moons.

1980

Mount St. Helens erupts after an earthquake triggers a landslide on the volcano's north face.

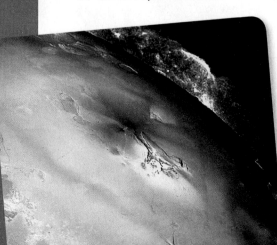

Io, one of Jupiter's moons

1883
When Krakatau erupts, more than 36,000 people are killed.

1896
Henry Ford builds his first car.

1906
San Francisco burns in the aftermath of an earthquake.

The Quadricycle, Henry Ford's first car

1935
Charles Richter devises a system for measuring the magnitude of earthquakes.

1951
Color television programming is introduced in the United States.

1962
A worldwide network of seismographs is established.

1982
Compact discs (CDs) and CD players are made available to the public.

1994
An eight-legged robot named *Dante II* descends into the crater of an active volcano in Alaska.

Dante II

1997
The population of the Caribbean island of Montserrat dwindles to less than half its original size as frequent eruptions of the Soufriere Hills volcano force evacuations.

2004
An earthquake of magnitude 9.0 strikes Indonesia and causes a tsunami that affects the coasts of Africa, India, and several Asian countries. The earthquake is one of the largest ever recorded.

Rocks

The Big Idea Earth is reshaped as rock is continuously created and destroyed in the rock cycle.

About the

The state of Florida is famous for its white, sandy beaches. The sand used to build these sand castles is a product of the weathering and erosion of rocks that contained the mineral quartz. Florida's quartz sand was transported southward by ocean currents from the Appalachian Mountains to present-day Florida. The Appalachians began to erode rapidly about 30 million to 35 million years ago.

PRE-READING ACTIVITY

Graphic Organizer **Spider Map** Before you read the chapter, create the graphic organizer entitled "Spider Map" described in the **Study Skills** section of the Appendix. Label the circle "Rock." Create a leg for each section in this chapter. As you read the chapter, fill in the map with details about the material presented in each section of the chapter.

START-UP ACTIVITY

Classifying Objects H.1.3.5 AA

Scientists use the physical and chemical properties of rocks to classify rocks. Classifying objects such as rocks requires close attention to many properties. Do this activity to practice classifying objects.

Procedure

1. Your teacher will give you a **bag containing several objects.** Examine the objects, and note features such as size, color, shape, texture, and smell plus any unique properties.

2. Invent three ways to sort these objects. You may have only 1 group or as many as 14 groups.

3. Use a **computer program or colored pencils and paper** to create an identification chart explaining how you organized the objects into groups.

Analysis

1. What properties did you use to sort the items?

2. Did you have any objects that could fit into more than one group? How did you solve this problem?

3. Which properties might you use to classify rocks? Explain your answer.

Types of Rocks

We live on a planet that is made almost entirely of rock. Yet can you identify a specific rock type when you see it?

Rock is a naturally occurring solid mixture of one or more minerals and organic matter. But before we learn about rock, let us begin the study of rock by taking a look at minerals.

Minerals

So, what is a mineral? A **mineral** is naturally formed solid matter that has a crystalline structure. Every mineral has a unique set of physical properties. These properties include color, hardness, density, and the way that the mineral breaks. These properties are determined by the elements that make up the mineral.

Minerals form in a variety of environments. Some minerals form at Earth's surface when bodies of salt water evaporate and minerals crystallize out of solution. Other minerals form within Earth as a result of heat and pressure, the circulation of hot liquid solutions, or the cooling of magma bodies.

Many minerals are important economically and industrially. Quartz sand, shown in **Figure 1,** calcite (in limestone), clay minerals, and minerals that contain the element titanium and the element phosphorus are important to Florida's economy. In fact, Florida produces 25% of the phosphate in the world and 80% of the phosphate in the United States. The phosphate that is mined in Florida is used mostly in agricultural fertilizers.

✓ **Reading Check** Identify four physical properties of minerals.

Figure 1 *The mineral quartz makes up most of the sand grains on the beaches of Florida.*

Quartz

How Rocks Are Classified

Scientists classify all rocks into three main classes based on how the rocks form. The three major classes of rocks are igneous rocks, metamorphic rocks, and sedimentary rocks. *Igneous rocks* form when hot, liquid rock—called *magma*—cools and hardens. *Metamorphic rocks* form when rock is heated or squeezed. *Sedimentary rocks* form when rocks break into smaller pieces and those pieces cement together. Each class of rock can be further classified into rock types based on composition and texture.

What Is the Rock Made Of?

The **composition** of a rock is the chemical makeup of the rock. So, a rock's composition is determined by the mineral or minerals that make up the rock. For instance, the limestone shown in **Figure 2** is a combination of the minerals calcite and aragonite. Both calcite and aragonite are forms of calcium carbonate, $CaCO_3$. Therefore, the chemical makeup of limestone is a combination of calcium, carbon, and oxygen.

What Does the Rock Look Like?

The **texture** of a rock depends on the sizes, shapes, and positions of the minerals in the rock. Some rocks are made of crystals that fit together like the pieces of a puzzle. Other rocks are made of fragments of rock or minerals. These fragments of rock or minerals are called *grains*. Grains range in size from very fine particles to boulders that measure several meters across.

Rocks that have a *fine-grained* texture are made of very small crystals or grains. *Coarse-grained* rocks are made of crystals or grains that can be seen with the eye. If a rock has a texture that is between fine- and coarse-grained, the rock has a *medium-grained* texture. Examples of these textures in three various types of sedimentary rocks are shown in **Figure 3**.

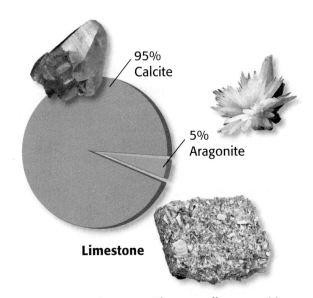

95% Calcite

5% Aragonite

Limestone

Figure 2 *The overall composition of a rock depends on the minerals that the rock contains.*

rock a naturally occurring solid mixture of one or more minerals and organic matter

mineral a naturally formed, inorganic solid that has a definite crystalline structure

composition the chemical makeup of a rock; describes either the minerals or other materials in the rock

texture the quality of a rock that is based on the sizes, shapes, and positions of the rock's grains

Figure 3   Examples of Sedimentary Rock Textures

Fine-grained Siltstone	**Medium-grained** Sandstone	**Coarse-grained** Conglomerate

Igneous Rocks

Igneous rocks form when hot, liquid rock—or magma—cools. Igneous rocks form within Earth and on Earth's surface. *Intrusive igneous rocks* form deep inside Earth. *Extrusive igneous rocks* form from lava that has erupted at Earth's surface.

The Composition of Igneous Rocks

The composition of magma depends on the type of rock that melted to make the liquid rock. Melted rock comes either from near Earth's surface or from deep inside Earth. The rocks from these two places are made of very different minerals. Look at **Figure 4.** Igneous rocks that form from melted crust commonly form light-colored igneous rocks, such as granite. Magma from deep inside Earth forms dark-colored igneous rocks, such as gabbro.

The Texture of Igneous Rocks

Magma that slowly cools deep inside Earth forms coarse-grained rocks that have large crystals. Magma that quickly cools at Earth's surface forms fine-grained rocks that have very small crystals. Sometimes, magma cools so quickly that it forms rocks that have no crystals. These rocks are called *volcanic glass*. Before rising to the surface, some magma cools deep inside Earth for a long time. **Figure 4** shows examples of igneous rocks that have coarse-grained and fine-grained textures.

Benchmark Check What assumptions can you make about an igneous rock that is made of large crystals? **D.1.3.5 CS**

Figure 4	Comparing Igneous Rocks	
	Coarse-grained	**Fine-grained**
Light-colored	Granite	Rhyolite
Dark-colored	Gabbro	Basalt

D.1.3.5 CS understands concepts of time and size relating to the interaction of Earth's processes.

Figure 5 Metamorphic Rock Textures

Foliated

Nonfoliated

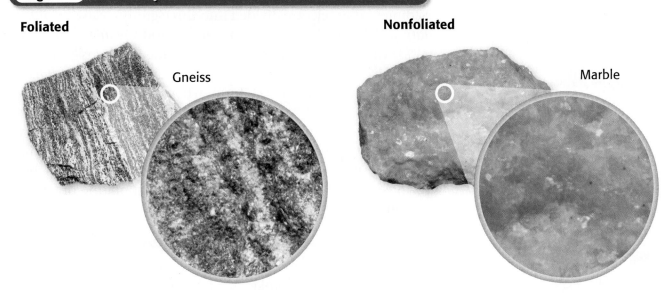

Gneiss

Marble

Metamorphic Rocks

A metamorphic rock is a rock whose structure, composition, and texture have changed, or *metamorphosed,* from those of the original rock. These changes take place when rock is placed under great pressure within Earth. Most metamorphic changes occur at depths greater than 2 km. At these depths, pressure can be many times greater than it is at Earth's surface. Likewise, temperatures at these depths are higher than the temperatures at Earth's surface. Metamorphism most commonly takes place at temperatures between 50°C and 1,000°C.

The Composition of Metamorphic Rocks

The minerals in metamorphic rocks vary depending on the type of rock that is being changed. When heated and squeezed, minerals in the original rock form new minerals. The depth at which the original minerals are squeezed and the temperature at which they are heated determine which new minerals form.

The Texture of Metamorphic Rocks

The texture of metamorphic rocks depends on how the mineral grains are arranged. During metamorphism, the pressure on the rock causes the grains of different minerals to form bands or layers. These rocks are said to have a *foliated,* or banded, texture. Rocks that contain grains of one mineral, such as quartz or calcite, commonly have a *nonfoliated* texture. When the texture is nonfoliated, the mineral grains do not form bands or layers. Examples of foliated and nonfoliated metamorphic rocks are shown in **Figure 5.**

Stretching Out

1. Using a **black pen,** sketch the crystals in **granite rock** on a **piece of paper.** Be sure to include the outline of the rock, and fill it with different crystal shapes.

2. Flatten some **plastic play putty** over your drawing, and slowly peel it off.

3. After making sure that the outline of your granite has been transferred to the putty, squeeze and stretch the putty. What happened to the crystals in the granite? What happened to the granite?

Halite

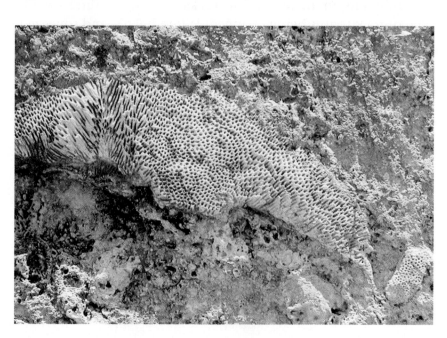

Shale

Figure 6 *Halite is a chemical sedimentary rock that crystallizes out of salt water. Shale is a clastic sedimentary rock that is composed of cemented clay particles.*

Figure 7 *The limestone that forms the Florida Keys is made up of ancient fossil coral reefs. A portion of a fossil reef is seen here in the wall of a quarry on Windley Key.*

Sedimentary Rocks

Sedimentary rocks are divided into three groups: *clastic sedimentary rocks, chemical sedimentary rocks,* and *organic sedimentary rocks.* Clastic sedimentary rocks are made of grains of rock or minerals. These grains of rock or minerals are called *sediment.* Clastic sedimentary rocks form when sediments are buried, squeezed together, and cemented by minerals such as calcite and quartz. Chemical sedimentary rocks form when minerals such as gypsum and halite crystallize out of a solution, such as ocean water, to become rock. Organic sedimentary rocks form when the shells and skeletons of dead marine organisms are buried and cemented by calcite or quartz.

The Composition of Sedimentary Rocks

The minerals in sedimentary rocks vary depending on the types of rocks that broke down to form the sediment and on the place where the sediment was *deposited,* or laid down. Clastic sedimentary rocks—such as sandstone, shale (shown in **Figure 6**), siltstone, and conglomerate—often contain silicate minerals. Silicate minerals contain a combination of silicon, Si, and oxygen, O. Quartz and clays are examples of silicate minerals found in clastic sedimentary rocks.

Halite, or common table salt, is an example of a chemical sedimentary rock. Halite, shown in **Figure 6,** is composed of the elements sodium, Na, and chlorine, Cl. Halite crystallizes out of salt water.

Limestone, one of the common types of rock in Florida, is an organic sedimentary rock. Limestone forms when the shells and skeletons of marine organisms are buried and cemented together. **Figure 7** shows an example of Florida limestone.

The Texture of Clastic Sedimentary Rocks

The texture of clastic sedimentary rocks depends in part on the size and shape of the grains that make up the rock. Coarse-grained rock is made up of large grains. The grains are large because they have traveled a short distance, which means that they have had less of a chance to grind against each other and to break into smaller pieces. Medium-grained or fine-grained rocks are made up of small grains that have traveled a long distance. The farther these grains travel, the more they grind and the smaller and more rounded they become.

Benchmark Check Explain why grains that make up sedimentary rocks are smaller when they have traveled a long distance.

D.1.3.5 CS

Rock Brochure Watch out world. Here come some new rock stars! Create a brochure that classifies "rock stars." Go to **go.hrw.com**, and type in the keyword **HZ5FOSW.**

SECTION
Review

Summary

- Minerals combine to form rocks.
- The three classes of rocks are igneous rocks, metamorphic rocks, and sedimentary rocks.
- Igneous rocks form when hot, liquid rock—called *magma*—cools either slowly or rapidly to form mineral crystals. D.1.3.5 CS
- Metamorphic rocks form when temperature and pressure change one type of rock into another type.
- Sedimentary rocks form when rock or mineral fragments are cemented together, when minerals crystallize out of a solution to become rock, or when the remains of once-living organisms become rock. D.1.3.1 CS

Using Key Terms

1. Use *rock, composition,* and *texture* in the same sentence.

Understanding Key Ideas

2. Identify four properties of minerals.

3. Explain the difference between the composition and texture of a rock.

4. Explain how the three classes of rock form.

5. Explain the difference between intrusive igneous rocks and extrusive igneous rocks.

6. Explain how the rate at which magma cools affects the texture of igneous rocks. D.1.3.5 CS

7. Explain the difference between foliated and nonfoliated metamorphic rocks.

8. Compare clastic, chemical, and organic sedimentary rocks.

Critical Thinking

9. **Making Comparisons** Compare the concepts of composition and texture.

FCAT Preparation

10. The composition of an igneous rock depends on the type of rock that melts to make the magma that forms the igneous rock. The texture of an igneous rock depends on the rate at which melted rock cools to form the igneous rock. If a geologist finds an igneous rock that slowly cooled near Earth's surface and that was made from melted crustal rock, what would the color and texture of the rock **most** likely be?

D.1.3.5 CS

A. dark and fine-grained

B. dark and coarse-grained

C. light and coarse-grained

D. light and fine-grained

SCLINKS

NSTA

Developed and maintained by the National Science Teachers Association

For a variety of links related to this chapter, go to www.scilinks.org

Topic: Rocks
SciLinks code: HSM1322

The Rock Cycle

You know how important it is to recycle paper, plastics, and aluminum. But did you know that Earth also recycles? As strange as it may sound, one of the things that Earth recycles is rock.

It may be hard to believe, but Earth's rocks are always changing. The **rock cycle** is the continuous process by which new rock forms from old rock material. Read on to learn about how rock changes as it moves through the rock cycle.

Around and Around It Goes

The rock cycle is illustrated in **Figure 1.** As you look at the figure, notice the directions in which the arrows point. Also notice that each arrow indicates not only direction but also a different geologic process that can change rock. From the figure, you can tell that sedimentary, metamorphic, and igneous rocks can change into other types of rock by different geologic processes. For example, a sedimentary rock can change into a metamorphic rock or an igneous rock and can even change back into a sedimentary rock.

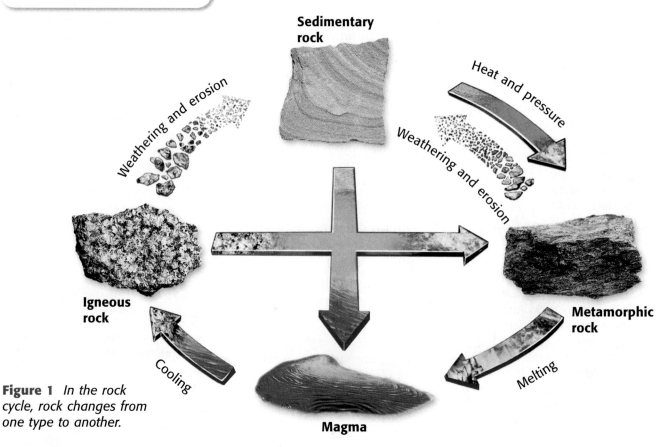

Figure 1 *In the rock cycle, rock changes from one type to another.*

Figure 2 Forces That Change Rock

Time

Burial with heat/pressure → Burial with heat/pressure → Melting and cooling →

Shale
(sedimentary)

Slate
(metamorphic)

Gneiss
(metamorphic)

Granite
(igneous)

Pathways in the Rock Cycle

Rocks may follow various pathways in the rock cycle. Time, heat, pressure, and cooling may alter a rock's identity as the rock changes from one type of rock to another. The location of a rock determines which geologic processes will have the biggest effect on change. For example, rock at Earth's surface is primarily affected by processes that break down rock. But deep inside Earth, rocks change because of extreme heat and pressure. Let's see how and where one type of rock turns into another type.

rock cycle the series of processes in which rock forms, changes from one type to another, is destroyed, and forms again by geologic processes

Forces That Change Rock

In **Figure 2,** you can see how heat, pressure, and cooling change shale, a sedimentary rock, into granite, an igneous rock. This process happens over millions of years.

To change into a metamorphic rock, shale must be forced down into or buried deep within Earth. Heat, pressure, or a combination of both may change shale that is buried within Earth into a metamorphic rock called *slate*. Slate is known as a low-grade metamorphic rock because it changes, or metamorphoses, only slightly. If the slate is subjected to even more heat and pressure, slate may change into a high-grade metamorphic rock called *gneiss* (NIES). Finally, if the temperature and pressure are high enough, the gneiss can melt to form magma. When the magma cools, the igneous rock granite forms.

D.1.3.1 CS knows that mechanical and chemical activities shape and reshape the Earth's land surface by eroding rock and soil in some areas and depositing them in other areas, sometimes in seasonal layers.

D.1.3.5 CS understands concepts of time and size relating to the interaction of Earth's processes.

Benchmark Check Use Figure 1 to determine which geologic processes would change granite into a sedimentary rock. **D.1.3.5 CS**

D.1.3.1 CS knows that mechanical and chemical activities shape and reshape the Earth's land surface by eroding rock and soil in some areas and depositing them in other areas, sometimes in seasonal layers.

D.1.3.5 CS understands concepts of time and size relating to the interaction of Earth's processes.

Illustrating the Rock Cycle

The diagram on these two pages illustrates one way that sand grains can change as different geologic processes act on the sand grains. In the following steps, you will see how these processes change the original sand grains into sedimentary rock, metamorphic rock, and igneous rock.

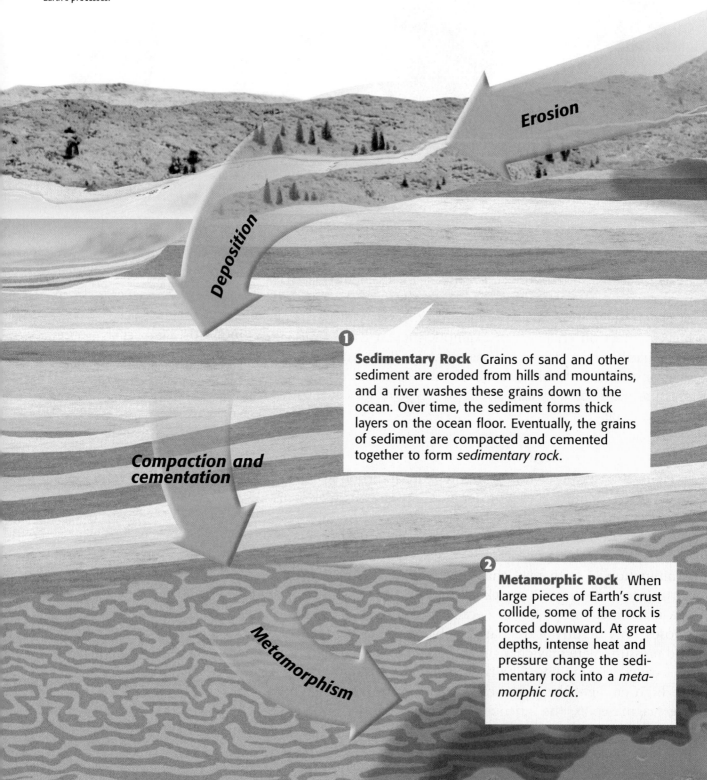

Erosion

Deposition

Compaction and cementation

Metamorphism

① Sedimentary Rock Grains of sand and other sediment are eroded from hills and mountains, and a river washes these grains down to the ocean. Over time, the sediment forms thick layers on the ocean floor. Eventually, the grains of sediment are compacted and cemented together to form *sedimentary rock*.

② Metamorphic Rock When large pieces of Earth's crust collide, some of the rock is forced downward. At great depths, intense heat and pressure change the sedimentary rock into a *metamorphic rock*.

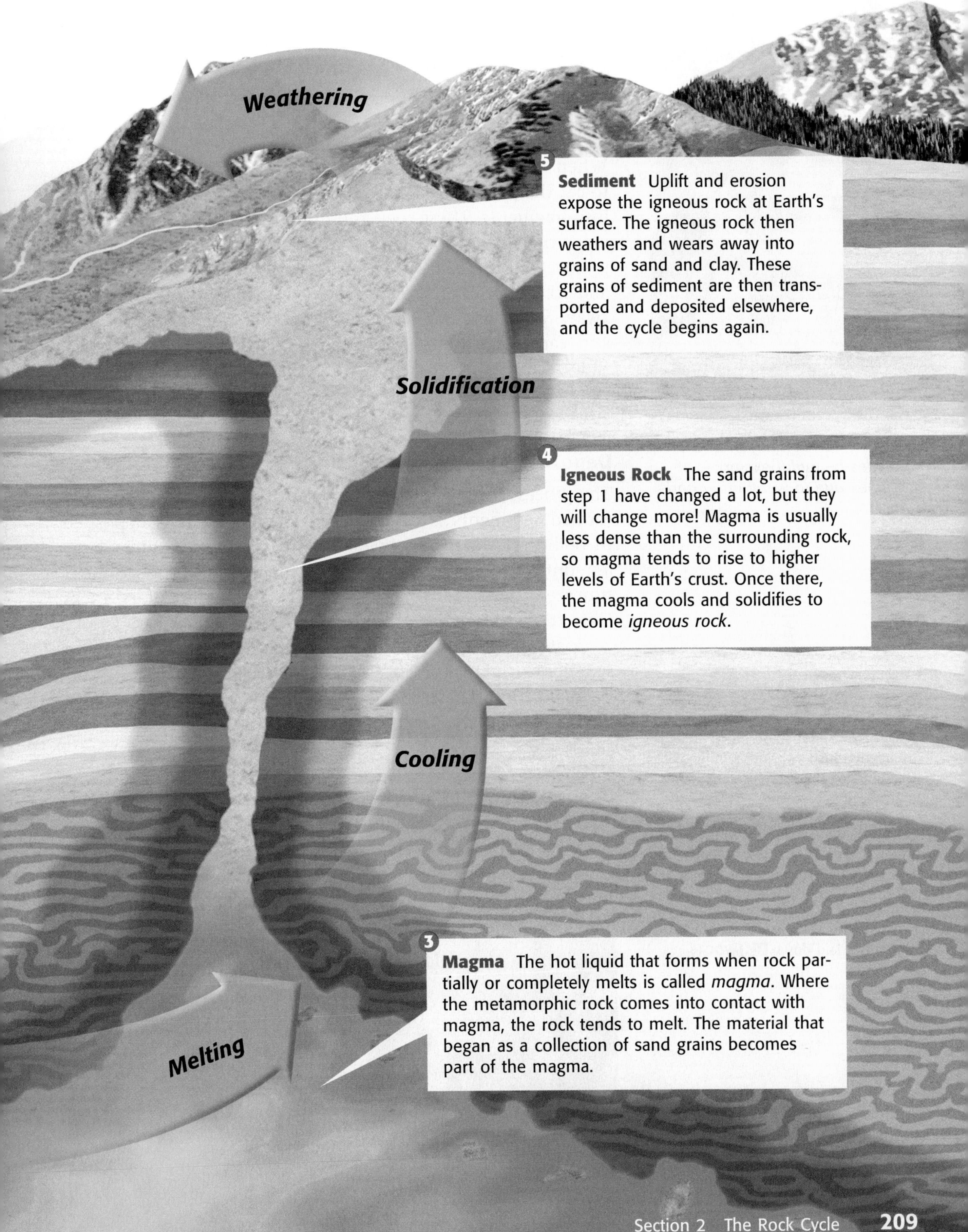

Weathering

Solidification

5

Sediment Uplift and erosion expose the igneous rock at Earth's surface. The igneous rock then weathers and wears away into grains of sand and clay. These grains of sediment are then transported and deposited elsewhere, and the cycle begins again.

4

Igneous Rock The sand grains from step 1 have changed a lot, but they will change more! Magma is usually less dense than the surrounding rock, so magma tends to rise to higher levels of Earth's crust. Once there, the magma cools and solidifies to become *igneous rock*.

Cooling

3

Magma The hot liquid that forms when rock partially or completely melts is called *magma*. Where the metamorphic rock comes into contact with magma, the rock tends to melt. The material that began as a collection of sand grains becomes part of the magma.

Melting

Figure 3 *Bryce Canyon in Utah provides beautiful examples of changes due to weathering and erosion.*

Processes That Shape Earth

In the rock cycle, geologic processes work alone or in combination to change one type of rock into another. The geologic processes that change rocks also shape the surface of Earth.

Weathering and Erosion

When water, ice, wind, heat, or living organisms break down rocks, the process is called **weathering.** Weathering breaks rocks into fragments. These rock and mineral fragments are the sediment that makes up sedimentary rock. Fragments of rock are removed from their source by a process called **erosion.** Water and ice break off fragments of rock and carry the fragments away. Wind can lift very small particles of dust and sand and can carry them long distances. Gravity can cause rock slides. The sediment moves to a place where it can collect. **Figure 3** shows one example of how land looks after weathering and erosion.

Deposition and Burial

The process in which water, ice, wind, and gravity drop newly formed sediments is called **deposition.** Sediment is deposited in bodies of water and in other low-lying areas. When large amounts of sediment are deposited, the weight of the sediment squeezes the underlying sediment. Many sedimentary rocks form from this burial of the underlying sediment.

Water carries dissolved minerals that can be deposited with sediment. Chemicals can also be released from sediment during deposition. These dissolved minerals and chemicals cement grains of sediment together to form sedimentary rocks.

Heat and Pressure

If buried sedimentary rock is under enough pressure, the sedimentary rock can change into metamorphic rock. Extreme heat can also cause the buried rock to metamorphose. In some cases, the rock gets hot enough to melt. This melting creates the magma that cools to form igneous rock.

weathering the natural process by which atmospheric and environmental agents, such as wind, rain, and temperature changes, disintegrate and decompose rocks

erosion the process by which wind, water, ice, or gravity transports soil and sediment from one location to another **FCAT** *VOCAB*

deposition the process in which material is laid down **FCAT** *VOCAB*

Figure 4 *Sediment piles up at the base of the mountain in large, triangular formations called alluvial fans.*

The Continuous Cycle

Rock that has been buried is brought to the surface of Earth again. Sometimes, uplift vertically moves rock to the surface of Earth. *Uplift* is the process by which regions of Earth rise to higher elevations. For example, mountains form when areas of Earth are uplifted. This uplift is followed by erosion. Buried rock is exposed at Earth's surface when overlying rocks erode away. When this buried rock is at the surface of Earth, the weathering, erosion, and deposition processes begin again. **Figure 4** shows that uplifted areas supply large amounts of sediment.

 Benchmark Check Would you conclude that uplift is a rapid process or a slow process? **D.1.3.5 CS**

D.1.3.1 CS knows that mechanical and chemical activities shape and reshape the Earth's land surface by eroding rock and soil in some areas and depositing them in other areas, sometimes in seasonal layers.

D.1.3.4 AA knows the ways in which plants and animals reshape the landscape.

D.1.3.5 CS understands concepts of time and size relating to the interaction of Earth's processes.

SECTION Review

Summary

- The continuous process by which new rock forms from old rock material is called the *rock cycle*.

- The sequence of events in the rock cycle depends on weathering, erosion, deposition, pressure, and heat, which change the rock material. **D.1.3.5 CS**

- Processes that change rock from one type to another often take millions of years in the rock cycle. **D.1.3.5 CS**

- Weathering, erosion, deposition, and uplift are processes that shape the surface features of Earth. **D.1.3.5 CS**

Using Key Terms

1. Write an original definition for *rock cycle, weathering, erosion,* and *deposition.* **D.1.3.1 CS** **FCAT VOCAB**

Understanding Key Ideas

2. Describe how the rock cycle changes rock from one type to every other type.

3. Over what period of time do processes in the rock cycle generally change rock? **D.1.3.5 CS**

4. What processes affect rocks at Earth's surface? **D.1.3.1 CS**

5. Explain how heat and pressure can change rock in Earth's crust.

6. Describe how buried rock is brought to Earth's surface.

Critical Thinking

7. **Analyzing Relationships** Which geologic processes in the rock cycle would change a sedimentary rock into another sedimentary rock, a metamorphic rock into another metamorphic rock, and an igneous rock into another igneous rock?

FCAT Preparation

8. The same geologic processes that change rock in the rock cycle also shape the surface of our planet. Some of these processes occur at Earth's surface. Other processes occur deep below the surface. The following example describes a geologic process that occurs at Earth's surface. After a long period of heavy rain, a portion of a hillside breaks away and slides downhill. What is the name of the process by which gravity carries the portion of the hillside downhill? **D.1.3.1 CS**

A. deposition

B. uplift

C. erosion

D. weathering

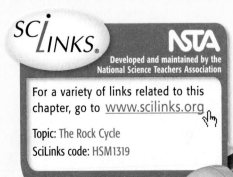

Developed and maintained by the National Science Teachers Association

For a variety of links related to this chapter, go to www.scilinks.org

Topic: The Rock Cycle
SciLinks code: HSM1319

Geology of Florida

Did you know that the Florida we see today began to form 20 million years after the last dinosaurs walked on Earth? But the part of Florida that you can see is only scratching the surface of Florida's geologic history.

Rocks that are thousands of meters below the surface of the state tell of a geologic history that is much, much older.

The Connection Between Florida and Africa

Did you know that present-day Florida was once part of present-day northwest Africa? As **Figure 1** shows, about 240 million years ago, the areas that would become Florida and northwest Africa were connected parts of the supercontinent Pangaea. Some 40 million years later, when Pangaea broke apart, Florida and northwest Africa separated and the Central Atlantic Ocean began to form. Geologists know that northwest Africa and Florida were connected because similar types of rock are found beneath both areas. In fact, the rocks underlying Florida resemble the rocks that lie beneath northwest Africa more than they resemble the rocks underlying the rest of North America.

Figure 1 **The Breakup of Pangaea**

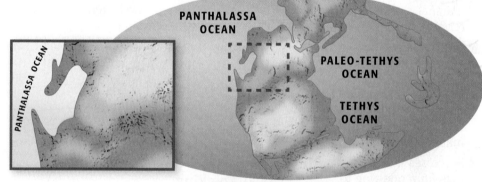

240 million years ago
Florida and northwest Africa were connected parts of a supercontinent called *Pangaea.*

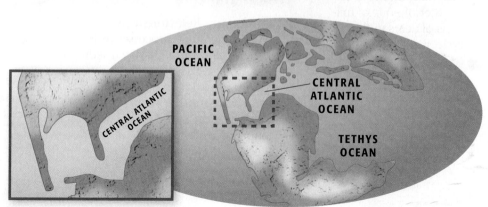

200 million years ago
Pangaea broke apart, and by 175 million years ago the Central Atlantic Ocean formed.

Building Present-Day Florida

The geology of present-day Florida is the result of a combination of factors. The limestone surface rocks seen in many parts of Florida are the product of the life, death, and burial of vast numbers of marine organisms. The white quartz sands for which Florida beaches are famous are the product of the erosion of the Appalachian Mountains and the movement of sediments carried southward by ocean currents. Finally, the changes in sea level during the ice ages reshaped sediments to form the land features that are present in Florida today.

The Florida Platform

After Pangaea broke apart, the area that would become Florida more than 100 million years later began sinking very, very slowly and was flooded by shallow seas. The marine organisms that lived abundantly in these shallow waters had shells and skeletons made of calcium carbonate. When these organisms died, the calcium carbonate in their shells and skeletons was preserved as rock, primarily limestone. Over time, this limestone formed layer after layer and became very thick. These layers of rock formed a **platform,** an area of continent that is composed of flat-lying layers of sedimentary rock. This platform, shown in **Figure 2,** is known as the *Florida Platform.*

Benchmark Check What is the relationship between marine organisms and the formation of the Florida Platform? **D.1.3.4 AA**

Figure 2 *The dark-green Florida Peninsula and the light-blue area offshore from the peninsula are the* Florida Platform. *The edge of the platform is only 5 to 6.5 km off the coast from Miami but is more than 160 km off the coast from Tampa.*

platform an area of a continent that is composed of flat-lying layers of sedimentary rock

D.1.3.1 CS knows that mechanical and chemical activities shape and reshape the Earth's land surface by eroding rock and soil in some areas and depositing them in other areas, sometimes in seasonal layers.

D.1.3.4 AA knows the ways in which plants and animals reshape the landscape.

Erosion of the Appalachian Mountains

The layers of limestone continued accumulating on the Florida Platform until 30 million to 35 million years ago. At that time, the Appalachian Mountains, which are located north of Florida, began to erode very rapidly. The sediments from the Appalachians were carried south by currents. The sediments were deposited over the platform, first over the northern part of the platform and later over the southern part. So, at that point, the Florida Platform was made of thick layers of limestone beneath thin layers of sedimentary rock formed from the Appalachian sediment. The whole platform was still underwater.

Florida During the Ice Ages

Over the last 1.8 million years, parts of the Florida Platform emerged from the sea and disappeared beneath the water again several times. These changes happened during periods of time called *glacial periods* and *interglacial periods*. During the glacial periods, the climate grew cold, ocean water froze into glaciers, and the sea level dropped. As the climate warmed during interglacial periods, glaciers melted, the sea level rose, and water covered much of the Florida Platform. When the sea level was high, waves and currents eroded rock on the platform. As the eroded sediments were spread across the platform, features that are seen across the state today, such as sand ridges, formed. The geologic map in **Figure 3** shows the ages of the formation of surface rocks that are visible in present-day Florida.

Figure 3 *The sediments that make up the surface rocks of Florida were deposited over the past 45 million years. The majority of these sediments were deposited during the last 1.8 million years.*

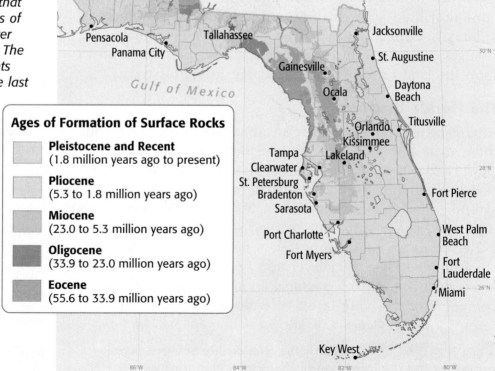

Ages of Formation of Surface Rocks

- **Pleistocene and Recent** (1.8 million years ago to present)
- **Pliocene** (5.3 to 1.8 million years ago)
- **Miocene** (23.0 to 5.3 million years ago)
- **Oligocene** (33.9 to 23.0 million years ago)
- **Eocene** (55.6 to 33.9 million years ago)

D.1.3.4 AA knows the ways in which plants and animals reshape the landscape.

Geology of the Florida Keys

The *Florida Keys,* which are an arc of low islands at the tip of South Florida, also began to form about 1.8 million years ago. At that time, a shallow sea covered what is now South Florida. Corals, such as those shown in **Figure 4,** established themselves in this sea along the edge of the Florida Platform. Over time, these corals formed reefs. As one reef died, a new reef grew on top of its remains. Eventually, dead reef material accumulated to a thickness of between 25 and 60 m. The ancient reefs were exposed when the global sea level last dropped. These ancient reefs form the present-day upper Florida Keys.

The lower Florida Keys formed in a slightly different way. Over time, large amounts of sand accumulated behind the reef and eventually covered it. When this accumulated sand emerged from beneath the ocean, the lower Florida Keys formed.

Benchmark Check What is the significance of coral in the formation of the Florida Keys? **D.1.3.4 AA**

Figure 4 *The rock that makes up the Florida Keys is composed largely of the accumulated remains of corals, such as the corals that form the reef shown here.*

SECTION Review

Summary

- Florida and northwest Africa were once connected parts of the supercontinent Pangaea.

- The Florida Platform formed from limestone made of the shells and skeletons of dead marine creatures and from sediments eroded from the Appalachian Mountains. **D.1.3.1 CS, D.1.3.4 AA**

- The Florida Keys formed when the remains of ancient coral reefs emerged from beneath the ocean. **D.1.3.4 AA**

Using Key Terms

1. Write an original definition for *platform.*

Understanding Key Ideas

2. What evidence supports the hypothesis that Florida was once a part of northwest Africa?

3. Describe three factors that combined to create the geology of present-day Florida. **D1.3.1 CS, D.1.3.4 AA**

4. Briefly describe the role that marine organisms played in the formation of the Florida Platform. **D.1.3.4 AA**

5. What is the relationship between coral and the formation of the Florida Keys? **D.1.3.4 AA**

Critical Thinking

6. **Making Inferences** What factor may have caused the land surface of Florida to be flat?

FCAT Preparation

7. The limestone of the Florida Peninsula was deposited underwater. What was the source of this limestone? **D.1.3.4 AA**

   A. the accumulation of quartz sand

   B. the shells and skeletons of marine organisms

   C. the evaporation of halite from ocean water

   D. metamorphosed shale

SCiLINKS®

NSTA

Developed and maintained by the National Science Teachers Association

For a variety of links related to this chapter, go to www.scilinks.org

Topic: Florida's Geology
SciLinks code: HSMF08

215

Skills Practice Lab

Let's Get Sedimental

How do we determine if sedimentary rock layers are undisturbed? The best way to do so is to be sure that fine-grained sediments near the top of a layer lie above coarse-grained sediments near the bottom of the layer. This lab activity will show you how to read rock features that will help you distinguish individual sedimentary rock layers. Then, you can look for the features in real rock layers.

Procedure

1 In a mixing bowl, thoroughly mix the sand, gravel, and soil. Fill the soda bottle about one-third full of the mixture.

2 Add water to the soda bottle until the bottle is two-thirds full. Twist the cap back onto the bottle, and shake the bottle vigorously until all of the sediment is mixed in the rapidly moving water.

3 Place the bottle on a tabletop. Use the scissors to carefully cut off the top of the bottle a few centimeters above the water, as shown. The open bottle will allow water to evaporate.

4 Immediately after you set the bottle on the tabletop, describe what you see from above and through the sides of the bottle.

5 Do not disturb the container. Allow the water to evaporate. After the container has sat for at least 24 hours, you may speed up the evaporation process by carefully using the dropper pipet to siphon off some of the clear water. You may also set the bottle in the sun or under a desk lamp to speed up evaporation.

6 After the sediment has dried and hardened, describe its surface.

7 Carefully lay the container on its side, and cut a wide, vertical strip of plastic down the length of the bottle to expose the sediments in the container. The strip may be easier to cut if you place pieces of clay on either side of the container to stabilize the container. (If the bottle is clear along its length, this step may not be required.)

8 Brush away the loose material from the sediment, and gently blow on the surface until it is clean. Examine the surface, and record your observations.

OBJECTIVES

Model the process of sedimentation. H.2.3.1 CS

Determine whether sedimentary rock layers are undisturbed. H.2.3.1 CS

MATERIALS

- clay
- dropper pipet
- gravel
- magnifying lens
- mixing bowl, 2 qt
- sand
- scissors
- soda bottle with a cap, plastic, 2 L
- soil, clay rich, if available
- water

SAFETY

 H.2.3.1 CS recognizes that patterns exist within and across systems.

Analyze the Results

1. **Identifying Patterns** Do you see through the side of the bottle anything that could help you determine if a sedimentary rock is undisturbed? Explain your answer.

2. **Identifying Patterns** Can you observe a pattern of deposition? If so, describe the pattern of deposition of sediment that you observe from top to bottom.

3. **Explaining Events** Explain how these features may be used to identify the top of a sedimentary layer in real rock and to decide if the layer has been disturbed.

4. **Identifying Patterns** Do you see through the side of the bottle any structures that might indicate which direction is up, such as a change in particle density or size?

5. **Identifying Patterns** Use the magnifying lens to examine the boundaries between the gravel, sand, and silt. Do the size of the particles and the type of sediment change dramatically in each layer?

Draw Conclusions

6. **Making Predictions** Imagine that a layer was deposited directly above the sediment in your bottle. Describe the composition of this new layer. Will the composition be the same as that of the mixture in Procedure steps 1–5?

Applying Your Data

With your class or with a parent, visit an outcrop of sedimentary rock. Apply the information that you have learned in this lab to see if you can determine whether the sedimentary rock layers are disturbed or undisturbed.

Chapter Review

USING KEY TERMS

1 Write an original definition for *rock cycle*.

Complete each of the following sentences by choosing the correct term from the word bank.

deposition **FCAT** **VOCAB**   foliated
platform   texture

2 The ___ of a rock is determined by the sizes, shapes, and positions of the minerals that the rock contains.

3 ___ metamorphic rock contains minerals that are arranged in layers.

4 ___ is the process in which material is laid down.

5 An area of a continent that is composed of flat-lying layers of sedimentary rock is a ___ .

UNDERSTANDING KEY IDEAS

Multiple Choice

6 Sedimentary rocks are classified into all of the following classes EXCEPT

a. clastic sedimentary rocks.

b. chemical sedimentary rocks.

c. foliated sedimentary rocks.

d. organic sedimentary rocks.

7 What kind of texture does an igneous rock that cools very slowly have? **D.1.3.5 CS**

a. a foliated texture

b. a fine-grained texture

c. a nonfoliated texture

d. a coarse-grained texture

8 Igneous rocks form when

a. dead marine organisms are buried.

b. sand grains are cemented together.

c. magma cools and solidifies.

d. mineral grains in a rock form bands.

9 A rock is located at the surface of Earth. Which of the following processes can change the rock? **D.1.3.1 CS** **FCAT**

a. weathering   **c.** melting

b. heat   **d.** pressure

10 What is the name of the process that removes and transports sediment from the source of the sediment? **D.1.3.1 CS**

a. deposition   **c.** weathering

b. erosion   **d.** uplift

11 A topographic map of Florida shows that the land surface is very flat. Which of the following geologic processes can you assume significantly contributed to the formation of Florida? **D.1.3.1 CS** **FCAT**

a. pressure   **c.** erosion

b. uplift   **d.** heat

12 The Florida Keys began to form along the southern edge of the Florida Platform approximately 1.8 million years ago. What caused the formation of the Florida Keys? **D.1.3.4 AA** **FCAT**

a. transported sediments eroded from the Appalachian Mountains

b. the breakup of Pangaea

c. the accumulation of dead coral reef material

d. the erosion of rock on the Florida Platform

Short Answer

13 How do the processes of weathering and erosion shape Earth's surface? **D.1.3.1 CS**

14 Describe the role that coral played in forming the Florida Keys. **D.1.3.4 AA**

15 Explain how the rate of cooling affects the texture of igneous rocks. **D.1.3.5 CS**

Math Skills

16 If sediment is deposited evenly in a layer at the rate of 5 mm every 100 years, in how many years will this layer of sediment be 5 m thick?

CRITICAL THINKING

Extended Response

17 **Analyzing Processes** Describe the geologic processes that are reshaping the surface features of Florida today. **D.1.3.1 CS**

18 **Applying Concepts** Give two examples of how texture can provide clues about how and where a rock formed.

19 **Identifying Relationships** Other than similar types of rock, what evidence would indicate that Florida was once part of northwest Africa?

Concept Mapping

20 Use the following terms to create a concept map: *rocks, metamorphic, sedimentary, igneous, foliated, nonfoliated, clastic, organic, chemical, intrusive,* and *extrusive.*

INTERPRETING GRAPHICS

The bar graph below shows the mineral composition of a sample of granite by percentage of mass. Use the graph below to answer the questions that follow.

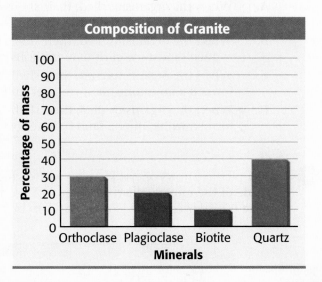

21 Your rock sample is made of four minerals. For each mineral, indicate the percentage of your sample that the mineral makes up.

22 Both plagioclase and orthoclase are feldspar minerals. What percentage of your sample of granite is made of minerals that are not feldspar minerals?

23 If your rock sample has a mass of 10 g, how many grams of quartz does your sample contain?

24 Use paper, a compass, and a protractor or a computer to make a pie chart that represents the composition of your sample of granite. Show the percentage of your sample that each of the four minerals makes up. (Look in the Appendix of this book for help on making a pie chart.)

For the following questions, write your answers on a separate sheet of paper.

1 Millions of years ago, the area that is Florida today was covered by a shallow sea. Organisms that had shells and skeletons made of calcium carbonate lived in this sea. How did these organisms affect the landscape of modern Florida?

A. When the organisms died, their shells and skeletons became sediment that eventually formed halite over millions of years.

B. When the organisms died, their shells and skeletons became sediment that eventually formed sandstone cliffs over millions of years.

C. When the organisms died, their shells and skeletons became sediment that eventually formed a limestone platform over millions of years.

D. When the organisms died, their shells and skeletons became sediment that eventually formed white, quartz sand beaches over millions of years.

2 The picture shows one of Florida's white-sand beaches. The sand grains on this beach are made of the mineral quartz. The quartz grains originated in the Appalachian Mountains and were transported to the Florida Platform by currents.

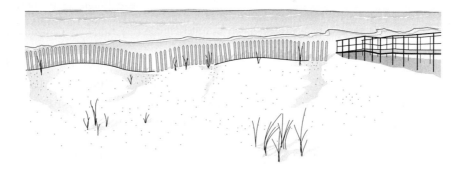

By what geological process were the quartz grains spread over the Florida Platform?

F. deposition

G. erosion

H. uplift

I. weathering

3 Scientists classify rocks based on how the rocks formed. What are the three main classes of rocks?

A. clastic, chemical, and organic rocks

B. extrusive, intrusive, and foliated rocks

C. igneous, metamorphic, and sedimentary rocks

D. fine-grained, medium-grained, and coarse-grained rocks

4 About 200 million years ago, the ancient supercontinent of Pangaea separated. The areas that would become modern Florida and modern northwest Africa split apart at that time. About 100 million years later, the area that would become modern Florida sank and was flooded by a shallow sea. During this period, limestone began to form. About 65 million years later, the Appalachian Mountains started to erode, and sediment carried south by currents covered the limestone. About how long ago (in millions of years) did sediment begin to cover the limestone?

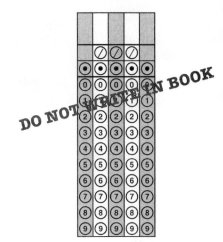

5 Which of the following statements describes a type of sedimentary rock?

  A. rock that forms when magma cools slowly deep beneath Earth's surface

  B. rock that forms when magma cools on the surface of Earth after a volcanic eruption

  C. rock that changes in structure, composition, or texture as a result of great pressure within Earth

  D. rock that forms when shells and skeletons of marine organisms build up layers on the bottom of the sea

6 The picture below shows Bryce Canyon in Utah. The rock in Bryce Canyon is composed of soft sedimentary rocks, including mudstones, sandstones, and limestones.

What processes were most important in shaping the land surface in Bryce Canyon?

  F. heat and pressure

  G. weathering and erosion

  H. compaction and cementation

  I. sedimentation and deposition

Science in Action

Science, Technology, and Society

The Moai of Easter Island

Easter Island is located in the Pacific Ocean more than 3,200 km from the coast of Chile. The island is home to mysterious statues that were carved from volcanic ash. The statues, called *moai*, have human heads and large torsos. The average moai weighs 14 tons and is more than 4.5 m tall, although some are as tall as 10 m! All together, 887 moai have been discovered. How old are the moai? Scientists believe that the moai were built 500 to 1,000 years ago. What purpose did moai serve for their creators? The moai may have been religious symbols or gods.

Social Studies ACTiViTY

WRITING SKILL Research the ancient Egyptians or members of another ancient society or civilization who are believed to have used stone to construct monuments to their gods or to important people. Report your findings in a short essay.

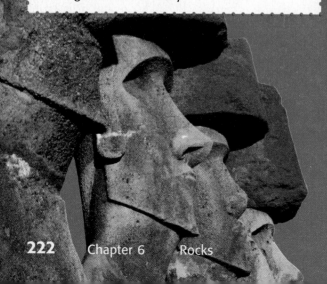

FOCUS ON FLORIDA

Place to Visit

Devil's Millhopper Geological State Park

As you descend a series of 236 steps, dense vegetation surrounds you. From within the vegetation, you hear the sound of water trickling over ancient limestone. Where are you? You are visiting Devil's Millhopper Geological State Park located near Gainesville. As the name of the park suggests, the main attraction is a geologic feature called the *Devil's Millhopper*. The Devil's Millhopper is a sinkhole that formed between 10,000 and 14,000 years ago when the ceiling of a large, limestone cavern collapsed. The collapse happened because acids in groundwater had dissolved away the limestone that supported the cavern ceiling.

Language Arts ACTiViTY

WRITING SKILL Using a map of Florida, locate other interesting names of places that are found around the state. Try to find the origin and meaning of the names that you select. Report your findings in a short paper.

Robert L. Folk

Petrologist For Robert Folk, the study of rock takes place on the microscopic level. Folk searches rock to find tiny life-forms that he has named *nannobacteria,* or *dwarf bacteria. Nannobacteria* may also be spelled *nanobacteria.* Because nannobacteria are so incredibly small—only 0.05 to 0.2 µm in diameter—Folk must use an extremely powerful microscope to see the shape of the bacteria in rock. The 100,000× microscope that Folk uses is called a *scanning electron microscope.* Research had already led Folk to discover that a certain type of Italian limestone is produced by bacteria. The bacteria were consuming the minerals, and the waste of the bacteria was forming the limestone. Further research led Folk to the discovery of the tiny nannobacteria.

The spherical or oval-shaped nannobacteria appeared as chains and grape-like clusters. From his research, Folk hypothesized that nannobacteria are responsible for many inorganic reactions that occur in rock. Many scientists are skeptical of Folk's nannobacteria. Some skeptics believe that the tiny size of nannobacteria makes the bacteria simply too small to contain the chemistry of life. Others believe that nannobacteria actually represent structures that do not come from living things.

Math ACTIVITY

If a nannobacterium is one-tenth of the length, one-tenth of the width, and one-tenth of the height of an ordinary bacterium, how many nannobacteria can fit in an ordinary bacterium? (Hint: Draw block diagrams of a nannobacterium and an ordinary bacterium.)

To learn more about these Science in Action topics, visit go.hrw.com and type in the keyword **HT6FRKFF.**

Current Science

Check out Current Science® articles related to this chapter by visiting go.hrw.com. Just type in the keyword HZ5CS04.

7

Weathering and Soil Formation

The Big Idea Earth is shaped and reshaped by the activity of wind, water, and living things.

About the

Need a nose job, Mr. President? The carving of Thomas Jefferson that is part of the Mount Rushmore National Memorial is having its nose inspected by a National Parks worker. The process of weathering has caused cracks to form in the carving of President Jefferson. National Parks workers use a sealant to protect the memorial from moisture, which can cause further cracking.

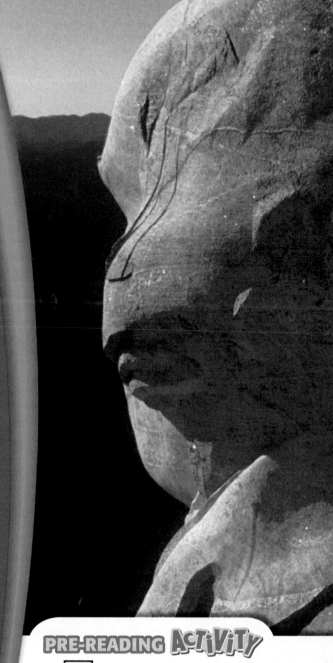

PRE-READING ACTIVITY

FOLDNOTES **Key-Term Fold** Before you read the chapter, create the FoldNote entitled "Key-Term Fold" described in the **Study Skills** section of the Appendix. Write a key term from the chapter on each tab of the key-term fold. Under each tab, write the definition of the key term.

START-UP ACTIVITY

What's the Difference? H.1.3.5 AA

In this chapter, you will learn about the processes and rates of weathering. Complete this activity to learn about how the size and surface area of a substance affects how quickly the substance breaks down.

Procedure

1. Fill **two small containers** about half full with **water.**

2. Add **one sugar cube** to one container.

3. Add **1 tsp of granulated sugar** to the other container.

4. Using **one spoon for each container,** stir the water and sugar in each container at the same rate.

5. Using a **stopwatch,** measure how long it takes for the sugar to dissolve in each container.

Analysis

1. Did the sugar dissolve at the same rate in both containers? Explain why or why not.

2. Do you think one large rock or several smaller rocks would wear away faster? Explain your answer.

Weathering

Did you know that the sand on the beach that you and your family visit may have come from rocks in mountains that are hundreds of miles away?

Sand grains come from larger rocks that are broken down. The process by which rock materials are broken down by the action of physical or chemical processes is called **weathering.**

Mechanical Weathering

If you were to strike one rock with another rock, you would be demonstrating one type of mechanical weathering. **Mechanical weathering** is the breakdown of rock into smaller pieces by physical means. Agents of mechanical weathering include ice, wind, water, gravity, plants, and animals.

Ice

The alternate freezing and thawing of soil and rock, called *frost action,* is a form of mechanical weathering. One type of frost action, *ice wedging,* is shown in **Figure 1.** Ice wedging starts when water seeps into cracks during warm weather. When temperatures drop, the water freezes and expands. The ice then pushes against the sides of the crack. This causes the crack to widen.

weathering the natural process by which atmospheric and environmental agents such as wind, rain, and temperature changes, disintegrate and decompose rocks

mechanical weathering the process by which rocks break down into smaller pieces by physical means

D.1.3.1 CS knows that mechanical and chemical activities shape and reshape the Earth's land surface by eroding rock and soil in some areas and depositing them in other areas, sometimes in seasonal layers.

Figure 1   Ice Wedging

The granite in the photo has been broken down by repeated ice wedging, which is shown below.

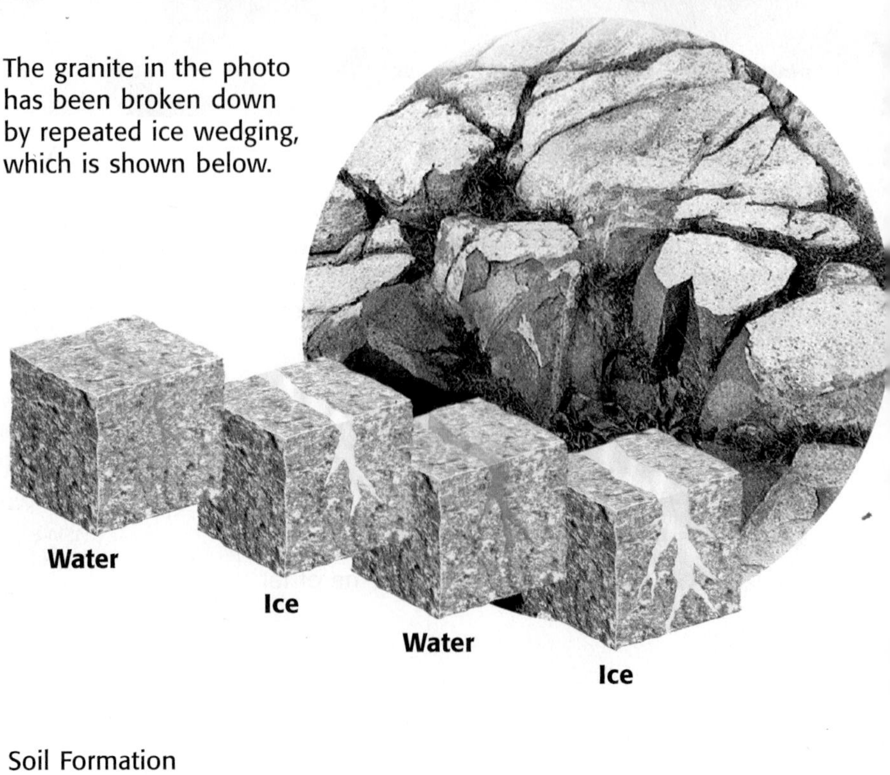

Water

Ice

Water

Ice

Figure 2 Three Forms of Abrasion

These river rocks are rounded because they have been tumbled in the riverbed by fast-moving water for many years.

This rock has been shaped by blowing sand. Such rocks are called *ventifacts*.

Rocks grind against each other in a rock slide, which creates smaller and smaller rock fragments.

Abrasion

As you scrape a piece of chalk against a board, particles of the chalk rub off to make a line on the board and the piece of chalk wears down and becomes smaller. The same process, called *abrasion,* happens with rocks. **Abrasion** is the grinding and wearing away of rock surfaces through the mechanical action of other rock or sand particles.

abrasion the grinding and wearing away of rock surfaces through the mechanical action of other rock or sand particles

Wind, Water, and Gravity

Abrasion can happen in different ways, as shown in **Figure 2.** When rocks and pebbles roll along the bottom of swiftly flowing rivers, they bump into and scrape against each other. The weathering that occurs eventually causes these rocks to become rounded and smooth.

Wind also causes abrasion. When wind blows sand and silt against exposed rock, the sand eventually wears away the rock's surface. The center photo in **Figure 2** shows what this kind of sandblasting can do to a rock.

Abrasion also occurs when rocks fall on one another. You can imagine the forces rocks exert on each other as they tumble down a mountainside. In fact, anytime one rock hits another, abrasion takes place.

Benchmark Check Explain how wind, water, and gravity erode rock by the process of abrasion. **D.1.3.1 CS**

Benchmark Activity

Demonstrating Abrasion

You have learned that water, wind, and gravity can all weather rock. Devise a simple demonstration that shows how one of these forces can weather rock. For example, you could devise a demonstration that illustrates how rocks grind against each other to create smaller rock fragments. Have your idea approved by your teacher. **D.1.3.1 CS**

Figure 3 *Although they grow slowly, tree roots are strong enough to break solid rock.*

Plants

You may not think of plants as being strong, but some plants can easily break rocks. Have you ever seen sidewalks and streets that are cracked because of tree roots? Roots don't grow fast, but they certainly are powerful! Plants often send their roots into existing cracks in rocks. As the plant grows, the force of the expanding root becomes so strong that the crack widens. Eventually, the entire rock can split apart, as shown in **Figure 3.**

Animals

Believe it or not, earthworms cause a lot of weathering! They burrow through the soil and move soil particles around. This exposes fresh surfaces to continued weathering. Would you believe that some kinds of tropical worms move an estimated 100 metric tons of soil per acre every year? Almost any animal that burrows causes mechanical weathering. Ants, worms, mice, ground squirrels, and rabbits are just some of the animals that contribute to weathering. **Figure 4** shows some animals that cause weathering. The mixing and digging that animals do often contribute to another type of weathering, called *chemical weathering.* You will learn about this type of weathering next.

Benchmark Check Explain how animals shape the landscape in which they live. D.1.3.4 AA

Figure 4 *Animals that live in the soil, such as moles, insects, worms, and gophers, cause a lot of weathering. When the animals burrow in the ground, they break up soil and loosen rocks to be exposed to further weathering.*

Figure 5   **Chemical Weathering of Granite**

After thousands of years of chemical weathering, even hard rock, such as granite, can turn to sediment.

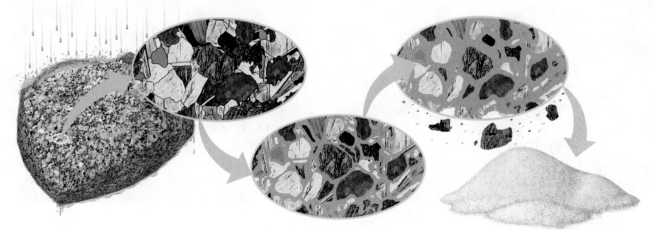

① Rain, weak acids, and air chemically weather granite.

② The bonds between mineral grains weaken as weathering proceeds.

③ When granite is weathered, it makes sand and clay, also called *sediment*.

Chemical Weathering

The process by which rocks break down as a result of chemical reactions is called **chemical weathering.** Common agents of chemical weathering are water, weak acids, and air.

Water

If you drop a sugar cube into a glass of water, the sugar cube will dissolve after a few minutes. This process is an example of chemical weathering. Even hard rock, such as granite, can be broken down by water. But, the process may take thousands of years. **Figure 5** shows how granite is chemically weathered.

Acid Precipitation

Rain, sleet, or snow that contains a high concentration of acids is called **acid precipitation.** Precipitation is naturally acidic. However, acid precipitation contains more acid than normal precipitation. The high level of acidity can cause very rapid weathering of rock. Small amounts of sulfuric and nitric acids from natural sources, such as volcanoes, can make precipitation acidic. However, acid precipitation can also be caused by air pollution from the burning of fossil fuels, such as coal and oil. When these fuels are burned, they give off gases, including sulfur oxides, nitrogen oxides, and carbon oxides. When these compounds combine with water in the atmosphere, they form weak acids, which then fall back to the ground in rain and snow. When the acidity is too high, acid precipitation can be harmful to plants and animals.

chemical weathering the process by which rocks break down as a result of chemical reactions
FCAT *VOCAB*

acid precipitation rain, sleet, or snow, that contains a high concentration of acids

D.1.3.1 CS knows that mechanical and chemical activities shape and reshape the Earth's land surface by eroding rock and soil in some areas and depositing them in other areas, sometimes in seasonal layers.

D.1.3.4 AA knows the ways in which plants and animals reshape the landscape.

D.1.3.5 CS understands concepts of time and size relating to the interaction of Earth's processes.

Figure 6 *Acid in groundwater has weathered limestone to form Diepolder Cave.*

 D.1.3.1 CS knows that mechanical and chemical activities shape and reshape the Earth's land surface by eroding rock and soil in some areas and depositing them in other areas, sometimes in seasonal layers.

 D.1.3.4 AA knows the ways in which plants and animals reshape the landscape.

D.1.3.5 CS understands concepts of time and size relating to the interaction of Earth's processes.

Figure 7 *Lichens, which consist of fungi and algae living together, contribute to chemical weathering.*

Acids in Groundwater

In certain places, groundwater contains weak acids, such as carbonic or sulfuric acid. These acids react with rocks in the ground, such as limestone. When groundwater comes in contact with limestone, a chemical reaction occurs. Over a long period of time, the dissolving of limestone forms *karst* features, such as caverns. The caverns, like the one shown in **Figure 6,** form from the dissolving away of the limestone.

Acids in Living Things

Another source of acids that cause weathering might surprise you. Take a look at the lichens in **Figure 7.** Lichens produce acids that can slowly break down rock. If you have ever taken a walk in a park or forest, you have probably seen lichens growing on the sides of trees or rocks. Lichens can also grow in places where some of the hardiest plants cannot. For example, lichens can grow in deserts, in arctic areas, and in areas high above the timberline, where even trees don't grow.

Acids React!

1. Vinegar is one example of a food that contains weak acids that react with certain substances. Immerse a piece of **calcite** in **vinegar,** and let it stand for several minutes.

2. Remove the calcite from the vinegar.

3. Does the calcite show any decrease in overall size?

4. How is this process similar to what happens to a rock when it is exposed to natural acids during weathering?

Air

The car shown in **Figure 8** is undergoing chemical weathering due to the air. The oxygen in the air is reacting with the iron in the car and is causing the car to rust. Water speeds up this process. But the iron would rust even if no water were present. Scientists call this process *oxidation*.

Oxidation is a chemical reaction in which an element, such as iron, combines with oxygen to form an oxide. This common form of chemical weathering is what causes rust. Old cars, aluminum cans, and your bike can oxidize if left exposed to air and rain for even short periods of time.

Benchmark Check Hypothesize why the mineral pyrite, which contains iron, oxidizes rapidly at Earth's surface. **D.1.3.5 CS**

Figure 8 *Rust is a result of chemical weathering.*

SECTION Review

Summary

- Wind, water, ice, and gravity cause mechanical weathering by abrasion. **D.1.3.1 CS**
- Plants cause mechanical weathering by breaking apart rocks. **D.1.3.4 AA**
- Animals cause mechanical weathering by turning soil. **D.1.3.4 AA**
- Water, acids, and air chemically weather rock slowly by weakening the bonds between mineral grains of the rock. **D.1.3.5 CS**

Using Key Terms

1. Use *weathering, mechanical weathering,* and *chemical weathering* in the same sentence. **FCAT VOCAB**

Understanding Key Ideas

2. List three agents that cause the mechanical weathering of rocks. **D.1.3.1 CS**

3. Describe three ways abrasion occurs in nature. **D.1.3.1 CS**

4. Compare the ways tree roots and ice mechanically weather rock. **D.1.3.1 CS, D.1.3.4 AA**

5. Describe five sources of chemical weathering. **D.1.3.1 CS, D.1.3.4 AA**

6. Describe the rate at which chemical weathering generally takes place. **D.1.3.5 CS**

Critical Thinking

7. **Making Comparisons** Compare the weathering processes that affect a rock on top of a mountain and a rock buried beneath the ground. **D.1.3.1 CS**

8. **Making Inferences** Why does acid precipitation weather rocks at a faster rate than normal precipitation does? **D.1.3.5 CS**

FCAT Preparation

9. The Grand Canyon is located in northwestern Arizona. It is more than 322 km long. In some places, the Grand Canyon is more than 1.6 km deep. The Colorado River has run through the Grand Canyon for millions of years. Which agent of mechanical weathering was most likely responsible for shaping the Grand Canyon? **D.1.3.1 CS**

   A. gravity

   B. water

   C. ice

   D. wind

SCiLINKS®

NSTA

Developed and maintained by the National Science Teachers Association

For a variety of links related to this chapter, go to www.scilinks.org

Topic: Weathering
SciLinks code: HSM1648

Rates of Weathering

Have you ever seen a cartoon in which a character falls off a cliff and lands on a ledge? Ledges exist in nature because the rock that makes up the ledge weathers more slowly than the surrounding rock.

Weathering is a process that generally takes a long time. However, some rock will weather faster than other rock. The rate at which a rock weathers depends on climate, elevation, and the makeup of the rock.

Differential Weathering

Hard rocks, such as granite, weather more slowly than softer rocks, such as limestone. **Differential weathering** is a process by which softer, less weather resistant rocks wear away at a faster rate than harder, more weather resistant rocks.

Figure 1 shows Devils Tower, in Wyoming, which was exposed by differential weathering. About 50 million years ago, a mass of molten rock cooled and hardened underground to form igneous rock. The surrounding rock was softer than the igneous rock. As the rocks were weathered for millions of years, the softer rock was completely worn away. The harder, more resistant rock of the tower is all that remains.

Figure 1 *Devils tower in Wyoming appears as it does today because of differential weathering. As surrounding rock was worn away, the hard rock of the tower was exposed.*

The Shape of Rocks

Weathering takes place on the outer surface of rocks. Therefore, the more surface area that is exposed to weathering, the faster the rock will be worn down. A large rock has a large surface area. But a large rock also has a large volume. Because of the large rock's volume, the large rock will take a long time to wear down.

If a large rock is broken into smaller fragments, weathering of the rock happens much more quickly because the fragments are smaller. The rate of weathering increases because a smaller rock has a larger ratio of surface area to volume than a larger rock has. So, more of a smaller rock is exposed to the weathering process. **Figure 2** shows this concept in detail.

Benchmark Check Explain the relationship between surface area and rates of weathering. **D.1.3.5 CS**

differential weathering the process by which softer, less weather resistant rocks wear away at a faster rate than harder, more weather resistant rocks do

D.1.3.5 CS understands concepts of time and size relating to the interaction of Earth's processes.

Figure 2 **Total Surface Area to Volume**

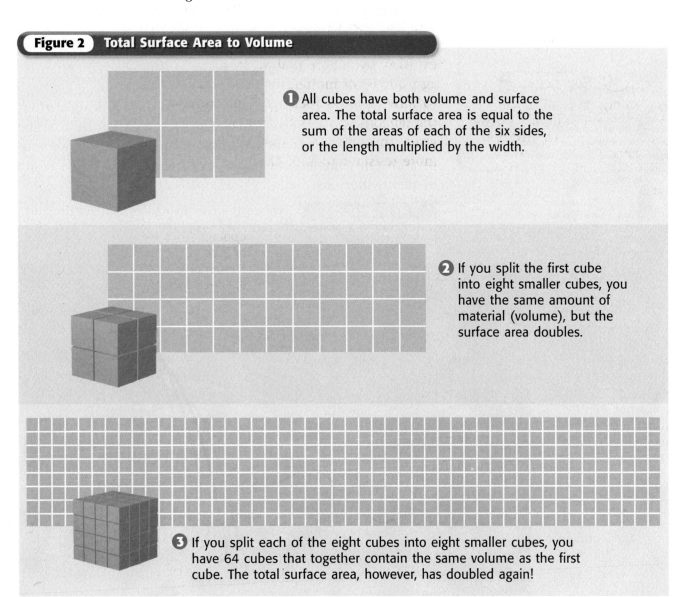

❶ All cubes have both volume and surface area. The total surface area is equal to the sum of the areas of each of the six sides, or the length multiplied by the width.

❷ If you split the first cube into eight smaller cubes, you have the same amount of material (volume), but the surface area doubles.

❸ If you split each of the eight cubes into eight smaller cubes, you have 64 cubes that together contain the same volume as the first cube. The total surface area, however, has doubled again!

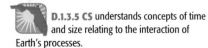

D.1.3.1 CS knows that mechanical and chemical activities shape and reshape the Earth's land surface by eroding rock and soil in some areas and depositing them in other areas, sometimes in seasonal layers.

D.1.3.5 CS understands concepts of time and size relating to the interaction of Earth's processes.

Weathering and Climate

The rate of weathering in an area is greatly affected by the climate of that area. *Climate* is the average weather condition in an area over a long period of time. Most of Florida has a climate that is subtropical. The subtropical climate of Florida is characterized by summers that are long, hot, and humid and by winters that are wet and mild.

Water and Temperature

The rate of chemical weathering happens faster in warm, humid climates, such as subtropical climates. The rusty channel marker shown in **Figure 3** has undergone oxidation. As you have learned, oxidation is a chemical reaction in which an element combines with oxygen to form an oxide. Oxidation, like other chemical reactions, happens at a faster rate when temperatures are higher and when water is present.

Water also increases the rate of mechanical weathering. Ice wedging is the process in which water that seeps into cracks in rocks freezes and causes rocks to break apart. Over time, this form of weathering can break down even the hardest rocks into soil.

Temperature is another major factor in mechanical weathering. For example, the rate of mechanical weathering may be faster in regions in which there is a large variation in temperature. In climates where cycles of freezing and thawing are frequent, more ice wedging takes place.

Benchmark Check Explain the way in which temperature and water can affect rates of weathering. **D.1.3.5 CS**

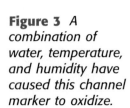

Figure 3 *A combination of water, temperature, and humidity have caused this channel marker to oxidize.*

Weathering and Elevation

Just like water and temperature, elevation also affects the rate of weathering. As shown in **Figure 4**, rocks at high elevations are exposed to wind, rain, ice, and snow. High winds and large amounts of precipitation cause these rocks to weather rapidly. On the other hand, rocks at sea level can be affected by wave action. The action of waves can weather rock rapidly, especially soft rocks.

Elevation and gravity work together to weather rock. The steep sides of mountains and hills increase the rate of weathering. Rainwater that runs quickly down the sides of mountains and hills breaks down rock. This broken rock is carried to lower elevations by the running water. New rock surfaces are also exposed to weathering when gravity causes rocks to slide down the sides of mountains and hills. The removal of rock exposes the fresh rock that was underneath the surface to the effects of weathering. The increased surface area allows weathering to happen at a faster rate.

Benchmark Check Explain how elevation and gravity work together to weather rocks. **D.1.3.5 CS**

Figure 4 *The ice, rain, and wind that these mountain peaks are exposed to cause them to weather at a fast rate.*

SECTION Review

Summary

- Weathering may be slow or rapid. The rate of weathering can be affected by climate, water, temperature, elevation, and gravity. **D.1.3.5 CS**

- The more surface area of a rock that is exposed to weathering, the faster the rock will be worn down. **D.1.3.5 CS**

- Chemical weathering occurs rapidly in warm, humid climates. **D.1.3.5 CS**

- Elevation affects the rate of weathering of rock. **D.1.3.5 CS**

Using Key Terms

1. Write an original definition for *differential weathering*.

Understanding Key Ideas

2. How does the hardness of a rock affect the rate of weathering? **D.1.3.5 CS**

3. How does surface area of a rock affect the rate of weathering? **D.1.3.5 CS**

4. How does climate affect rates of weathering? **D.1.3.5 CS**

5. Why do the rocks at the peak of a mountain weather faster than the rocks at the bottom of the mountain? **D.1.3.5 CS**

Critical Thinking

6. **Making Inferences** Does the rate of chemical weathering increase or stay the same when a rock becomes more mechanically weathered? Why? **D.1.3.5 CS**

FCAT Preparation

7. One process that alters Earth's surface is differential weathering. What event would most likely occur in a longer time frame than the time it would take the soft rock of a volcano to weather away? **D.1.3.5 CS**

   A. a lightning strike

   B. a hurricane season

   C. the evaporation of a lake

   D. the birth and death of a star

SCILINKS®

NSTA

Developed and maintained by the National Science Teachers Association

For a variety of links related to this chapter, go to www.scilinks.org

Topic: Rates of Weathering
SciLinks code: HSM1269

From Bedrock to Soil

Most plants need soil to grow. But what exactly is soil? Where does it come from?

READING WARM-UP

Objectives

● Describe how mechanical and chemical activities aid in the formation and deposition of soil. **D.1.3.1 CS**

● Explain how the different properties of soil affect plant growth.

● Describe how various climates affect soil.

● Describe how plants and animals reshape the landscape and add to soil fertility. **D.1.3.4 AA**

● Describe the positive and negative consequences of human activities that affect soil. **D.2.3.2, G.2.3.4 AA**

Terms to Learn

soil	soil texture
parent rock	soil structure
bedrock	humus

READING STRATEGY

Prediction Guide Before you read this section, write the title of each heading in this section. Next, under each heading, write what you think you will learn.

The Source of Soil

To a scientist, **soil** is a loose mixture of small mineral fragments, organic material, water, and air that can support the growth of vegetation. But not all soils are the same. Because soils are made from weathered rock fragments, the type of soil that forms depends on the type of rock that weathers. The rock formation that is the source of mineral fragments in the soil is called **parent rock.**

Bedrock is the layer of rock beneath soil. In this case, the bedrock is the parent rock because the soil above it formed from the bedrock below. Soil that remains above its parent rock is called *residual soil.*

Soil can be blown or washed away from its parent rock. This soil is called *transported soil.* **Figure 1** shows one way that soil is moved from one place to another. Both wind and the movement of glaciers are also responsible for transporting soil.

Benchmark Check Explain how soil is transferred from one place to another. **D.1.3.1 CS**

Figure 1 *Transported soil may be moved long distances from its parent rock by rivers, such as this one.*

D.1.3.1 CS knows that mechanical and chemical activities shape and reshape the Earth's land surface by eroding rock and soil in some areas and depositing them in other areas, sometimes in seasonal layers.

Figure 2 **Soil Texture**

The proportion of these different-sized particles in soil determine the soil's texture.

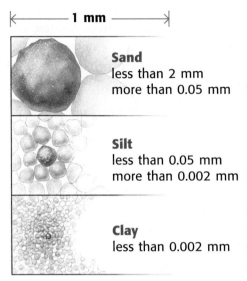

Sand	less than 2 mm more than 0.05 mm
Silt	less than 0.05 mm more than 0.002 mm
Clay	less than 0.002 mm

← 1 mm →

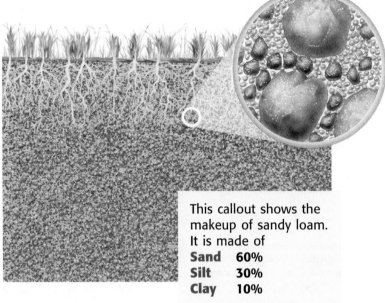

This callout shows the makeup of sandy loam. It is made of
Sand **60%**
Silt **30%**
Clay **10%**

Soil Properties

Some soils are great for growing plants. Other soils cannot support the growth of plants. To better understand soil, you will next learn about its properties, such as soil texture, soil structure, and soil fertility.

Soil Texture and Soil Structure

Soil is made of different-sized particles. These particles can be as large as 2 mm, such as sand. Other particles can be too small to see without a microscope. **Soil texture** is the soil quality that is based on the proportions of soil particles. **Figure 2** shows the soil texture for one type of soil.

Soil texture affects the soil's consistency. Consistency describes a soil's ability to be worked and broken up for farming. For example, soil that has a large proportion of clay can be hard and difficult for farmers to break up.

Soil texture influences the *infiltration,* or ability of water to move through soil. Soil should allow water to get to the plants' roots without causing the soil to be completely saturated.

Water and air movement through soil is also influenced by soil structure. **Soil structure** is the arrangement of soil particles. Soil particles are not always evenly spread out. Often, one type of soil particle will clump in an area. A clump of one type of soil can either block water flow or help water flow, which affects soil moisture.

soil a loose mixture of rock fragments, organic material, water, and air that can support the growth of vegetation

parent rock a rock formation that is the source of soil

bedrock the layer of rock beneath soil

soil texture the soil quality that is based on the proportions of soil particles

soil structure the arrangement of soil particles

Soil Fertility

Nutrients in soil, such as iron, are necessary for plants to grow. Some soils are rich in nutrients. Other soils may not have many nutrients or are not able to supply the nutrients to the plants. A soil's ability to hold nutrients and to supply nutrients to a plant is described as *soil fertility*. Many nutrients in soil come from the parent rock. Other nutrients come from **humus,** which is the organic material formed in soil from the decayed remains of plants and animals. These remains are broken down into nutrients by decomposers, such as bacteria and fungi.

humus the dark, organic material formed in soil from the decayed remains of plants and animals

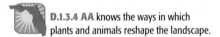 **Benchmark Check** **Explain how organisms contribute to soil fertility. D.1.3.4 AA**

Soil Horizons

Because of the way soil forms, soil often occurs in a series of layers. Humus-rich soil is on top, sediment is below that, and bedrock is on the bottom. Geologists call these layers *horizons*. The word *horizon* tells you that the layers are horizontal. **Figure 3** shows what these horizons can look like.

The top layer of soil is often called the *topsoil*. Topsoil contains more humus than the layers below it. The humus is rich in the nutrients plants need to be healthy.

D.1.3.1 CS knows that mechanical and chemical activities shape and reshape the Earth's land surface by eroding rock and soil in some areas and depositing them in other areas, sometimes in seasonal layers.

D.1.3.4 AA knows the ways in which plants and animals reshape the landscape.

Figure 3 **Soil Horizons**

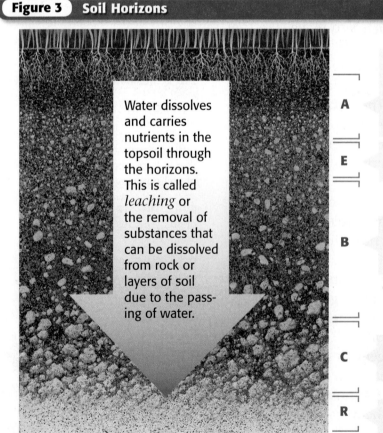

Water dissolves and carries nutrients in the topsoil through the horizons. This is called *leaching* or the removal of substances that can be dissolved from rock or layers of soil due to the passing of water.

A This horizon consists of the topsoil. Topsoil contains more humus than any other soil horizon. Soil in forests often has an O horizon. The O horizon is made up of litter from dead plants and animals.

E This horizon experiences intense leaching of nutrients.

B This horizon collects the dissolved substances and nutrients deposited from the upper horizons.

C This horizon is made of partially weathered bedrock.

R This horizon is made of bedrock that has little or no weathering.

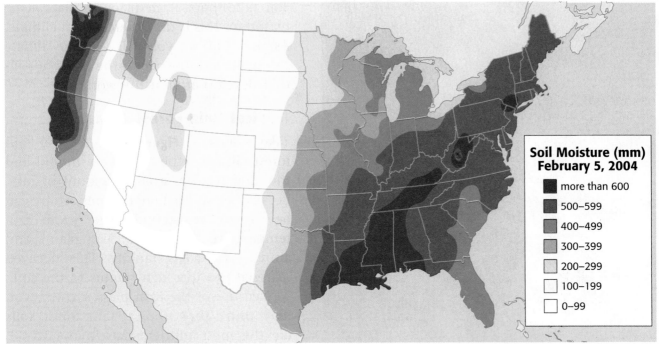

Source: NOAA Climate Prediction Center

Figure 4 *The map above models the depth of soil moisture in the continental United States on February 5, 2004. Soil moisture values in Florida were 400 to more than 600 mm.*

Soil Moisture (mm)
February 5, 2004

- more than 600
- 500–599
- 400–499
- 300–399
- 200–299
- 100–199
- 0–99

Soil Temperature and Moisture

Soil temperature is important to plant growth. Plant growth is slowed if soil temperature is too high or too low. So, soil temperature must be monitored by growers to make sure that it is optimum for plant growth.

The water that is held in the spaces between soil particles is called *soil moisture*. Soil moisture is important because the amount of moisture in the soil determines whether precipitation will infiltrate or run off the soil. A map that models soil moisture in the United States is shown in **Figure 4.**

Soil pH

Soil pH influences which nutrients will be available to plants from the soil. Certain nutrients will not be available to plants in soils that are basic, or have a high pH. Other nutrients will not be available to plants in soils that are acidic, or have low pH. Because nutrient needs vary between plant types, the best soil pH for growing varies between plant types, too.

Soil Color

Soil color can be related to soil fertility. Soils that are black or dark brown usually contain organic matter and are fertile. Reddish or yellowish soils often contain oxidized iron. These soils are fertile, too. However, soils that are whitish may contain salts. Salts may make soils unsuitable for farming.

CONNECTION TO Meteorology

Soil Moisture and Weather Forecasting Did you realize that soil moisture plays an important role in weather forecasting? The amount of moisture that soil contains can be directly linked to air temperature. For example, high soil moisture can increase the dewpoint and keep nighttime low temperatures from dropping significantly. Soil moisture can also be used to forecast precipitation. High soil moisture, which supplies moisture to the atmosphere through evaporation, can increase the chance of precipitation.

Figure 5 *Lush tropical rain forests have very thin topsoil.*

Soil and Climate

Soil types vary from place to place. One reason for this is the differences in climate. As you read on, you will see that climate can make a difference in the types of soils that develop around the world.

Tropical Rain Forest Climates

Take a look at **Figure 5.** In tropical rain forest climates, the air is very humid and the land receives a large amount of rain. Because of warm temperatures, crops can be grown year-round. The warm soil temperature also allows dead plants and animals to decay rapidly. This decayed material provides rich humus to the soil.

Because of the lush plant growth, you may think that tropical rain forest soils are the most nutrient-rich in the world. However, tropical rain forest soils are nutrient poor. The heavy rains in this climate leach precious nutrients from the topsoil into deeper layers of soil. The result is that tropical topsoil is very thin. Another reason tropical rain forest soil is nutrient poor is that the lush vegetation has a great demand for nutrients. The nutrients that are not leached away are quickly taken up by plants and trees that live off the soil.

Deforestation

Clearing trees from an area without replacing them is called *deforestation*. As populations increase and the demand for lumber products and wood for fuel increases, parts of the world are becoming deforested. Nowhere is the rate of deforestation as rapid as in tropical rain forests, where land is being converted for agriculture and for cattle grazing. Because the soil of tropical rain forests is thin, nutrients can be depleted quickly. Farmers must move from one plot of land to another to find fertile soil to farm. Each plot must be cleared of forest to make it suitable for agriculture. If land for farming is not quickly planted with cover crops, the thin soil will wash away. Similarly, if land is cleared by logging or by the collection of wood for fuel and if trees are not rapidly replanted, the soil will wash away.

Benchmark Check Explain how human activities can cause soil erosion. **D.2.3.2, G.2.3.4 AA**

D.2.3.2 knows the positive and negative consequences of human action on the Earth's systems.

G.2.3.4 AA understands that humans are a part of an ecosystem and their activities may deliberately or inadvertently alter the equilibrium in ecosystems.

Desert Climates

While tropical climates get a lot of rain, deserts get less than 25 cm a year. Leaching of nutrients is not a problem in desert soils. But the lack of rain causes many other problems, such as very low rates of chemical weathering and less ability to support plant and animal life. A low rate of weathering means soil is created at a slower rate.

Some water is available from groundwater. Groundwater can trickle in from surrounding areas and seep to the surface. But as soon as the water is close to the surface, the water evaporates. So, any materials that were dissolved in the water are left behind in the soil. Without the water to dissolve the minerals, the plants are unable to take them up. Often, the chemicals left behind are various types of salts. These salts can sometimes become so concentrated that the soil becomes toxic, or poisonous, even to desert plants! Death Valley, shown in **Figure 6,** is a desert that has toxic levels of salt in the soil.

INTERNET ACTIVITY

Older than Dirt

Explore how a mountain changes over millions of years. Go to **go.hrw.com,** and type in the keyword **HZ5WSFW.**

Land Degradation

Land degradation occurs when either natural processes or human activity damage land to the point that it can no longer support plants and animals. In areas that have dry climates, a process called *desertification* can take place. Through this process, land becomes more desertlike as a result of a change in climate or human activity. Desertification may be caused by drought, a long period during which rainfall is below average. Human activities that can cause desertification include farming methods that cause soil to lose its fertility and productivity, livestock overgrazing, and deforestation.

Figure 6 *The dry conditions and salt content of desert soils make it difficult for many plants to survive.*

Figure 7 *The rich soils in areas that have a temperate climate support a vast farming industry.*

D.2.3.2 knows the positive and negative consequences of human action on the Earth's systems.

G.2.3.4 AA understands that humans are a part of an ecosystem and their activities may deliberately or inadvertently alter the equilibrium in ecosystems.

Figure 8 *Until recently, farmland in the Everglades has been subsiding at a rate of between 2.5 and 3 cm per year.*

Temperate Forest and Grassland Climates

Much of the continental United States has a temperate climate. A large amount of weathering occurs in temperate climates. Temperate areas get enough rain to cause a high level of chemical weathering, but they do not get enough rain to cause the nutrients to be leached out of the soil. Frequent changes in temperature lead to frost action. As a result, thick, fertile soils develop, as shown in **Figure 7.**

Temperate soils are some of the most productive soils in the world. In fact, the midwestern part of the United States has earned the nickname "breadbasket" for the many crops the region's soil supports.

Reading Check **Which climate has the most productive soil?**

Arctic Climates

Arctic areas have so little precipitation that they are like cold deserts. In arctic climates, as in desert climates, chemical weathering occurs very slowly. So, soil formation also occurs slowly. Slow soil formation is why soil in arctic areas is thin and unable to support many plants.

Arctic climates also have low soil temperatures. At low temperatures, decomposition of plants and animals happens more slowly or stops completely. Slow decomposition limits the amount of humus in the soil, which limits the nutrients available. These nutrients are necessary for plant growth.

Soil in Florida

Most of the soil in Florida is sandy. The most common sandy soil in Florida is Myakka (mie AK kuh). Myakka is a fine sand and is found over more than 6,000 km² of the state. The Florida citrus crop is grown in Myakka soil.

Organic soils, which are commonly called *peat,* are found in the Everglades. Sugar cane, vegetables, and rice are the main crops farmed in these soils. Farming began in the Everglades during the 20th century. Since that time, a process called *subsidence* has caused organic soils in the Everglades to sink to a lower level. Much of the subsidence was caused when water drained from the soil. The soil has shrunk and has been reduced in thickness. Across the Everglades, soil thickness has reduced from between 1.5 and 3.5 m to approximately 15 cm.

Summary

- Mechanical and chemical activities aid in the formation and deposition of soil. **D.1.3.1 CS**

- Soil temperature affects how soil can be worked for farming and how well water passes through it.

- Plants and animals reshape the landscape and add to soil fertility. **D.1.3.4 AA**

- The ability of soil to provide nutrients so that plants can survive and grow is called *soil fertility*.

- For plants to grow well, soil temperature must be optimum.

- The amount of moisture in the soil determines whether precipitation will infiltrate or run off the soil.

- The pH of a soil influences which nutrients plants can take up from the soil.

- Soil color is related to soil fertility.

- Different climates have different types of soil, depending on the temperature and rainfall.

- Deforestation and desertification cause soil to lose its fertility and productivity and to be washed away. **D.2.3.2, G.2.3.4 AA**

- Temperate soils are some of the most productive soils in the world.

Using Key Terms

1. Use *soil, soil texture,* and *soil structure* in the same sentence.

Understanding Key Ideas

2. Describe how mechanical and chemical activities aid in the formation and deposition of soil. **D.1.3.1 CS**

3. Explain how different properties of soil affect plant growth.

4. Describe how plants and animals reshape the landscape and add to soil fertility. **D.1.3.4 AA**

5. Describe the positive and negative consequences of human activities that affect soil. **D.2.3.2, G.2.3.4 AA**

6. Describe how various climates affect soil.

Critical Thinking

7. **Identifying Relationships** In which type of climate would leaching be more common—tropical rain forest climate or desert climate?

8. **Making Comparisons** Explain why arctic soils and desert soils are similar even though arctic climates and desert climates are different.

FCAT Preparation

9. Soils vary from place to place on Earth. In some climates, soils are thin and nutrient poor but support many plants. In other climates, soil is formed at a slow rate and is unable to support many plants. And in other climates, thick, fertile soils are able to support a large farming economy. In which of the following climates is deforestation most rapidly causing the loss of a thin, nutrient-poor soil? **G.2.3.4 AA**

   A. in arctic climates

   B. in desert climates

   C. in tropical climates

   D. in grassland climates

For a variety of links related to this chapter, go to www.scilinks.org

Topic: Soil and Climate
SciLinks code: HSM1408

Soil Conservation

Believe it or not, soil can be endangered, just like plants and animals. Because soil takes thousands of years to form, it is not easy to replace. Practicing good stewardship of the soil helps maintain fertile soil for future generations.

If we do not take care of our soils, we can ruin them or even lose them. Soil is a resource that must be conserved. **Soil conservation** is a method used to maintain the fertility of the soil by protecting the soil from erosion and nutrient loss.

The Importance of Soil

Soil provides minerals and other nutrients for plants. If the soil loses these nutrients, then plants will not be able to grow. Take a look at the plants shown in **Figure 1.** The plants on the right look unhealthy because they are not getting enough nutrients. There is enough soil to support the plant's roots, but the soil is not providing them with the food they need. The plants on the left are healthy because the soil they live in is rich in nutrients.

All animals get their energy from plants. The animals get their energy either by eating the plants or by eating animals that have eaten plants. So, if plants can't get their nutrients from the soil, animals can't get their nutrients from plants.

Benchmark Check Explain the interrelationship between soil, plants, and animals. **G.2.3.2 CS**

soil conservation a method to maintain the fertility of the soil by protecting the soil from erosion and nutrient loss

Figure 1 *Both of these photos show the same crop, but the soil in the photo on the right is poor in nutrients.*

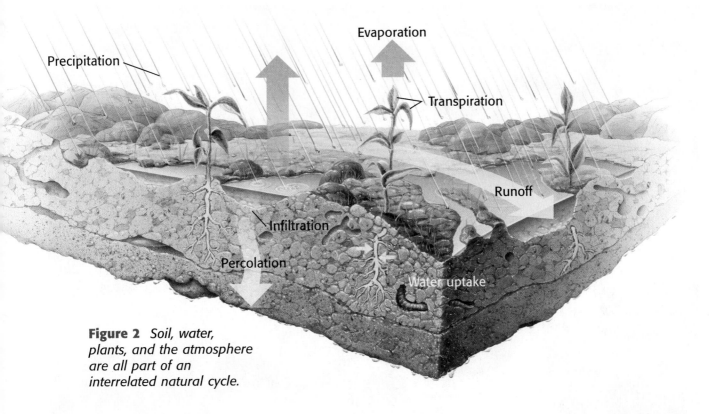

Precipitation

Evaporation

Transpiration

Runoff

Infiltration

Percolation

Water uptake

Figure 2 *Soil, water, plants, and the atmosphere are all part of an interrelated natural cycle.*

Soil and Water

Soil, water, plants, and the atmosphere are all part of a natural cycle that is shown in **Figure 2.** When it rains, the force of gravity causes water that collects on the ground to infiltrate the soil and move downward, or percolate, through the spaces between soil particles. Some of this water seeps down to the water table. The water that remains between soil particles acts as water storage for plants. The water also contains the nutrients that plants need to survive. Plants take in this water through their roots and release it through their leaves in a process called *transpiration*. The water vapor that is released by plants becomes low-level moisture in the atmosphere.

Soil and Organisms

Did you know that 1 g of fertile soil can contain as many as 1 billion bacterial cells? These bacterial cells are the most numerous organisms of the soil ecosystem. Other organisms that live in the soil include plants, fungi, worms, insects, and small mammals. Each of these organisms plays an important role in the soil ecosystem. For example, certain bacteria can convert nitrogen into chemical compounds that plants use. And the burrowing activity of earthworms not only mixes and binds soil but also creates channels in the soil through which plant roots grow. If the soil disappears, the habitat for these organisms does, too.

CONNECTION TO Biology

The Museum of Entomology One of the largest collections of spiders, insects, and related organisms in the United States is found in Florida. The collection is located at the Museum of Entomology (entomology is the study of insects) in Gainesville. Scientists study organisms from the collection to learn how to best protect the agricultural economy of Florida. The museum currently offers tours to local classes.

D.1.3.4 AA knows the ways in which plants and animals reshape the landscape.

G.2.3.2 CS knows that all biotic and abiotic factors are interrelated and that if one factor is changed or removed, it impacts the availability of other resources within the system.

Figure 3 *Providence Canyon, located near Columbus, Georgia, began forming in the early 1800s. Erosion of the soft sand in the canyon continues today.*

Soil Damage and Loss

What would happen if there were no soil? Soil loss is a serious problem around the world. Soil damage can lead to soil loss. Soil can be damaged from overuse by poor farming techniques or by overgrazing. Overused soil can lose its nutrients and become infertile. Plants can't grow in soil that is infertile.

Most farming methods can increase the rate at which soil erodes. For example, plowing loosens topsoil and removes plants that hold the soil in place. The plowed topsoil is more easily blown or washed away than the unplowed topsoil is.

Benchmark Check **Explain how humans can damage soil and cause soil loss. D.2.3.2, G.2.3.4 AA**

Soil Erosion

When soil is left unprotected, it can be exposed to erosion. **Erosion** is the process by which wind, water, or gravity transport soil and sediment from one location to another. **Figure 3** shows Providence Canyon, which was formed from the erosion of soil when trees were cut down to clear land for farming. Roots from plants and trees are like anchors to the soil. Roots keep topsoil from being eroded. Therefore, plants and trees protect the soil. Taking care of vegetation helps take care of soil.

erosion the process by which wind, water, ice, or gravity transport soil and sediment from one location to another

Salinization

The accumulation of salts in the soil is known as **salinization.** Salinization is a major problem in parts of the world where rainfall amounts are low and the soil is naturally salty. In these areas, water used for irrigation is salty. So, when irrigation water evaporates from farmland, salt is left behind. In time, the soil may become so salty that plants cannot grow in it.

salinization the accumulation of salts in soil

Soil-Conservation Methods

A number of soil-conservation methods that protect topsoil are available to farmers. Some methods, such as contour plowing, terracing, and no-till farming, are used to reduce soil erosion. Crop rotation is a method that is used to slow nutrient depletion and reduce damage caused by insect pests. Finally, farmers can restore nutrients to soil by planting cover crops.

Contour Plowing and Terracing

If farmers plowed rows so that the rows ran up and down hills, what might happen during a heavy rain? The rows would channel the rainwater down the hill, which would erode the soil. To prevent erosion from happening in this way, a farmer could plow across the slope of the hills instead of up and down the slope. This method of soil conservation is called *contour plowing*. In contour plowing, the rows act as a series of dams instead of a series of rivers. If the hills are very steep, farmers can use a soil-conservation method known as *terracing*. Terracing changes one steep field into a series of small, flat fields. **Figure 4** illustrates the contour-plowing and terracing methods of soil conservation.

D.1.3.1 CS knows that mechanical and chemical activities shape and reshape the Earth's land surface by eroding rock and soil in some areas and depositing them in other areas, sometimes in seasonal layers.

D.2.3.2 knows the positive and negative consequences of human action on the Earth's systems.

G.2.3.4 AA understands that humans are a part of an ecosystem and their activities may deliberately or inadvertently alter the equilibrium in ecosystems.

Figure 4   Contour Plowing and Terracing

Contour plowing helps prevent erosion caused by heavy rains.

Terracing prevents erosion caused by heavy rains on steep hills.

Figure 5 *George Washington Carver taught soil-conservation methods to farmers.*

![MATH PRACTICE]

Making Soil

Suppose it takes 500 years for 2 cm of new soil to form in a certain area. But the soil is eroding at a rate of 1 mm per year. Is the soil eroding faster than it can be replaced? Explain.

Figure 6 *Soybeans are a cover crop that restores nutrients to soil.*

D.2.3.2 knows the positive and negative consequences of human action on the Earth's systems.

G.2.3.4 AA understands that humans are a part of an ecosystem and their activities may deliberately or inadvertently alter the equilibrium in ecosystems..

Crop Rotation

One way to slow down nutrient depletion is through *crop rotation*. If the same crop is grown year after year in the same field, certain nutrients become depleted. To slow this process, a farmer can plant different crops. A different crop will use up fewer nutrients or different nutrients from the soil.

Another benefit to practicing crop rotation is that insect pests cause less damage to crops. How does crop rotation decrease insect damage? The answer is relatively simple. Most insect pests eat one or only a few kinds of plants. One example of such a pest is the tomato hornworm. If farmers plant tomatoes on the same land year after year, the hornworm population grows rapidly and the tomato crop will be destroyed. However, if a different crop is planted on the same land every other year, the hornworms will not find food and will die.

Benchmark Check Describe the two ways in which practicing crop rotation benefits farmers. **D.2.3.2, G.2.3.4 AA**

Cover Crops

In the southern United States, during the early 1900s, the soil had become nutrient poor by the farming of only one crop, cotton. George Washington Carver, the scientist shown in **Figure 5,** urged farmers to plant soybeans and peanuts instead of cotton. Some plants, such as soybeans and peanuts, shown in **Figure 6,** helped to restore important nutrients to the soil. These plants are called cover crops. *Cover crops* are crops that are planted between harvests to replace certain nutrients and prevent erosion. Cover crops prevent erosion by providing cover from wind and rain.

No-Till Farming

In a soil-conservation method known as *no-till farming,* a farmer harvests a crop without turning over the soil. As shown in **Figure 7,** the farmer simply leaves the remains of a newly harvested crop on the ground and plants the next crop in these remains. As the new crop develops, the remains of the first crop hold the soil in place. Water runoff is reduced, and soil erosion is slowed by the cover provided by the remains of the first crop.

Compared with other farming methods, no-till farming saves time. Unfortunately, no-till farming is not suitable for all crops.

Figure 7 *No-till farming prevents erosion by providing cover that reduces water runoff.*

SECTION Review

Summary

● Soil is important for plants to grow, for animals to live in, and for water to be stored. If left unprotected, soil can be exposed to erosion. **D.2.3.2, G.2.3.2 CS, G.2.3.4 AA**

● Contour plowing and terracing prevent soil erosion by keeping water from running directly downhill. **D.2.3.2 , G.2.3.4 AA**

● Crop rotation slows nutrient depletion and reduces insect damage. **D.2.3.2, G.2.3.4 AA**

● Cover crops restore nutrients to soil and prevent soil erosion. **D.2.3.2, G.2.3.4 AA**

● No-till farming reduces water runoff and slows soil erosion. **D.2.3.2, G.2.3.4 AA**

Using Key Terms

1. Write an original definition for *soil conservation, erosion,* and *salinization.*

Understanding Key Ideas

2. What are three important benefits that soil provides? **G.2.3.2 CS**

3. List two ways in which soils can be damaged. **D.2.3.2, G.2.3.4 AA**

4. Describe two soil-conservation methods that prevent downhill soil erosion. **D.2.3.2, G.2.3.4 AA**

5. Explain two ways in which crop rotation benefits soils. **D.2.3.2, G.2.3.4 AA**

6. List two reasons that farmers plant cover crops. **D.2.3.2, G.2.3.4 AA**

7. Explain how no-till farming slows soil erosion. **D.2.3.2, G.2.3.4 AA**

Critical Thinking

8. **Applying Concepts** Why do land animals, including carnivores, depend on soil to survive? **G.2.3.2 CS**

9. **Making Predictions** How would drought affect the interrelationship between soil, water, plants, and the atmosphere? **G.2.3.2 CS**

FCAT Preparation

10. A number of soil-conservation methods are available to farmers. Some methods are used to reduce soil erosion. Other methods are used to slow nutrient depletion and to store nutrients in soil. And other methods are used to reduce damage caused by insect pests. Which of the following soil conservation methods would a farmer use to slow nutrient depletion and reduce damage caused by insects? **G.2.3.4 AA**

   A. contour plowing

   B. terracing

   C. crop rotation

   D. no-till farming

Model-Making Lab

OBJECTIVES

Design a model to understand how abrasion breaks down rocks. D.1.3.1 CS, H.1.3.5 AA

Evaluate the effects of abrasion. D.1.3.1 CS, H.1.3.5 AA

MATERIALS

- bottle, plastic, wide-mouthed, with lid, 3 L
- graph paper or computer
- markers
- pieces of limestone, all about the same size (24)
- poster board
- tap water

SAFETY

D.1.3.1 CS knows that mechanical and chemical activities shape and reshape the Earth's land surface by eroding rock and soil in some areas and depositing them in other areas, sometimes in seasonal layers.

H.1.3.5 AA knows that a change in one or more variables may alter the outcome of an investigation.

Rockin' Through Time

Wind, water, and gravity constantly change rocks. As wind and water rush over the rocks, the rocks may be worn smooth. As rocks bump against one another, their shapes change. The form of mechanical weathering that occurs as rocks collide and scrape together is called *abrasion*. In this activity, you will shake some pieces of limestone to model the effects of abrasion.

Ask a Question

1 How does abrasion break down rocks? How can I use this information to identify rocks that have been abraded in nature?

Form a Hypothesis

2 Formulate a hypothesis that answers the questions above.

Test the Hypothesis

3 Copy the chart on the next page onto a piece of poster board. Allow enough space to place rocks in each square.

4 Lay three of the limestone pieces on the poster board in the area marked "0 shakes." Be careful not to bump the poster board after you have added the rocks.

5 Place the remaining 21 rocks in the 3 L bottle. Then, fill the bottle halfway with water.

6 Close the lid of the bottle securely. Shake the bottle vigorously 100 times.

7 Remove three rocks from the bottle, and place them on the poster board in the box that indicates the number of times the rocks have been shaken.

8 Repeat steps 6 and 7 six times until all of the rocks have been added to the board.

Analyze the Results

1 **Examining Data** Describe the surface of the rocks that you placed in the area marked "0 shakes." Are they smooth or rough?

2 **Describing Events** How did the shape of the rocks change as you performed this activity?

3 **Constructing Graphs** Using graph paper or a computer, construct a graph, table, or chart that describes how the shapes of the rocks changed as a result of the number of times they were shaken.

Rocks Table	
0 shakes	100 shakes
200 shakes	300 shakes
400 shakes	500 shakes
600 shakes	700 shakes

Draw Conclusions

4 **Drawing Conclusions** Why did the rocks change?

5 **Evaluating Results** How did the water change during the activity? Why did it change?

6 **Making Predictions** What would happen if you used a much harder rock, such as granite, for this experiment?

7 **Interpreting Information** How do the results of this experiment compare with what happens in a river?

Chapter Review

USING KEY TERMS

1 Write an original definition for *soil structure* and *soil texture*.

2 Use *erosion* and *soil conservation* in separate sentences.

For each pair of terms, explain how the meanings of the terms differ.

3 *mechanical weathering* and *chemical weathering* **FCAT VOCAB**

4 *bedrock* and *parent rock*

UNDERSTANDING KEY IDEAS

Multiple Choice

5 Which of the following is a biotic factor that reshapes Earth's landscape? **D.1.3.4 AA**

a. gravity

b. water

c. plants

d. wind

6 In which climate would you find the fastest rate of chemical weathering? **D.1.3.5 CS**

a. a warm, humid climate

b. a cold, humid climate

c. a cold, dry climate

d. a warm, dry climate

7 Which of the following is a benefit that bacteria and fungi provide? **D.1.3.4 AA**

a. They form parent rock.

b. They maintain soil temperature.

c. They break down organic matter.

d. They enable ice wedging.

8 Which of the following properties describes a soil's ability to supply nutrients?

a. soil structure

b. infiltration

c. soil fertility

d. soil consistency

9 Soil is important because it provides

a. housing for animals.

b. nutrients for plants.

c. storage for water.

d. All of the above

10 Which of the following soil conservation techniques prevents erosion? **D.2.3.2, G.2.3.4 AA**

a. contour plowing

b. terracing

c. no-till farming

d. All of the above

11 Caverns are structures that form in karst landscapes. Which of the following processes causes caverns to form? **D.1.3.1 CS FCAT**

a. abrasion

b. dissolution

c. oxidation

d. ice wedging

12 Some organisms produce acids that can slowly break down rocks. Which of the following organisms produces acid that breaks down rocks? **D.1.3.4 AA, D.1.3.5 CS FCAT**

a. earthworms

b. oak trees

c. ants

d. lichens

Short Answer

13 Describe the two major types of weathering. D.I.3.I CS

14 Why is soil in temperate forests thick and fertile?

15 Describe the process of desertification. D.2.3.2, G.2.3.4 AA

16 How do cover crops help prevent soil erosion? D.2.3.2, G.2.3.4 AA

Math Skills

17 If 5 mm of bedrock weathers to form topsoil in 100 years, how many millimeters of topsoil is produced per year?

CRITICAL THINKING

Extended Response

18 **Drawing Conclusions** What can happen to soil when soil conservation is not practiced? D.2.3.2, G.2.3.4 AA

19 **Analyzing Processes** What are the positive and negative consequences of human activities that alter the soil? D.2.3.2, G.2.3.4 AA

20 **Applying Concepts** If you had to plant a crop on a steep hill, what soil conservation techniques would you use to prevent erosion? D.2.3.2, G.2.3.4 AA

Concept Mapping

21 Use the following terms to create a concept map: *weathering, chemical weathering, mechanical weathering, abrasion, ice wedging, oxidation,* and *soil.*

INTERPRETING GRAPHICS

The graph below shows how the density of water changes when temperature changes. The denser a substance is, the less volume it occupies. In other words, as most substances become colder, they contract and become denser. But water is unlike most other substances. When water freezes, it expands and becomes less dense. Use the graph to answer the questions that follow.

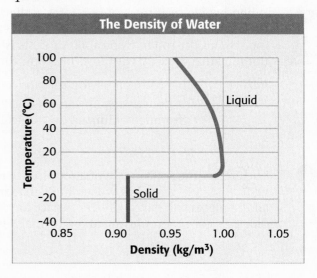

22 Which has a greater density: water at 40°C or water at −20°C?

23 How would the line in the graph appear if water had the same properties as most other liquids?

24 Which substance would be a more effective agent of mechanical weathering: water or another liquid? Why?

For the following questions, write your answers on a separate sheet of paper.

1 Weathering is a natural process that changes Earth's surface. Most weathering is caused by ice, water, and wind. Organisms, such as earthworms and other burrowing animals, can also cause weathering. What kind of weathering do earthworms and burrowing animals cause?

A. abrasion

B. oxidation

C. differential weathering

D. mechanical weathering

2 When people clear tropical rain forests, the consequences for the ecosystem can be extremely negative. People need lumber, fuel, and agricultural land, which is why they clear forests. But the soil in tropical rain forests is very thin and nutrient-poor. If cleared land is not replanted quickly with trees or crops, the soil will wash away.

READ
INQUIRE
EXPLAIN

Part A Why is the soil of tropical rainforests thin and nutrient-poor?

Part B Why do farmers move from one plot of land to another, increasing the negative environmental impact on tropical rain forests?

3 The greater the surface area of a rock is, the faster the rock will weather. If a large rock is broken into smaller pieces, the total of all the pieces will have a greater surface area than the original rock did. This concept is illustrated by the diagram.

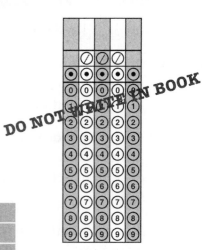

DO NOT WRITE IN BOOK

Total Surface Area to Volume

If the rock in illustration 1 were a cube in which each side measures 100 meters, the cube would have a total surface area of 60000 square meters. If the same rock were broken into eight smaller cubes, as illustration 2 shows, what would be the total surface area exposed to weathering in square meters?

4 Desertification is a form of land degradation that takes place in areas that have dry climates. In the process of desertification, the land becomes like a desert and will not support the same plants and animals it did before desertification began. What causes desertification?

F. high amounts of rainfall and flooding
G. earthquakes, volcanoes, and landslides
H. industrial waste, chemical waste, and other pollutants
I. climate change, drought, and human activities such as poor farming methods, overgrazing, and deforestation

5 The picture below shows a process of mechanical weathering that can cause cracks in rock to widen.

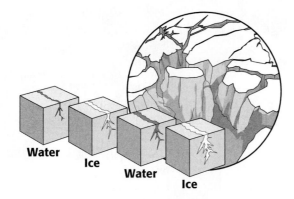

What is this process called?

A. abrasion
B. dissolution
C. ice wedging
D. oxidation

6 The soils in temperate climates are some of the most productive soils in the world. Temperate areas get enough rain to cause a high level of chemical weathering but not enough rain that the nutrients are leached out of the soil. What types of soils **most likely** form in temperate climates?

F. thin, fertile soils
G. thick, fertile soils
H. thin, nutrient-poor soils
I. thick, nutrient-poor soils

Science in Action

FOCUS ON FLORIDA

Science, Technology, and Society

African Dust

Did you know that dust blown across the Atlantic Ocean from northwestern Africa may be responsible for some environmental problems in Florida? Scientists studying samples of the dust have discovered that live bacteria, fungi, and viruses are being transported across the ocean from Africa. Research suggests that some of these organisms may cause diseases that are killing certain marine animals, such as corals, and certain marine plants, such as sea grasses. In addition, elements such as iron and phosphorus, which are found in the dust, may be causing toxic algal blooms in the Gulf of Mexico.

Social Studies ACTIVITY

Find pictures on the Internet or in magazines that show how people in arid regions of northwestern Africa live. Make a poster by using the pictures you find.

Scientific Discoveries

Strange Soil

Mysterious patterns of circles, polygons, and stripes were discovered in the soil in remote areas in Alaska and the Norwegian islands. At first, scientists were puzzled by these strange designs in remote areas. Then, the scientists discovered that these patterns were created by the area's weathering process, which includes cycles of freezing and thawing. When the soil freezes, the soil expands. When the soil thaws, the soil contracts. This process moves and sorts the particles of the soil into patterns.

Language Arts ACTIVITY

WRITING SKILL Write a creative short story describing what life would be like if you were a soil circle on one of these remote islands.

J. David Bamberger

Habitat Restoration J. David Bamberger knows how important taking care of the environment is. Therefore, he has turned his ranch into the largest habitat restoration project in Texas. For Bamberger, restoring the habitat started with restoring the soil. One way Bamberger restored the soil was to manage the grazing of the grasslands and to make sure that grazing animals didn't expose the soil. Overgrazing causes soil erosion. When cattle clear the land of its grasses, the soil is exposed to wind and rain, which can wash the topsoil away.

Bamberger also cleared his land of most of the shrub, *juniper*. Juniper requires so much water per day that it leaves little water in the soil for the grasses and wildflowers. The change in the ranch since Bamberger first bought it in 1959 is most obvious at the fence-line border of his ranch. Beyond the fence is a small forest of junipers and little other vegetation. On Bamberger's side, the ranch is lush with grasses, wildflowers, trees, and shrubs.

Math ACTIVITY

Bamberger's ranch is 2,300 hectares. There are 0.405 hectares in 1 acre. How many acres is Bamberger's ranch?

To learn more about these Science in Action topics, visit go.hrw.com and type in the keyword HT6FWFFF.

Current Science

Check out Current Science® articles related to this chapter by visiting go.hrw.com. Just type in the keyword HZ5CS10.

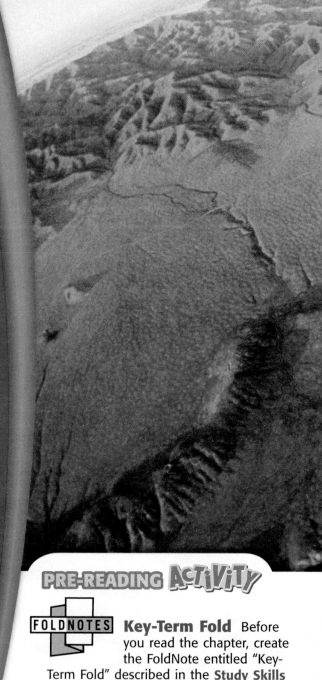

8

The Restless Earth

The Big Idea Earth's crust is constantly changing in measurable ways.

About the PHOTO

The San Andreas fault stretches across the California landscape like a giant wound. The fault, which is 1,000 km long, breaks the Earth's crust from Northern California to Mexico. Because the North American plate and Pacific plate are slipping past one another along the fault, many earthquakes happen.

PRE-READING ACTIVITY

FOLDNOTES **Key-Term Fold** Before you read the chapter, create the FoldNote entitled "Key-Term Fold" described in the **Study Skills** section of the Appendix. Write a key term from the chapter on each tab of the key-term fold. Under each tab, write the definition of the key term.

STARTUP ACTIVITY

Continental Collisions

As you can see, continents not only move but also can crash into each other. In this activity, you will model the collision of two continents.

Procedure

1. Obtain **two stacks of paper** that are each about 1 cm thick.
2. Place the two stacks of paper on a **flat surface,** such as a desk.
3. Very slowly, push the stacks of paper together so that they collide. Continue to push the stacks until the paper in one of the stacks folds over.

Analysis

1. What happens to the stacks of paper when they collide with each other?
2. Are all of the pieces of paper pushed upward? If not, what happens to the pieces that are not pushed upward?
3. What type of landform will most likely result from this continental collision?

Inside the Earth

If you tried to dig to the center of the Earth, what do you think you would find? Would the Earth be solid or hollow? Would it be made of the same material throughout?

Actually, the Earth is made of several layers. Each layer is made of different materials that have different properties. Scientists think about physical layers in two ways—by their composition and by their physical properties.

The Composition of the Earth

The Earth is divided into three layers—the crust, the mantle, and the core—based on the compounds that make up each layer. A *compound* is a substance composed of two or more elements. The less dense compounds make up the crust and mantle, and the densest compounds make up the core. The layers form because heavier elements are pulled toward the center of the Earth by gravity, so elements of lesser mass are found farther from the center.

The Crust

The outermost layer of Earth covering the mantle is the **crust.** The crust is 5 to 100 km thick. It is the thinnest layer of the Earth. As **Figure 1** shows, there are two types of crust—continental and oceanic. Both continental crust and oceanic crust are made mainly of the elements oxygen, silicon, and aluminum. However, the denser oceanic crust has almost twice as much iron, calcium, and magnesium, which form minerals that are denser than those in the continental crust.

READING WARM-UP

Objectives

● Identify the layers of the Earth by their composition.

● Identify the layers of the Earth by their physical properties.

● Describe a tectonic plate.

● Explain how seismic waves helped scientists learn about Earth's interior.

C.1.3.2, B.1.3.6 AA

Terms to Learn

crust *FCAT VOCAB*   asthenosphere
mantle   mesosphere
core   tectonic plate
lithosphere

READING STRATEGY

Reading Organizer As you read this section, create an outline of the section. Use the headings from the section in your outline.

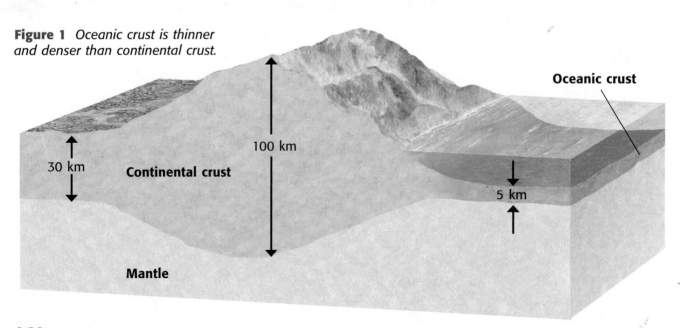

Figure 1 *Oceanic crust is thinner and denser than continental crust.*

Oceanic crust

100 km

30 km   **Continental crust**

5 km

Mantle

The Mantle

The layer of the Earth between the crust and the core is the **mantle.** The mantle is much thicker than the crust and contains most of the Earth's mass.

No one has ever visited the mantle. The crust is too thick to drill through to reach the mantle. Scientists must draw conclusions about the composition and other physical properties of the mantle from observations made on the Earth's surface. In some places, mantle rock pushes to the surface, which allows scientists to study the rock directly.

As you can see in **Figure 2,** another place scientists look for clues about the mantle is the ocean floor. Magma from the mantle flows out of active volcanoes on the ocean floor. These underwater volcanoes have given scientists many clues about the composition of the mantle. Because the mantle has more magnesium and less aluminum and silicon than the crust does, the mantle is denser than the crust.

The Core

The layer of the Earth that extends from below the mantle to the center of the Earth is the **core.** Scientists think that the Earth's core is made mostly of iron and contains smaller amounts of nickel but almost no oxygen, silicon, aluminum, or magnesium. As shown in **Figure 3,** the core makes up roughly one-third of the Earth's mass.

✓ Reading Check Briefly describe the layers that make up Earth.

Figure 2 *Volcanic vents on the ocean floor, such as this vent off the coast of Hawaii, allow magma to rise up through the crust from the mantle.*

crust the thin and solid outermost layer of the Earth above the mantle **FCAT VOCAB**

mantle the layer of rock between the Earth's crust and core

core the central part of the Earth below the mantle

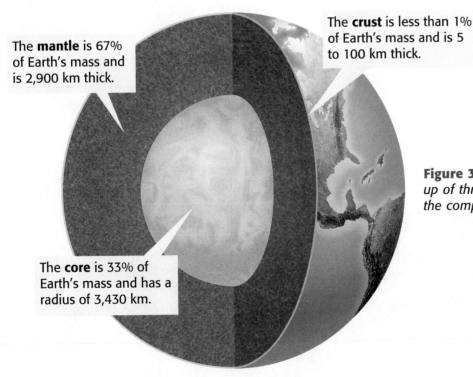

The **mantle** is 67% of Earth's mass and is 2,900 km thick.

The **crust** is less than 1% of Earth's mass and is 5 to 100 km thick.

The **core** is 33% of Earth's mass and has a radius of 3,430 km.

Figure 3 *The Earth is made up of three layers based on the composition of each layer.*

Using Models

Imagine that you are building a model of the Earth that will have a radius of 1 m. You find out that the average radius of the Earth is 6,380 km and that the thickness of the lithosphere is about 150 km. What percentage of the Earth's radius is the lithosphere? How thick (in centimeters) would you make the lithosphere in your model? Using these two facts and the other measurements given on this page, make both a pie graph and a bar graph showing the relative sizes of each of the Earth's layers.

The Physical Structure of the Earth

Another way to look at the Earth is to examine the physical properties of its layers. The Earth is divided into five physical layers—the lithosphere, asthenosphere, mesosphere, outer core, and inner core. As shown in the figure below, each layer has its own set of physical properties.

✓ Reading Check What are the five physical layers of the Earth?

Lithosphere The outermost, rigid layer of the Earth is the **lithosphere.** The lithosphere is made of two parts—the crust and the rigid upper part of the mantle. The lithosphere is divided into pieces called *tectonic plates*.

Asthenosphere The **asthenosphere** is a plastic layer of the mantle on which pieces of the lithosphere move. The asthenosphere is made of solid rock that flows very slowly.

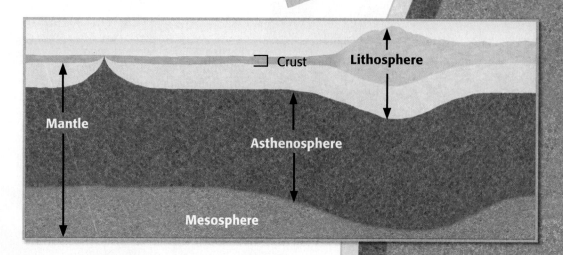

Crust

Lithosphere

Mantle

Asthenosphere

Mesosphere

lithosphere the solid, outer layer of the Earth that consists of the crust and the rigid upper part of the mantle

asthenosphere the soft layer of the mantle on which the tectonic plates move

mesosphere the strong, lower part of the mantle between the asthenosphere and the outer core

Mesosphere Beneath the asthenosphere is the strong, lower part of the mantle called the **mesosphere.** The mesosphere extends from the bottom of the asthenosphere to the Earth's core.

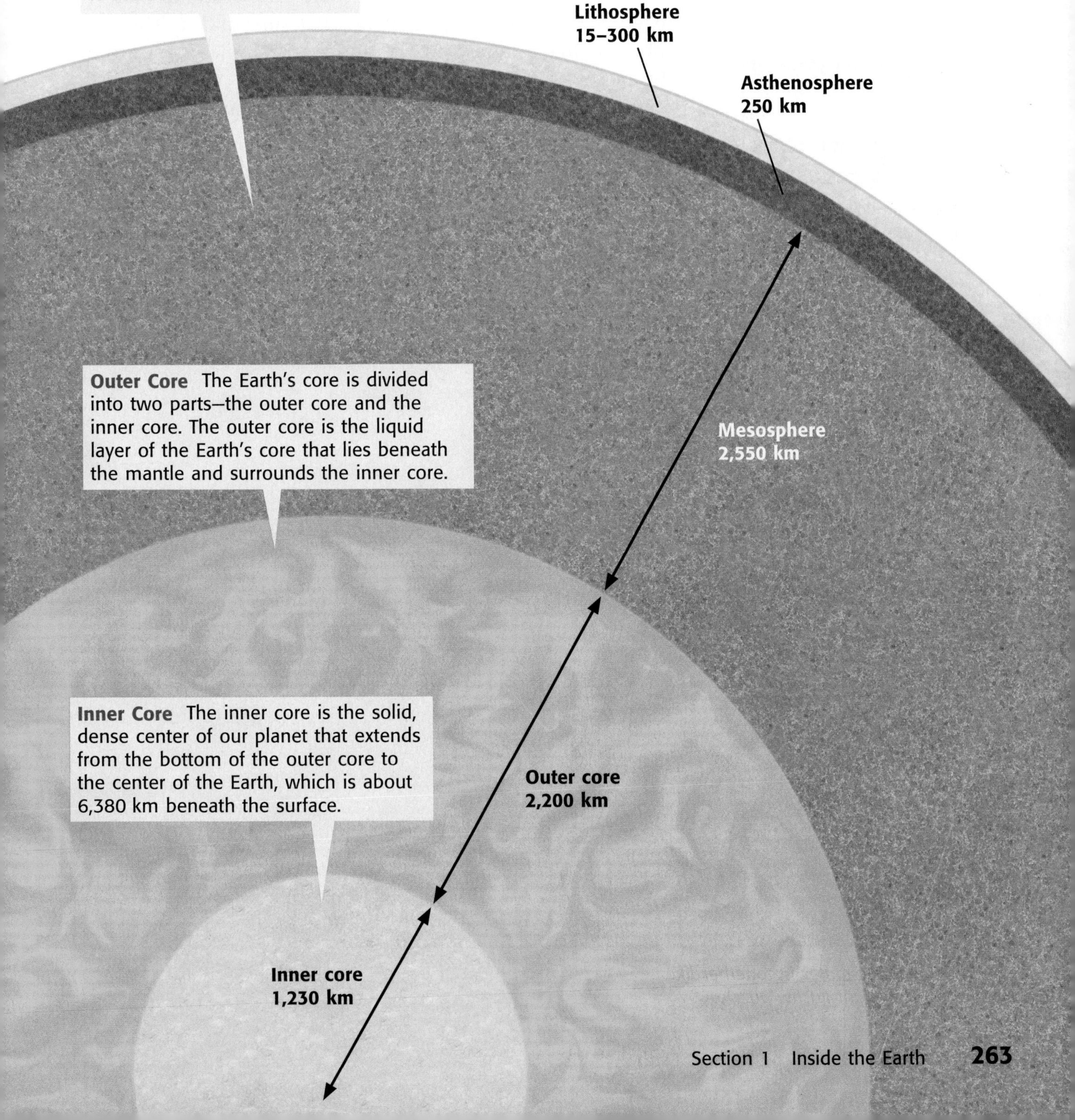

Lithosphere
15–300 km

Asthenosphere
250 km

Mesosphere
2,550 km

Outer Core The Earth's core is divided into two parts—the outer core and the inner core. The outer core is the liquid layer of the Earth's core that lies beneath the mantle and surrounds the inner core.

Inner Core The inner core is the solid, dense center of our planet that extends from the bottom of the outer core to the center of the Earth, which is about 6,380 km beneath the surface.

Outer core
2,200 km

Inner core
1,230 km

Tectonic Plates

Pieces of the lithosphere that move around on top of the asthenosphere are called **tectonic plates.** But what exactly does a tectonic plate look like? How big are tectonic plates? How and why do they move around? To answer these questions, begin by thinking of the lithosphere as a giant jigsaw puzzle.

A Giant Jigsaw Puzzle

All of the tectonic plates have names, some of which you may already know. Some of the major tectonic plates are named on the map in **Figure 4.** Notice that each tectonic plate fits together with the tectonic plates that surround it. The lithosphere is like a jigsaw puzzle, and the tectonic plates are like the pieces of a jigsaw puzzle.

Notice that not all tectonic plates are the same. For example, compare the size of the South American plate with that of the Cocos plate. Tectonic plates differ in other ways, too. For example, the South American plate has an entire continent on it and has oceanic crust, but the Cocos plate has only oceanic crust. Some tectonic plates, such as the South American plate, include both continental and oceanic crust.

tectonic plate a block of lithosphere that consists of the crust and the rigid, outermost part of the mantle

Major Tectonic Plates

1. Pacific plate
2. North American plate
3. Cocos plate
4. Nazca plate
5. South American plate
6. African plate
7. Eurasian plate
8. Indian plate
9. Australian plate
10. Antarctic plate

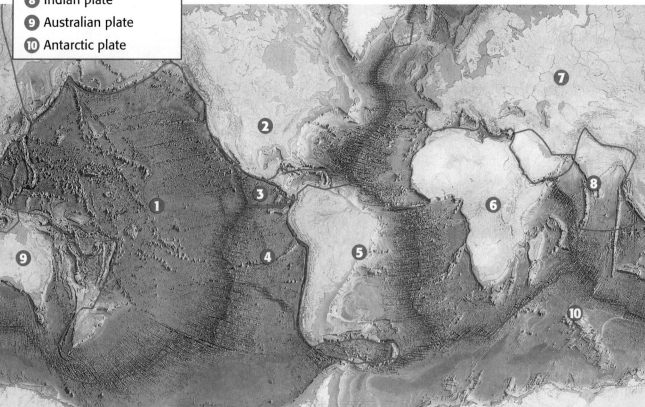

Figure 4 *Tectonic plates fit together like the pieces of a giant jigsaw puzzle.*

Figure 5 **The South American Plate**

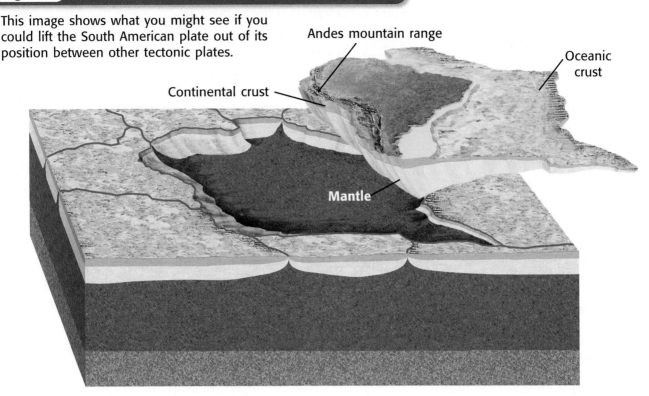

This image shows what you might see if you could lift the South American plate out of its position between other tectonic plates.

Andes mountain range

Oceanic crust

Continental crust

Mantle

A Tectonic Plate Close-Up

What would a tectonic plate look like if you could lift it out of its place? **Figure 5** shows what the South American plate might look like if you could. Notice that this tectonic plate not only consists of the upper part of the mantle but also consists of both oceanic crust and continental crust. The thickest part of the South American plate is the continental crust. The thinnest part of this plate is in the mid-Atlantic Ocean.

Like Ice Cubes in a Bowl of Punch

Think about ice cubes floating in a bowl of punch. If there are enough cubes, they will cover the surface of the punch and bump into one another. Parts of the ice cubes are below the surface of the punch and displace the punch. Large pieces of ice displace more punch than small pieces of ice do. Tectonic plates "float" on the asthenosphere in a similar way. The plates cover the surface of the asthenosphere, and they touch one another and move around. The lithosphere displaces the asthenosphere. Thick tectonic plates, such as those made of continental crust, displace more asthenosphere than do thin plates, such as those made of oceanic lithosphere.

✓ Reading Check Why do tectonic plates made of continental lithosphere displace more asthenosphere than tectonic plates made of oceanic lithosphere do?

QUICK Lab

Tectonic Ice Cubes

1. Take the bottom half of a **clear, 2 L soda bottle** that has been cut in half. Remove the label.
2. Fill the bottle with **water** to about 1 cm below the top edge of the bottle.
3. Get **three pieces of irregularly shaped ice** that are small, medium, and large.
4. Float the ice in the water, and note how much of each piece is below the surface of the water.
5. Do all pieces of ice float mostly below the surface? Which piece is mostly below the surface? Why?

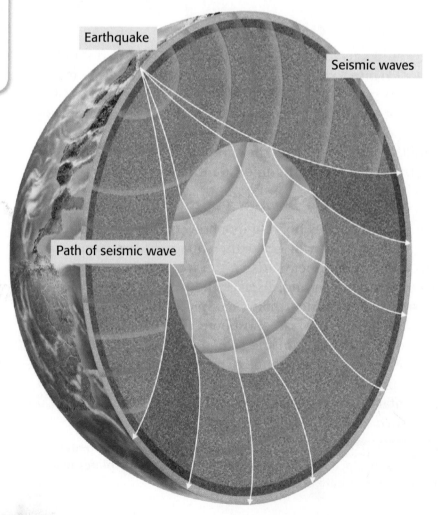

Mapping the Earth's Interior

How do scientists know about the deepest parts of the Earth? Scientists have never even drilled through the crust, which is only a thin skin on the surface of the Earth. So, how do we know so much about the mantle and the core?

Would you be surprised to know that some of the answers come from earthquakes? When an earthquake happens, vibrations called *seismic waves* are produced. Seismic waves travel at different speeds through the Earth. Their speed depends on the density and composition of material that they pass through. For example, a seismic wave traveling through a solid will move faster than a seismic wave traveling through a liquid.

When an earthquake happens, machines called *seismographs* measure the times at which seismic waves arrive at different distances from the earthquake. Seismologists can then use these distances and travel times to calculate the density and thickness of each physical layer of the Earth. **Figure 6** shows how seismic waves travel through the Earth.

Benchmark Check How do vibrations from an earthquake move through Earth's interior? **C.1.3.2, B.1.3.6 AA**

Figure 6 *By measuring changes in the speed of seismic waves that travel through Earth's interior, seismologists have learned that the Earth is made of different layers.*

Earthquake

Seismic waves

Path of seismic wave

Summary

- The Earth is made up of three layers—the crust, the mantle, and the core—based on chemical composition. Less dense compounds make up the crust and mantle. Denser compounds make up the core.

- The Earth is made up of five main physical layers: the lithosphere, the asthenosphere, the mesosphere, the outer core, and the inner core.

- Tectonic plates are large pieces of the lithosphere that move around on the Earth's surface.

- The crust in some tectonic plates is mainly continental or oceanic crust. Other plates include both kinds of crust.

- Thick tectonic plates, such as those with mainly continental crust, displace more asthenosphere than thin plates, such as those with mainly oceanic crust do.

- Seismic waves spread through Earth's interior away from the disturbances caused by an earthquake. **C.1.3.2, B.1.3.6 AA**

Using Key Terms

For each pair of terms, explain how the meanings of the terms differ.

1. *crust* and *mantle* **FCAT VOCAB**

2. *lithosphere* and *asthenosphere*

Understanding Key Ideas

3. The part of the Earth on which the tectonic plates move is the
   a. lithosphere.
   b. asthenosphere.
   c. mesosphere.
   d. crust.

4. Identify the layers of the Earth by their chemical composition.

5. Identify the layers of the Earth by their physical properties.

6. Describe a tectonic plate.

7. Explain how the movement of seismic waves helped scientists learn about the structure of the Earth's interior. **C.1.3.2**

Critical Thinking

8. **Making Comparisons** Explain the difference between the crust and the lithosphere.

9. **Analyzing Ideas** Why does a seismic wave travel faster through solid rock than through water?

FCAT Preparation

10. When an earthquake happens, seismic waves travel from the earthquake's center. The seismic waves travel at different speeds through different layers of Earth. The speed that seismic waves travel is determined by the density of each physical layer of Earth. Seismic waves are detected by machines called *seismographs*. Scientists can use the information from seismographs to determine the structure of Earth's interior. If an earthquake happens, through which of the following layers of Earth will the seismic waves travel slowest? **B.1.3.6 AA**

    A. the crust
    B. the mantle
    C. the outer core
    D. the inner core

SCiLINKS

NSTA
Developed and maintained by the National Science Teachers Association

For a variety of links related to this chapter, go to www.scilinks.org

Topic: Composition of the Earth; Structure of the Earth

SciLinks code: HSM0329; HSM1468

Restless Continents

Have you ever looked at a map of the world and noticed that the coastlines of continents on opposite sides of the oceans appear to fit together like the pieces of a puzzle? Is it just coincidence that the coastlines fit together well? Is it possible that the continents were actually together sometime in the past?

READING WARM-UP

Objectives

- Describe Wegener's hypothesis of continental drift.
- Explain how sea-floor spreading provides a way for continents to move.
- Describe how new oceanic lithosphere forms at mid-ocean ridges.
- Explain how magnetic reversals provide evidence for sea-floor spreading.

Terms to Learn

continental drift
sea-floor spreading

READING STRATEGY

Paired Summarizing Read this section silently. In pairs, take turns summarizing the material. Stop to discuss ideas that seem confusing.

continental drift the hypothesis that states that the continents once formed a single landmass, broke up, and drifted to their present locations

Wegener's Continental Drift Hypothesis

One scientist who looked at the pieces of this puzzle was Alfred Wegener (VAY guh nuhr). In the early 1900s, he wrote about his hypothesis of *continental drift.* **Continental drift** is the hypothesis that states that the continents once formed a single landmass, broke up, and drifted to their present locations. This hypothesis seemed to explain a lot of puzzling observations, including the observation of how well continents fit together.

Continental drift also explained why fossils of the same plant and animal species are found on continents that are on different sides of the Atlantic Ocean. Many of these ancient species could not have crossed the Atlantic Ocean. As you can see in **Figure 1,** without continental drift, this pattern of fossils would be hard to explain. In addition to fossils, similar types of rock and evidence of the same ancient climatic conditions were found on several continents.

✓ Reading Check How did fossils provide evidence for Wegener's hypothesis of continental drift?

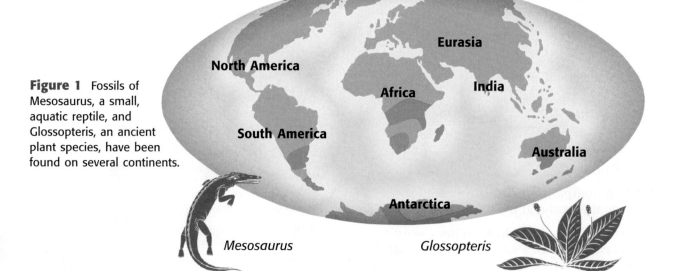

Figure 1 Fossils of Mesosaurus, a small, aquatic reptile, and Glossopteris, an ancient plant species, have been found on several continents.

Mesosaurus   *Glossopteris*

Figure 2 The Drifting Continents

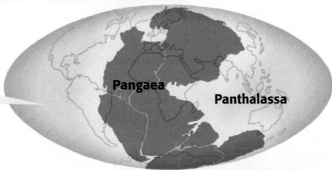

245 Million Years Ago
Pangaea existed when some of the earliest dinosaurs were roaming the Earth. The continent was surrounded by a sea called *Panthalassa*, which means "all sea."

135 Million Years Ago
Gradually, Pangaea broke into two big pieces. The northern piece is called *Laurasia*. The southern piece is called *Gondwana*.

65 Million Years Ago
By the time the dinosaurs became extinct, Laurasia and Gondwana had split into smaller pieces.

The Breakup of Pangaea

Wegener made many observations before proposing his hypothesis of continental drift. He thought that all of the present continents were once joined in a single, huge continent. Wegener called this continent *Pangaea* (pan JEE uh), which is Greek for "all earth." We now know from the theory of plate tectonics that Pangaea existed about 245 million years ago. We also know that Pangaea further split into two huge continents—Laurasia and Gondwana—about 180 million years ago. As shown in **Figure 2,** these two continents split again and formed the continents we know today.

Sea-Floor Spreading

When Wegener put forth his hypothesis of continental drift, many scientists would not accept it. From the calculated strength of the rocks, it did not seem possible for the crust to move in this way. During Wegener's life, no one knew the answer. It wasn't until many years later that evidence provided some clues to the forces that moved the continents.

Figure 3 Sea-Floor Spreading

Sea-floor spreading creates new oceanic lithosphere at mid-ocean ridges.

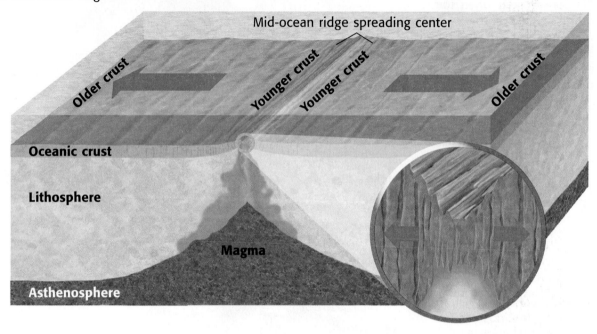

sea-floor spreading the process by which new oceanic lithosphere (sea floor) forms as magma rises to Earth's surface and solidifies at a mid-ocean ridge

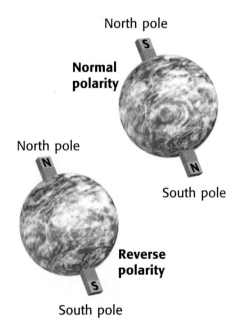

Figure 4 *The polarity of Earth's magnetic field changes over time.*

Mid-Ocean Ridges and Sea-Floor Spreading

A chain of submerged mountains runs through the center of the Atlantic Ocean. The chain is part of a worldwide system of mid-ocean ridges. *Mid-ocean* ridges are underwater mountain chains that run through Earth's ocean basins.

Mid-ocean ridges are also places where sea-floor spreading takes place. **Sea-floor spreading** is the process by which new oceanic lithosphere forms as magma rises toward the surface and solidifies. As the tectonic plates move away from each other, the sea floor spreads apart and magma fills in the gap. As this new crust forms, the older crust gets pushed away from the mid-ocean ridge. As **Figure 3** shows, the older crust is farther away from the mid-ocean ridge than the younger crust is.

Evidence for Sea-Floor Spreading: Magnetic Reversals

Some of the most important evidence of sea-floor spreading comes from magnetic reversals recorded in the ocean floor. Throughout Earth's history, the north and south magnetic poles have changed places many times. When the poles change places, the polarity of Earth's magnetic poles changes, as shown in **Figure 4.** When Earth's magnetic poles change places, this change is called a *magnetic reversal.*

Magnetic Reversals and Sea-Floor Spreading

The molten rock at the mid-ocean ridges contains tiny grains of magnetic minerals. These mineral grains contain iron and are like compasses. They align with the magnetic field of the Earth. When the molten rock cools, the record of these tiny compasses remains in the rock. This record is then carried slowly away from the spreading center of the ridge as sea-floor spreading occurs.

As you can see in **Figure 5,** when the Earth's magnetic field reverses, the magnetic mineral grains align in the opposite direction. The new rock records the direction of the Earth's magnetic field. As the sea floor spreads away from a mid-ocean ridge, it carries with it a record of magnetic reversals. This record of magnetic reversals was the final proof that sea-floor spreading does occur.

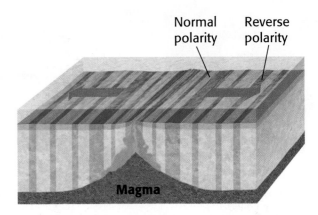

Normal polarity   Reverse polarity

Magma

Figure 5 *Magnetic reversals in oceanic crust are shown as bands of light blue and dark blue. Light blue bands indicate normal polarity, and dark blue bands indicate reverse polarity.*

✓ **Reading Check** How is a record of magnetic reversals recorded in molten rock at mid-ocean ridges?

SECTION Review

Summary

- Wegener hypothesized that continents drift apart from one another and have done so in the past.
- The process by which new oceanic lithosphere forms at mid-ocean ridges is called sea-floor spreading.
- As tectonic plates separate, the sea floor spreads apart and magma fills in the gap.
- Magnetic reversals are recorded over time in oceanic crust.

Using Key Terms

1. Write an original definition for *continental drift* and *sea-floor spreading*.

Understanding Key Ideas

2. At mid-ocean ridges,
   a. the crust is older.
   b. sea-floor spreading occurs.
   c. oceanic lithosphere is destroyed.
   d. tectonic plates are colliding.

3. Explain how oceanic lithosphere forms at mid-ocean ridges.

4. What is magnetic reversal?

5. Describe Wegener's hypothesis of continental drift.

Critical Thinking

6. **Identifying Relationships** Explain how magnetic reversals provide evidence for sea-floor spreading.

FCAT Preparation

7. Wegener developed a hypothesis of continental drift. What evidence supported this new hypothesis? H.1.3.1 AA

   A. the similarities of fossils found on landmasses that are far away from each other

   B. the movement of tides

   C. the relationship between the mantle and the crust

   D. the relationship between the north and south poles

SCI LINKS®

NSTA
Developed and maintained by the
National Science Teachers Association

For a variety of links related to this chapter, go to www.scilinks.org

Topic: Tectonic Plates
SciLinks code: HSM1497

The Theory of Plate Tectonics

It takes an incredible amount of force to move a tectonic plate! But where does this force come from?

As scientists' understanding of mid-ocean ridges and magnetic reversals grew, scientists formed a theory to explain how tectonic plates move. **Plate tectonics** is the theory that explains how large pieces of the lithosphere, called *plates,* move and change shape. In this section, you will learn what causes tectonic plates to move. First, you will learn about the different types of tectonic plate boundaries.

Tectonic Plate Boundaries

A tectonic plate boundary is a place where tectonic plates touch. These boundaries are divided into three types: convergent, divergent, and transform. The type of boundary depends on how the tectonic plates move relative to one another. Tectonic plates can collide, separate, or slide past each other. Earthquakes can occur at all three types of plate boundaries. The figure below shows examples of tectonic plate boundaries.

READING WARM-UP

Objectives

- Describe the three types of tectonic plate boundaries.
- Describe the three forces thought to move tectonic plates.
- Explain how the rate of tectonic plate movement is measured. **D.1.3.5 CS**

Terms to Learn

plate tectonics **FCAT** *VOCAB*
convergent boundary
divergent boundary
transform boundary

READING STRATEGY

Brainstorming The key idea of this section is plate tectonics. Brainstorm words and phrases related to plate tectonics.

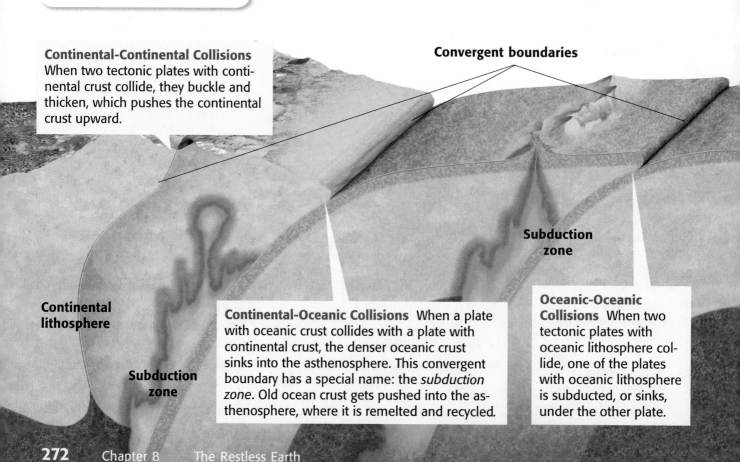

Continental-Continental Collisions
When two tectonic plates with continental crust collide, they buckle and thicken, which pushes the continental crust upward.

Convergent boundaries

Subduction zone

Continental lithosphere

Subduction zone

Continental-Oceanic Collisions When a plate with oceanic crust collides with a plate with continental crust, the denser oceanic crust sinks into the asthenosphere. This convergent boundary has a special name: the *subduction zone*. Old ocean crust gets pushed into the asthenosphere, where it is remelted and recycled.

Oceanic-Oceanic Collisions When two tectonic plates with oceanic lithosphere collide, one of the plates with oceanic lithosphere is subducted, or sinks, under the other plate.

Convergent Boundaries

When two tectonic plates collide, the boundary between them is a **convergent boundary.** What happens at a convergent boundary depends on the kind of crust at the leading edge of each tectonic plate. The three types of convergent boundaries are continental-continental boundaries, continental-oceanic boundaries, and oceanic-oceanic boundaries.

Divergent Boundaries

When two tectonic plates separate, the boundary between them is called a **divergent boundary.** New sea floor forms at divergent boundaries. Mid-ocean ridges are the most common type of divergent boundary.

Transform Boundaries

When two tectonic plates slide past each other horizontally, the boundary between them is a **transform boundary.** The San Andreas fault in California is a good example of a transform boundary. This fault marks the place where the Pacific and North American plates are sliding past each other.

Reading Check Define the term *transform boundary.*

plate tectonics the theory that explains how large pieces of the lithosphere, called *plates,* move and change shape **FCAT**VOCAB

convergent boundary the boundary formed by the collision of two lithospheric plates

divergent boundary the boundary between two tectonic plates that are moving away from each other

transform boundary the boundary between tectonic plates that are sliding past each other horizontally

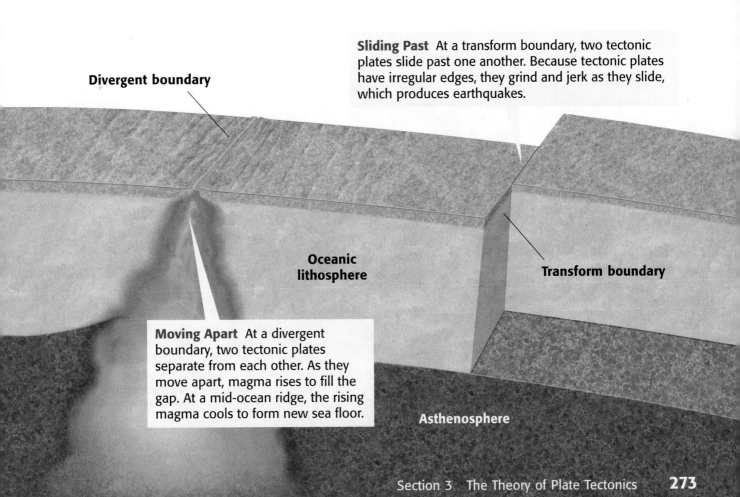

Divergent boundary

Sliding Past At a transform boundary, two tectonic plates slide past one another. Because tectonic plates have irregular edges, they grind and jerk as they slide, which produces earthquakes.

Oceanic lithosphere

Transform boundary

Moving Apart At a divergent boundary, two tectonic plates separate from each other. As they move apart, magma rises to fill the gap. At a mid-ocean ridge, the rising magma cools to form new sea floor.

Asthenosphere

Possible Causes of Tectonic Plate Motion

You have learned that plate tectonics is the theory that the lithosphere is divided into tectonic plates that move around on top of the asthenosphere. What causes the motion of tectonic plates? Remember that the solid rock of the asthenosphere flows very slowly. This movement occurs because of changes in density within the asthenosphere. These density changes are caused by the outward flow of thermal energy from deep within the Earth. When rock is heated, it expands, becomes less dense, and tends to rise to the surface of the Earth. As the rock gets near the surface, the rock cools, becomes more dense, and tends to sink. **Figure 1** shows three possible causes of tectonic plate motion.

D.1.3.5 CS understands concepts of time and size relating to the interaction of Earth's processes.

Benchmark Check What causes the motion of the tectonic plates? **D.1.3.5 CS**

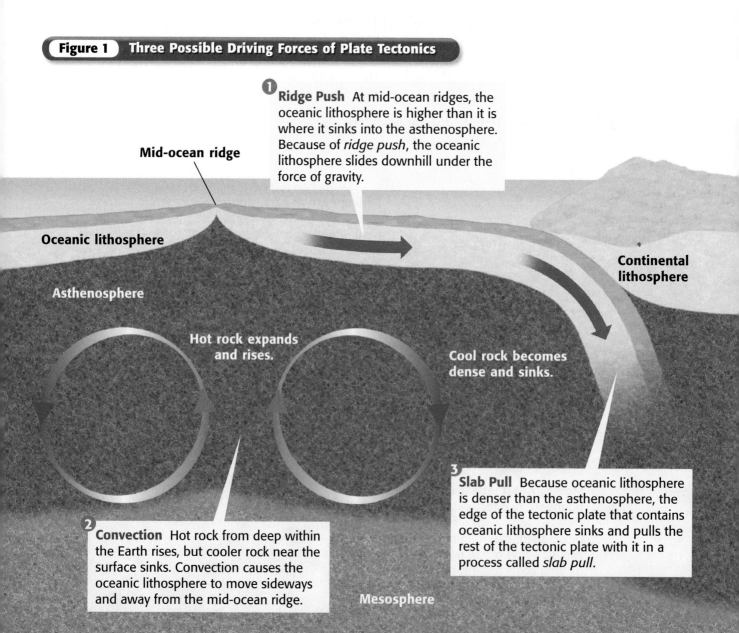

Figure 1 **Three Possible Driving Forces of Plate Tectonics**

❶ Ridge Push At mid-ocean ridges, the oceanic lithosphere is higher than it is where it sinks into the asthenosphere. Because of *ridge push*, the oceanic lithosphere slides downhill under the force of gravity.

Mid-ocean ridge

Oceanic lithosphere

Continental lithosphere

Asthenosphere

Hot rock expands and rises.

Cool rock becomes dense and sinks.

❷ Convection Hot rock from deep within the Earth rises, but cooler rock near the surface sinks. Convection causes the oceanic lithosphere to move sideways and away from the mid-ocean ridge.

❸ Slab Pull Because oceanic lithosphere is denser than the asthenosphere, the edge of the tectonic plate that contains oceanic lithosphere sinks and pulls the rest of the tectonic plate with it in a process called *slab pull*.

Mesosphere

Tracking Tectonic Plate Motion

How fast do tectonic plates move? The answer to this question depends on many factors, such as the type and shape of the tectonic plate and the way that the tectonic plate interacts with the tectonic plates that surround it. Tectonic plate movements are so slow and gradual that you can't see or feel them—the movement is measured in centimeters per year.

The Global Positioning System

Scientists use a system of satellites called the *global positioning system* (GPS), shown in **Figure 2,** to measure the rate of tectonic plate movement. Radio signals are continuously beamed from satellites to GPS ground stations, which record the exact distance between the satellites and the ground station. Over time, these distances change slightly. By recording the time it takes for the GPS ground stations to move a given distance, scientists can measure the speed at which each tectonic plate moves.

GPS satellite

Figure 2 *The image above shows the orbits of the GPS satellites.*

SECTION Review

Summary

- Boundaries between tectonic plates are classified as convergent, divergent, or transform.
- Ridge push, convection, and slab pull are three possible driving forces of plate tectonics.
- Scientists use data from a system of satellites called the global positioning system to measure the rate of motion of tectonic plates.

Using Key Terms

1. Write an original definition for *plate tectonics.* **FCAT** *VOCAB*

Understanding Key Ideas

2. The speed that a tectonic plate moves per year is best measured
   a. in kilometers per year.
   b. in centimeters per year.
   c. in meters per year.
   d. in millimeters per year. **D.1.3.5 CS**

3. Describe three possible driving forces of plate movement.

4. Explain how GPS can measure the rate of plate movement.

5. Identify the three types of plate boundaries

Critical Thinking

6. **Analyzing Processes** Why does oceanic crust sink beneath continental crust at convergent boundaries?

SCiLINKS.

NSTA

Developed and maintained by the
National Science Teachers Association

For a variety of links related to this chapter, go to www.scilinks.org

Topic: Plate Tectonics
SciLinks code: HSM1171

Deforming the Earth's Crust

Have you ever tried to bend something, only to have it break? Take long, uncooked pieces of spaghetti, and bend them very slowly but only a little. Now, bend them again farther and faster. What happened?

Why does a material bend at one time but break at another time? The answer is that the stress on the material was different each time. *Stress* is the amount of force per unit area on a given material. The same principle applies to the rocks in the Earth's crust. Different things happen to rock when different types of stress are applied. The different types of stress applied to rock and the activities that wear away rock shape the features of Earth's surface.

Deformation

The process by which the shape of a rock changes because of stress is called *deformation*. The spaghetti in **Figure 1** deformed in two different ways—by bending and by breaking. The same thing happens in rock layers. Rock layers bend when stress is placed on them. But when enough stress is placed on rocks, they can reach their elastic limit and break.

Compression and Tension

The type of stress that occurs when an object is squeezed, such as when two tectonic plates collide, is called **compression.** When compression occurs at a convergent boundary, mountains form.

Another form of stress is tension. **Tension** is stress that occurs when forces act to stretch an object. As you might guess, tension occurs at divergent plate boundaries, such as mid-ocean ridges, when two tectonic plates pull away from each other.

✓ Reading Check How do the forces of plate tectonics cause rock to deform?

READING WARM-UP

Objectives

- Identify how the movement of tectonic plates affects Earth's land surface. **D.1.3.3 CS**
- Describe two types of stress that deform rocks.
- Describe three major types of folds.
- Compare the three types of faults.
- Identify the most common types of mountains.
- Contrast uplift and subsidence.

Terms to Learn

compression   fault
tension   uplift
folding   subsidence

READING STRATEGY

Discussion Read this section silently. Write down questions that you have about this section. Discuss your questions in a small group.

Figure 1 *When a small amount of stress is placed on uncooked spaghetti, the spaghetti bends. Additional stress causes the spaghetti to break.*

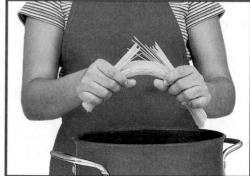

Figure 2 **Folding: When Rock Layers Bend Because of Stress**

Unstressed

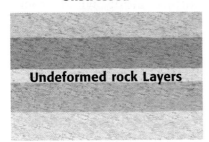

Undeformed rock Layers

Horizontal stress

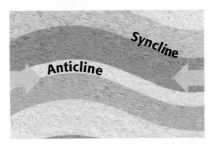

Syncline

Anticline

Vertical stress

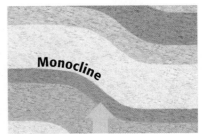

Monocline

Folding

The bending of rock layers due to stress in the Earth's crust is called **folding.** Scientists assume that all rock layers started as horizontal layers. So, when scientists see a fold, they know that deformation has taken place.

Types of Folds

Depending on how the rock layers deform, different types of folds are made. **Figure 2** shows the two most common types of folds—*anticlines*, or upward-arching folds; and *synclines*, downward, troughlike folds. Another type of fold is a monocline. In a *monocline,* rock layers are folded so that both ends of the fold are horizontal. Imagine taking a stack of paper and laying it on a table. Think of the sheets of paper as different rock layers. Now, put a book under one end of the stack. You can see that both ends of the sheets are horizontal, but all of the sheets are bent in the middle.

Folds can be large or small. The largest folds are measured in kilometers. Other folds are also obvious but are much smaller. These small folds can be measured in centimeters. **Figure 3** shows examples of large and small folds.

compression stress that occurs when forces act to squeeze an object

tension stress that occurs when forces act to stretch an object

folding the bending of rock layers due to stress

Figure 3 *The large photo shows mountain-sized folds in the Rocky Mountains. The small photo shows a rock that has folds smaller than a penknife.*

Faulting

Some rock layers break when stress is applied to them. The surface along which rocks break and slide past each other is called a **fault.** The blocks of crust on each side of the fault are called *fault blocks.*

When a fault is not vertical, understanding the difference between its two sides—the *hanging wall* and the *footwall*—is useful. **Figure 4** shows the difference between a hanging wall and a footwall. Two main types of faults can form. The type of fault that forms depends on how the hanging wall and footwall move in relationship to each other.

Normal Faults

A *normal fault* is shown in **Figure 5.** When a normal fault moves, it causes the hanging wall to move down relative to the footwall. Normal faults usually occur when tectonic forces cause tension that pulls rocks apart.

Reverse Faults

A *reverse fault* is shown in **Figure 5.** When a reverse fault moves, it causes the hanging wall to move up relative to the footwall. This movement is the reverse of a normal fault. Reverse faults usually happen when tectonic forces cause compression that pushes rocks together.

Reading Check How does the hanging wall in a normal fault move in relation to a reverse fault?

Fault

Footwall   **Hanging wall**

Figure 4 *The position of a fault block determines whether it is a hanging wall or a footwall.*

fault a break in a body of rock along which one block slides relative to another

---

Figure 5 **Normal and Reverse Faults**

Normal Fault When rocks are pulled apart because of tension, normal faults often form.

Reverse Fault When rocks are pushed together by compression, reverse faults often form.

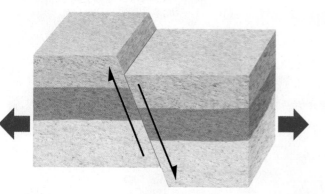

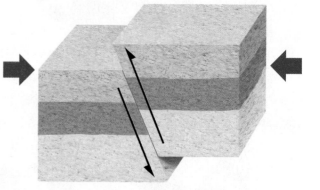

Figure 6 *The photo at left is a normal fault. The photo at right is a reverse fault.*

Telling the Difference Between Faults

It's easy to tell the difference between a normal fault and a reverse fault in drawings with arrows. But what types of faults are shown in **Figure 6**? You can certainly see the faults, but which one is a normal fault, and which one is a reverse fault? In the top left photo in **Figure 6,** one side has obviously moved relative to the other side. You can tell that this fault is a normal fault by looking at the order of sedimentary rock layers. If you compare the two dark layers near the surface, you can see that the hanging wall has moved down relative to the footwall.

Strike-Slip Faults

A third major type of fault is a *strike-slip fault.* A strike-slip fault is shown in **Figure 7.** Strike-slip faults form when opposing forces cause rock to break and move horizontally. If you were standing on one side of a strike-slip fault and looking across the fault when it moved, the ground on the other side would appear to move to your left or right. The San Andreas fault in California is a spectacular example of a strike-slip fault.

Quick Lab

Modeling Strike-Slip Faults

1. Use **modeling clay** to construct a box that is 6 in. × 6 in. × 4 in. Use different colors of clay to represent different horizontal layers.

2. Using **scissors,** cut the box down the middle. Place **two 4 in. × 6 in. index cards** inside the cut so that the two sides of the box slide freely.

3. Using gentle pressure, slide the two sides horizontally past one another.

4. How does this model illustrate the motion that occurs along a strike-slip fault?

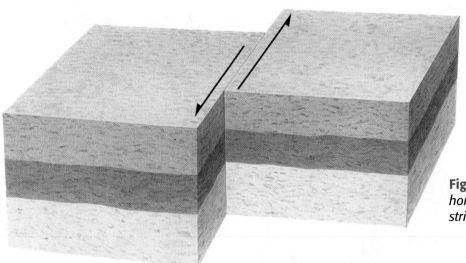

Figure 7 *When rocks are moved horizontally by opposing forces, strike-slip faults often form.*

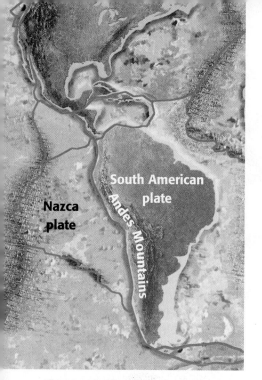

Figure 8 *The Andes Mountains formed on the edge of the South American plate where it converges with the Nazca plate.*

Figure 9 *The Appalachian Mountains were once as tall as the Himalaya Mountains but have been worn down by hundreds of millions of years of weathering and erosion.*

Plate Tectonics and Mountain Building

You have just learned about several ways that the Earth's crust changes because of the forces of plate tectonics. When tectonic plates collide, land features that start as folds and faults can eventually become large mountain ranges. Mountains exist because tectonic plates are continually moving around and colliding with one another. As shown in **Figure 8,** the Andes Mountains formed above the subduction zone where two tectonic plates converge.

When tectonic plates undergo compression or tension, they can form mountains in several ways. The three most common types of mountains are folded mountains, fault-block mountains, and volcanic mountains.

Folded Mountains

The highest mountain ranges in the world are made up of folded mountains. These ranges form at convergent boundaries where continents have collided. *Folded mountains* form when rock layers are squeezed together and pushed upward. If you place a pile of paper on a table and push on opposite edges of the pile, you will see how folded mountains form.

An example of a folded mountain range that formed at a convergent boundary is shown in **Figure 9.** About 390 million years ago, the Appalachian Mountains formed when the landmasses that are now North America and Africa collided. Other examples of mountain ranges that consist of very large and complex folds are the Alps in central Europe, the Ural Mountains in Russia, and the Himalaya Mountains, in Asia.

Benchmark Check **Explain how folded mountains form. D.1.3.3 CS**

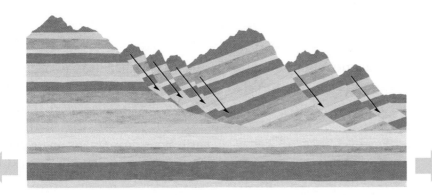

Figure 10 When the crust is subjected to tension, the rock can break along a series of normal faults, which creates fault-block mountains.

Fault-Block Mountains

When tectonic forces put enough tension on the Earth's crust, a large number of normal faults can result. *Fault-block mountains* form when this tension causes large blocks of the Earth's crust to drop down relative to other blocks. **Figure 10** shows one way that fault-block mountains form.

When sedimentary rock layers are tilted up by faulting, they can produce mountains that have sharp, jagged peaks. As shown in **Figure 11,** the Tetons in western Wyoming are a spectacular example of fault-block mountains.

Volcanic Mountains

Most of the world's major volcanic mountains are located at convergent boundaries where oceanic crust sinks into the asthenosphere at subduction zones. The rock that is melted in subduction zones forms magma, which rises to the Earth's surface and erupts to form *volcanic mountains*. Volcanic mountains can also form under the sea. Sometimes, these mountains can rise above the ocean surface to become islands. The majority of tectonically active volcanic mountains on the Earth have formed around the tectonically active rim of the Pacific Ocean. The rim has become known as the *Ring of Fire*.

Figure 11 The Tetons formed as a result of tectonic forces that stretched the Earth's crust and caused it to break in a series of normal faults.

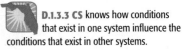
D.1.3.3 CS knows how conditions that exist in one system influence the conditions that exist in other systems.

In a World of Your Own
Create a planet that might be described in a science fiction book. Describe the interactions of the planet's core, mantle, and crust. Go to **go.hrw.com,** and type in the keyword **HZ5TECW.**

uplift the rising of regions of the Earth's crust to higher elevations

subsidence the sinking of regions of the Earth's crust to lower elevations

Uplift and Subsidence

Vertical movements in the crust are divided into two types—uplift and subsidence. The rising of regions of Earth's crust to higher elevations is called **uplift.** Rocks that are uplifted may or may not be highly deformed. The sinking of regions of Earth's crust to lower elevations is known as **subsidence** (suhb SIED'ns). Unlike some uplifted rocks, rocks that subside do not undergo much deformation.

Uplifting of Depressed Rocks

The formation of mountains is one type of uplift. Uplift can also occur when large areas of land rise without deforming. One way that areas rise without deforming is through a process known as *rebound*. When the crust rebounds, it slowly springs back to its previous elevation. Uplift often happens when a weight is removed from the crust.

Subsidence of Cooler Rocks

Rocks that are hot take up more space than cooler rocks do. For example, the lithosphere is relatively hot at mid-ocean ridges. The farther the lithosphere is from the ridge, the cooler and denser the lithosphere becomes. Because the oceanic lithosphere now takes up less volume, the ocean floor subsides.

Tectonic Letdown

Subsidence can also occur when the lithosphere becomes stretched in rift zones. A *rift zone* is a set of deep cracks that forms between two tectonic plates that are pulling away from each other. As tectonic plates pull apart, stress between the plates causes a series of faults to form along the rift zone. As shown in **Figure 12,** the blocks of crust in the center of the rift zone subside.

Figure 12 *The East African rift, from Ethiopia to Kenya, is part of a divergent boundary, but you can see how the crust has subsided relative to the blocks at the edge of the rift zone.*

Summary

- Deformation and folding are two activities shape Earth's land surface.

- Compression and tension are two forces of plate tectonics that deform rock.

- Folding occurs when rock layers bend because of stress.

- Faulting occurs when rock layers break and then move on either side of the break.

- Mountains are classified as either folded, fault-block, or volcanic.

- Mountain building is caused by the movement of tectonic plates. Folded mountains and volcanic mountains form at convergent boundaries. Fault-block mountains form at divergent boundaries. **D.1.3.3 CS**

- Uplift and subsidence are the two types of vertical movement in the Earth's crust. Uplift occurs when regions of the crust rise to higher elevations. Subsidence occurs when regions of the crust sink to lower elevations.

Using Key Terms

For each pair of terms, explain how the meanings of the terms differ.

1. *compression* and *tension*

2. *uplift* and *subsidence*

Understanding Key Ideas

3. The type of fault in which the hanging wall moves up relative to the footwall is called a
   a. strike-slip fault.
   b. fault-block fault.
   c. normal fault.
   d. reverse fault.

4. Describe three types of folds.

5. Compare the three types of faults.

6. Identify the most common types of mountains.

7. Describe two activities that shape Earth's land features. **D.1.3.3 CS**

8. What are rift zones, and how do they form?

Critical Thinking

9. **Predicting Consequences** If a fault occurs in an area where rock layers have been folded, which type of fault is it likely to be? Why?

10. **Identifying Relationships** Would you expect to see a folded mountain range at a mid-ocean ridge? Explain your answer. **D.1.3.3 CS**

FCAT Preparation

11. Most of the world's major volcanic mountains are located at convergent boundaries where oceanic crust sinks into the asthenosphere at subduction zones. The rock that is melted in subduction zones forms magma, which rises to the Earth's surface and erupts to form volcanic mountains. Volcanic mountains can also form under the ocean. Which of the following is most likely to happen if lava from an undersea volcano flows above the surface of the ocean? **D.1.3.3 CS**

    A. A mountain range of folded mountains will form.

    B. A mountain range of fault-block mountains will form.

    C. A volcanic island will form.

    D. Earth's crust will move vertically, so uplifting will occur.

SCiLINKS®

NSTA
Developed and maintained by the
National Science Teachers Association

For a variety of links related to this chapter, go to www.scilinks.org

Topic: Faults; Mountain Building
SciLinks code: HSM0566; HSM0999

What Are Earthquakes?

Have you ever felt the earth move under your feet? Many people have. Every day, somewhere within this planet, an earthquake is happening.

The word *earthquake* defines itself fairly well. But there is more to earthquakes than just the shaking of the ground. An entire branch of Earth science, called **seismology** (siez MAHL uh jee), is devoted to studying earthquakes. Earthquakes are complex, and they present many questions for *seismologists,* the scientists who study them.

Where Do Earthquakes Occur?

Most earthquakes take place near the edges of tectonic plates. Tectonic plates are giant pieces of Earth's thin, outermost layer. Tectonic plates move around on top of a layer of plastic rock. **Figure 1** shows the Earth's tectonic plates and the locations of recent major earthquakes.

Tectonic plates move in different directions and at different speeds. Two plates can push toward or pull away from each other. They can also slip slowly past each other. As a result of these movements, numerous features called faults exist in the Earth's crust. A *fault* is a break in the Earth's crust along which blocks of the crust slide relative to one another. Earthquakes occur along faults because of this sliding.

READING WARM-UP

Objectives

- Explain where earthquakes take place.
- Explain what causes earthquakes.
- Identify three different types of faults that occur at plate boundaries.
- Describe how energy from earthquakes travels through the Earth.

  B.1.3.6 AA, C.1.3.2

Terms to Learn

seismology   P waves
deformation   S waves
elastic rebound
seismic waves

READING STRATEGY

Paired Summarizing Read this section silently. In pairs, take turns summarizing the material. Stop to discuss ideas that seem confusing.

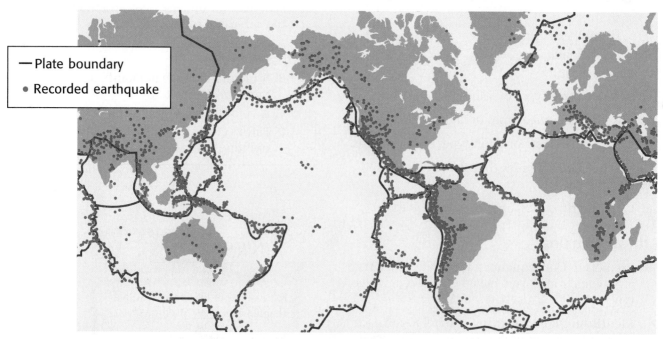

— Plate boundary
• Recorded earthquake

Figure 1 *The largest and most active earthquake zone lies along the plate boundaries surrounding the Pacific Ocean.*

What Causes Earthquakes?

As tectonic plates push, pull, or slip past each other, stress increases along faults near the plates' edges. In response to this stress, rock in the plates deforms. **Deformation** is the change in the shape of rock in response to stress. Rock along a fault deforms in mainly two ways. It deforms in a plastic manner, like a piece of molded clay, or in an elastic manner, like a rubber band. *Plastic deformation,* which is shown in **Figure 2,** does not lead to earthquakes.

Elastic deformation, however, does lead to earthquakes. Rock can stretch farther without breaking than steel can, but rock will break at some point. Think of elastically deformed rock as a stretched rubber band. You can stretch a rubber band only so far before it breaks. When the rubber band breaks, it releases energy. Then, the broken pieces return to their unstretched shape.

Elastic Rebound

The sudden return of elastically deformed rock to its original shape is called **elastic rebound.** Elastic rebound is like the return of the broken rubber-band pieces to their unstretched shape. Elastic rebound occurs when more stress is applied to rock than the rock can withstand. During elastic rebound, energy is released. Some of this energy travels as seismic waves. These seismic waves cause an earthquake, as shown in **Figure 3.**

✓ Reading Check How does elastic rebound relate to earthquakes?

Figure 2 *This road cut is adjacent to the San Andreas fault in Southern California. The rocks in the cut have undergone deformation because of the continuous motion of the fault.*

seismology the study of earthquakes

deformation the bending, tilting, and breaking of the Earth's crust; the change in the shape of rock in response to stress

elastic rebound the sudden return of elastically deformed rock to its undeformed shape

---

Figure 3 **Elastic Rebound and Earthquakes**

Before earthquake

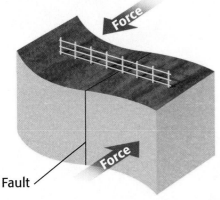

Fault

❶ Tectonic forces push rock on either side of the fault in opposite directions, but the rock is locked together and does not move. The rock deforms in an elastic manner.

After earthquake

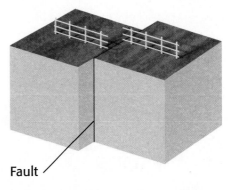

Fault

❷ When enough stress is applied, the rock slips along the fault and releases energy.

Faults at Tectonic Plate Boundaries

A specific type of plate motion takes place at different tectonic plate boundaries. Each type of motion creates a particular kind of fault that can produce earthquakes. Examine **Table 1** and the diagram below to learn more about plate motion.

Table 1 Plate Motion and Fault Types	
Plate motion	**Major fault type**
Transform	strike-slip fault
Convergent	reverse fault
Divergent	normal fault

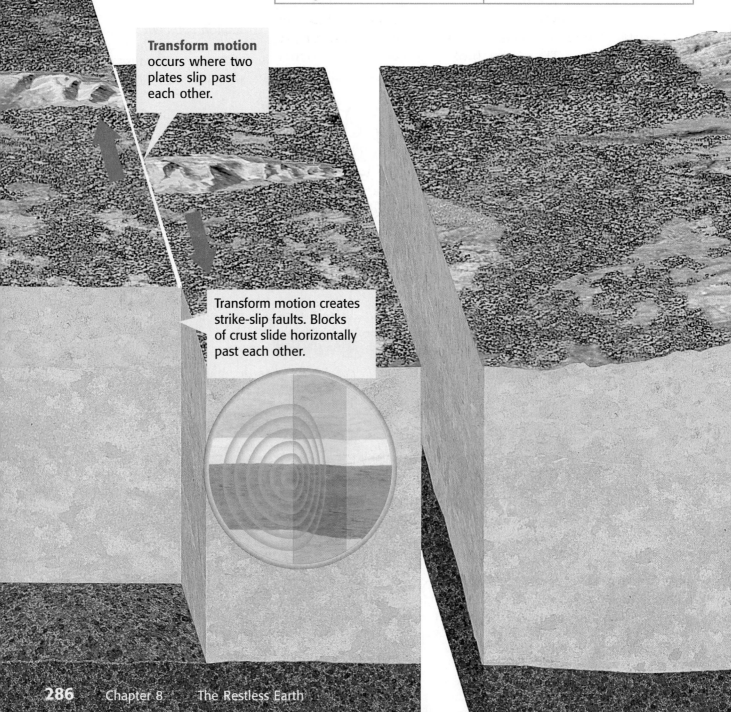

Transform motion occurs where two plates slip past each other.

Transform motion creates strike-slip faults. Blocks of crust slide horizontally past each other.

Earthquake Zones

Earthquakes can happen both near Earth's surface or far below it. Most earthquakes happen in the earthquake zones along tectonic plate boundaries. *Earthquake zones* are places where a large number of faults are located. The San Andreas fault zone in California is an example of an earthquake zone. But not all faults are located at tectonic plate boundaries. Sometimes, earthquakes happen along faults in the middle of tectonic plates.

Reading Check Where are earthquake zones located?

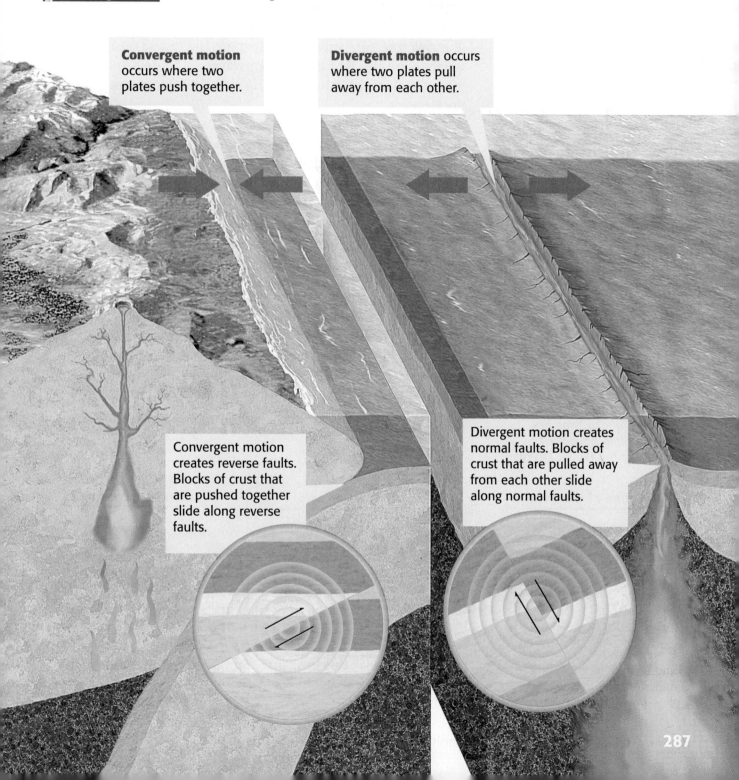

Convergent motion occurs where two plates push together.

Divergent motion occurs where two plates pull away from each other.

Convergent motion creates reverse faults. Blocks of crust that are pushed together slide along reverse faults.

Divergent motion creates normal faults. Blocks of crust that are pulled away from each other slide along normal faults.

Quick Lab

Modeling Seismic Waves

1. Stretch a **spring toy** lengthwise on a **table**.

2. Hold one end of the spring while a partner holds the other end. Push your end toward your partner's end. Observe what happens.

3. Repeat step 2, but this time shake the spring from side to side.

4. Which type of seismic wave is represented in step 2? in step 3?

seismic wave a wave of energy that travels through the Earth, away from an earthquake in all directions

P wave a seismic wave that causes particles of rock to move in a back-and-forth direction

S wave a seismic wave that causes particles of rock to move in a side-to-side direction

Figure 4 *The largest and most active earthquake zone lies along the plate boundaries surrounding the Pacific Ocean.*

How Do Earthquake Waves Travel?

Waves of energy that travel through the Earth are called **seismic waves.** Seismic waves that travel through the Earth's interior are called *body waves*. There are two types of body waves: P waves and S waves. Seismic waves that travel along the Earth's surface are called *surface waves*. Each type of seismic wave travels through Earth's layers in a different way and at a different speed. Also, the speed of a seismic wave depends on the kind of material the wave travels through.

P Waves and S Waves

Waves that travel through solids, liquids, and gases are called **P waves** (pressure waves). P waves are the fastest seismic waves, so they are the first earthquake waves to be detected. P waves move back and forth, squeezing and stretching rock as shown in **Figure 4.**

Rock can also be deformed from side to side. After being deformed from side to side, the rock springs back to its original position and S waves are created. **S waves,** or shear waves, are the second-fastest seismic waves. S waves shear rock side to side, as shown in **Figure 4,** which means they stretch the rock sideways. Unlike P waves, S waves cannot travel through parts of the Earth that are completely liquid.

Surface Waves

Surface waves move along the Earth's surface mostly in the upper few kilometers of Earth's crust. There are two types of surface waves. One type produces motion up, down, and around. The other type produces back-and-forth motion like the motion produced by S waves. Surface waves travel more slowly than body waves and are more destructive.

✓ Reading Check Explain the difference between surface waves and body waves.

P waves move rock back and forth, which squeezes and stretches the rock, as they travel through the rock.

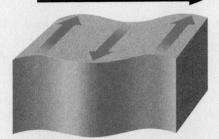

S waves shear rock side to side as they travel through the rock.

Surface waves move the ground in much the same way that ocean waves move water particles.

Earthquakes and Buildings

In many places, buildings, such as those shown in **Figure 5,** are not designed or constructed to withstand an earthquake's forces. Scientists and engineers study buildings that fail during earthquakes. As a result, they have learned a lot about making buildings more earthquake resistant.

Architects and engineers combine what they have learned with the newest technology to design and construct buildings and bridges to better withstand earthquakes. Today, older structures in California and other earthquake-prone areas are being made more earthquake resistant. The process of making older structures more earthquake resistant is called *retrofitting*.

Figure 5 *During the January 17, 1995, earthquake, the fronts of entire buildings collapsed into the streets of Kobe, Japan.*

SECTION Review

Summary

- Earthquakes occur mainly near the edges of tectonic plates.
- Elastic rebound is the direct cause of earthquakes.
- Three major types of faults occur at tectonic plate boundaries: normal faults, reverse faults, and strike-slip faults.
- Earthquake energy travels as body waves through the Earth's interior or as surface waves along the surface of the Earth.
B.1.3.6 AA, C.1.3.2

Using Key Terms

Use a term from the section to complete the sentence below.

1. _____ is the change in shape of rock in response to stress.

Understanding Key Ideas

2. Seismic waves that shear rock side to side are called
   a. surface waves.
   b. S waves.
   c. P waves.
   d. Both (b) and (c)

3. Where do earthquakes occur?

4. How do seismic waves move through Earth? **B.1.3.6 AA, C.1.3.2**

5. Describe the three types of plate motion and the faults that are related to each type of motion.

Critical Thinking

6. **Applying Concepts** Given what you know about elastic rebound, why do you think some earthquakes are stronger than others?

7. **Identifying Relationships** Why do you think that the majority of earthquake zones are located at tectonic plate boundaries?

FCAT Preparation

8. Waves of energy that travel through the Earth are called seismic waves. Seismic waves that travel through the Earth's interior are called body waves. A certain type of body wave, called a P wave, travels through granite at 5.8 km/s. Which of the following is a good estimate of how far a P wave would travel in 30 s? **B.1.3.6 AA**

   A. 115 km
   B. 130 km
   C. 175 km
   D. 190 km

SCiLINKS

NSTA
Developed and maintained by the
National Science Teachers Association

For a variety of links related to this chapter, go to www.scilinks.org

Topic: What Is an Earthquake?
SciLinks code: HSM1658

Model-Making Lab

Convection Connection

Some scientists think that convection currents within the Earth's mantle cause tectonic plates to move. Because these convection currents cannot be observed directly, scientists use models to simulate the process. In this activity, you will make your own model to simulate tectonic plate movement.

OBJECTIVES

Model convection currents to simulate tectonic plate movement.

Draw conclusions about the role of convection in plate tectonics.

MATERIALS

- craft sticks (2)
- food coloring
- gloves, heat-resistant
- hot plates, small (2)
- pan, aluminum, rectangular
- pencil
- ruler, metric
- thermometers (3)
- water, cold
- wooden blocks

SAFETY

Ask a Question

1 How can I make a model of convection currents in the Earth's mantle?

Form a Hypothesis

2 Turn the question above into a statement in which you give your best guess about what factors will have the greatest effect on your convection model.

Test the Hypothesis

3 Place two hot plates side by side in the center of your lab table. Be sure that they are away from the edge of the table.

4 Place the pan on top of the hot plates. Slide the wooden blocks under the pan to support the ends. Make sure that the pan is level and secure.

5 Fill the pan with cold water. The water should be at least 4 cm deep. Turn on the hot plates, and put on your gloves.

6 After a minute or two, tiny bubbles will begin to rise in the water above the hot plates. Gently place two craft sticks on the water's surface.

7 Use the pencil to align the sticks parallel to the short ends of the pan. The sticks should be about 3 cm apart and near the center of the pan.

8 As soon as the sticks begin to move, place a drop of food coloring in the center of the pan. Observe what happens to the food coloring.

9 With the help of a partner, hold one thermometer bulb just under the water at the center of the pan. Hold the other two thermometers just under the water near the ends of the pan. Record the temperatures.

10 When you are finished, turn off the hot plates. After the water has cooled, carefully empty the water into a sink.

Analyze the Results

1 **Explaining Events** Based on your observations of the motion of the food coloring, how does the temperature of the water affect the direction in which the craft sticks move?

Draw Conclusions

2 **Drawing Conclusions** How does the motion of the craft sticks relate to the motion of the water?

3 **Applying Conclusions** How does this model relate to plate tectonics and the movement of the continents?

4 **Applying Conclusions** Based on your observations, what can you conclude about the role of convection in plate tectonics?

Applying Your Data

Suggest a substance other than water that might be used to model convection in the mantle. Consider using a substance that flows more slowly than water.

Chapter Review

1 Use *crust*, *mantle*, and *core* in the same sentence. **FCAT VOCAB**

Complete each of the following sentences by choosing the correct term from the word bank.

asthenosphere   uplift

deformation   continental drift

2 The hypothesis that continents can drift apart and have done so in the past is known as _____.

3 The _____ is the soft layer of the mantle on which the tectonic plates move.

4 _____ is the change in the shape of rock in response to stress.

5 The rising of regions of the Earth's crust to higher elevations is called _____.

6 The theory of global dynamics in which Earth's crust is divided into large, rigid plates whose movements cause seismic activity is called _____. **FCAT VOCAB**

UNDERSTANDING KEY IDEAS

Multiple Choice

7 Deformation of the crust is a process that can be described in what terms? **D.1.3.3 CS**

  a. gradual and rare

  b. sudden and rare

  c. gradual and common

  d. sudden and common

8 Earthquakes can cause changes in the Earth's surface along faults. In what type of fault does the hanging wall move up relative to the footwall? **D.1.3.3 CS FCAT**

  a. strike-slip fault

  b. fault-block fault

  c. normal fault

  d. reverse fault

9 The type of mountain that forms when rock layers are squeezed together and pushed upward is a

  a. folded mountain.

  b. fault-block mountain.

  c. volcanic mountain.

  d. strike-slip mountain.

10 Seismic waves travel through Earth at different speeds depending on the density of the layers that they travel through. Where does scientific knowledge of the Earth's interior primarily come from? **B.1.3.6 AA FCAT**

  a. studying magnetic reversals in seismic waves

  b. studying seismic waves using the *global positioning system*

  c. studying the path of seismic waves generated by earthquakes

  d. studying the movement of tectonic plates

Short Answer

11 Explain how seismic waves move through Earth's interior during an earthquake. **B.1.3.6 AA FCAT**

12 How do magnetic reversals provide evidence of sea-floor spreading?

13 Explain how sea-floor spreading provides a way for continents to move.

14 Explain how different seismic waves affect rock as they travel through it.

B.1.3.6 AA, C.1.3.2

15 What is the global positioning system (GPS), and how does GPS allow scientists to measure the rate of motion of tectonic plates?

CRITICAL THINKING

Extended Response

16 **Applying Concepts** Why does oceanic lithosphere sink at subduction zones but not at mid-ocean ridges?

17 **Applying Concepts** Japan is located near a point where three tectonic plates converge. What would you imagine the earthquake-hazard level in Japan to be? Explain why.

Concept Mapping

18 Use the following terms to create a concept map: *sea-floor spreading, convergent boundary, divergent boundary, subduction zone, transform boundary,* and *tectonic plates.*

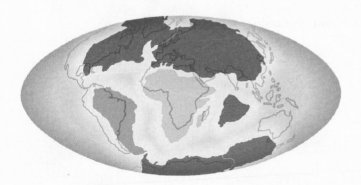

INTERPRETING GRAPHICS

Imagine that you could travel to the center of the Earth. Use the diagram below to answer the questions that follow.

Composition	Structure
Crust (50 km)	Lithosphere (150 km)
Mantle (2,900 km)	Asthenosphere (250 km)
	Mesosphere (2,550 km)
Core (3,430 km)	Outer core (2,200 km)
	Inner core (1,228 km)

19 How far beneath the Earth's surface would you have to go before you were no longer passing through rock that had the composition of granite?

20 How far beneath the Earth's surface would you have to go to find liquid material in the Earth's core?

21 At what depth would you find mantle material but still be within the lithosphere?

22 How far beneath the Earth's surface would you have to go to find solid iron and nickel in the Earth's core?

For the following questions, write your answers on a separate sheet of paper.

1 Earthquakes occur when tectonic plates move against each other. Which one of the following conditions could be the cause of an earthquake?

A. tsunamis
B. landslides
C. Earth's magnetic field
D. convergent plate motion

2 There have been many theories about the causes of tectonic plate movement. Which of the following is thought to be the cause of tectonic plate movement?

F. convection
G. deformation
H. faulting
I. folding

3 Andres and his family are driving through the countryside. They saw a chain of mountains like those shown in the picture below.

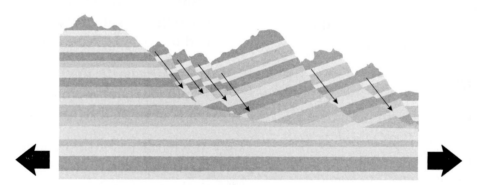

Mountain Formation

What type of mountain formation did Andres and his family observe?

A. folded
B. volcanic
C. transform
D. fault-block

4 Carlotta lives in California and has become very interested in the San Andreas fault because she knows that it may produce earthquakes. She has been studying what causes earthquakes and how their waves travel. She knows there are both body waves and surface waves. Which type of wave is more destructive and will cause the most damage to buildings and roadways? Why does this type of wave cause more damage?

5 The diagram below shows tectonic plates.

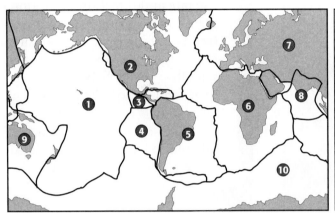

❶	Pacific Plate
❷	North American Plate
❸	Cocos Plate
❹	Nazca Plate
❺	South American Plate
❻	African Plate
❼	Eurasian Plate
❽	Indian Plate
❾	Australian Plate
❿	Antarctic Plate

Major Tectonic Plates

Which tectonic plate borders the Mid-Atlantic Ridge?

F. Cocos plate
G. Nazca plate
H. Pacific plate
I. African plate

FCAT Preparation

Science in Action

Science, Technology, and Society

Using Satellites to Track Plate Motion

When you think of laser beams firing, you may think of science fiction movies. However, scientists use laser beams to determine the rate and direction of motion of tectonic plates. From ground stations on Earth, laser beams are fired at several small satellites orbiting 5,900 km above Earth. From the satellites, the laser beams are reflected back to ground stations. Differences in the time it takes signals to be reflected from targets are measured over a period of time. From these differences, scientists can determine the rate and direction of plate motion.

Tallahassee
Jacksonville
St. Augustine
Gainesville
Daytona Beach

Key West

Weird Science

Earthquakes in Florida?

Even though Florida is nowhere near a tectonic plate boundary, Florida residents have experienced a few earthquakes in history. In January 1879, an earthquake was felt near St. Augustine, in northeastern Florida. The ground shook so hard that plaster fell off walls, and objects toppled off of shelves. Other Florida cities, such as Gainesville, Jacksonville, Tallahassee, and Daytona Beach also felt the earthquake. A year later, Key West felt strong shock waves from two earthquakes. The town did not suffer damage from the aftershocks because the center of the earthquake was located in Cuba. Despite these historic earthquakes, scientists think that the chance of an earthquake happening in Florida is pretty rare.

Social Studies ACTiViTY

WRITING SKILL Research a society that lives at an active plate boundary. Find out how the people live with dangers such as volcanoes and earthquakes. Include your findings in a short report.

Language Arts ACTiViTY

Research the effects of earthquakes, and write a journal entry from the perspective of someone who experienced an earthquake.

This scientist is using a laser to test one of the satellites that will be used to track plate motion.

Alfred Wegener

Continental Drift Alfred Wegener's greatest contribution to science was the hypothesis of continental drift. This hypothesis states that continents drift apart from one another and have done so in the past. To support his hypothesis, Wegener used geologic, fossil, and glacial evidence gathered on both sides of the Atlantic Ocean. For example, Wegener recognized similarities between rock layers in North America and Europe and between rock layers in South America and Africa. He believed that these similarities could be explained only if these geologic features were once part of the same continent.

Although continental drift explained many of his observations, Wegener could not find scientific evidence to develop a complete explanation of how continents move. Most scientists were skeptical of Wegener's hypothesis and dismissed it as foolishness. It was not until the 1950s and 1960s that the discoveries of magnetic reversals and sea-floor spreading provided evidence of continental drift.

Math ACTiViTY

The distance between South America and Africa is 7,200 km. As new crust is created at the mid-ocean ridge, South America and Africa are moving away from each other at a rate of about 3.5 cm per year. How many millions of years ago were South America and Africa joined?

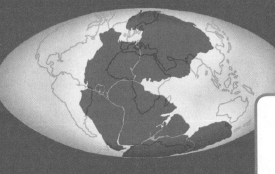

To learn more about these Science in Action topics, visit go.hrw.com and type in the keyword **HT6FTRFF**.

Current Science

Check out Current Science® articles related to this chapter by visiting go.hrw.com. Just type in the keyword HZ5CS07.

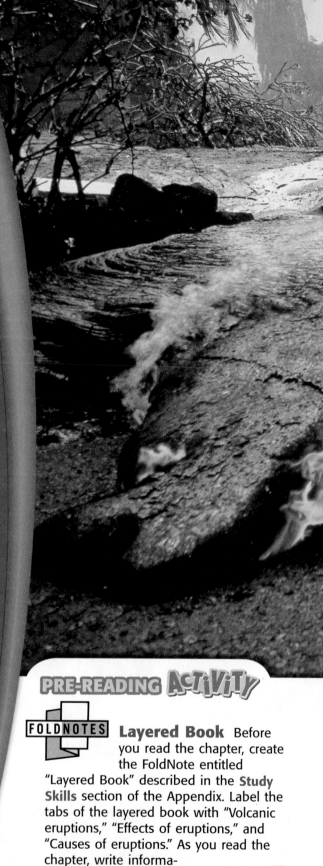

9

Volcanoes

 **The Big Idea** The Earth is shaped and reshaped by the activity of volcanoes.

About the PHOTO

When you think of a volcanic eruption, you probably think of a cone-shaped mountain exploding and sending huge clouds of ash into the air. Some volcanic eruptions do just that! Most volcanic eruptions, such as the one shown here, which is flowing over a road in Hawaii, are slow and quiet. Volcanic eruptions happen throughout the world, and they play a major role in shaping the Earth's surface.

PRE-READING ACTIVITY

FOLDNOTES Layered Book Before you read the chapter, create the FoldNote entitled "Layered Book" described in the **Study Skills** section of the Appendix. Label the tabs of the layered book with "Volcanic eruptions," "Effects of eruptions," and "Causes of eruptions." As you read the chapter, write information you learn about each category under the appropriate tab.

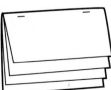

START-UP ACTIVITY

Anticipation H.1.3.5 AA

In this activity, you will build a simple model of a volcano, and you will try to predict an eruption.

Procedure

1. Place **10 mL of baking soda** on a **sheet of tissue.** Fold the corners of the tissue over the baking soda, and place the tissue packet in a **large pan.**

2. Put **modeling clay** around the top edge of a **funnel.** Press that end of the funnel over the tissue packet to make a tight seal with the pan.

3. After you put on **safety goggles,** add **50 mL of vinegar** and **several drops of liquid dish soap** to a **200 mL beaker** and stir.

4. Predict how long it will take the volcano to erupt after the liquid is poured into the funnel. Then, carefully pour the liquid into the funnel, and use a **stopwatch** to measure how long the volcano takes to begin erupting.

Analysis

1. Based on your observations, explain what happened to cause the eruption.

2. How accurate was your prediction? By how many seconds did the class predictions vary?

3. How do the size of the funnel opening and the amount of baking soda and vinegar affect the amount of time that the volcano takes to erupt?

Volcanic Eruptions

Think about the force released when the first atomic bomb exploded during World War II. Now imagine an explosion 10,000 times stronger, and you will get an idea of how powerful a volcanic eruption can be.

The explosive pressure of a volcanic eruption can turn an entire mountain into a billowing cloud of ash and rock in a matter of seconds. But eruptions are also creative forces—they help form fertile farmland. They also create some of the largest mountains on Earth. During an eruption, molten rock, or *magma,* is forced to the Earth's surface. Magma that flows onto the Earth's surface is called *lava.* **Volcanoes** are areas of Earth's surface through which magma and volcanic gases pass.

Nonexplosive Eruptions

At this moment, volcanic eruptions are occurring around the world—on the ocean floor and on land. Nonexplosive eruptions are the most common type of eruption. These eruptions produce relatively calm flows of lava, such as those shown in **Figure 1.** Nonexplosive eruptions can release huge amounts of lava. Vast areas of the Earth's surface, including much of the sea floor and the Northwest region of the United States, are covered with lava from nonexplosive eruptions.

volcano a vent or fissure in the Earth's surface through which magma and gases are expelled

Figure 1 Examples of Nonexplosive Eruptions

Sometimes, nonexplosive eruptions can spray lava into the air. Lava fountains, such as this one, pulse with the pressure of escaping gases.

▲ The speed of a lava flow can range from a slow creep to as fast as 60 km/h.

Explosive Eruptions

Explosive eruptions, such as the eruption of the Soufriere Hills volcano shown in **Figure 2,** are much rarer than nonexplosive eruptions. However, the effects of explosive eruptions can be incredibly destructive. During an explosive eruption, clouds of hot debris, ash, and gas rapidly shoot out from a volcano. Instead of producing lava flows, explosive eruptions cause molten rock to be blown into tiny particles that harden in the air. The dust-sized particles, called *ash,* can reach the upper atmosphere and can circle Earth for years. Larger pieces of debris fall close to the volcano. An explosive eruption can blast millions of tons of lava and rock from a volcano. In a matter of seconds, an explosive eruption can demolish an entire mountainside, as shown in **Figure 3.**

Benchmark Check Identify some of the devastating effects that an explosive volcanic eruption can have on the area surrounding a volcano. **D.1.3.5 CS**

Figure 2 *Smoke and ash shoot skyward during the eruption of the Soufriere Hills volcano on the Caribbean island of Montserrat in August 1997.*

D.1.3.5 CS understands concepts of time and size relating to the interaction of Earth's processes.

Figure 3 *Within seconds, the 1980 eruption of Mount St. Helens in Washington State caused the side of the mountain to collapse. The blast scorched and flattened 600 km^2 of forest.*

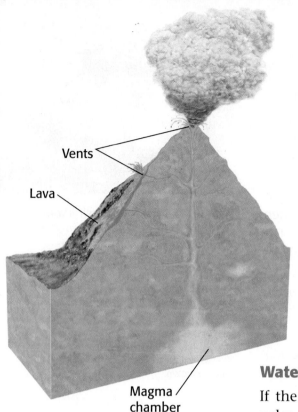

Vents

Lava

Magma chamber

Figure 4 *Volcanoes form when lava is released from vents.*

magma chamber the body of molten rock that feeds a volcano

vent an opening at the surface of the Earth through which volcanic material passes

Living with Volcanoes
Investigate the unique characteristics of communities near volcanoes. Go to **go.hrw.com,** and type in the keyword **HZ5VOLW.**

D.1.3.5 CS understands concepts of time and size relating to the interaction of Earth's processes.

What Is Inside a Volcano?

If you could look inside an erupting volcano, you would see the features shown in **Figure 4.** A **magma chamber** is a body of molten rock deep underground that feeds a volcano. Magma rises from the magma chamber through cracks in Earth's crust to openings called **vents.** Magma is released from the vents during an eruption.

What Makes Up Magma?

By comparing the composition of magma from different eruptions, scientists have made an important discovery. The composition of the magma affects how explosive a volcanic eruption is. The key to whether an eruption will be explosive lies in the silica, water, and gas content of the magma.

Water and Magma—An Explosive Combination

If the water content of the magma in a volcano is high, the volcano is more likely to undergo an explosive eruption. Because magma is underground, it is under intense pressure, and water stays dissolved in it. If the magma quickly moves to the surface, the pressure suddenly decreases and the water and other compounds, such as carbon dioxide, become gases. As the gases expand rapidly, an explosion can result. This process is similar to what happens when you shake and open a can of soda. When a can of soda is shaken, the CO_2 that is dissolved in the soda is released, and pressure inside the can builds up. When the can is opened, the soda shoots out, just as lava shoots out of a volcano during an explosive eruption.

Silica-Rich Magma Traps Explosive Gases

A volcano in which the magma has a high silica content is also likely to undergo explosive eruptions. Silica-rich magma has a stiff consistency. It flows slowly and tends to harden in a volcano's vents, which plugs the vents. As more magma pushes up from below, upward pressure increases. If enough pressure builds up, an explosive eruption takes place. Stiff magma prevents water vapor and other gases from easily escaping. Gas bubbles that are trapped in magma can expand until they explode. When they explode, the magma shatters and ash and pumice are blasted from the vent. Magma that contains less silica has a runnier, more fluid consistency. Gases escape this type of magma more easily, so explosive eruptions are less likely to occur where low-silica magma is present.

Benchmark Check What is the relationship between high silica content in magma and an explosive eruption? **D.1.3.5 CS**

What Erupts from a Volcano?

Magma erupts as either lava or pyroclastic (PIE roh KLAS tik) material. *Lava* is liquid magma that flows from a volcanic vent. *Pyroclastic material* forms when magma is blasted into the air and hardens. Nonexplosive eruptions produce mostly lava. Explosive eruptions produce mostly pyroclastic material. Over many years—or even during the same eruption—a volcano's eruptions may alternate between lava and pyroclastic eruptions.

Types of Lava

The viscosity of lava, or how lava flows, varies greatly. To understand viscosity, remember that a milkshake has high viscosity and a glass of milk has low viscosity. Lava that has high viscosity is stiff. Lava that has low viscosity is more fluid. The viscosity of lava affects the surface of a lava flow in different ways, as shown in **Figure 5.** *Blocky lava* and *pahoehoe* (puh HOY HOY) have a high viscosity and flow slowly. Other types of lava flows, such as *aa* (AH AH) and *pillow lava,* have lower viscosities and flow more quickly.

CONNECTION TO Social Studies

Fertile Farmlands Volcanic ash helps create some of the most fertile farmland in the world. Use a world map and reference materials to find the location of volcanoes that have helped create farmland in Italy, Africa, South America, and the United States. Make an illustrated map on a piece of poster board to share your findings.

ACTIVITY

Figure 5   Four Types of Lava

Aa is so named because of the painful experience of walking barefoot across its jagged surface. This lava pours out quickly and forms a brittle crust. The crust is torn into jagged pieces as molten lava continues to flow underneath.

Pahoehoe lava flows slowly, like wax dripping from a candle. Its glassy surface has rounded wrinkles.

Pillow lava forms when lava erupts underwater. As you can see here, this lava forms rounded lumps that are the shape of pillows.

Blocky lava is cool, stiff lava that does not travel far from the erupting vent. Blocky lava usually oozes from a volcano and forms jumbled heaps of sharp-edged chunks.

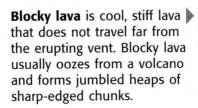

Figure 6 Four Types of Pyroclastic Material

Volcanic bombs are large blobs of magma that harden in the air. The shape of this bomb was caused by the magma spinning through the air as it cooled.

Lapilli, which means "little stones" in Italian, are pebblelike bits of magma that hardened before they hit the ground.

Volcanic ash forms when the gases in stiff magma expand rapidly and the walls of the gas bubbles explode into tiny, glasslike slivers. Ash makes up most of the pyroclastic material in an eruption.

Volcanic blocks, the largest pieces of pyroclastic material, are pieces of solid rock erupted from a volcano.

Types of Pyroclastic Material

Pyroclastic material forms when magma explodes from a volcano and solidifies in the air. This material also forms when powerful eruptions shatter existing rock. The size of pyroclastic material ranges from boulders that are the size of houses to tiny particles that can remain suspended in the atmosphere for years. **Figure 6** shows four types of pyroclastic material: volcanic bombs, volcanic blocks, lapilli (lah PIL IE), and volcanic ash.

D.1.3.5 CS understands concepts of time and size relating to the interaction of Earth's processes.

✓ **Reading Check** Describe four types of pyroclastic material.

Modeling an Explosive Eruption

1. Inflate a **large balloon,** and place it in a **cardboard box.**

2. Spread a **sheet** on the floor. Place the box in the middle of the sheet. Mound a thin layer of **sand** over the balloon to make a volcano that is taller than the edges of the box.

3. Lightly mist the volcano with **water.** Sprinkle **tempera paint** on the volcano until the volcano is completely covered.

4. Place **small objects** such as **raisins** randomly on the volcano. Draw a sketch of the volcano.

5. Put on your **safety goggles.** Pop the balloon with a **pin.**

6. Use a **metric ruler** to calculate the average distance that 10 grains of sand and 10 raisins traveled.

7. How did the relative weight of each type of material affect the average distance that the material traveled?

8. Draw a sketch of the exploded volcano.

Pyroclastic Flows

One particularly dangerous type of volcanic flow is called a *pyroclastic flow*. Pyroclastic flows are produced when enormous amounts of hot ash, dust, and gases are ejected from a volcano. This glowing cloud of pyroclastic material can race downhill at speeds of more than 200 km/h—faster than most hurricane-force winds! The temperature at the center of a pyroclastic flow can exceed 700°C. A pyroclastic flow from the eruption of Mount Pinatubo is shown in **Figure 7.** Fortunately, scientists were able to predict the eruption and a quarter of a million people were evacuated before the eruption.

Figure 7 *The 1991 eruption of Mount Pinatubo in the Philippines released terrifying pyroclastic flows.*

SECTION
Review

Summary

- Volcanic eruptions can be both explosive and nonexplosive. **D.1.3.5 CS**
- Magma that has a high level of water, CO_2, or silica tends to erupt explosively. **D.1.3.5 CS**
- Lava can be classified by its viscosity and by the surface texture of lava flows.
- Pyroclastic material, such as ash and volcanic bombs, forms when magma solidifies as it travels through the air.

Using Key Terms

1. Write an original definition for *volcano, magma chamber,* and *vent.*

Understanding Key Ideas

2. Classify four types of lava. Explain the characteristics that you used in your classification.

3. Which produces more pyroclastic material: an explosive eruption or a noneruptive explosion.

4. Explain how the presence of silica and water in magma increases the chances of an explosive eruption. **D.1.3.5 CS**

5. What is a pyroclastic flow?

Critical Thinking

6. **Analyzing Ideas** How would you compare an explosive eruption to opening a can of soda that has been shaken? Be sure to describe the role of carbon dioxide. **D.1.3.5 CS**

7. **Making Inferences** Predict the silica content of aa, pillow lava, and blocky lava.

FCAT Preparation

8. A volcanologist is studying the conditions under which an explosive volcanic eruption takes place. Which of the following conditions in magma would be least likely to lead to an explosive eruption? **D.1.3.5 CS**

A. Gas escapes easily.

B. Gas expands rapidly.

C. Pressure builds up beneath a vent that is plugged with magma.

D. The pressure suddenly decreases as the magma moves quickly to the surface.

SCI LINKS®

NSTA
Developed and maintained by the
National Science Teachers Association

For a variety of links related to this chapter, go to www.scilinks.org

Topic: Volcanic Eruptions
SciLinks code: HSM1616

Effects of Volcanic Eruptions

In 1816, Chauncey Jerome, a resident of Connecticut, wrote that the clothes his wife had laid out to dry the day before had frozen during the night. This event would not have been unusual except that the date was June 10!

At that time, residents of New England did not know that the explosion of a volcanic island on the other side of the world had severely changed the global climate and was causing "The Year Without a Summer."

Volcanic Eruptions and Climate Change

The explosion of Mount Tambora in 1815 blanketed most of Indonesia in darkness for three days. It is estimated that 12,000 people died directly from the explosion and 80,000 people died from the resulting hunger and disease. The global effects of the eruption were not felt until the next year, however. During large-scale eruptions, enormous amounts of volcanic ash and gases are ejected into the upper atmosphere.

As volcanic ash and gases spread throughout the atmosphere, they can block enough sunlight to cause global temperatures to drop. The Tambora eruption affected the global climate enough to cause food shortages in North America and Europe. More recently, the eruption of Mount Pinatubo, shown in **Figure 1,** caused average global temperatures to drop by as much as 0.5°C. Although this may seem insignificant, such a shift can disrupt climates all over the world.

Benchmark Check **Explain the relationship between explosive volcanic eruptions and global climate change.** D.1.3.3 CS, D.1.3.5 CS

Figure 1 *Ash from the eruption of Mount Pinatubo blocked out the sun in the Philippines for several days. The eruption also affected global climate.*

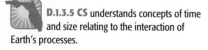

D.1.3.3 CS knows how conditions that exist in one system influence the conditions that exist in other systems.

D.1.3.5 CS understands concepts of time and size relating to the interaction of Earth's processes.

Different Types of Volcanoes

Volcanic eruptions can cause profound changes in climate. But the changes to Earth's surface caused by eruptions are probably more familiar. Perhaps the best known of all volcanic landforms are the volcanoes themselves. The three basic types of volcanoes are illustrated in **Figure 2.**

Shield Volcanoes

Shield volcanoes are built of layers of lava released from repeated nonexplosive eruptions. Because the lava is very runny, it spreads out over a wide area. Over time, the layers of lava create a volcano that has gently sloping sides. Although their sides are not very steep, shield volcanoes can be enormous. Hawaii's Mauna Kea, the shield volcano shown here, is the tallest mountain on Earth. Measured from its base on the sea floor, Mauna Kea is taller than Mount Everest.

Cinder Cone Volcanoes

Cinder cone volcanoes are made of pyroclastic material usually produced from moderately explosive eruptions. The pyroclastic material forms steep slopes, as shown in this photo of the Mexican volcano Paricutín. Cinder cones are small and usually erupt for only a short time. Paricutín appeared in a cornfield in 1943 and erupted for only nine years before stopping at a height of 400 m. Cinder cones often occur in clusters, commonly on the sides of other volcanoes. They usually erode quickly because the pyroclastic material is not cemented together.

Composite Volcanoes

Composite volcanoes, sometimes called *stratovolcanoes*, are one of the most common types of volcanoes. They form from explosive eruptions of pyroclastic material followed by quieter flows of lava. The combination of both types of eruptions forms alternating layers of pyroclastic material and lava. Composite volcanoes, such as Japan's Mount Fuji (shown here), have broad bases and sides that get steeper toward the top. Composite volcanoes in the western region of the United States include Mount Hood, Mount Rainier, Mount Shasta, and Mount St. Helens.

Figure 2 Three Types of Volcanoes

Shield volcano

Cinder cone volcano

Composite volcano

Figure 3 *A crater, such as this one in Kamchatka, Russia, forms around the central vent of a volcano.*

crater a bowl-shaped depression that forms on the surface of an object when a falling body strikes the object's surface or when an explosion occurs

caldera a large, circular depression that forms when the magma chamber below a volcano partially empties and causes the ground above to sink

Other Types of Volcanic Landforms

In addition to volcanoes, other landforms are produced by volcanic activity. These landforms include craters, calderas, and lava plateaus. Read on to learn more about these landforms.

Craters

Around the central vent at the top of many volcanoes is a funnel-shaped pit called a **crater.** An example of a crater is shown in **Figure 3.** During less explosive eruptions, lava flows and pyroclastic material can pile up around the vent creating a cone with a central crater. As the eruption stops, the lava that is left in the crater often drains back underground. The vent may then collapse to form a larger crater. If the lava hardens in the crater, the next eruption may blast it away. In this way, a crater becomes larger and deeper.

Calderas

Calderas can appear to be similar to craters, but they are many times larger than craters. A **caldera** is a large, circular depression that forms when the chamber that supplies magma to a volcano partially empties and the chamber's roof collapses. As a result, the ground above the magma chamber sinks, as shown in **Figure 4.** Much of Yellowstone Park is made up of three large calderas that formed when volcanoes collapsed between 1.9 million and 0.6 million years ago. Today, hot springs, such as Old Faithful, are heated by the thermal energy left over from those events.

Reading Check How do calderas form?

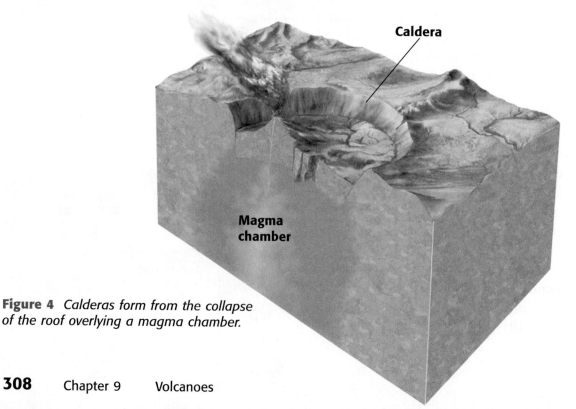

Caldera

Magma chamber

Figure 4 *Calderas form from the collapse of the roof overlying a magma chamber.*

Lava Plateaus

The most massive outpourings of lava do not come from individual volcanoes. Most of the lava on Earth's surface erupted from long cracks, or *rifts*, in the crust. In this type of eruption, runny lava can pour out for millions of years and spread over huge areas. A landform that results from repeated eruptions of lava spread over a large area is called a **lava plateau.** The Columbia River Plateau, part of which is shown in **Figure 5,** is a lava plateau that formed between 17 million and 14 million years ago in the northwestern region of the United States. In some places, the Columbia River Plateau is 3 km thick.

Figure 5 *The Columbia River Plateau formed from a massive outpouring of lava that began 17 million years ago.*

lava plateau a wide, flat landform that results from repeated nonexplosive eruptions of lava that spread over a large area

SECTION Review

Summary

- The large volumes of gas and ash released from volcanic eruptions can affect climate. D.1.3.3 CS
- Shield volcanoes result from many eruptions of relatively runny lava.
- Cinder cone volcanoes result from mildly explosive eruptions of pyroclastic material.
- Composite volcanoes result from alternating explosive and nonexplosive eruptions.
- Craters, calderas, and lava plateaus are volcanic landforms.

Using Key Terms

1. Use each of the following terms in a separate sentence: *crater, caldera,* and *lava plateau.*

Understanding Key Ideas

2. Predict the effects that ash and gases from an explosive volcanic eruption can have on Earth's climate. D.1.3.3 CS, D.1.3.5 CS

3. Explain why cinder cone volcanoes have narrower bases and steeper sides than shield volcanoes do.

4. Compare the three types of volcanoes.

5. Compare craters and calderas.

Critical Thinking

6. **Making Inferences** Hypothesize why it took a year for the Tambora eruption's effects to be felt in New England. D.1.3.3 CS, D.1.3.5 CS

FCAT Preparation

7. Which of the following is the most likely effect of a volcanic eruption that releases a large amount of ash and gas? D.1.3.3 CS

   A. an increase in the amount of sunlight reaching Earth

   B. a decrease in average global temperature

   C. a drop in global sea level

   D. an increase in crop yield

For a variety of links related to this chapter, go to www.scilinks.org

Topic: Volcanic Effects
SciLinks code: HSM1615

Causes of Volcanic Eruptions

More than 2,000 years ago, Pompeii was a busy Roman city near the sleeping volcano Mount Vesuvius. People did not see Vesuvius as much of a threat. Everything changed when Vesuvius suddenly erupted and buried the city in a deadly blanket of ash that was almost 20 ft thick!

Today, even more people are living on and near active volcanoes. Scientists closely monitor volcanoes to avoid this type of disaster. They study the gases coming from active volcanoes and look for slight changes in the volcano's shape that could indicate that an eruption is near. Scientists know much more about the causes of eruptions than the ancient Pompeiians did, but there is much more to be discovered.

READING WARM-UP

Objectives

● Describe the formation and movement of magma.

● Explain the relationship between volcanoes and plate tectonics. **D.1.3.3 CS**

● Summarize four methods scientists use to predict volcanic eruptions.

Terms to Learn

rift zone
hot spot

READING STRATEGY

Reading Organizer As you read this section, make a flowchart of the steps of magma formation in different tectonic environments.

The Formation of Magma

Understanding how magma forms helps explain why volcanoes erupt. Magma forms in the deeper regions of the Earth's crust and in the uppermost layers of the mantle where the temperature and pressure are very high. Changes in pressure and temperature cause magma to form.

Pressure and Temperature

Part of the upper mantle is made of very hot, puttylike rock that flows slowly. The rock of the mantle is hot enough to melt at Earth's surface, but it remains a puttylike solid because of pressure. This pressure is caused by the weight of the rock above the mantle. In other words, the rock above the mantle presses the atoms of the mantle so close together that the rock cannot melt. As **Figure 1** shows, rock melts when its temperature increases or when the pressure on the rock decreases.

Figure 1 *The curved line indicates the melting point of a rock. As pressure decreases and temperature increases, the rock begins to melt.*

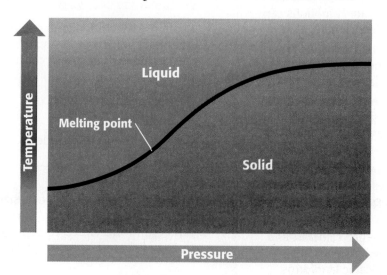

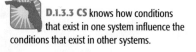
D.1.3.3 CS knows how conditions that exist in one system influence the conditions that exist in other systems.

Magma Formation in the Mantle

Because the temperature of the mantle is fairly constant, a decrease in pressure is the most common cause of magma formation. Magma often forms at the boundary between separating tectonic plates, where pressure is decreased. Once formed, the magma is less dense than the surrounding rock, so the magma slowly rises toward the surface like an air bubble in a jar of honey.

Where Volcanoes Form

The locations of volcanoes give clues about how volcanoes form. The map in **Figure 2** shows the location of some of the world's major active volcanoes. The map also shows the boundaries between tectonic plates. A large number of volcanoes lie directly on tectonic plate boundaries. In fact, the plate boundaries surrounding the Pacific Ocean have so many volcanoes that the area is called the *Ring of Fire.*

Tectonic plate boundaries are areas where tectonic plates either collide, separate, or slide past one another. At these boundaries, it is possible for magma to form and travel to the surface. About 80% of active volcanoes on land form where plates collide, and about 15% form where plates separate. The remaining few occur far from tectonic plate boundaries.

✓ **Reading Check** Why are most volcanoes located on plate boundaries?

Reaction to Stress

1. Make a pliable "rock" by pouring **60 mL of water** into a **plastic cup** and adding **150 mL of cornstarch,** 15 mL at a time. Stir well each time.

2. Pour half of the cornstarch mixture into a **clear bowl.** Carefully observe how the "rock" flows. Be patient—this process is slow!

3. Scrape the rest of the "rock" out of the cup with a **spoon.** Observe the behavior of the "rock" as you scrape.

4. What happened to the "rock" when you let it flow by itself? What happened when you put stress on the "rock"?

5. How is this pliable "rock" similar to the rock of the upper part of the mantle?

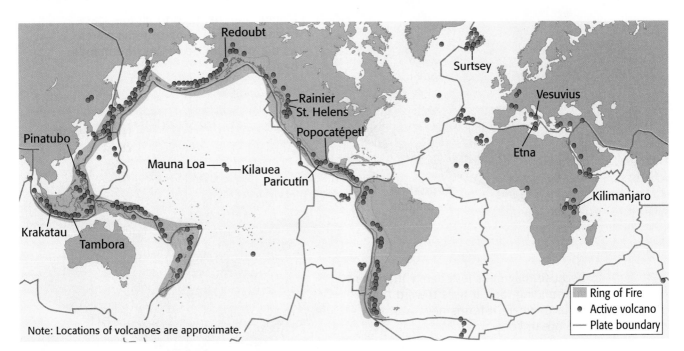

Note: Locations of volcanoes are approximate.

Figure 2 *Tectonic plate boundaries are likely places for volcanoes to form. The Ring of Fire contains nearly 75% of the world's active volcanoes on land.*

Determining the Origin of Volcanoes Use the Internet or another source to find a map that shows volcanoes of the world. Select 10 volcanoes in different parts of the world. Choose some volcanoes that are on land and some volcanoes that are in the ocean. Determine whether each volcano formed at a divergent boundary, at a convergent boundary, or at a hot spot. Turn in your completed research to your teacher. **D.1.3.3 CS**

rift zone an area of deep cracks that forms between two tectonic plates that are pulling away from each other

When Tectonic Plates Separate

At a *divergent boundary,* tectonic plates move away from each other. As tectonic plates separate, a set of deep cracks called a **rift zone** forms between the plates. Mantle rock then rises to fill in the gaps. When mantle rock gets closer to the surface, the pressure decreases. The pressure decrease causes the mantle rock to melt and form magma. Because magma is less dense than the surrounding rock, it rises through the rifts. When the magma reaches the surface, it spills out and hardens, creating new crust, as shown in **Figure 3.**

Mid-Ocean Ridges Form at Divergent Boundaries

Lava that flows from undersea rift zones produces volcanoes and mountain chains called *mid-ocean ridges*. Just as a baseball has stitches, the Earth is circled with mid-ocean ridges. At these ridges, lava flows out and creates new crust. Most volcanic activity on Earth occurs at mid-ocean ridges. While most mid-ocean ridges are underwater, Iceland, with its volcanoes and hot springs, was created by lava from the Mid-Atlantic Ridge. In 1963, enough lava poured out of the Mid-Atlantic Ridge near Iceland to form a new island called *Surtsey*. Scientists watched this new island being born!

Figure 3 **How Magma Forms at a Divergent Boundary**

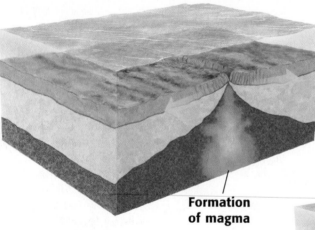

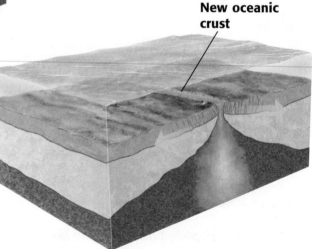

◀ Mantle material rises to fill the space opened by separating tectonic plates. As the pressure decreases, the mantle begins to melt.

New oceanic crust

Formation of magma

Because magma is less dense than the ▶ surrounding rock, it rises toward the surface, where it forms new crust on the ocean floor.

Figure 4 How Magma Forms at a Convergent Boundary

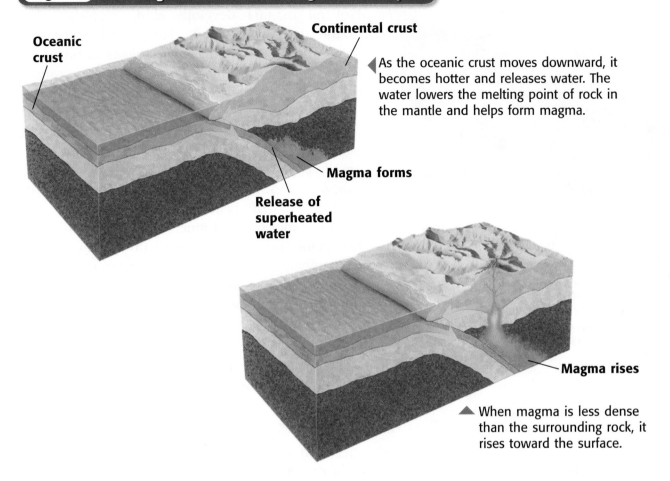

Oceanic crust

Continental crust

◀ As the oceanic crust moves downward, it becomes hotter and releases water. The water lowers the melting point of rock in the mantle and helps form magma.

Magma forms

Release of superheated water

Magma rises

▲ When magma is less dense than the surrounding rock, it rises toward the surface.

When Tectonic Plates Collide

If you slide two pieces of notebook paper into one another on a flat desktop, the papers will either buckle upward or one piece of paper will move under the other. This is similar to what happens at a convergent boundary. A *convergent boundary* is a place where tectonic plates collide. When an oceanic plate collides with a continental plate, the oceanic plate usually slides underneath the continental plate. The process of *subduction,* the movement of one tectonic plate underneath another, is shown in **Figure 4.** Oceanic crust is subducted because it is denser and thinner than continental crust.

Subduction Produces Magma

As the descending oceanic crust scrapes past the continental crust, the temperature and pressure increase. The combination of increased heat and pressure causes the water contained in the oceanic crust to be released. The water then mixes with the mantle rock, which lowers the rock's melting point, causing it to melt. This body of magma can rise to form a volcano.

Benchmark Check How does subduction produce magma? **D.I.3.3 CS**

SCHOOL to HOME

Tectonic Models Create models of convergent and divergent boundaries by using materials of your choice. Have your teacher approve your list before you start building your model at home with a family member. In class, use your model to explain how each type of boundary leads to the formation of magma.

ACTIVITY

D.I.3.3 CS knows how conditions that exist in one system influence the conditions that exist in other systems.

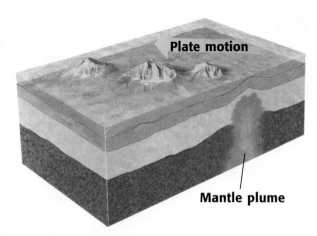

Hot Spots

Not all magma develops along tectonic plate boundaries. For example, the Hawaiian Islands, some of the most well-known volcanoes on Earth, are nowhere near a plate boundary. The volcanoes of Hawaii and several other places on Earth are known as *hot spots*. **Hot spots** are volcanically active places on the Earth's surface that are far from plate boundaries. Some scientists think that hot spots are directly above columns of rising magma, called *mantle plumes*. Other scientists think that hot spots are the result of cracks in the Earth's crust.

A hot spot often produces a long chain of volcanoes. One theory is that the mantle plume stays in the same spot while the tectonic plate moves over it, as shown in **Figure 5.** Another theory argues that hot-spot volcanoes occur in long chains because they form along the cracks in the Earth's crust. Both theories may be correct.

Figure 5 *According to one theory, a string of volcanic islands forms as a tectonic plate passes over a mantle plume.*

hot spot a volcanically active area of Earth's surface, commonly far from a tectonic plate boundary

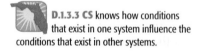 **D.1.3.3 CS** knows how conditions that exist in one system influence the conditions that exist in other systems.

✓ **Reading Check** Describe two theories that explain the existence of hot spots.

Predicting Volcanic Eruptions

You now understand some of the processes that produce volcanoes, but how do scientists predict when a volcano is going to erupt? Volcanoes are classified in three categories. *Extinct volcanoes* have not erupted in recorded history and probably never will erupt again. *Dormant volcanoes* are currently not erupting, but the record of past eruptions suggests that they may erupt again. *Active volcanoes* are currently erupting or show signs of erupting in the near future. Scientists study active and dormant volcanoes for signs of a future eruption.

Figure 6 *As if being this close to an active volcano is not dangerous enough, the gases being collected are extremely poisonous.*

Measuring Small Quakes and Volcanic Gases

Most active volcanoes produce small earthquakes as the magma within them moves upward and causes the surrounding rock to shift. Just before an eruption, the number and intensity of the earthquakes increase and the occurrence of quakes may be continuous. Monitoring these quakes is one of the best ways to predict an eruption.

As **Figure 6** shows, scientists also study the volume and composition of volcanic gases. The ratio of certain gases, especially that of sulfur dioxide, SO_2, to carbon dioxide, CO_2, may be important in predicting eruptions. Changes in this ratio may indicate changes in the magma chamber below.

Measuring Slope and Temperature

As magma moves upward prior to an eruption, it can cause the Earth's surface to swell. The side of a volcano may even bulge as the magma moves upward. An instrument called a *tiltmeter* helps scientists detect small changes in the angle of a volcano's slope. Scientists also use satellite technology such as the Global Positioning System (GPS) to detect the changes in a volcano's slope that may signal an eruption.

One of the newest methods for predicting volcanic eruptions includes using satellite images. Infrared satellite images record changes in the surface temperature and gas emissions of a volcano over time. If the site is getting hotter, the magma below is probably rising!

SECTION
Review

Summary

- Temperature and pressure influence magma formation.
- Most volcanoes form at tectonic boundaries.
- As tectonic plates separate, magma rises to fill the cracks, or rifts, that develop. **D.1.3.3 CS**
- As oceanic and continental plates collide, the oceanic plate tends to subduct and cause the formation of magma. **D.1.3.3 CS**
- To predict eruptions, scientists study the frequency and type of earthquakes associated with the volcano as well as changes in slope, changes in the gases released, and changes in the volcano's surface temperature.

Using Key Terms

1. Use *hot spot* and *rift zone* in separate sentences.

Understanding Key Ideas

2. Describe how magma forms and moves.

3. Explain how convergent and divergent plate boundaries cause magma formation. **D.1.3.3 CS**

4. Summarize four methods that scientists use to predict volcanic eruptions.

5. Explain why oceanic plates tend to subduct when they collide with a continental plate.

Critical Thinking

6. **Making Inferences** New crust is constantly created at mid-ocean ridges, but the oldest oceanic crust is only about 150 million years old? What can you infer from these data?

7. **Identifying Relationships** Identify the relationship that exists between a volcanic deposit and the age of the layers of which it is made. Which layers are the youngest, and which are the oldest? Explain your answer.

FCAT Preparation

8. A volcanologist is studying the conditions under which magma forms at tectonic plate boundaries. Under which of the following conditions will the volcanologist find that subduction produces magma? **D.1.3.3 CS**

   A. when pressure on mantle rock decreases

   B. when mantle rock rises to fill the gap in a rift zone

   C. when the Earth's surface passes over a hot spot

   D. when the melting point of rock is lowered

SCI LINKS®

NSTA
Developed and maintained by the
National Science Teachers Association

For a variety of links related to this chapter, go to www.scilinks.org

Topic: What Causes Volcanoes?
SciLinks code: HSM1654

Skills Practice Lab

Volcano Verdict

OBJECTIVES

Build a working apparatus to test carbon dioxide levels.
H.3.3.4 CS

Test the levels of carbon dioxide emitted from a model volcano. H.1.3.5 AA

MATERIALS

- baking soda, 15 mL
- bottle, drinking, 16 oz
- box or stand for plastic cup
- clay, modeling
- coin
- cup, clear plastic, 9 oz
- graduated cylinder
- limewater, 1 L
- straw, drinking, flexible
- tissue, bathroom (2 sheets)
- vinegar, white, 140 mL
- water, 100 mL

SAFETY

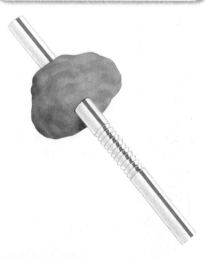

You will need to pair up with a partner for this exploration. You and your partner will act as geologists who work in a city located near a volcano. City officials are counting on you to predict when the volcano will erupt next. You and your partner have decided to use limewater as a gas-emissions tester. You will use this tester to measure the levels of carbon dioxide emitted from a simulated volcano. The more active the volcano is, the more carbon dioxide it releases.

Procedure

1. Put on your safety goggles, and carefully pour limewater into the plastic cup until the cup is three-fourths full. You have just made your gas-emissions tester.

2. Now, build a model volcano. Begin by pouring 50 mL of water and 70 mL of vinegar into the drink bottle.

3. Form a plug of clay around the short end of the straw, as shown at left. The clay plug must be large enough to cover the opening of the bottle. Be careful not to get the clay wet.

4. Sprinkle 5 mL of baking soda along the center of a single section of bathroom tissue. Then, roll the tissue, and twist the ends so that the baking soda can't fall out.

5 Drop the tissue into the drink bottle, and immediately put the short end of the straw inside the bottle to make a seal with the clay.

6 Put the other end of the straw into the lime-water, as shown at right.

7 You have just taken your first measurement of gas levels from the volcano. Record your observations.

8 Imagine that it is several days later and you need to test the volcano again to collect more data. Before you continue, toss a coin. If it lands heads up, go to step 9. If it lands tails up, go to step 10. Write down the step that you follow.

9 Repeat steps 1–7. This time, add 2 mL of baking soda to the vinegar and water. (Note: You must use fresh water, vinegar, and limewater.) Write down your observations. Go to step 11.

10 Repeat steps 1–7. This time, add 8 mL of baking soda to the vinegar and water. (Note: You must use fresh water, vinegar, and limewater.) Write down your observations. Go to step 11.

11 Return to step 8 once. Then, answer the questions below.

Analyze the Results

1 **Explaining Events** How do you explain the difference in the appearance of the limewater from one trial to the next?

2 **Recognizing Patterns** What does the data that you collected indicate about the activity in the volcano?

Draw Conclusions

3 **Evaluating Results** Based on your results, do you think it would be necessary to evacuate the city?

4 **Applying Conclusions** How would a geologist use a gas-emissions tester to predict volcanic eruptions?

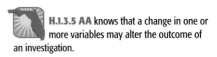

H.1.3.5 AA knows that a change in one or more variables may alter the outcome of an investigation.

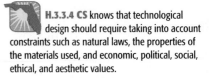

H.3.3.4 CS knows that technological design should require taking into account constraints such as natural laws, the properties of the materials used, and economic, political, social, ethical, and aesthetic values.

Chapter Review

USING KEY TERMS

For each pair of terms, explain how the meanings of the terms differ.

1 *caldera* and *crater*

2 *volcano* and *magma chamber*

3 *rift zone* and *hot spot*

UNDERSTANDING KEY IDEAS

Multiple Choice

4 The type of magma that tends to cause explosive eruptions has a

  a. high silica content and high viscosity.

  b. high silica content and low viscosity.

  c. low silica content and low viscosity.

  d. low silica content and high viscosity.

  D.1.3.5 CS

5 Lava that flows slowly to form a glassy surface with rounded wrinkles is called

  a. aa lava.   **c.** pillow lava.

  b. pahoehoe lava.   **d.** blocky lava.

6 Magma forms within the mantle most often as a result of

  a. high temperature and high pressure.

  b. high temperature and low pressure.

  c. low temperature and high pressure.

  d. low temperature and low pressure.

7 A theory that helps explain the causes of both earthquakes and volcanoes is the theory of

  a. pyroclastics.

  b. plate tectonics.

  c. climatic fluctuation.

  d. mantle plumes.

8 Before a volcanic eruption, volcanologists record an increasing number of small earthquakes. What is the most likely cause of these earthquakes? **D.1.3.5 CS** *FCAT*

  a. the movement of magma

  b. the formation of pyroclastic material

  c. the hardening of magma

  d. the movement of tectonic plates

9 A volcanic eruption sends large amounts of volcanic dust and ash into the atmosphere. If this volcanic dust and ash remain in the atmosphere for months or years, what do you predict will happen? **D.1.3.3 CS, D.1.3.5 CS** *FCAT*

  a. Solar reflection will decrease, and temperatures will increase.

  b. Solar reflection will increase, and temperatures will increase.

  c. Solar reflection will decrease, and temperatures will decrease.

  d. Solar reflection will increase, and temperatures will decrease.

10 At divergent plate boundaries,

  a. heat from Earth's core causes mantle plumes.

  b. oceanic plates sink, which causes magma to form.

  c. tectonic plates move apart.

  d. hot spots cause volcanoes. **D.1.3.3 CS**

Short Answer

11 Explain how the presence of water in magma affects a volcanic eruption. **D.1.3.5 CS**

12 Identify four clues that scientists use to predict eruptions.

13 Identify the characteristics of the three types of volcanoes.

14 Describe the positive effects of volcanic eruptions.

Math Practice

15 A pyroclastic flow travels a distance of 2 km in 2.5 min. What is the rate of speed of the flow in kilometers per hour? **D.1.3.5 CS**

CRITICAL THINKING

Extended Response

16 **Identifying Relationships** What is the relationship between rift zones and the production of magma? **D.1.3.3 CS**

17 **Making Comparisons** Compare the way in which cinder cone volcanoes are formed to the way in which composite volcanoes are formed.

18 **Evaluating Hypotheses** What evidence could confirm the existence of mantle plumes?

19 **Making Predictions** Predict some of the possible consequences that would result from a decrease in average global temperature following an explosive volcanic eruption. **D.1.3.3 CS, D.1.3.5 CS**

Concept Mapping

20 Use the following terms to create a concept map: *volcanic bombs, aa, pyroclastic material, pahoehoe, lapilli, lava,* and *volcano.*

INTERPRETING GRAPHICS

The graph below illustrates the average change in temperature above or below normal for a community over several years. Use the graph below to answer the questions that follow.

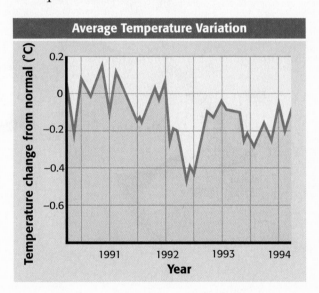

21 If the variation in temperature over the years was influenced by a major volcanic eruption, when did the eruption most likely take place? Explain. **D.1.3.3 CS, D.1.3.5 CS**

22 If the temperature were measured only once each year (at the beginning of the year), how would your interpretation be different? **D.1.3.5 CS**

For the following questions, write your answers on a separate sheet of paper.

1 Why do large volcanic eruptions sometimes affect natural systems on Earth, such as global climate?

A. Trees, which help cool Earth, are destroyed.

B. The extreme heat produced by an eruption increases global temperatures.

C. Water released into the atmosphere by an eruption increases global precipitation.

D. The ash and gases released into the atmosphere by an eruption block sunlight and thus reduce global temperatures.

2 The dots on the map below indicate the locations of active volcanoes.

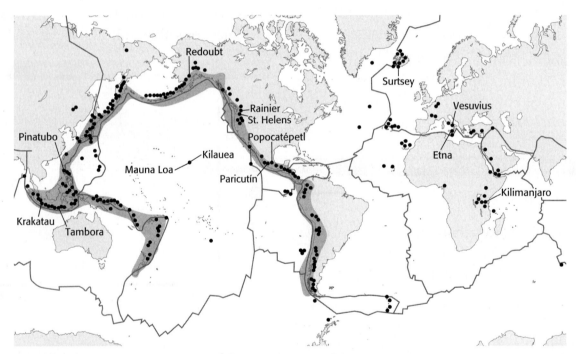

Distribution of Active Volcanoes

The majority of these volcanoes are located around the Pacific Ocean in an area called the Ring of Fire. How is the location of volcanoes in the Ring of Fire related to tectonic plate boundaries?

F. Most volcanoes in the Ring of Fire are located at hot spots.

G. Most volcanoes in the Ring of Fire are located along a mid-ocean ridge.

H. There is no consistent pattern in the location of volcanoes in the Ring of Fire.

I. Most volcanoes in the Ring of Fire are located where an oceanic plate collides with a continental plate.

3 Sometimes, lava can flow as fast as 30 kilometers per hour. If lava is flowing from a volcanic eruption at that rate, in how many minutes will the lava flow 15 kilometers?

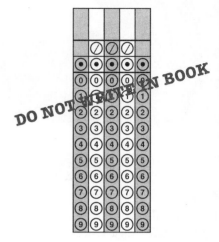

4 Magma can form at both convergent and divergent tectonic plate boundaries. How does magma form at a divergent tectonic plate boundary?

A. Magma forms from columns of rising magma called magma plumes.

B. Magma forms when pressure decreases and the mantle begins to melt.

C. Magma forms when the roof of a magma chamber collapses and melts.

D. Magma forms when water mixes with mantle rock, which increases the rock's melting point and causes the rock to melt.

5 Examine the illustration of a volcano shown below.

What is the term for the area to which the arrow is pointing?

F. lava

G. crater

H. caldera

I. magma chamber

FCAT Preparation

Science in Action

Weird Science

Pele's Hair

It is hard to believe that the fragile specimen shown below is a volcanic rock. This strange type of lava, called *Pele's hair,* forms when volcanic gases spray molten rock high into the air. When conditions are right, the lava can harden into strands of volcanic glass as thin as a human hair. This type of lava is named after Pele, the Hawaiian goddess of volcanoes. Several other types of lava are named in Pele's honor. Pele's tears are tear-shaped globs of volcanic glass often found at the end of strands of Pele's hair. Pele's diamonds are green, gemlike stones found in hardened lava flows.

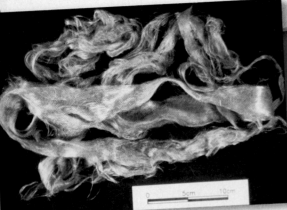

Science, Technology, and Society

Fighting Lava with Fire Hoses

What would you do if a 60 ft wall of lava was advancing toward your home? Most people would head for safety. But when an eruption threatened to engulf the Icelandic fishing village of Heimaey in 1973, some villagers held their ground and fought back. Working 14-hour days in conditions so hot that their boots would catch on fire, villagers used fire-hoses to spray sea water on the lava flow. For several weeks, the lava advanced toward the town, and it seemed as if there was no hope. But the water eventually cooled the lava fast enough to divert the flow and save the village. It took 5 months and about 1.5 billion gallons of water to fight the lava flow. When the eruption stopped, villagers found that the island had grown by 20%!

Language Arts ACTiViTY

Volcanic terms come from many languages. Research some volcanic terms on the Internet, and create an illustrated volcanic glossary to share with your class.

Social Studies ACTiViTY

WRITING SKILL To try to protect the city of Hilo, Hawaii, from an eruption in 1935, planes dropped bombs on the lava. Find out if this mission was successful, and write a report about other attempts to stop lava flows.

Kristin Martin

Volcanologist Kristin Martin is a graduate student who is studying volcanology at the University of South Florida (USF) in Tampa. As an undergraduate student majoring in geology at USF, Martin found herself instantly attracted to volcanology. So, after earning her bachelor's degree, she decided to stay at USF and study volcanoes.

Martin has focused her studies on Cerro Negro volcano, which is located in the Central American nation of Nicaragua. She is modeling the way tephra, which is ejected ash and rock fragments, is distributed around Cerro Negro so that she can understand what happens when a volcano erupts. Her research has led her to a better understanding of previous eruptions of Cerro Negro volcano. Understanding Cerro Negro volcano is important, because the volcano will most likely erupt again.

Martin is fascinated by volcanoes and knows the importance of her work. "Millions of people live in the shadows of active volcanoes all over the world," Martin explains. "Understanding the volcanoes and how and when they may erupt is critical in order to ensure the safety of all the people."

Math ACTIVITY

The 1912 eruption of Mt. Katmai in Alaska could be heard 5,620 km away in Atlanta, Georgia. If the average speed of sound in the atmosphere is 342 m/s, how many hours after the eruption did the citizens of Atlanta hear the explosion?

.com
To learn more about these Science in Action topics, visit go.hrw.com and type in the keyword **HT6FVOFF.**

Current Science

Check out Current Science® articles related to this chapter by visiting go.hrw.com. Just type in the keyword **HZ5CS09.**

UNIT 4

TIMELINE

Earth and Space

In this unit, you will learn about astronomy and about Earth's movement around the sun. Long before science was called *science*, people looked up at the night sky and tried to understand the twinkling lights above. Early astronomers charted the stars and built calendars based on the movement of the sun, moon, and planets. Today, scientists from around the world work together to maintain a space station in orbit around Earth. This timeline shows some of the events that have occurred as scientists have learned more about our planet's "neighborhood" in space.

1054

Chinese and Korean astronomers record the appearance of a supernova, an exploding star. Strangely, no European observations of this event have ever been found.

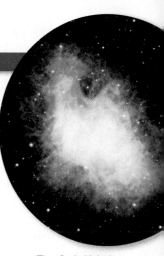

The Crab Nebula

Andromeda Galaxy (M31)

1924

An astronomer named Edwin Hubble confirms the existence of other galaxies.

1983

Sally Ride becomes the first American woman to travel in space.

1582

Ten days are dropped from October when the Gregorian calendar replaces the Julian calendar.

1666

Using a prism, Isaac Newton discovers that white light is composed of different colors.

1898

The War of the Worlds, by H. G. Wells, is published.

1958

The National Aeronautics and Space Administration (NASA) is established to oversee the exploration of space.

1970

Apollo 13 is damaged shortly after leaving orbit. The spacecraft's three astronauts navigate around the moon to return safely to Earth.

1977

Voyager 1 and *Voyager 2* are launched on missions to Jupiter, Saturn, and beyond. Now more than 10 billion kilometers away from Earth, they are still sending back information about space.

Voyager 2

1992

Astronomers discover the first planet that is outside the solar system.

1998

John Glenn becomes the oldest human in space. His second trip into space comes 36 years after he became the first American to orbit Earth.

2003

Astronomers discover three distant quasars that date back to a time when the universe was only 800 million years old. Light takes 13 billion years to reach Earth from the farthest of the three quasars.

Astronomy

The Big Idea Earth, the sun, and the stars are part of a galaxy within a vast universe.

About the PHOTO

Gas and dust stream outward from the dying star IC 4406. IC 4406 has been called the "Retina Nebula" because of its similarity to the retina of the human eye. In this side view of the dying star, light from different gas atoms appears as different colors. Oxygen appears blue, hydrogen appears green, and nitrogen appears red.

PRE-READING ACTIVITY

Three-Panel Flip Chart Before you read the chapter, create the FoldNote entitled "Three-Panel Flip Chart" described in the **Study Skills** section of the Appendix. Label the flaps of the three-panel flip chart with "Stars," "Galaxies," and "Our solar system." As you read the chapter, write information you learn about each category under the appropriate flap.

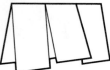

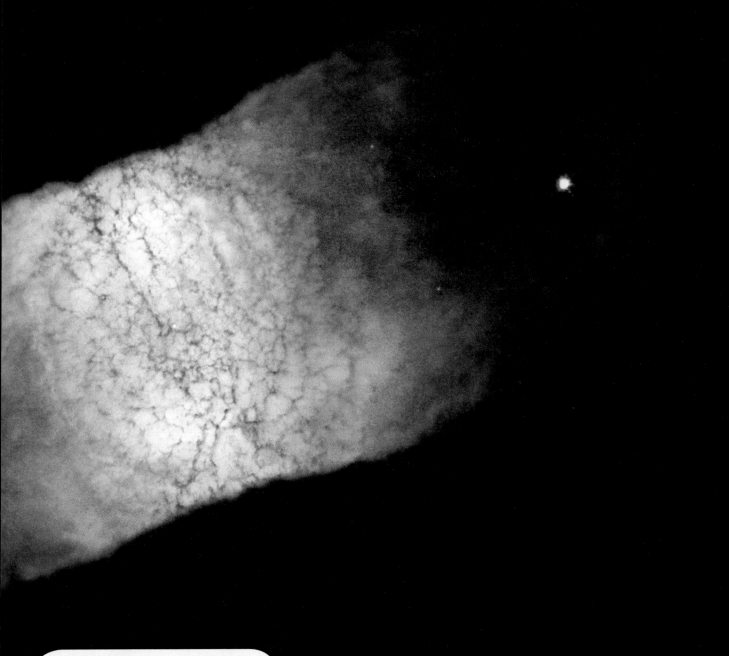

START-UP ACTIVITY

Strange Gravity

If you drop a heavy object, will it fall faster than a lighter one will? According to the law of gravity, the answer is no. In 1971, *Apollo 15* astronaut David Scott stood on the moon and dropped a feather and a hammer. Television audiences were amazed to see both objects strike the moon's surface at the same time. Now, you can perform a similar experiment.

Procedure

1. Select **two pieces of identical notebook paper.** Crumple one piece of paper into a ball.

2. Place the flat piece of paper on top of a **book** and the paper ball on top of the flat piece of paper.

3. Hold the book waist high, and then drop it to the floor.

Analysis

1. Which piece of paper reached the bottom first? Did either piece of paper fall slower than the book did? Explain your observations.

2. Now, hold the paper ball in one hand and the flat piece of paper in the other. Drop both pieces of paper at the same time. Besides gravity, what affected the speed of the falling paper? Record your observations.

Stars and Galaxies

One night, when the sky is clear and the moon is dim, go outside and look at the stars. Humans have been looking at these points of light since the beginning of human history. What are stars, and what makes stars shine?

Stars are giant bodies of hot gases that are held together by gravity. Unlike matter on Earth, stars produce their own light. Most stars make light when they combine, or fuse, four atoms of one element, hydrogen, and make another element, helium. This process releases huge amounts of thermal energy and light. Humans took thousands of years to figure out this very basic secret of why stars shine.

Composition of Stars

How do astronomers know what stars are made of? They use an instrument called a **spectroscope** to study the light from stars. Every atom produces its own special pattern of light. As **Figure 1** shows, this pattern looks like the bar code on soup cans and cereal boxes. Astronomers can use a spectroscope to study these "bar codes" and to identify the elements that are in a star.

Stars are made mostly of hydrogen and helium gases. But stars also have traces of many other elements. Carbon, nitrogen, and oxygen are the most common of these elements. Stars also contain calcium, iron, and sodium. In fact, some of the elements in your body were once a part of a star!

READING WARM-UP

Objectives

● Describe the composition of stars. **E.1.3.4 CS**

● Explain how stars differ in temperature, brightness, distance, size, and age. **E.1.3.4 CS**

● Describe the three types of galaxies. **E.2.3.1 CS**

● Describe a star cluster.

Terms to Learn

spectroscope *FCAT VOCAB*
light-year   open cluster
nebula   globular cluster

READING STRATEGY

Reading Organizer As you read this section, create an outline of the section. Use the headings from the section in your outline.

spectroscope an instrument that splits white light into a band of colors *FCAT VOCAB*

E.1.3.4 CS knows that stars appear to be made of similar chemical elements, although they differ in age, size, temperature, and distance.

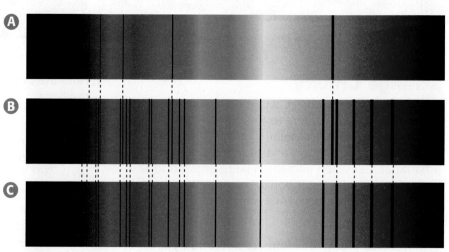

Figure 1 *When light is passed through hydrogen gas (A) or helium gas (C) and through a slit and prism, lines appear in the spectrum. If both hydrogen and helium are present, both sets of lines appear (B).*

Figure 2 *The stars Betelgeuse and Rigel are located in the constellation Orion. Betelgeuse (upper left) is a star that is nearing the end of its life. Rigel (lower right) is a young star that shines with the light of 40,000 suns.*

Types of Stars

Some stars are very bright. Other stars are very faint. Stars differ in other ways, too. These differences have helped astronomers classify stars and learn more about how stars are born and about how stars change over time.

Differences in Temperature and Color

If you look closely, you will see that some of the brightest stars show hints of color. Capella, like the sun, is yellowish. Betelgeuse (BET'l JOOZ) is reddish, and Rigel (RIE juhl) has the faintest tinge of blue. **Figure 2** shows the reddish color of Betelgeuse and the bluish color of Rigel.

Color is one of a star's most basic properties that can be measured. Color helps astronomers classify stars by temperature. Cool stars, such as Betelgeuse (3,000°C), are red. Medium-hot stars, such as the sun (6,000°C), are yellowish. The hottest stars, such as Rigel (15,000°C), shine with a bluish tinge.

Benchmark Check **Explain how temperature is related to the color of a star.** E.1.3.4 CS

Differences in Brightness

Stars also differ in the amount of light that they produce. Astronomers call this property *luminosity* (LOO muh NAHS uh tee). Stars have a variety of luminosities. A large star, such as Aldebaran (al DEB uh ruhn), produces more than 100 times as much light as the sun does. A very large star, such as Betelgeuse, produces more than 1 million times as much light as the sun does. Stars can also be very dim. It would take 1,000 dim stars to make as much light as the sun makes.

The brightness of a star in the sky has as much to do with the star's distance as with the star's luminosity. A nearby dim star can look as bright as a distant star that is very bright. If the sun were far enough away, its blazing light would look as dim as the faintest star that you can see in the night sky.

Light Pollution

WRITING SKILL With a parent or guardian, go outside one night and see if you can see stars. If you live near a large city or town, you probably see very few stars because of all of the light from streetlights and buildings. Astronomers call this condition *light pollution*. Research the topic of light pollution. Think about ways that you could reduce light pollution around your neighborhood. Use these suggestions to create a pamphlet that you could distribute throughout your neighborhood.

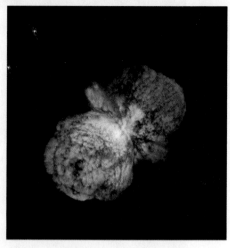

Figure 3 *The image at left shows Proxima Centauri, a star that is 4.22 light years from Earth. Eta Carinae, the star shown at right, is about 7,500 light years from Earth.*

Calculating Distance
Proxima Centauri is approximately 4.22 light-years from Earth. If 1 light-year equals approximately 9.5 trillion kilometers, what is the approximate distance of Proxima Centauri from Earth?

light-year the distance that light travels in one year; about 9.46 trillion kilometers

Distances to Stars

For thousands of years, people thought that stars were located just outside our solar system. In the 1800s, however, astronomers carefully measured the positions of stars and discovered that stars are incredibly far from Earth. These scientists measured the positions of certain stars at different times of the year. In this way, the measurements would be taken at different locations in Earth's orbit. The scientists found very slight changes in the positions of these stars. The apparent shifts in the positions of these stars could then be calculated to find the distances to these stars.

The distances to stars are so large—many trillions of kilometers—that by the 1900s, astronomers started to measure the distances in light-years. A **light-year** is the distance that a beam of light travels in one year, at a speed of 300,000 km/s. A light-year equals nearly 6 trillion miles or about 9.46 trillion kilometers.

The stars shown in **Figure 3** are so far away from Earth that they are invisible to the naked eye. Proxima Centauri, the star closest to the sun, is 4.22 light-years from Earth. Eta Carinae is about 7,500 light years from Earth.

The End of Stars

The life span of a star depends on the star's mass. Eta Carinae, shown in **Figure 3,** has a mass that is 150 times the mass of the sun and has a life span of only 10 million years. Stars such as the sun last 10 billion years. The smallest stars, called *brown dwarfs,* have masses that are only one-tenth of the sun's mass. They can last more than 200 billion years.

Every star eventually dies, usually after billions of years. Stars whose masses are more than 10 times the mass of the sun become supernovas. Supernovas are large stars that explode and spread their elements into space. Stars that are similar to the sun burn out with no explosions at all.

E.1.3.3 understands that our sun is one of many stars in our galaxy.

E.1.3.4 CS knows that stars appear to be made of similar chemical elements, although they differ in age, size, temperature, and distance.

Origins of Galaxies

Stars are not randomly spread throughout space. Instead, stars form vast groupings called *galaxies*. Our galaxy, the Milky Way, is one of billions of galaxies in the universe. A galaxy can have billions of stars orbiting together as a family.

According to a theory called the *big bang*, the universe began with a tremendous explosion about 14 billion years ago. Elements, energy, and forces—such as gravity—formed relationships as the universe rapidly expanded outward. Matter collected in various parts of the universe and formed galaxies.

Benchmark Check Explain why other galaxies may have the same elements, forces, and forms of energy that our solar system does. E.2.3.1 CS

Types of Galaxies

The light from individual stars in another galaxy comes to Earth from so far away that the light blurs together. From Earth, other galaxies look cloudy and have a spiral shape, a snowball shape, or no shape at all. An astronomer classifies galaxies as spirals, ellipticals, or irregulars according to their shape.

Spiral Galaxies

Spiral galaxies, such as NGC 1232, look like flat, delicate pinwheels of light, as shown in **Figure 4.** A typical spiral galaxy contains stars and nebulas. **Nebulas** are bright clouds of dust and gas that are the birthplaces of the next generation of stars. The blurred light from a spiral galaxy is made up of billions of stars. The Milky Way is a spiral galaxy that contains about 200 billion stars. The sun is located about two-thirds of the way between the center of the galaxy and the galaxy's edge.

Galactic Whirlpool

1. Fill a **medium mixing bowl** two-thirds full of **water.**

2. Place **1 tsp of black pepper** in the center of the bowl.

3. Use your fingers to rapidly swirl the water in the bowl in a clockwise direction.

4. What kind of pattern does the pepper form? Does this pattern resemble the shape of a spiral galaxy?

nebula a large cloud of dust and gas in interstellar space; a region in space where stars are born

Figure 4 *NGC 1232 is located about 100 million light-years from Earth. NGC 1232 is approximately twice the size of the Milky Way galaxy.*

E.2.3.1 CS knows that thousands of other galaxies appear to have the same elements, forces, and forms of energy found in our Solar System.

Figure 5 *The Magellanic Clouds are two irregular galaxies that orbit the Milky Way galaxy. The Large Magellanic Cloud, shown in this photo, can be seen with the naked eye from the Southern Hemisphere.*

INTERNET ACTIVITY

Astronomer Biographies
Write a biography of an interesting astronomer. Go to **go.hrw.com,** and type in the keyword **HZ5OBSW.**

open cluster a group of stars that are close together relative to surrounding stars

globular cluster a tight group of stars that looks like a ball and contains up to 1 million stars

E.2.3.1 CS knows that thousands of other galaxies appear to have the same elements, forces, and forms of energy found in our Solar System.

Elliptical Galaxies

Because most elliptical galaxies are very round, they can be thought of as "cosmic snowballs." However, some elliptical galaxies are slightly flattened, but not as much as spiral galaxies are. Unlike spiral galaxies, whose gas clouds are still creating stars, elliptical galaxies seem to have stopped making new stars more than 10 billion years ago. Astronomers are still not sure why spiral galaxies that are the same age as elliptical galaxies form stars at such very different rates than elliptical galaxies do. Elliptical galaxies are also among the largest galaxies in the universe. They can contain up to 5 trillion stars!

Irregular Galaxies

Scientists have discovered more irregular galaxies than any other kind of galaxy. The smallest irregular galaxies have only about 10 million stars. The largest irregular galaxies can have several billion stars. Many of these galaxies are nearly as old as the Milky Way. Irregular galaxies form new stars slowly. The most spectacular irregular galaxies near the Milky Way are the Magellanic Clouds. The Large Magellanic Cloud is shown in **Figure 5.** The Milky Way is consuming these two galaxies. In about 100 million years, the Magellanic Clouds will be gone.

Star Clusters

Some stars within galaxies occur in small groups called *star clusters*. If you look closely at a magnified photograph of a spiral galaxy, you will see groups of stars everywhere. These groups are the star clusters to which many stars belong. Many stars are found in star clusters because these stars were born in clouds of gas that tend to produce more than one star at a time.

Open Clusters and Globular Clusters

Clouds of gas within the Milky Way tend to give birth to thousands of stars at a time. These stars form close together in a group called an **open cluster.** In the winter sky, the open cluster Pleiades, or Seven Sisters, can be seen with the naked eye. This cluster is shown in **Figure 6.**

When the Milky Way was forming, millions of stars were created in clouds of gas that were orbiting the Milky Way. These tight groups of stars, called **globular clusters,** are located in a spherical halo that surrounds the Milky Way. More than 130 globular clusters are known to orbit the Milky Way.

✓ Reading Check Compare open clusters and globular clusters.

Figure 6 *The open cluster Pleiades, which is located about 400 light-years from Earth in the constellation Taurus, can be seen without using a telescope.*

SECTION Review

Summary

- Stars are made mostly of hydrogen gas and helium gas. **E.1.3.4 CS**
- Stars mostly differ from one another by their mass, temperature, and luminosity. **E.1.3.4 CS**
- Stars and star clusters are found in vast systems called *galaxies.*
- Other galaxies appear to have the same elements, forces, and forms of energy found in our solar system. **E.2.3.1 CS**
- The sun is only one of 200 billion stars in the Milky Way galaxy. **E.1.3.3**
- Star clusters are collections of a few thousand stars that formed close together from the same cloud.

Using Key Terms

1. Use *nebula, open cluster,* and *globular cluster* in separate sentences.

Understanding Key Ideas

2. Compare and contrast stars. **E.1.3.4 CS**

3. Describe the composition of a star. **E.1.3.4 CS**

4. Explain the difference between spiral, irregular, and elliptical galaxies.

Critical Thinking

5. **Applying Concepts** If all galaxies formed from the matter that expanded into space after the big bang, what physical properties might galaxies other than the Milky Way share with our solar system? **E.2.3.1 CS**

6. **Predicting Consequences** The Milky Way galaxy will collide with the Andromeda galaxy, which is another spiral galaxy, in 5 billion years. Use what you know about spiral, irregular, and elliptical galaxies to predict what kind of galaxy might result from this collision.

FCAT Preparation

7. Scientists use a spectroscope to find out what stars are made of. A spectroscope allows scientists to study light from stars. From the study of starlight, scientists have discovered that stars are made mostly of two elements. What are these two elements? **E.1.3.4 CS**

A. oxygen and hydrogen

B. hydrogen and helium

C. helium and carbon

D. carbon and oxygen

SCiLINKS. **NSTA**

Developed and maintained by the National Science Teachers Association

For a variety of links related to this chapter, go to www.scilinks.org

Topic: Stars; Galaxies
SciLinks code: HSM1448; HSM0632

Our Solar System

Distances in our solar system are almost too great to imagine. Pluto, which is the outermost planet, averages 5.9 billion miles from the sun!

The vast region of space called the *solar system* includes planets, moons, comets, asteroids, meteoroids, and our very own star, the sun. Although Earth may seem large to us, it is only the fifth-largest planet in the solar system.

The Sun: Center of the Solar System

The sun is located at the center of the solar system. The sun is 1,390,000 km in diameter and makes up more than 99% of the mass in the solar system. Like other stars in the universe, the sun is made mostly of hydrogen and helium. However, the sun contains traces of almost every other element.

The sun's energy is produced when hydrogen atoms fuse to form helium. The energy that is released in this process causes the sun to shine. This same energy causes the sun's high temperatures, which may reach 1,000,000°C in the sun's outer atmosphere. Energy from the sun also lights and heats the surface of Earth.

Benchmark Check) **Explain how the sun produces light.** E.1.3.3

READING WARM-UP

Objectives

● Explain the process by which stars, such as the sun, produce light. **E.1.3.3**

● Compare the planets and moons of the inner solar system with the planets and moons of the outer solar system. **E.1.3.1 AA**

● Describe three important discoveries that satellite probes have helped scientists make about planets and moons in the solar system. **E.1.3.2**

Terms to Learn

comet   meteor
asteroid   meteorite
meteoroid

READING STRATEGY

Reading Organizer As you read this section, make a table comparing the properties of the terrestrial planets with the properties of the gas-giant planets.

Figure 1 *These images show the relative sizes of the planets and the sun.*

Mercury

Venus

Earth

Jupiter

Mars

Sun

The Inner Solar System

The region of space called the *inner solar system* contains the four planets closest to the sun: Mercury, Venus, Earth, and Mars. They are sometimes called the *terrestrial planets* because they have a rocky composition and their size is similar to Earth's.

Mercury: Closest to the Sun

Mercury, shown in **Figure 1,** is the planet that is closest to the sun. Mercury is barren and has a thin, highly unstable atmosphere. Like our moon, Mercury has a heavily cratered surface. Mercury also has mountains and plains. Temperatures on Mercury can vary greatly. Daytime temperatures can reach 427°C. At night, temperatures can plunge to –173°C. Astronomers have discovered that despite its high temperatures, Mercury may have ice below the surface of its polar regions.

Venus: Earth's Twin

Venus, shown in **Figure 1,** is the second planet from the sun. Venus is slightly smaller, less massive, and less dense than Earth is. Like Earth, Venus has mountains, volcanoes, and plains. But unlike Earth, Venus has an atmosphere that contains mostly carbon dioxide and that is so dense that the atmosphere would instantly crush a human. The atmosphere also has layers of thick clouds that are made up of sulfuric acid. Because of Venus's dense atmosphere, surface temperatures average 464°C. At this temperature, metals such as lead would melt and flow.

Benchmark Activity

The Vast Solar System To understand the vastness of our solar system, complete the following mathematical calculation. Mercury is 58 million kilometers from the sun. Use 1 m to represent this distance. Now, use meters to calculate the distance between Pluto and the sun. Pluto is 5.9 billion kilometers from the sun. What percentage of the distance between the sun and Pluto is the distance between the sun and Mercury? E.1.3.1 AA

E.1.3.1 AA understands the vast size of our Solar System and the relationship of the planets and their satellites.

E.1.3.3 understands that our sun is one of many stars in our galaxy.

Saturn

Uranus

Neptune

Pluto

Earth and Its Moon

Earth, shown in **Figure 2,** is the third planet from the sun. Earth is the only planet in the solar system that is known to have the combination of factors that support life: liquid water, atmospheric oxygen and nitrogen, and other materials that cycle continuously. Earth is very geologically active. Landmasses slowly move around the surface of Earth, so the shapes of the continents are continuously changing. Forces such as weathering and erosion also constantly reshape Earth's surface.

Earth has one moon. Although the moon's average distance from Earth is only 384,000 km, the moon is very different from Earth. The moon's gravity is too weak to hold an atmosphere. As a result, temperatures vary greatly on the moon. In addition, small bodies can strike the moon's surface instead of burning up, which accounts for the moon's heavily cratered surface.

Mars: Our Intriguing Neighbor

Mars, shown in **Figure 3,** is the last of the inner planets. It is located an average distance of 228 million kilometers from the sun. Unlike Earth, Mars has a very thin atmosphere that is composed largely of carbon dioxide and that has lesser amounts of nitrogen and argon. Surface temperatures vary widely. In summer, temperatures near the equator may be as high as 20°C. In winter, temperatures near the poles may be as low as –130°C. Two small moons, Phobos and Deimos, orbit Mars.

The surface of Mars is highly variable. High mountains, deep canyons, huge impact craters, flat plains, and polar ice caps are a part of the Martian landscape. Of great interest to scientists are surface features that are characteristic of erosion by water. In 2004, data from NASA's Mars rovers, *Spirit* and *Opportunity,* indicated that liquid water once existed on Mars's surface. Scientists now wonder if this water existed long enough for organisms to have evolved on the planet.

Benchmark Check Explain the important new information that astronomers have learned about Mars from NASA's rovers. E.I.3.2

Figure 2 *Earth's land masses, cloudy atmosphere, and oceans are visible from space.*

E.I.3.1 AA understands the vast size of our Solar System and the relationship of the planets and their satellites.

E.I.3.2 knows that available data from various satellite probes show the similarities and differences among planets and their moons in the Solar System.

Figure 3 *In this photograph, which the Mars rover* Spirit *took, a rock outcrop named* Longhorn *is visible in the foreground. The plains of Gusev Crater sweep off into the distance behind this rock.*

The Outer Solar System

The vast region of space called the *outer solar system* includes the gas giants Jupiter, Saturn, Uranus, and Neptune. They are gigantic balls of gas that have no solid surfaces on which to stand. Each of these planets is 4 to 12 times as big as Earth. Pluto, which is the farthest planet from the sun, is not a gas-giant planet.

Jupiter: A Giant Among Giants

Jupiter, shown in **Figure 4,** is the largest planet in the solar system. The planet has a diameter of 142,984 km. Jupiter is also the most massive planet. It is made mostly of hydrogen, which exists as both a liquid and a solid. The planet's atmosphere consists of molecular hydrogen, helium, and trace amounts of ammonia, methane, and water. Violent disturbances occur in Jupiter's atmosphere. They include winds of up to 540 km/h and enormous areas of high pressure that scientists think are storms.

Jupiter has at least 63 moons! Europa has a thick, icy crust that may float on top of a deep ocean of liquid water.

Saturn: The Ringed World

Saturn is the second-largest but the least dense planet in the solar system. Like Jupiter, Saturn is made mostly of hydrogen. Saturn's atmosphere also consists of molecular hydrogen, helium, traces of other gases, and water. Spectacular rings, which are shown in **Figure 5,** orbit Saturn's equator. They are more than 250,000 km in diameter but less than 1 km thick. Trillions of small particles of water ice make up these rings. The particles mostly range from a centimeter to several meters across.

Titan is the largest of Saturn's 31 known moons. Titan's atmosphere is nearly twice as thick as Earth's atmosphere and is made of nitrogen gas.

Figure 4 *Io, one of Jupiter's larger moons, can be seen in the lower right-hand portion of this image of the planet.*

CONNECTION TO Meteorology

The Great Red Spot
The red, circular area in the southern hemisphere of Jupiter is known as the *Great Red Spot.* Astronomers think that the Great Red Spot is a storm that is similar to a hurricane on Earth. The storm is enormous. It is twice as large as Earth. The storm is also quite old. It has been viewed by astronomers for at least 350 years.

Figure 5 *Ammonia and methane clouds give Saturn its banded appearance. The different colors of the planet's ice rings indicate different amounts of other materials, such as rock and carbon compounds, that occur in the rings.*

Figure 6 *Scientists think that a massive object may have struck Uranus and tipped the planet over on its side.*

Uranus: A Small Giant

Uranus is the third gas giant and the third-largest planet in the solar system. Uranus has a diameter of 51,118 km. The planet is made mostly of rock and ice. Hydrogen, helium, and traces of methane make up the planet's atmosphere. The methane in the atmosphere filters incoming sunlight and gives Uranus the greenish blue tinge that is shown in **Figure 6.** Unlike other planets, Uranus is tipped over on its side.

Uranus has 27 moons. Six of these moons have not yet been named. Uranus's moon Miranda has a radius of only 240 km. But images from the spacecraft *Voyager 2* show that a huge impact has nearly turned the moon inside out. The impact shattered the moon and caused the moon to re-form in a mixed-up state. Rock and ice from the deep interior of Miranda are spread out on the surface of the moon.

Neptune: The Blue World

Neptune, the last of the gas giants, is a beautiful blue planet. It has a diameter of 49,532 km and is made of rock and ice. Like Uranus, Neptune has an atmosphere that contains hydrogen, helium, and traces of methane. The blue color of the planet results from trace gases, such as methane. The deeper layers of Neptune's atmosphere, unlike Uranus's, are visible. Clouds and changes in weather can be seen, as shown in **Figure 7.** Neptune has the fastest winds of any planet in the solar system. Neptune's winds travel at more than 1,000 km/h. No one really knows what causes these winds to blow so hard.

Neptune has 13 moons. The largest moon, Triton, has a surface temperature of –235°C and polar ice caps made of frozen nitrogen. Active ice volcanoes on Triton's surface spew out dark nitrogen and methane gas clouds.

Benchmark Check Compare the atmospheres of Uranus and Neptune with the atmosphere of Earth. E.1.3.1 AA

E.1.3.1 AA understands the vast size of our Solar System and the relationship of the planets and their satellites.

E.1.3.2 knows that available data from various satellite probes show the similarities and differences among planets and their moons in the Solar System.

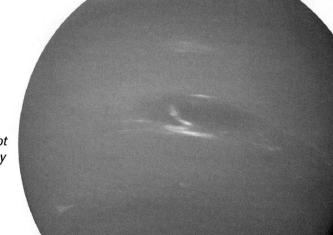

Figure 7 *The Great Dark Spot, shown at the center of this image, was visible when* Voyager 2 *visited Neptune. The spot has since disappeared or been hidden by Neptune's atmosphere.*

Pluto: The Mystery Planet

Pluto, the most distant planet, is located an average of 5.9 billion miles from the sun. Pluto is so far from the sun's warming rays that the planet's surface temperature reaches only –235°C. Having a diameter of 2,390 km, Pluto is the smallest planet in the solar system. Pluto is made of rock and ice. The planet's atmosphere is thin and is composed of methane and nitrogen. Pluto's moon, Charon (KER uhn), is a little more than half the size of Pluto. Both Pluto and Charon are shown in **Figure 8.**

Smaller Bodies in the Solar System

In the vast space between the planets, small bodies of rock and ice orbit the sun. Astronomers theorize that these bodies are materials left over from the formation of the solar system.

Comets

Loosely packed bodies of ice, rock, and cosmic dust orbiting the sun are called **comets.** Scientists think most comets come from the far outer regions of the solar system in a spherical region called the *Oort cloud.* The gravity of stars passing near the Oort cloud may cause comets to enter the solar system. The comets fall into new orbits, which brings the comets much closer to the sun. If comets come close enough to the sun, solar radiation heats their ice and gas forms. This gas forms a glowing tail, shown in **Figure 9,** that can be millions of kilometers long.

Figure 8 *Pluto (left) and its moon, Charon (right), are shown in this image taken from the* Hubble Space Telescope. *Both Pluto and Charon are smaller than Earth's moon.*

comet a small body of ice, rock, and cosmic dust that follows an elliptical orbit around the sun and that gives off gas and dust in the form of a tail as it passes close to the sun

Figure 9 *This is Comet Hale-Bopp as seen from Earth in April 1997. Astronomers determined that the comet was 40 km in diameter.*

Figure 10 *This view of the cratered surface of the asteroid Eros was taken from an altitude of 200 km. The large crater at the top of the asteroid is 5.3 km in diameter.*

asteroid a small, rocky object that orbits the sun; most asteroids are located in a band between the orbits of Mars and Jupiter

meteoroid a relatively small, rocky body that travels through space

meteor a bright streak of light that results when a meteoroid burns up in Earth's atmosphere

meteorite a meteoroid that reaches Earth's surface without burning up completely

Asteroids

Between the orbits of Mars and Jupiter lies the *asteroid belt.* This region of space is about 300 million kilometers across. In this region, millions of small bodies called *asteroids* orbit the sun as though they were tiny planets. **Asteroids** are cratered objects that are made of either carbon materials or combinations of iron and rock. Astronomers think that asteroids are material that Jupiter's gravity prevented from forming into a planet. The smallest asteroids are only a few meters in diameter. Ceres, the largest asteroid discovered, has a diameter of about 1,000 km. In 2001, NASA's *NEAR* spacecraft landed on the asteroid Eros. This potato-shaped rock, shown in **Figure 10,** has hundreds of craters and strange pools of dust on its surface.

Meteoroids

The space within our solar system contains dust and debris from asteroids and comets. These pieces of dust and debris are called **meteoroids.** Most are about the size of sand grains.

Meteoroids that enter Earth's atmosphere reach speeds of between 35,000 and 250,000 km/h. Friction heats the speeding meteoroids to thousands of degrees Celsius, which causes them to glow brightly. The atmosphere around the meteoroid's path also heats and glows because of friction with air molecules. The glowing trails that result when meteoroids burn up in Earth's atmosphere are called **meteors.** A meteor trail can be a few hundred meters in diameter and tens of kilometers long before it fades. Meteor trails are commonly called *shooting stars.*

Once every few days, larger bodies that are sometimes the size of basketballs or bigger enter our atmosphere. They create fireballs that light up the night sky. The largest of these bodies can pass through Earth's atmosphere without burning up and can strike Earth. The bodies that reach Earth's surface are called **meteorites. Figure 11** shows a meteorite that struck Earth.

Reading Check Explain the difference between a meteoroid, a meteorite, and a meteor.

Figure 11 *In March 2003, hundreds of meteorites, such as the one shown at the right, pelted Park Forest, Illinois.*

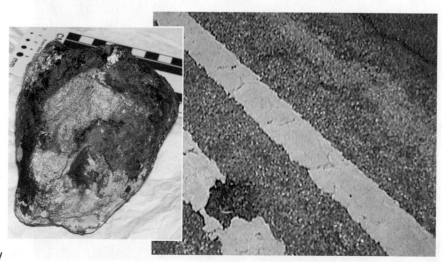

Summary

- The sun's energy, like the energy of other stars in our universe, is produced when hydrogen atoms fuse to form helium. E.1.3.3

- The small, rocky planets Mercury, Venus, Earth, and Mars are very different from the gas giants Jupiter, Saturn, Uranus, and Neptune. E.1.3.1 AA

- Most planets that orbit the sun are orbited by their own satellites, which are called *moons*. E.1.3.1 AA

- The smaller bodies in the solar system are rocky and icy and have diameters ranging from a few meters to nearly 2,000 km.

- Comets are icy bodies that orbit the sun and that form glowing tails when heated by the sun.

- Asteroids are rocky bodies that orbit mostly between the orbits of Mars and Jupiter, and meteoroids are rocky bodies that are debris from comet and asteroid collisions.

Using Key Terms

1. Use *comet*, *asteroid*, and *meteoroid* in the same sentence.

Understanding Key Ideas

2. Explain the process by which the sun and other stars produce light. E.1.3.3

3. Compare Earth's atmosphere with the atmospheres of Earth's neighbors, Venus and Mars.

4. Describe the difference between the planets in the inner solar system and the planets in the outer solar system. E.1.3.1 AA

5. Describe the information that *Voyager 2* provided about Uranus's moon Miranda. E.1.3.2

6. Explain why Uranus and Neptune are tinged with color when they are seen from a distance.

7. Describe the three types of smaller bodies that can be found in the solar system.

Critical Thinking

8. **Identifying Relationships** Astronauts are flying a spacecraft to the planet Mars. They will land the spacecraft on the planet's surface. Use what you know about Mars to describe the equipment that the astronauts will need to take with them to explore the surface of the planet.

FCAT Preparation

9. Stars fuse atoms of a particular element to form helium. What is this element? E.1.3.4 CS

   A. oxygen

   B. hydrogen

   C. nitrogen

   D. calcium

10. An astronomer is observing a planet that is smaller than our moon and that has an atmosphere composed of methane and nitrogen. The planet has a single moon that is more than half as large as the planet itself. Which planet is the astronomer observing? E.1.3.1 AA

    F. Neptune

    G. Uranus

    H. Pluto

    I. Saturn

Skills Practice Lab

OBJECTIVES

Discover what the color of a glowing object reveals about the temperature of that object.

Describe how the color and temperature of a star are related. E.1.3.4 CS

MATERIALS

- battery, D cell (2)
- battery, D cell, weak
- flashlight bulb
- tape, electrical
- wire, insulated copper, with ends stripped, 20 cm long (2)

SAFETY

E.1.3.4 CS knows that stars appear to be made of similar chemical elements, although they differ in age, size, temperature, and distance.

Red Hot or Not?

Some stars in the night sky look brighter than other stars do. Some are even different colors. Betelgeuse, a bright star in the constellation Orion, glows red. Sirius, one of the brightest stars in the sky, glows bluish white. Astronomers use a star's color to estimate the temperature of the star. In this activity, you will experiment with a light bulb and some batteries to discover what the color of a glowing object reveals about the temperature of that object.

Ask a Question

1 How are the color and temperature of a star related?

Form a Hypothesis

2 On a sheet of paper, write a few sentences that answer the above question about the relationship between the color and the temperature of a star.

Test the Hypothesis

3 Tape one end of an insulated copper wire to the positive pole of the weak D-cell battery. Tape one stripped end of a second wire to the negative pole of the battery.

4 Touch the free end of each wire to the light bulb. Hold one of the wires against the bottom tip of the light bulb. Hold the second wire against the side of the metal portion of the bulb. The bulb should light.

5 Record the color of the light bulb's filament. Carefully touch your hand to the bulb. Observe the temperature of the bulb. Record your observations.

6 Repeat steps 3–5 with one of the two fresh D-cell batteries.

7 Use the electrical tape to connect the two fresh D-cell batteries to each other. Be sure to connect the positive pole of the first battery to the negative pole of the second battery.

8 Using the fresh D-cell batteries that are taped together, repeat steps 3–5.

Analyze the Results

1 **Describing Events** What was the color of the filament in each of the three trials? Compare the temperature of the bulb in each of those trials with the temperature of the bulb in the other two trials.

2 **Analyzing Results** What can you tell about a star from its color?

3 **Classifying** What color are stars that have relatively high surface temperatures? What color are stars that have relatively low surface temperatures?

Draw Conclusions

4 **Applying Conclusions** Arrange the following stars in order from highest to lowest surface temperature: Sirius, which is bluish white; Aldebaran, which is orange; Procyon, which is yellow-white; Capella, which is yellow; and Betelgeuse, which is red.

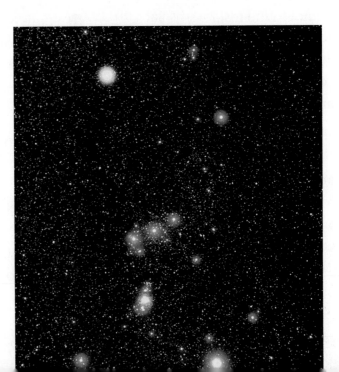

343

Chapter Review

USING KEY TERMS

For each pair of terms, explain how the meanings of the terms differ.

1 *open cluster* and *globular cluster*

2 *comet* and *asteroid*

3 *meteor* and *meteorite*

UNDERSTANDING KEY IDEAS

Multiple Choice

4 Stars usually form from

  a. galaxies.

  b. gas clouds.

  c. open clusters.

  d. globular clusters.

5 The distances to stars are incredibly large. Which of the following units do astronomers use to measure distances to stars? E.1.3.4 CS *FCAT*

  a. meters

  b. miles

  c. light-years

  d. light-minutes

6 Which of the following statements about star clusters is true?

  a. They are not found inside our solar system.

  b. They are bigger than galaxies.

  c. They contain only very old stars.

  d. They are smaller than galaxies.

7 Which of the following statements about galaxies is true? E.2.3.1 CS

  a. They are larger than star clusters.

  b. They form into many different shapes.

  c. They contain billions of stars.

  d. All of the above

8 The Milky Way contains about 200 billion stars, including the sun. The Milky Way is an example of which of the following groups of stars? E.2.3.1 CS *FCAT*

  a. a star cluster

  b. a nebula

  c. a galaxy

  d. a solar system

9 Jupiter, Saturn, Uranus, and Neptune are examples of

  a. gas-giant planets.

  b. terrestrial planets.

  c. inner planets.

  d. planets that you can stand on.

10 In 2004, NASA launched the rovers *Spirit* and *Opportunity*. The NASA rovers were designed to gather information about which of the following? E.1.3.2 *FCAT*

  a. the surface of Mars

  b. the rings of Saturn

  c. the surface of Eros

  d. the composition of Miranda

11 Many planets have moons. Which of the following satellites is Pluto's only moon? E.1.3.4 CS *FCAT*

  a. Europa

  b. Charon

  c. Io

  d. Miranda

12 Which of the following is NOT debris that has been left over from the formation of our solar system?

  a. planets

  b. asteroids

  c. comets

  d. meteoroids

Short Answer

13 How do stars, such as the sun, produce light? E.1.3.3

14 Explain the difference between spiral, elliptical, and irregular galaxies. E.2.3.1 CS

15 Explain how astronomers determine the elements that make up stars. E.1.3.4 CS

Math Skills

16 Very massive stars last only 1 million years before they become supernovas. How many generations of supernovas may have happened by the time the universe was 1 billion years old?

Extended Response

17 **Making Inferences** You are outside looking at stars. You see a star that is bluish in color and another star that is orangish in color. What can you conclude about the temperatures of these two stars? E.1.3.4 CS

18 **Making Comparisons** An astronomer discovers a star cluster in the Andromeda galaxy. What kind of star cluster do you think the astronomer has found? E.1.3.4 CS

19 **Analyzing Ideas** Mercury has a thin, unstable atmosphere and is the planet closest to the sun. Venus has a thick atmosphere and is farther away from the sun. Why is Venus's surface temperature much hotter than Mercury's?

20 **Making Comparisons** More than 500 small objects have been found beyond Neptune. Use what you know about the smaller bodies in the solar system to describe these distant bodies.

Concept Mapping

21 Use the following terms to create a concept map: *universe, big bang, nebula, elliptical galaxies, spiral galaxies, irregular galaxies,* and *galaxies.* E.1.3.4 CS

INTERPRETING GRAPHICS

The graph below shows Hubble's law, which relates how far galaxies are from Earth to how fast they are moving away from Earth. Use the graph below to answer the questions that follow.

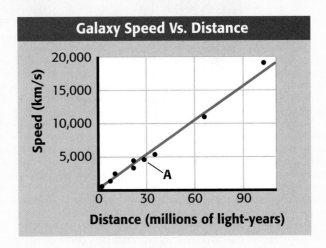

22 Look at the point that represents Galaxy A in the graph. How far is Galaxy A from Earth, and how fast is it moving away from Earth?

23 If a galaxy is moving away from Earth at 15,000 km/s, how far is the galaxy from Earth?

Standardized Test Preparation

For the following questions, write your answers on a separate sheet of paper.

1 Astronomers classify stars by temperature according to color. The hottest stars can be 40000°C. Medium-hot stars, such as our Sun, can be about 6000°C. Cool stars can have temperatures around 3000°C. What color are cool stars?

A. blue
B. orange
C. red
D. yellow

2 The picture below was made by using a spectroscope. Atoms of an element produce a special light pattern that the spectroscope records. Although stars differ in age, size, temperature, and distance from Earth, the spectroscope tells astronomers that stars are made mostly of hydrogen and helium.

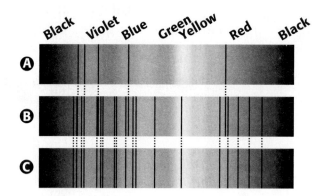

When light is passed through hydrogen gas (A) or helium gas (C) and through a slit and prism, lines appear in the spectrum. If both hydrogen and helium are present, both sets of lines appear (B).

What other elements are **most** commonly found in stars?

F. carbon, iron, and sodium
G. calcium, iron, and sodium
H. carbon, nitrogen, and oxygen
I. calcium, nitrogen, and oxygen

3 The solar system is made up of planets in orbit around the Sun. Those planets include Earth, Saturn, Mercury, Venus, Pluto, and Jupiter.

Part A   Put the following planets in order starting with the planet closest to the Sun and ending with the planet farthest from the Sun: Earth, Jupiter, Pluto, Mercury, and Saturn. Which of these planets are in the inner solar system? Which of these planets are in the outer solar system?

Part B   Put the following planets in order from largest to smallest: Earth, Jupiter, Pluto, Mercury, and Saturn.

4 Our solar system is located in the Milky Way. Which one of the following answers **best** describes the Milky Way?

A.   a nebula containing about 200 billion stars

B.   a spiral galaxy containing about 200 billion stars

C.   an irregular galaxy containing about 200 billion stars

D.   an elliptical galaxy containing about 200 billion stars

5 Pluto is the farthest planet in the solar system from the Sun. It is an average of 9.535 billion kilometers from the Sun. Earth is about 149669000 kilometers from the Sun. Visualize Pluto, Earth, and the Sun in a straight line with Earth between the Sun and Pluto. If Pluto was at its average distance from the Sun, what would be the approximate distance from Earth to Pluto in billions of kilometers?

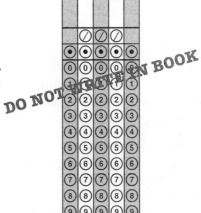

DO NOT WRITE IN BOOK

6 In February of 1996, *NASA's NEAR* spacecraft was launched into space. The *NEAR* spacecraft was designed to gather information about which of the following?

F.   the rings of Saturn

G.   the surface of Eros

H.   the surface of Mars

I.   the composition of Miranda

Science in Action

Place to Visit

Orlando Science Center Planetarium

There is a place in Florida where you can explore the wonders of the universe from the comfort of your own seat. This place is the Orlando Science Center Planetarium—the largest planetarium in the United States. It is located within a dome that is 24 m wide and 8 stories high! A specialized star projector displays scientifically accurate three-dimensional images of the night sky onto the interior of the dome. The projector creates the movement and relative positions of the sun, moon, and five visible planets. Star systems, constellations, galaxies, and nebulas are also projected onto the dome.

Math ACTiViTY

The base of the dome that houses the Orlando Science Center Planetarium is 24 m in diameter. What is the approximate area of the base of the dome? (Hint: The area of a circle is πr^2.)

Scientific Discoveries

The Oort Cloud

Have you ever wondered where comets come from? In 1950, Dutch astronomer Jan Oort decided to find out where comets originated. Oort studied 19 comets. He found that all of these comets had very long orbits, which indicated that the comets had come from the far outer regions of the solar system. Oort thought that all of the comets had come from an area at the far edge of the solar system. In addition, he believed that the comets had entered the planetary system from different directions. These conclusions led Oort to theorize that comets come from an area that surrounds the solar system like a sphere and that comets can come from any point within that sphere. Today, this spherical zone at the edge of the solar system is called the *Oort cloud*. Astronomers believe that billions or even trillions of comets may exist within the Oort cloud.

Social Studies ACTiViTY

WRITING SKILL Before astronomers understood the nature of comets, comets were a source of much fear and misunderstanding among humans. Research some of the myths that humans have created about comets. Summarize your findings in a short essay.

Subrahmanyan Chandrasekhar

From White Dwarfs to Black Holes You may be familiar with the *Chandra X-Ray Observatory*. You may also know that in July 1999, NASA launched this observatory—the most powerful x-ray telescope ever built—to search for x-ray sources in space. But do you know how the observatory got its name? The *Chandra X-Ray Observatory* was named after Subrahmanyan Chandrasekhar (SOOB ruh MAHN yuhn CHUHN druh SAY kuhr), an Indian American astrophysicist.

One of the most influential astrophysicists of the 20th century, Chandrasekhar was simply known as *Chandra* by his fellow scientists. Chandrasekhar made many contributions to physics and astrophysics. The contribution for which Chandrasekhar is best known was made in 1933, when he was a 23-year-old graduate student at Cambridge University in England. At the time, astrophysicists thought that all stars eventually became planet-sized stars known as *white dwarfs*. But from his calculations, Chandrasekhar believed that not all stars end their lives as white dwarfs. He determined that a white dwarf's mass has an upper limit that is 1.4 times the mass of the sun. He believed that if a star was more massive than this limit, it would collapse and would become a very dense object. This object is now known as a *neutron star*. Even more massive objects will become *black holes*. Chandrasekhar's ideas revolutionized astrophysics. In 1983, at the age of 73, Chandrasekhar was awarded the Nobel Prize in physics for his work on the evolution of stars.

Language Arts ACTIVITY

WRITING SKILL Use the Internet or another source to research the meaning of the word *chandra*. Write a paragraph describing your findings.

go.hrw.com
To learn more about these Science in Action topics, visit go.hrw.com and type in the keyword HT6FASFF.

Current Science
Check out Current Science® articles related to this chapter by visiting go.hrw.com. Just type in the keyword HZ5CS20.

11

Earth, Sun, and Moon

 The Big Idea The interactions of bodies in our solar system affect life on Earth.

About the

The lunar eclipse shown in this time-lapse photo was seen by people all over the world. A lunar eclipse happens when Earth comes between the sun and the moon and the shadow of Earth falls on the moon. Earth's atmosphere causes the moon to be cast in a red light. In this chapter, you will learn about how the changing positions of Earth, the sun, and the moon cause eclipses, the seasons, and the tides.

PRE-READING ACTIVITY

FOLDNOTES **Layered Book** Before you read the chapter, create the FoldNote entitled "Layered Book" described in the **Study Skills** section of the Appendix. Label the tabs of the layered book with "Planetary motion," "Days and seasons," "Lunar cycles," and "Tides." As you read the chapter, write information you learn about each category under the appropriate tab.

START-UP ACTIVITY

How Long Is Your Day? E.1.3.1 AA

In this activity, you will show how Earth's tilt in relation to the sun affects the number of daylight hours.

Procedure

1. Set a **globe that has a base** on a **table** so that the globe's North Pole points toward the ceiling and the globe's South Pole points toward the tabletop. Turn off the lights.

2. Have your partner hold a **flashlight** so that the flashlight's beam is parallel to the tabletop and points toward the globe's equator.

3. Turn the globe so that Florida faces the beam. Tilt the globe slightly so that its North Pole points away from the flashlight.

4. Make sure that the flashlight and globe remain in these positions throughout the activity.

5. Use a **piece of removable tape** to mark the width of the lighted area of the globe along the line of latitude that is nearest your hometown.

6. Repeat step 4 at 45°N latitude and 75°N latitude.

7. Measure the number of minutes of longitude that each piece of tape represents.

Analysis

1. Compare the length of the pieces of tape. What does the difference in length of the tape indicate?

2. Given that each 1° of longitude equals 4 min of time, how many hours of daylight does each piece of tape represent?

Planetary Motion

Why do Earth and the other planets revolve around the sun? Why don't they fly off into space? Does something hold them in their paths?

To answer these questions, you need to go back in time to look at the discoveries made by the scientists of the 1500s and 1600s. Danish astronomer Tycho Brahe (TIE koh BRAH uh) carefully observed the positions of planets for more than 25 years. When Brahe died in 1601, a German astronomer named Johannes Kepler (yoh HAHN uhs KEP luhr) continued Brahe's work. Kepler set out to understand the motions of planets and to describe the solar system.

A Revolution in Astronomy

Each planet spins on its axis. The spinning of a body, such as a planet, on its axis is called **rotation.** As Earth rotates, only one-half of Earth faces the sun. The half that faces the sun is light and is experiencing daytime. The half that faces away from the sun is dark and is experiencing nighttime.

The path that a body follows as it travels around another body in space is called an **orbit.** One complete trip along an orbit is called a **revolution.** The amount of time that a planet takes to complete a single trip around the sun is called a *period of revolution.* Each planet takes a different amount of time to circle the sun. Earth's period of revolution is about 365.25 days (a year), but Mercury orbits the sun in only 88 days. **Figure 1** illustrates the orbit and revolution of Earth around the sun as well as the rotation of Earth on its axis.

rotation the spin of a body on its axis

orbit the path that a body follows as it travels around another body in space

revolution the motion of a body that travels around another body in space; one complete trip along an orbit

Figure 1 *A planet rotates on its axis and revolves around the sun in a path called an* orbit.

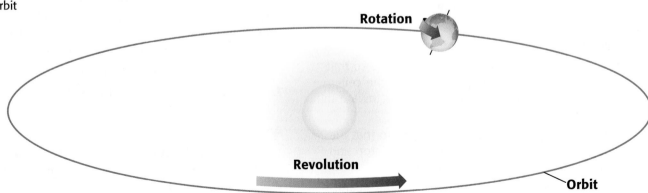

Figure 2 Parts of an Ellipse

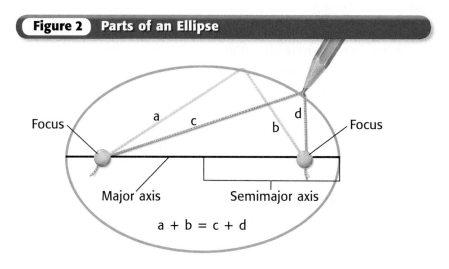

a + b = c + d

Kepler's First Law of Motion

Kepler's first discovery came from his study of Mars. Kepler discovered that Mars moved around the sun in an elongated circle called an *ellipse*. The finding that each planet moves in an ellipse became Kepler's first law of motion. An ellipse is a closed curve in which the sum of the distances between any point on the curve and two fixed points inside the ellipse is always the same, as **Figure 2** shows. The two fixed points are called *foci* (singular, *focus*). Kepler's first law also says that the sun is always located at one of these foci. An ellipse's maximum length is its *major axis*. Half this length is the *semimajor axis*, which is often used to describe an ellipse's size.

Kepler's Second Law of Motion

Kepler's second discovery was that the closer a planet is to the sun, the faster the planet moves. This discovery led to Kepler's second law of motion, which is that a line connecting the sun and a planet sweeps equal areas in equal times, as **Figure 3** shows. For this to happen, the planet must move faster when the line is shorter, or when the planet is closer to the sun.

Kepler's Third Law of Motion

Kepler saw that the farther a planet is from the sun, the more time the planet takes to orbit the sun. So, Saturn takes longer to orbit the sun than Earth does. This finding led to Kepler's third law of motion, which describes the relationship between a planet's period of revolution and its semimajor axis. By using period of revolution, Kepler calculated distance from the sun.

Benchmark Check Describe Kepler's third law. E.1.3.1 AA

Kepler's Formula

Kepler's third law can be expressed by the formula

$$P^2 = a^3$$

where P is the period of revolution and a is the semimajor axis of an orbiting body. For example, Mars's period is 1.88 years, and its semimajor axis is 1.523 AU. Thus, $1.88^2 = 1.523^3 = 3.53$. Calculate a planet's period of revolution if the semimajor axis is 5.74 AU. (The symbol AU stands for *astronomical unit,* which is a measure of distance.)

E.1.3.1 AA understands the vast size of our solar system and the relationship of the planets and their satellites.

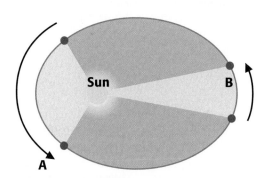

Figure 3 *According to Kepler's second law, area* A *is equal to area* B, *and the time that the planet takes to move in orbit along area* A *is equal to the time that the planet takes to move along area* B. *For the times to be equal, the planet must move faster the closer it is to the sun.*

Newton to the Rescue!

Kepler wondered what caused the planets closest to the sun to move faster than the planets farther away. However, he never found an answer. Sir Isaac Newton finally put the puzzle together when he described the force of gravity. Newton didn't understand why gravity worked or what caused it. Even today, scientists do not fully understand gravity. But Newton combined the work of earlier scientists and used mathematics to explain the effects of gravity.

The Law of Universal Gravitation

Newton reasoned that an object falls toward Earth because Earth and the object are attracted to each other by gravity. He discovered that this attraction depends on the masses of the objects and the distance between the objects.

Newton's *law of universal gravitation* states that the force of gravity depends on the product of the masses of the objects divided by the square of the distance between the objects. The larger the masses of two objects and the closer together the objects are, the greater the force of gravity between the objects. For example, if the distance between two objects doubles, the gravitational attraction between them will decrease by 2 × 2 (a factor of 4), as shown in **Figure 4.** If the distance between two objects increases by a factor of 10, the gravitational attraction between them will decrease by 10 × 10 (a factor of 100).

Both Earth and the moon are attracted to each other. Although it may seem as if Earth does not orbit the moon, Earth and the moon actually orbit each other.

Benchmark Check Explain Newton's law of universal gravitation. **E.1.3.1 AA**

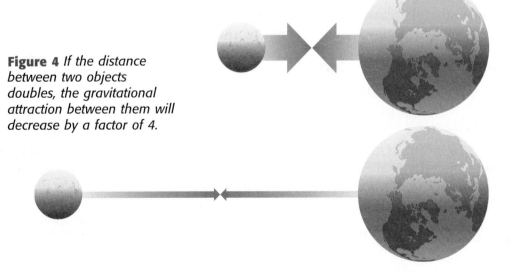

Figure 4 *If the distance between two objects doubles, the gravitational attraction between them will decrease by a factor of 4.*

Orbits Falling Down and Around

If you drop a rock, it falls to the ground. So, why doesn't the moon come crashing into Earth? The answer has to do with the moon's inertia. *Inertia* is an object's resistance to a change in speed or direction until an outside force acts on the object. In space, there is not any air to cause resistance and slow the movement of the moon. Therefore, the moon continues to move, and gravity keeps the moon in orbit, as **Figure 5** shows.

Imagine twirling a ball on the end of a string. As long as you hold the string, the ball will orbit your hand. As soon as you let go of the string, the ball will fly off in a straight path. Gravity acts on orbiting bodies in the same way that the string acts on the ball. Gravity keeps the moon from flying off in a straight path. In this way, gravity affects all bodies in orbit, including Earth and other planets in our solar system.

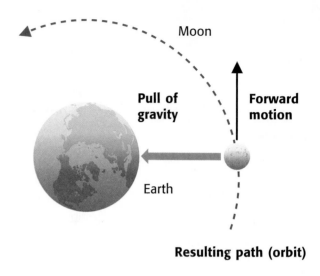

Figure 5 *Gravity causes the moon to fall toward Earth and changes a straight-line path into a curved orbit.*

SECTION Review

Summary

- Rotation is the spinning of a body on its axis, and revolution is a body's motion along an orbit around another body.

- Planets move in an ellipse around the sun. The closer a planet is to the sun, the faster it moves. A planet's period of revolution depends on the semimajor axis of its orbit. **E.I.3.I AA**

- Gravitational attraction decreases as distance increases and decreases as mass decreases.

Using Key Terms

1. Write an original definition for *revolution* and *rotation*.

Understanding Key Ideas

2. How did Kepler's theories help explain the relationship between a planet and the planet's distance from the sun? **E.I.3.I AA**

3. How does gravity keep a planet moving in an orbit around the sun? **E.I.3.I AA**

Math Skills

4. Earth's period of revolution is 365.25 days. Convert this period of revolution into hours.

Critical Thinking

5. **Making Comparisons** Describe the three laws of planetary motion. How is each law related to the other two laws? **E.I.3.I AA**

FCAT Preparation

6. When Planet X orbits a star, the distance between Planet X and the star doubles. When this distance doubles, how does the gravitational attraction between Planet X and the star change? **E.I.3.I AA**

A. It decreases by a factor of 4.

B. It increases by a factor of 6.

C. It decreases by a factor of 9.

D. It remains the same.

SECTION

2

READING WARM-UP

Objectives

● Explain the cause of daylight and night. E.1.3.1 AA

● Explain how the tilt and movement of Earth cause changes in seasons and in the length of a day. D.1.3.3 CS

● Describe the causes of equinoxes and solstices. E.1.3.1 AA

● Describe how latitude affects the amount of seasonal change that an area experiences. D.1.3.3 CS

Terms to Learn

day
equinox
solstice

READING STRATEGY

Reading Organizer As you read this section, create an outline of the section. Use the headings from the section in your outline.

Days and Seasons on Earth

Have you ever noticed that a winter day has fewer hours of daylight than a summer day does? During the winter, a day may get dark as early as 6:00 P.M. However, in the summer, a day may not get dark until 9:00 P.M. What causes these differences in hours of daylight?

The answer to this question has to do with the motion of Earth as it revolves around the sun. Learning more about how Earth moves will help you understand why we have daylight and night and why we have the seasons of the year.

The Earth-Sun System

You now know that Earth revolves around the sun in an ellipse, or elongated circle. It takes 1 year, or $365\frac{1}{4}$ days, for Earth to revolve once around the sun. But it is Earth's rotation that is a direct cause of daylight and night.

Earth's Rotation

It takes Earth 23 hours and 56 minutes to rotate once on its axis. Earth's axis is an imaginary line that runs through Earth's center from the North Pole to the South Pole. **Figure 1** shows Earth's rotation on its axis and revolution around the sun.

We usually think of a day as the hours of light that we experience. But a **day** is also the time required for Earth to rotate once on its axis. A day includes the time of light and dark. Earth's rotation causes daylight and night. Because Earth rotates counterclockwise as seen from above the North Pole, the sun appears to rise in the east and set in the west.

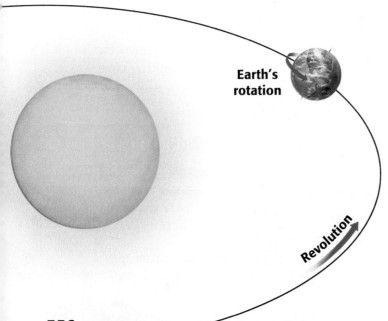

Earth's rotation

Revolution

Figure 1 *The side of Earth that faces the sun is light, which is daylight. The side of Earth that faces away from the sun is dark, which is night.*

Figure 2 The Seasons

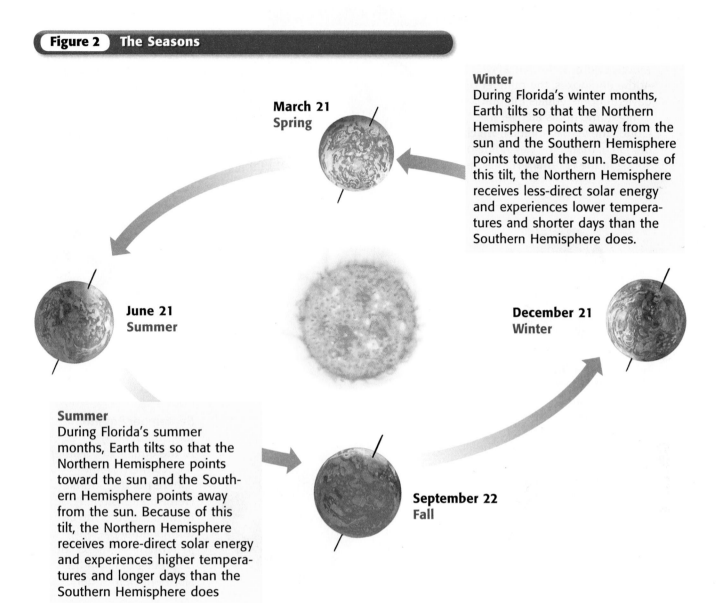

March 21
Spring

Winter
During Florida's winter months, Earth tilts so that the Northern Hemisphere points away from the sun and the Southern Hemisphere points toward the sun. Because of this tilt, the Northern Hemisphere receives less-direct solar energy and experiences lower temperatures and shorter days than the Southern Hemisphere does.

June 21
Summer

December 21
Winter

Summer
During Florida's summer months, Earth tilts so that the Northern Hemisphere points toward the sun and the Southern Hemisphere points away from the sun. Because of this tilt, the Northern Hemisphere receives more-direct solar energy and experiences higher temperatures and longer days than the Southern Hemisphere does

September 22
Fall

Earth's Tilt

Seasons are caused mainly by the 23.5° tilt of Earth's axis. This tilt causes the number of daylight hours to change as the time of year changes. An area has fewer daylight hours in winter than in summer. Winter in the Northern Hemisphere is caused by the tilt of the Northern Hemisphere away from the sun. In summer, an area has more daylight hours than in winter. Summer in the Northern Hemisphere is caused by the tilt of the Northern Hemisphere toward the sun. **Figure 2** shows how Earth's tilt affects the amount of sunlight in an area.

day the time required for Earth to rotate once on its axis

Benchmark Check How does Earth's tilt cause summer in the Northern Hemisphere? **D.1.3.3 CS**

D.1.3.3 CS knows how conditions that exist in one system influence the conditions that exist in other systems.

Figure 3 The Seasons' Yearly Cycle

1

March Equinox (March 21)
At the equinoxes, the number of daylight hours equals the number of nighttime hours all over the world. The vernal equinox, which is in March, marks the beginning of spring in the Northern Hemisphere.

4

December Solstice (December 22)
The North Pole is tilted away from the sun. The winter solstice marks the beginning of winter in the Northern Hemisphere. There are fewer daylight hours in the Northern Hemisphere than in the Southern Hemisphere.

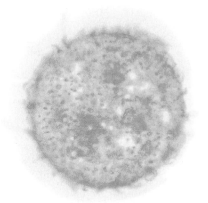

2

June Solstice (June 22)
The North Pole is tilted toward the sun. The summer solstice marks the beginning of summer in the Northern Hemisphere. There are more daylight hours in the Northern Hemisphere than in the Southern Hemisphere.

3

September Equinox (September 23)
At the equinoxes, neither the Northern Hemisphere nor the Southern Hemisphere is tilted toward the sun. The autumnal equinox, which is in September, marks the beginning of fall in the Northern Hemisphere.

The Seasons' Yearly Cycle

Earth's tilt and shape affect the amount of sunlight that an area receives. But what does the Earth-sun system look like at different times of the year? The seasons' yearly cycle is caused by Earth's tilt and revolution around the sun.

Equinoxes

equinox the moment when the sun appears to cross the celestial equator

solstice the point at which the sun is as far north or as far south of the equator as possible

Figure 3 shows that in March and September, neither end of Earth's axis is tilted toward the sun. So, both hemispheres receive the same amount of solar energy because the sun is directly above the equator. The time when the sun is directly above the equator is called **equinox** (EE kwi NAHKS).

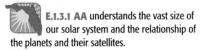

E.1.3.1 AA understands the vast size of our solar system and the relationship of the planets and their satellites.

Benchmark Check During an equinox, what is the position of Earth relative to the position of the sun? E.1.3.1 AA

Solstices

A **solstice** happens when the sun is farthest north or south of the equator. In the month of June, the Northern Hemisphere tilts toward the sun, so the Northern Hemisphere is warmer than the Southern Hemisphere. At this time, the Northern Hemisphere has more daylight hours than the Southern Hemisphere does. In December, the opposite happens because the Southern Hemisphere tilts toward the sun.

The Amount of Seasonal Change

Some places on Earth do not have much seasonal change because their position in relation to the sun does not change. For example, near the equator, the temperature and the amount of daylight stay about the same year-round. But the tilt of the North Pole and South Pole in relation to the sun changes throughout the year. Position in relation to the sun determines the angle and amount of sunlight that an area receives, as **Figure 4** shows.

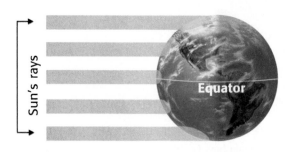

Figure 4 *Areas near the equator do not have much seasonal change because their position in relation to the sun does not change when Earth's tilt changes.*

D.1.3.3 CS knows how conditions that exist in one system influence the conditions that exist in other systems.

SECTION
Review

Summary

- Daylight and night are caused by the rotation of Earth on its axis. **E.1.3.1 AA**

- Seasons and the number of daylight hours are caused by the tilt of Earth's axis. **D.1.3.3 CS**

- Equinoxes and solstices are caused by Earth's tilt and by Earth's revolution around the sun. **E.1.3.1 AA**

- The amount of seasonal change in an area is determined by the amount of change in the area's position in relation to the sun. **D.1.3.3 CS**

Using Key Terms

Correct the statement below by replacing the underlined term.

1. A(n) <u>day</u> is the time at which the sun is farthest north or south of the equator.

Understanding Key Ideas

2. What causes daylight and night on Earth? **E.1.3.1 AA**

Math Skills

3. Light travels about 300,000 km/s. If the distance between the sun and Earth is 150 million kilometers, how long does light take to travel from the sun to Earth? **E.1.3.1 AA**

Critical Thinking

4. **Applying Concepts** If Earth's tilt did not change, would Earth have seasons? **D.1.3.3 CS**

SCILINKS

NSTA
Developed and maintained by the
National Science Teachers Association

For a variety of links related to this chapter, go to www.scilinks.org

Topic: Latitude and Longitude; The Sun
SciLinks code: HSTE035; HSM1477

Lunar Cycles

Have you ever wondered why the moon seems to change throughout the month? Sometimes, the moon is a big glowing ball; other times, it's just a sliver.

Since the earliest times, people have looked at the sky to learn more about the moon. They wondered about the changing appearance of the moon and noticed that the same changes happened month after month. When you look up at the moon, you see what ancient people saw. These changes in the moon's appearance are called the *phases of the moon.*

The Earth-Moon System

You now know that Earth rotates on its axis and revolves around the sun. But did you know that the moon rotates on its axis as it moves around Earth? Take a look at **Figure 1.** Every 27.3 days, the moon rotates once on its axis and revolves once around Earth. The rate at which the moon rotates on its axis is the same as the rate at which the moon revolves around Earth. Because these rates are the same, the same side of the moon always faces Earth.

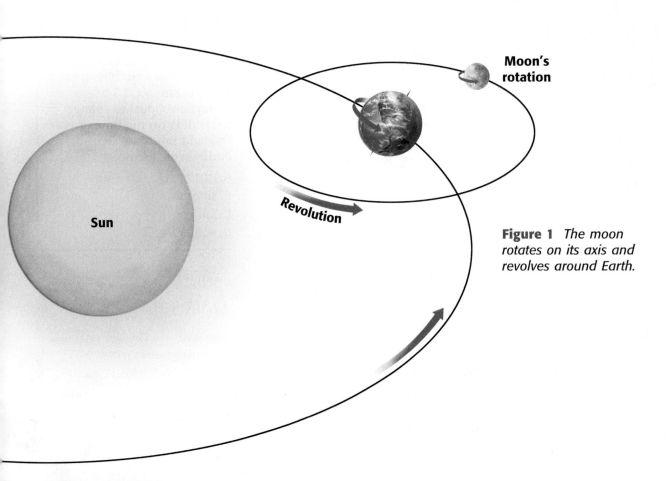

Moon's rotation

Revolution

Sun

Figure 1 *The moon rotates on its axis and revolves around Earth.*

Figure 2 **The Phases of the Moon**

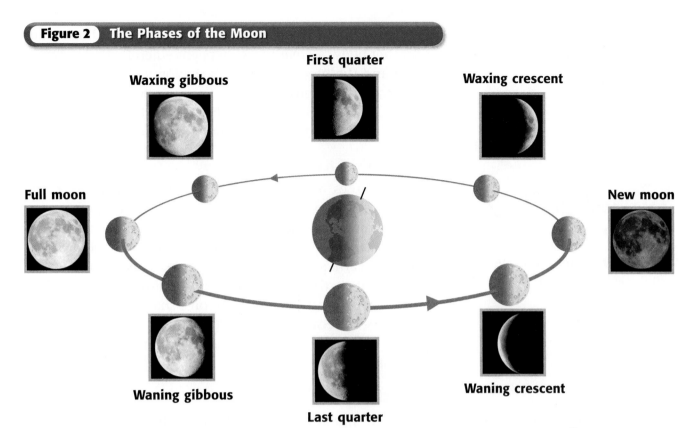

Phases of the Moon

From Earth, one of the most noticeable features of the moon is its continually changing appearance. When viewed from Earth over a one-month period, the moon appears to change from a fully lit circle to a thin crescent and back to a circle. This changing appearance of the moon results from the changing position of the moon in relation to Earth and the sun. As the moon revolves around Earth, the amount of sunlight reflected toward Earth by the face of the moon changes. The various appearances of the moon due to its changing position are called **phases.** The phases of the moon are shown in **Figure 2.**

Waxing and Waning

When the moon is *waxing*, the sunlit part that can be seen from Earth appears to get larger. When the moon is *waning*, the sunlit part seen from Earth appears to get smaller. Notice that even as the phases of the moon change, the total amount of sunlight that the moon receives remains the same. Half of the moon is always in sunlight, just as half of Earth is always in sunlight. But because the moon's rate of rotation is equal to its period of revolution, the side of the moon that is visible from Earth is always the same side.

Benchmark Check During a full moon, where is Earth in relation to the sun and the moon? **E.1.3.1 AA**

MATH PRACTICE

Orbits Within Orbits

The average distance between Earth and the moon is about 384,400 km. The average distance between Earth and the sun is about 150 million kilometers. Assume that the orbit of Earth around the sun and the orbit of the moon around Earth are perfectly circular and in the same plane. Using the distances given above, calculate the maximum and minimum distances between the moon and the sun.

phase the change in the sunlit area of one celestial body as seen from another celestial body

 **E.1.3.1 AA** understands the vast size of our solar system and the relationship of the planets and their satellites.

eclipse an event in which the shadow of one celestial body falls on another

Solar Jam Research the sun, sun spots, and solar flares. Go to **go.hrw.com,** and type in the keyword **HZ5SOLW.**

E.1.3.1 AA understands the vast size of our solar system and the relationship of the planets and their satellites.

Figure 3 *On the left is a diagram of the positions of Earth and the moon during a solar eclipse. On the right is a picture of the sun's outer atmosphere, or corona, which is visible only when the moon appears to block the entire disk of the sun.*

Eclipses

An **eclipse** happens when the shadow of one celestial body falls on another body. A *lunar eclipse* happens when Earth is between the sun and the moon and Earth's shadow falls on the moon. A *solar eclipse* happens when the moon is between Earth and the sun and the moon's shadow falls on Earth. **Figure 3** shows the positions of Earth and the moon in a solar eclipse.

The Moon's Tilted Orbit

If lunar eclipses and solar eclipses happen when Earth, the moon, and the sun are aligned, why doesn't the moon's revolution around Earth cause eclipses every month? The reason is that the moon's orbit around Earth is tilted—by about 5°—in relation to Earth's orbit around the sun. This tilt places the moon out of Earth's shadow for most full-moon phases. The tilt also places Earth out of the moon's shadow for most new-moon phases. Because the moon's orbit is tilted, the moon, the sun, and Earth are not aligned every month. So, eclipses do not happen every month.

Solar Eclipses

Because the moon's orbit is elliptical, the distance between the moon and Earth changes. During a type of solar eclipse called an *annular eclipse,* the moon is at a point in its orbit that is far from Earth. In an annular eclipse, the moon does not appear to fully cover the disk of the sun—some of the sun shows around the moon's edge. During an eclipse called a *total solar eclipse,* the moon is at a point in its orbit that is closer to Earth. During a total solar eclipse, the moon appears to be the same size as the sun and appears to fully cover the disk of the sun, as **Figure 3** shows. Only the sun's *corona,* or faint outer atmosphere, is visible during a total solar eclipse.

Benchmark Check Describe a solar eclipse. E.1.3.1 AA

Solar eclipse

NEVER look directly at the sun! You can permanently damage your eyes.

Lunar eclipse

Lunar Eclipses

During a lunar eclipse, Earth comes between the sun and the moon, as shown in **Figure 4.** Lunar eclipses can happen only during a full moon. As you can see, the moon appears to be a brightly glowing red ball during a lunar eclipse. Earth's atmosphere acts like a lens and bends some of the sunlight into Earth's shadow. When sunlight hits the particles in Earth's atmosphere, the atmosphere filters the blue light out. With the blue light removed, most of the remaining light that lights the moon is red.

Figure 4 *On the left, you can see that the moon can have a reddish color during a lunar eclipse. On the right, you can see the positions of Earth and the moon during a lunar eclipse.*

SECTION Review

Summary

- Every 27.3 days, the moon rotates once on its axis and revolves once around Earth.

- Earth's movement and the moon's orbit cause the phases of the moon. **E.1.3.1 AA**

- A solar eclipse occurs when the shadow of the moon falls on Earth.

- A lunar eclipse occurs when the shadow of Earth falls on the moon.

Using Key Terms

Use a term from the section to complete each sentence below.

1. A(n) ___ happens when the shadow of one celestial body falls on another body.

2. The various appearances of the moon that are due to changes in the moon's position are ___.

Math Skills

3. The diameter of the moon is 3,475 km. What is the moon's radius?

Critical Thinking

4. **Applying Concepts** Explain why people on Earth always see the same side of the moon. **E.1.3.1 AA**

5. **Identifying Relationships** Describe how the movement of Earth and the moon's orbit cause the phases of the moon. **E.1.3.1 AA**

FCAT Preparation

6. As the moon revolves around Earth, the amount of sunlight that the moon reflects toward Earth changes. When the sun and moon form a 90° angle with Earth, the moon is in which phase? **E.1.3.1 AA**

   A. waning crescent

   B. new moon

   C. last quarter

   D. waxing gibbous

SCi**LINKS**®

NSTA

Developed and maintained by the National Science Teachers Association

For a variety of links related to this chapter, go to www.scilinks.org

Topic: The Earth's Moon
SciLinks code: HSTE490

Tides, the Sun, and the Moon

If you stand at an ocean shore long enough, you may see the edge of the ocean shrink away from you. If you wait longer, you may see it return to its original place on the shore. Would you believe that the moon causes this movement?

Did you know that the movement of Earth, the sun, and the moon affects the movement of the oceans? **Tides** are daily changes in the level of ocean water. Tides are influenced by the sun and the moon, as shown in **Figure 1.**

The Lure of the Moon

The tides are influenced by gravity. The gravity of the moon pulls on every particle of Earth. But because liquids move more easily than solids do, the pull on liquids is much more noticeable than the pull on solids is. Even the liquid in an open soft drink is slightly pulled by the moon's gravity. The gravity of the sun also has an effect on the oceans.

High Tide and Low Tide

How often tides occur and how tidal levels vary depend on the position of the moon as it revolves around Earth. The moon's pull is strongest on the part of Earth that directly faces the moon.

Benchmark Check How does the moon affect Earth's oceans? E.1.3.1 AA

READING WARM-UP

Objectives

● Explain tides and their relationship with Earth, the sun, and the moon. D.1.3.3 CS, E.1.3.1 AA

● Describe four types of tides.

● Analyze the relationship between tides and coastal land. D.1.3.3 CS

Terms to Learn

tide
tidal range
spring tide *FCAT* VOCAB
neap tide *FCAT* VOCAB

READING STRATEGY

Discussion Read this section silently. Write down questions that you have about this section. Discuss your questions in a small group.

tide the periodic rise and fall of the water level in the oceans and other large bodies of water

Figure 1 *Although gravitational forces from both the sun and moon continuously pull on Earth, the moon's gravity is the force that most affects Earth's tides.*

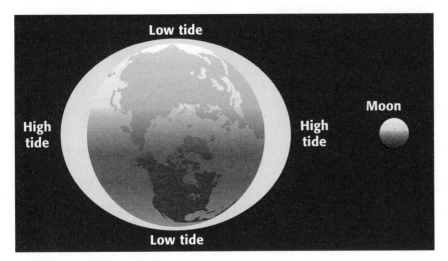

Low tide

High tide

High tide

Moon

Low tide

Figure 2 *High tide occurs on the part of Earth that is closest to the moon. At the same time, high tide also occurs on the opposite side of Earth.*

Battle of the Bulge

When a part of the ocean faces the moon, the water there bulges toward the moon. At the same time, water on the opposite side of Earth bulges because of Earth's rotation and the motion of the moon around Earth. These bulges are called *high tides*. **Figure 2** shows how the moon's position causes the water to bulge. High tides draw water away from the area between the high tides and cause *low tides* to form in those areas.

Timing Tides

Tides are determined by Earth's rotation and by the moon's revolution around Earth. The speed at which the moon revolves around Earth is too slow for the moon to always have the same position in relation to Earth. Tides would not alternate between high and low if the moon orbited Earth in one day—fast enough to always have the same position in relation to Earth. As **Figure 3** shows, a spot on Earth that is facing the moon takes longer than a day—24 h 50 min—to rotate and face the moon again.

Figure 3 *Tides occur on Earth because the moon revolves around Earth too slowly to always have the same position in relation to Earth.*

Tuesday, 11:00 A.M.

Wednesday, 11:50 A.M.

CONNECTION TO Language Arts

WRITING SKILL **Mont-St-Michel: Sometimes an Island** Mont-St-Michel is located off the coast of France. Mont-St-Michel experiences extreme tides. The tides are so extreme that Mont-St-Michel is an island during high tide and is connected to the mainland during low tide. Research the history of Mont-St-Michel, and write a short story describing what living there for a day would be like. Include a description of Mont-St-Michel at high tide and at low tide.

Benchmark Activity

Tidal Charts

Investigate the relationship between tides on Earth and the position of the moon. Research the measured tidal changes in the Bay of Fundy, including how they relate to the phases of the moon. Make a chart or graph that shows this relationship. E.1.3.1 AA

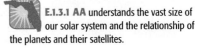

E.1.3.1 AA understands the vast size of our solar system and the relationship of the planets and their satellites.

Tidal Variations

The sun also affects tides. The sun is much larger than the moon, but the sun is also much farther from Earth than the moon is. As a result, the sun's influence on tides is less powerful than the moon's influence. The combined forces of the sun and the moon on Earth result in tidal ranges that vary based on the positions of all three bodies. A **tidal range** is the difference between the level of ocean water at high tide and the level at low tide.

✓ Reading Check What is a tidal range?

Spring Tides

When the sun, Earth, and moon are aligned, spring tides occur. **Spring tides** are tides that have the largest daily tidal range and occur during the new and full moons, or every 14 days. Spring tides occur when the moon is between the sun and Earth. Spring tides also occur when the moon and the sun are on opposite sides of Earth. **Figure 4** shows the positions of the sun, Earth, and the moon during spring tides.

Neap Tides

When the sun, Earth, and moon form a 90° angle, neap tides occur. **Neap tides** are tides that have the smallest daily tidal range and occur during the first and third quarters of the moon. Neap tides occur halfway between the occurrences of spring tides. During neap tides, the gravitational forces of the sun and moon work against each other on Earth. **Figure 4** shows the positions of the sun, Earth, and the moon during neap tides.

tidal range the difference in levels of ocean water at high tide and low tide

spring tide a tide of increased range that occurs two times a month, at the new and full moons *FCAT VOCAB*

neap tide a tide of minimum range that occurs during the first and third quarters of the moon *FCAT VOCAB*

E.1.3.1 AA understands the vast size of our solar system and the relationship of the planets and their satellites.

Figure 4 **Spring Tides and Neap Tides**

Spring Tides During spring tides, the gravitational forces of the sun and moon pull on Earth either from the same direction (left) or from opposite directions (right).

Neap Tides During neap tides, the sun and moon are at right angles relative to Earth. This arrangement lessens the gravitational effect of the sun and the moon on Earth.

Tides and Topography

After a tidal range has been measured, the times that tides occur can be accurately predicted. This information can be useful for people near the coast, as shown in **Figure 5**. In some coastal areas that have narrow inlets, movements of water called *tidal bores* occur. A tidal bore is a body of water that rushes up through a narrow bay, estuary, or river channel during the rise of high tide and causes a sudden tidal rise.

Benchmark Check **How might tidal bores affect rocks in coastal areas?** D.1.3.3 CS

Figure 5 *It's a good thing that the people on this beach (left) knew when high tide occurred (right). These photos show the Bay of Fundy in New Brunswick, Canada. The Bay of Fundy has the greatest tidal range on Earth.*

D.1.3.3 CS knows how conditions that exist in one system influence the conditions that exist in other systems.

SECTION
Review

Summary

- Tides are caused by the gravitational forces of the moon and sun on Earth. E.1.3.1 AA

- The moon's gravity is the main force behind the tides. D.1.3.3 CS, E.1.3.1 AA

- The positions of the sun and moon relative to the Earth cause tidal ranges. D.1.3.3 CS, E.1.3.1 AA

- The four types of tides are high tides, low tides, spring tides, and neap tides.

Using Key Terms

1. Write an original definition for *spring tide* and *neap tide*. E.1.3.1 AA *FCAT VOCAB*

Understanding Key Ideas

2. Which tides have minimum tidal range? Which tides have maximum tidal range?

3. What causes tidal bores? D.1.3.3 CS

Math Skills

4. A spot on Earth that is facing the moon takes 24 h and 50 min to rotate to face the moon again. How many minutes does this rotation take? E.1.3.1 AA

Critical Thinking

5. **Analyzing Processes** Explain how the position of the moon relates to the occurrence of tides. D.1.3.3 CS, E.1.3.1 AA

FCAT Preparation

6. When part of the ocean is directly facing the moon, the water at that part bulges toward the moon. What is this bulge called? D.1.3.3 CS
   - **A.** low tide
   - **B.** high tide
   - **C.** neap tide
   - **D.** spring tide

For a variety of links related to this chapter, go to www.scilinks.org

Topic: Tides; Florida's Coasts
SciLinks code: HSM1525; HSMF05

Model-Making Lab

E.1.3.1 AA understands the vast size of our solar system and the relationship of the planets and their satellites.

OBJECTIVES

- **Build** a working model of the Earth-moon system.
- **Explain** how the Earth-moon system works using your model. E.1.3.1 AA

MATERIALS

- cardboard, 1 cm × 1 cm piece
- corrugated cardboard disk, about 4 cm in diameter, with center marked
- corrugated cardboard disk, about 16 cm in diameter, with center marked
- dowel, $\frac{1}{4}$ in. in diameter and 36 cm in length
- glue, white
- pencil, sharp
- stapler
- string, 5 cm length

SAFETY

Turning the Tides

Daily tides are caused by two "bulges" on the ocean's surface—one on the side of Earth facing the moon and the other on the opposite side of Earth. The bulge in the water on the side facing the moon is caused by the moon's gravitational pull on the water. But the bulge on the opposite side of Earth is slightly more difficult to explain. Whereas the moon pulls the water on one side of Earth, the combined rotation of Earth and the moon "pushes" the water on the opposite side of Earth. In this activity, you will model the motion of Earth and the moon to investigate the tidal bulge on the side of Earth facing away from the moon.

Procedure

1. Draw a line from the center of each disk along the folds in the cardboard to the edge of the disk. This line is the radius.

2. Place a drop of white glue on one end of the dowel. Lay the large disk flat, and align the dowel with the line for the radius that you drew in step 1. Insert about 2.5 cm of the dowel into the edge of the disk.

3. Add a drop of glue to the other end of the dowel, and push that end into the smaller disk, along the smaller disk's radius. The setup should look like a two-headed lollipop, as shown below. This setup is a model of the Earth-moon system.

4. Staple the string to the edge of the large disk on the side opposite the dowel. Staple the cardboard square to the other end of the string. This smaller piece of cardboard represents Earth's oceans that face away from the moon.

5️⃣ Place the tip of the pencil at the center of the large disk, as shown in the figure on the next page, and spin the model. You may poke a small hole in the bottom of the disk with your pencil, but DO NOT poke all the way through the cardboard. Record your observations. **Caution:** Be sure that you are at a safe distance from other people before spinning your model.

6️⃣ Now, find your model's center of mass. The center of mass is the point at which the model can be balanced on the end of the pencil. (Hint: It might be easier to find the center of mass by using the eraser end. Then, use the sharpened end of the pencil to balance the model.) This balance point should be just inside the edge of the large disk.

7️⃣ Place the pencil at the center of mass, and spin the model around the pencil. Again, you may wish to poke a small hole in the disk. Record your observations.

Analyze the Results

1️⃣ What happened when you tried to spin the model around the center of the large disk? This model, called the *Earth-centered model,* represents the incorrect view that the moon orbits the center of Earth.

2️⃣ What happened when you tried to spin the model around its center of mass? This point, called the *barycenter,* is the point around which both Earth and the moon rotate.

3️⃣ In each case, what happened to the string and cardboard square when the model was spun?

Draw Conclusions

4️⃣ Which model explains why Earth has a tidal bulge on the side opposite the moon: the Earth-centered model or the barycentric model? Explain.

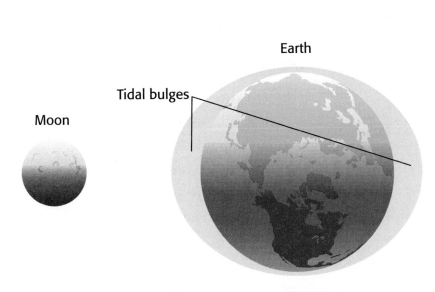

Earth

Tidal bulges

Moon

Chapter Review

USING KEY TERMS

For each pair of terms, explain how the meanings of the terms differ.

1 *rotation* and *revolution*

2 *equinox* and *solstice*

3 *spring tide* and *neap tide* **FCAT VOCAB**

Use a term from the chapter to complete each sentence below.

4 The daily changes of ocean water levels are commonly called ___.

5 A(n) ___ happens when one celestial body casts a shadow on another celestial body.

6 The path that a planet travels around the sun is called the ___.

7 A(n) ___ is the difference between the level of ocean water at high tide and the level of ocean water at low tide.

UNDERSTANDING KEY IDEAS

Multiple Choice

8 Eclipses occur when the shadow of one celestial body, such as a planet, falls on another celestial body. When might an eclipse happen? **E.1.3.1 AA FCAT**

a. every high tide

b. only during a full moon

c. when the moon is between the Earth and the sun

d. when the sun is between the moon and the Earth

9 Which of the following happens at the solstices?

a. The number of daylight hours equals the number of nighttime hours.

b. Either spring or fall begins.

c. The sun is directly above the equator.

d. Either the Northern or Southern Hemisphere tilts toward the sun.

10 The seasons are caused by Earth's tilt as it travels around the sun. What causes winter in the Southern Hemisphere? **D.1.3.3 CS FCAT**

a. The North Pole tilts away from the sun.

b. The equator receives direct sunlight.

c. Earth moves closer to the sun.

d. The South Pole tilts away from the sun.

11 Planetary orbits are not perfect circles. Which of the following is the shape that planetary orbits have? **E.1.3.1 AA FCAT**

a. solstice   c. ellipse

b. spiral   d. period

Short Answer

12 Describe how changes in Earth's tilt affect the amount of seasonal change that an area experiences. **D.1.3.3 CS**

13 What causes the changes in seasons and changes in day length? **D.1.3.3 CS**

14 Compare solar and lunar eclipses. **E.1.3.1 AA**

15 What causes the moon's phases? **E.1.3.1 AA**

16 What determines a planet's period of revolution? **E.1.3.1 AA**

17 Why do the sun and the moon appear to move across the sky each day? E.1.3.1 AA

18 During which moon phase do solar eclipses happen? E.1.3.1 AA

19 Why is the tidal range relatively small during a neap tide? E.1.3.1 AA

CRITICAL THINKING

Extended Response

20 Making Comparisons How did Newton's law of universal gravitation help explain the work of Johannes Kepler?

21 Identifying Relationships Describe Kepler's three laws of motion in your own words. Describe how each law relates to either the revolution, rotation, or orbit of a planetary body.

22 Analyzing Ideas Your family is planning to build a home near the beach. Which time is better for choosing the place to build the house: during spring tides or neap tides? E.1.3.1 AA *FCAT*

Concept Mapping

23 Use the following terms to create a concept map: *phases, eclipse, revolution, solar eclipse,* and *lunar eclipse.*

INTERPRETING GRAPHICS

Use the diagram below to answer the questions that follow.

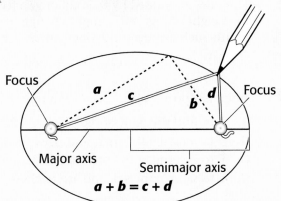

$$a + b = c + d$$

24 Which of Kepler's laws of motion does the illustration represent?

25 How does the equation shown in the diagram support the law?

26 What is an ellipse's maximum length called?

Standardized Test Preparation

For the following questions, write your answers on a separate sheet of paper.

1 The tides are caused by the pull of gravity from the Sun and Moon. Explain one reason why the height of high tides might change over the course of a month. Do not include weather events such as storms in your answer.

2 What is a principal reason for sending probes to Mars?

A. to find the path of the planet's solar orbit
B. to measure the mass and size of the planet
C. to determine the presence of planetary moons
D. to sample the soil and atmosphere of the planet

3 Which of the following events takes the longest period of time to occur?
F. Earth orbits the Sun once.
G. The Moon orbits Earth twice.
H. Earth rotates on its axis five times.
I. Eleven full moons are seen from Earth.

4 Ixion is a recently discovered body in our solar system. The table below contains data about Ixion's orbit and Earth's orbit around the Sun.

ORBITS OF IXION AND EARTH

	Orbit Radius (Billions of Kilometers)	Orbit Time (Earth Years)
Earth	0.15	1.00
Ixion	6.00	248

In billions of kilometers, how much greater is the radius of Ixion's orbit than Earth's orbit?

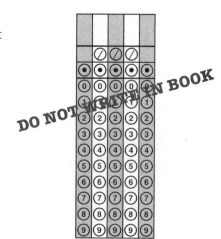

5 Many people enjoy watching the full moon disappear and reappear during lunar eclipses. A lunar eclipse results when Earth, the Moon, and the Sun are aligned in a certain way. Which of the following drawings shows the correct relative positions of Earth, the Moon, and the Sun during a lunar eclipse?

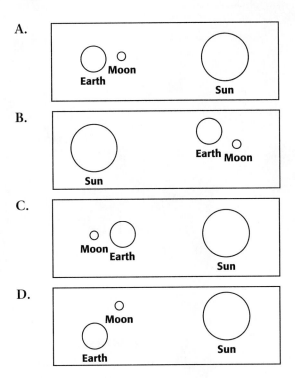

A.

B.

C.

D.

6 The Moon is much smaller than the Sun. Explain why the Sun and the Moon appear to be approximately the same size when they are viewed from Earth.

Science in Action

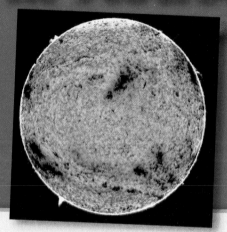

FOCUS ON FLORIDA

Science, Technology, and Society

Don't Look at the Sun!

How do we learn about the sun if we don't look at it directly? We look at the sun indirectly by using a telescope called a *solar telescope*. The world's three largest solar telescopes are at Kitt Peak National Observatory near Tucson, Arizona. The largest of these telescopes, the McMath-Pierce solar telescope, creates an image of the sun that is almost 1 m wide. The McMath-Pierce solar telescope creates this image by using a mirror that is more than 2 m in diameter. The sun's rays are directed from this mirror down a diagonal shaft to a mirror that is 152 m underground. This second mirror can be adjusted to focus the sunlight and direct it to a third mirror, which directs the light to an observing room and instrument shaft.

Weird Science

The JAMSTAR Project

In 2003, engineering and meteorology students at Florida Tech designed, built, and launched one of the largest amateur rockets in history. This exciting rocket development project was called the JAMSTAR Project. The rocket was successfully launched early one April morning in 2003. When the rocket reached about 80,000 ft, the nose cone broke off and a parachute opened. The parachute carried meteorological instruments that transmitted weather data to Earth. The rocket launch was a thrilling success. The JAMSTAR Project is a great example of Florida students aiming high and working together to accomplish great things.

Math Activity

The outer skin of the McMath-Pierce solar telescope consists of 140 copper panels that measure 10.4 m × 2.4 m each. How many square meters of copper were used to construct the outer skin of the telescope?

Language Arts Activity

WRITING SKILL Find out more about Florida Tech's JAMSTAR Project and write a brief news article describing the project.

Sandra Faber

Astronomer What do you do when you send a telescope into space and then find out that the telescope is broken? You call Sandra Faber, Ph.D., a professor of astronomy at the University of California, Santa Cruz (UCSC). After the *Hubble Space Telescope* went into orbit in April 1990, scientists found that the images collected by the telescope were not turning out as expected. Faber's team at UCSC was in charge of a device on *Hubble* called the *Wide Field Planetary Camera*. Faber and her team decided to use the camera to test the telescope and determine what was wrong.

To perform the test, Faber and her team pointed *Hubble* toward a bright star and took several photos. Information from those photos enabled Faber's team to create a model of what was wrong. After the team reported the team's findings of error to NASA and presented the model, Faber and a group of other experts began to correct the problem. The group's efforts were a success and put *Hubble* back into operation so that astronomers could continue researching stars and other objects in space.

Social Studies ACTiViTY

Research the history of the telescope. Make a timeline that includes the dates of major events in telescope history. For example, include in your timeline the first use of a telescope to see the rings of Saturn.

The Study of Living Things

All living things share certain characteristics of life. For example, all living things are made up of cells. Some living things are made up of only one cell, but other living things, such as humans, are made up of trillions of cells. In this unit, you will learn about the characteristics of living things and cells.

There are many kinds of cells, such as bacterial cells, plant cells, and animal cells. These cells differ in some ways, but all cells help a living thing survive. This timeline shows some of the discoveries that have been made as scientists have studied living things and cells.

1620
The Pilgrims settle Plymouth Colony.

1665
Robert Hooke discovers cells after observing a thin piece of cork under a microscope.

1861
The American Civil War begins.

1952
Martha Chase and Alfred Hershey demonstrate that DNA is the hereditary material.

1831
Robert Brown discovers the nucleus in a plant cell.

1838
Matthias Schleiden discovers that all plant tissue is made up of cells.

1839
Theodor Schwann shows that all animal tissue is made up of cells.

1858
Rudolf Virchow determines that all cells are produced from cells.

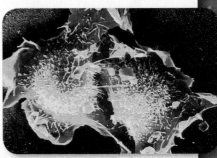

1873
Anton Schneider observes and accurately describes mitosis.

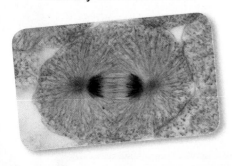

1937
The Golden Gate Bridge opens in San Francisco.

1941
George Beadle and Edward Tatum discover that genes control the chemical reactions in cells by directing protein production.

1956
Scientists determine that proteins are made in cell organelles called *ribosomes*.

1971
Lynn Margulis proposes the endosymbiotic theory of the origin of cell organelles.

1997
A sheep named Dolly becomes the first animal to be cloned from a single body cell.

2002
Scientists test a cancer vaccine that can be given orally. Tests on mice lead scientists to be hopeful that the vaccine can be tested on humans.

It's Alive!! Or Is It?

The Big Idea Living things have specific characteristics and needs.

About the

What does it mean to say that something is *alive*? Machines have some of the characteristics of living things, but machines do not have all of these characteristics. This amazing robot insect can respond to changes in its environment. It can walk over obstacles. It can perform some tasks. But it is still not alive. How is it like and unlike a living insect?

PRE-READING ACTIVITY

Graphic Organizer

Concept Map Before you read the chapter, create the graphic organizer entitled "Concept Map" described in the **Study Skills** section of the Appendix. As you read the chapter, fill in the concept map with details about the characteristics of living things.

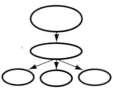

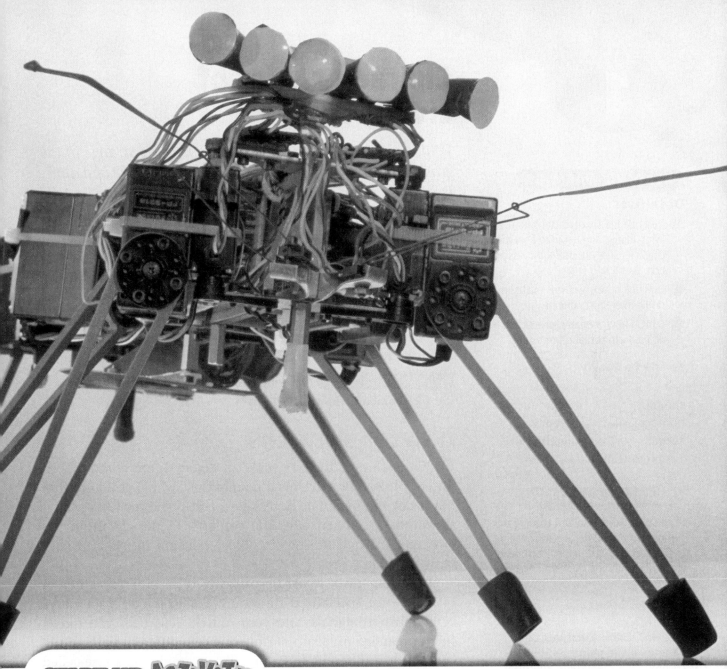

Lights On! F.1.3.7 CS

In this activity, you will work with a partner to see how eyes react to changes in light.

Procedure

1. Observe a classmate's eyes in a lighted room. Note the size of your partner's pupils.

2. Have your partner keep both eyes open. Ask him or her to cover each one with a cupped hand. Wait about one minute.

3. Instruct your partner to pull away both hands quickly. Immediately, look at your partner's pupils. Record what happens.

4. Now, briefly shine a **flashlight** into your partner's eyes. Record how this affects your partner's pupils. **Caution:** Do not use the sun as the source of the light.

5. Change places with your partner, and repeat steps 1–4 so that your partner can observe your eyes.

Analysis

1. How did your partner's eyes respond to changes in the level of light?

2. How did changes in the size of your pupils affect your vision? What does this tell you about why pupils change size?

Characteristics of Living Things

While outside one day, you notice something strange in the grass. It's slimy, bright yellow, and about the size of a dime. Is it a plant part from a tree? Is it alive? How can you tell?

cell the smallest unit that can perform all life processes; cells are covered by a membrane and have DNA and cytoplasm

An amazing variety of living things exists on Earth. But living things are all alike in several ways. What does a dog have in common with a mushroom? And what do *you* have in common with a slimy, yellow blob, known as a *slime mold*? All living things share six characteristics. These characteristics help us decide whether something is living or not. These characteristics also help us classify living things by their similarities and differences. Read on to find out about these six characteristics.

Benchmark Check Describe two ways in which scientists use the six characteristics of life. G.1.3.3 CS

Living Things Have Cells

All living things, such as those in **Figure 1,** are composed of one or more cells. A **cell** is a membrane-covered structure that has all of the materials necessary for life. The membrane that surrounds a cell separates the contents of the cell from the environment outside the cell. Most cells are too small to see with the naked eye.

In an organism made up of many cells, different kinds of cells perform specialized functions. For example, your nerve cells transport signals, and your muscle cells help you move. In an organism made up of only one cell, different parts of the cell perform different functions. For example, in a one-celled paramecium, some parts of the cell take in food. Other parts of the cell excrete wastes.

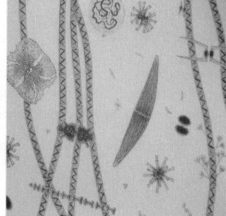

Figure 1 *Some organisms, such as the protists shown on the right, are made of one cell or a few cells. The Florida flatwoods salamander shown on the left is made of millions of cells.*

Figure 2 *The touch of an insect triggers the Venus' flytrap to close its leaves quickly.*

Living Things Sense and Respond to Change

All organisms have the ability to sense changes in their environment and to respond to those changes. For example, when your pupils are exposed to light, they respond by becoming smaller. A change that affects the activity of the organism is called a **stimulus** (plural, *stimuli*).

Stimuli can be chemicals, gravity, light, sounds, hunger, or anything that causes organisms to respond in some way. A gentle touch causes a response in the plant shown in **Figure 2.**

Homeostasis

Even though an organism's outside environment may change, conditions inside an organism's body must stay the same. Many chemical reactions keep an organism alive. These reactions can take place only when conditions are exactly right, so an organism must maintain stable internal conditions to survive. The maintenance of a stable internal environment is called **homeostasis** (HOH mee OH STAY sis).

Reading Check Why is homeostasis important?

Responding to External Changes

Your body maintains a temperature of about 37°C. When you get hot, your body responds by sweating. When you get cold, your muscles twitch in an attempt to warm you up. This twitching is called *shivering*. Whether you are sweating or shivering, your body is trying to return itself to normal.

Other animals also need to have stable internal conditions. But many cannot respond the way you do. They have to control their body temperature by moving from one environment to another. If they get too warm, they move to the shade. If they get too cool, they move out into the sunlight.

stimulus anything that causes a reaction or change in an organism or any part of an organism

homeostasis the maintenance of a constant internal state in a changing environment

Benchmark Activity

Is It a Living Thing?

With the help of your teacher, choose two interesting organisms. Then, research the organisms to see whether they have all six characteristics of life. Create a poster of your organisms. Include their similar and different characteristics. **G.1.3.3 CS**

G.1.3.3 CS understands that the classification of living things is based on a given set of criteria and is a tool for understanding biodiversity and interrelationships.

F.1.3.7 CS knows that behavior is a response to the environment and influences growth, development, maintenance, and reproduction.

Figure 3 *Like most animals, bears produce offspring by sexual reproduction.*

Figure 4 *The hydra can reproduce asexually by forming buds that break off and grow into new individuals.*

sexual reproduction reproduction in which the sex cells from two parents unite to produce offspring that share traits from both parents

asexual reproduction reproduction that does not involve the union of sex cells and in which one parent produces offspring that are genetically identical to the parent

heredity the passing of genetic traits from parent to offspring

metabolism the sum of all chemical processes that occur in an organism

Living Things Reproduce

Organisms make other organisms similar to themselves. They do so in one of two ways: by sexual reproduction or by asexual reproduction. In **sexual reproduction,** two parents produce offspring that will share characteristics of both parents. Most animals and plants reproduce in this way. The bear cubs in **Figure 3** were produced sexually by their parents.

In **asexual reproduction,** a single parent produces offspring that are identical to the parent. **Figure 4** shows an organism that reproduces asexually. Most single-celled organisms reproduce in this way.

Living Things Have DNA

The cells of all living things contain the molecule **d**eoxyribo-**n**ucleic (dee AHKS uh RIE boh noo KLEE ik) **a**cid, or DNA. *DNA* controls the structure and function of cells. When organisms reproduce, they pass copies of their DNA to their offspring. Passing DNA ensures that offspring resemble parents. The passing of traits from one generation to the next is called **heredity.**

Living Things Use Energy

Organisms use energy to carry out the activities of life. These activities include such things as making food, breaking down food, moving materials into and out of cells, and building cells. An organism's **metabolism** (muh TAB uh LIZ uhm) is the total of all of the chemical activities that the organism performs.

☑ Reading Check Name four chemical activities that take place in living things and that require energy.

Living Things Grow and Develop

All living things grow during periods of their lives. In a single-celled organism, the cell grows and divides to make other organisms. In organisms that are made of many cells, the number of cells increases, and the organism grows larger. In addition to becoming larger, living things may develop and change as they grow. For example, you will pass through different stages in your life as you develop into an adult, just as the acorn passes through many stages as it develops into a tree, as seen in **Figure 5.**

Figure 5 *Over time, acorns develop into oak seedlings, which become oak trees.*

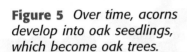

SECTION Review

Summary

- All living things share six characteristics that are also used to classify organisms. **G.1.3.3 CS**
- Organisms are made of one or more cells.
- Organisms detect and respond to stimuli.
- Organisms reproduce asexually or sexually.
- Organisms have DNA.
- Organisms use energy for their metabolism.
- Organisms grow.
- Homeostasis is the maintenance of a stable internal environment.

Using Key Terms

Use a term from the section to complete each sentence below.

1. Living things pass on ___ from parent to offspring.

2. Living things are made of ___.

Understanding Key Ideas

3. Differentiate between asexual reproduction and sexual reproduction?

4. Describe the six characteristics of living things.

Critical Thinking

5. **Applying Concepts** You find what you think is an organism. How can you tell if it was living?

6. **Applying Concepts** How do you respond to some stimuli in your environment? **F.1.3.7 CS**

FCAT Preparation

7. You laugh when somebody tickles you. Which of the following characteristics of life are you showing? **G.1.3.3 CS**

   A. that you are made of cells

   B. that your cells have DNA

   C. that you respond to stimuli

   D. that you grow and develop

SCILINKS

NSTA

Developed and maintained by the National Science Teachers Association

For a variety of links related to this chapter, go to www.scilinks.org

Topic: Characteristics of Living Things
SciLinks code: HSM0258

SECTION 2

The Necessities of Life

Would it surprise you to learn that you have the same basic needs as a tree, a frog, and a fly?

In fact, almost every organism has the same basic needs: water, air, a place to live, and food.

READING WARM-UP

Objectives

- Explain why organisms need water, air, living space, and food.
- Describe the chemical building blocks of cells.

Terms to Learn

producer
consumer
decomposer
protein
carbohydrate
lipid
phospholipid
ATP
nucleic acid

READING STRATEGY

Discussion Read this section silently. Write down questions that you have about this section. Discuss your questions in a small group.

Water

You may know that your body is made mostly of water. In fact, your cells and the cells of almost all living organisms are approximately 70% water. Most of the chemical reactions involved in metabolism require water.

Organisms differ greatly in terms of how much water they need and how they get it. You could survive for only about three days without water. You get water from the fluids you drink and the food you eat. The desert-dwelling kangaroo rat never drinks. It gets all of its water from its food.

Air

Air is a mixture of several different gases, including oxygen and carbon dioxide. Most living things use oxygen in the chemical process that releases energy from food. Many organisms living on land get oxygen from the air. Many organisms living in water either take in dissolved oxygen from the water or come to the water's surface to get oxygen from the air. The European diving spider shown in **Figure 1** goes to great lengths to get oxygen.

Green plants, algae, and some bacteria need carbon dioxide gas in addition to oxygen. These organisms produce food and oxygen by performing photosynthesis (FOHT oh SIN thuh sis). In *photosynthesis*, green organisms convert the energy in sunlight to energy stored in food.

Reading Check What process do plants use to make food?

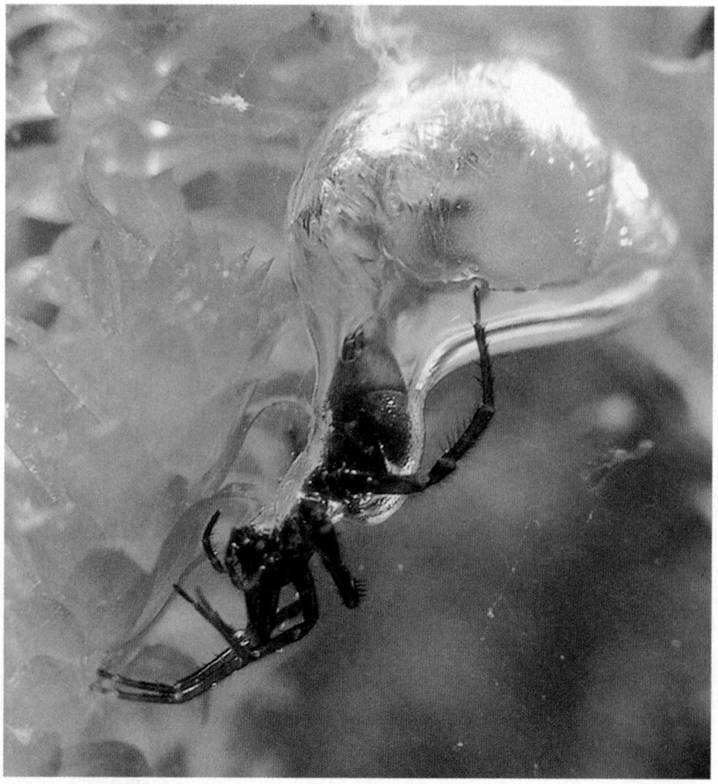

Figure 1 *This spider surrounds itself with an air bubble that provides the spider with a source of oxygen underwater.*

A Place to Live

All organisms need a place to live that contains all of the things they need to survive. Some organisms, such as elephants, require a large amount of space. Other organisms may live their entire life in one small place. Space on Earth is limited. So, organisms often compete with each other for food, water, and other necessities. The tricolored heron in **Figure 2,** competes with other birds and predators for the fish and other animals it eats.

Figure 2 *This tricolored heron is wading in a lagoon off Fort Myer's Beach in Florida. It competes with many other organisms for space to live and food to eat.*

Food

All living things need food. Food gives organisms the raw materials and the energy needed to carry on life processes. Organisms use the nutrients and energy from food for activites such as making new cells to replace damaged or dead cells, and growing. But not all organisms get food in the same way. In fact, organisms can be divided into three different groups based on how they get their food.

producer an organism that can make its own food by using energy from its surroundings

consumer an organism that eats other organisms or organic matter

decomposer an organism that gets energy by breaking down the remains of dead organisms or animal wastes and consuming or absorbing the nutrients

Making Food

Some organisms, such as plants, are called producers. **Producers** are organisms that can make their own food. Like most producers, plants use energy from the sun to make food from water and carbon dioxide. Some producers get energy and food from the chemicals in their environment.

Taking Food

Other organisms are called **consumers** because they must eat, or consume, other organisms to get food. The frog in **Figure 3** is an example of a consumer. It gets the energy it needs by eating insects and other organisms.

Some consumers are decomposers. **Decomposers** are organisms that get their food by breaking down the nutrients in dead organisms or animal wastes. The mushroom in **Figure 3** is a decomposer.

Figure 3 *The frog is a consumer. The mushroom is a decomposer. The green plants are producers.*

protein a molecule that is made up of amino acids and that is needed to build and repair body structures and to regulate processes in the body

Putting It All Together

Some organisms make their own food. Some organisms get food from eating other organisms. But all organisms need to break down that food in order to use the nutrients in it.

Nutrients are made up of molecules. A *molecule* is a particle that is made of two or more atoms combine. Molecules made of different kinds of atoms are *compounds*. Molecules found in living things are usually made of different combinations of six elements: carbon, hydrogen, nitrogen, oxygen, phosphorus, and sulfur. These elements combine to form proteins, carbohydrates, lipids, ATP, and nucleic acids.

Proteins

Almost all of the life processes of a cell involve proteins. **Proteins** are large molecules that are made up of smaller molecules called *amino acids*.

Making Proteins

Organisms break down the proteins in food to supply their cells with amino acids. These amino acids are then linked together to form new proteins. Some proteins are made up of only a few amino acids, but others contain more than 10,000 amino acids.

Proteins in Action

Proteins have many different functions. Some proteins form structures that are easy to see, such as those in **Figure 4.** Other proteins are very small and help cells do their jobs. Inside red blood cells, the protein hemoglobin (HEE moh GLOH bin) binds to oxygen to deliver and release oxygen throughout the body. Some proteins protect cells. Other proteins, called *enzymes* (EN ZIEMZ), start or speed up chemical reactions in cells.

Figure 4 *Spider webs, hair, horns, and feathers are all made from proteins.*

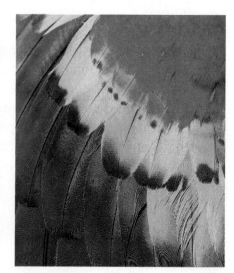

Figure 5 *The extra sugar in a potato plant is stored in the potato as starch, a complex carbohydrate.*

Carbohydrates

Molecules made of sugars are called **carbohydrates.** Cells use carbohydrates as a source of energy and for energy storage. An organism's cells break down carbohydrates to release the energy stored in them. There are two kinds of carbohydrates—simple carbohydrates and complex carbohydrates.

Simple Carbohydrates

Simple carbohydrates are made up of one sugar molecule or a few sugar molecules linked together. Table sugar and the sugar in fruits are examples of simple carbohydrates.

Complex Carbohydrates

When an organism has more sugar than it needs, its extra sugar may be stored as complex carbohydrates. *Complex carbohydrates* are made of hundreds of sugar molecules that are linked together. Plants, such as the potato plant in **Figure 5,** store extra sugar as starch. When you eat mashed potatoes, you are eating a potato plant's stored starch. Your body then breaks down this complex carbohydrate to release the energy stored in the potato.

Reading Check What is the difference between simple carbohydrates and complex carbohydrates?

carbohydrate a class of energy-giving nutrients that includes sugars, starches, and fiber; contains carbon, hydrogen, and oxygen

How Much Oxygen?

Each red blood cell carries about 250 million molecules of hemoglobin. How many molecules of oxygen could a single red blood cell deliver throughout the body if every hemoglobin molecule attached to four oxygen molecules?

Starch Search

1. Obtain several **food samples** from your teacher.
2. Put **a few drops of iodine** on each sample. Record your observations. **Caution:** Iodine can stain clothing.
3. When iodine comes into contact with starch, a black substance appears. Which samples contain starch?

Figure 6 **Phospholipid Membranes**

The head of a phospholipid molecule is attracted to water, but the tail is not.

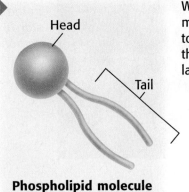

Head

Tail

Phospholipid molecule

When phospholipid molecules come together in water, they form two layers.

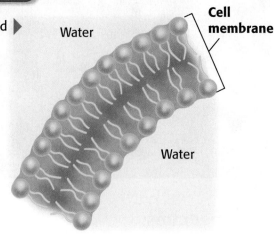

Cell membrane

Water

Water

lipid a type of biochemical that does not dissolve in water; fats and steroids are lipids

phospholipid a lipid that contains phosphorus and that is a structural component in cell membranes

ATP **a**denosine **tri**phosphate, a molecule that acts as the main energy source for cell processes

Lipids

Lipids are compounds that cannot mix with water. Lipids have many important jobs in the cell. Like carbohydrates, some lipids store energy. Other lipids form the membranes of cells.

Phospholipids

All cells are surrounded by a cell membrane. The cell membrane helps protect the cell and keep the internal conditions of the cell stable. **Phospholipids** (FAHS foh LIP idz) are the molecules that form much of the cell membrane. The head of a phospholipid molecule is attracted to water. The tail is not. Cells are mostly water. When phospholipids are in water, the tails come together, and the heads face out into the water. **Figure 6** shows how phospholipid molecules form two layers in water.

Fats and Oils

Fats and oils are lipids that store energy. When an organism has used up most of its carbohydrates, it can get energy from these lipids. The structures of fats and oils are almost the same, but at room temperature, most fats are solid, and most oils are liquid. Most of the lipids stored in plants are oils. Most of the lipids stored in animals are fats.

✓ **Reading Check** What is one difference between oils and fats?

ATP

Adenosine **tri**phosphate (uh DEN uh SEEN trie FAHS FAYT), also called ATP, is another important molecule. **ATP** is the major energy-carrying molecule in the cell. The energy in carbohydrates and lipids must be transferred to ATP, which then provides fuel for cellular activities.

CONNECTION TO **Social Studies**

Whaling Since about 800 C.E., whales have been hunted and killed for their oil. Whale oil was often used as fuel for oil lamps. Most of the oil taken from whales was taken from their fat, or *blubber*. Some whales had blubber more than 18 in. thick, producing more than 40 barrels of oil per whale. Research whether anyone still hunts whales or uses whale oil. Make a presentation to the class on your findings.

Nucleic Acids

Nucleic acids are sometimes called the blueprints of life because they have all the information needed for a cell to make proteins. **Nucleic acids** are large molecules made up of molecules called *nucleotides* (NOO klee oh TIEDZ). A nucleic acid may have thousands of nucleotides. The order of those nucleotides stores information. DNA is a nucleic acid. A DNA molecule is like a recipe book that describes how to make proteins. When a cell needs to make a certain protein, the cell gets information from the order of the nucleotides in DNA. This order of nucleotides tells the cell the order of the amino acids that are linked together to make that protein.

nucleic acid a molecule made up of subunits called *nucleotides*

New Found Pet Write a short story about taking care of an unusual pet. Go to **go.hrw.com,** and type in the keyword **HL5ALVW.**

SECTION Review

Summary

- Organisms need water for cellular processes.
- Organisms need oxygen to release the energy contained in their food.
- Organisms must have a place to live.
- Cells store energy in carbohydrates, which are made of sugars.
- Proteins are made up of amino acids. Some proteins are enzymes.
- Fats and oils store energy and make up cell membranes.
- Cells use molecules of ATP to fuel their activities.
- Nucleic acids, such as DNA, are made up of nucleotides.

Using Key Terms

For each pair of terms, explain how the meanings of the terms differ.

1. *producer* and *consumer*
2. *lipid* and *phospholipid*

Understanding Key Ideas

3. Explain why organisms need water, air, living space, and food.

4. Describe the chemical building blocks of cells.

5. Why are decomposers categorized as consumers? How do decomposers obtain the energy they need?

6. What are the subunits of proteins?

Critical Thinking

7. **Making Inferences** Could life as we know it exist on Earth if air contained only oxygen? Explain your answer.

8. **Predicting Consequences** What would happen to the supply of ATP in your cells if you did not eat enough carbohydrates? How would this affect your cells?

FCAT Preparation

9. At one time, scientists classified all organisms as plants or animals. Today, there are six kingdoms, including Fungi. This kingdom includes organisms such as mushrooms. Why have mushrooms been classified in their own group? G.1.3.3 CS

   A. because mushrooms have only two of the characteristics of life

   B. because mushrooms have very different characteristics than those of plants or animals

   C. because mushrooms are hard to grow

   D. because mushrooms are very hard to find

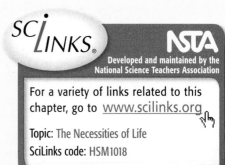

SCILINKS®

Developed and maintained by the National Science Teachers Association

For a variety of links related to this chapter, go to www.scilinks.org

Topic: The Necessities of Life
SciLinks code: HSM1018

Inquiry Lab

OBJECTIVES

Observe responses to stimuli.

Analyze responses to stimuli.

MATERIALS

- chalk (1 stick)
- container, plastic, small, with lid
- gloves, protective
- isopod (4)
- potato, raw (1 small slice)
- ruler, metric
- soil (8 oz)
- stopwatch

SAFETY

Roly-Poly Races

Have you ever watched a bug run? Did you wonder why it was running? The bug you saw running was probably reacting to a stimulus. In other words, something happened to make the bug run! One characteristic of living things is that they respond to stimuli. In this activity, you will study the movement of roly-polies. Roly-polies are also called *pill bugs*. But they are not really bugs; they are land-dwelling animals called *isopods*. Isopods live in dark, moist areas under rocks or wood. You will provide stimuli to determine how fast your isopod can move and what affects its speed and direction. Remember that isopods are living things and must be treated gently and respectfully.

Ask a Question

1 Ask a question such as, "Which stimuli cause pill bugs to run?"

Form a Hypothesis

2 Using your question as a guide, form a hypothesis. For example, you could form the following hypothesis: "Light, sound, and touch stimulate pill bugs to run."

Test the Hypothesis

3 Choose a partner, and decide together how you will run your roly-poly race. Discuss some gentle ways to stimulate your isopods to move. Choose five or six things that might cause movement, such as a gentle nudge or a change in temperature, sound, or light. Check your choices with your teacher.

4 Make a data table similar to the table below. Label the columns with the stimuli that you've chosen. Label the rows "Isopod 1," "Isopod 2," "Isopod 3," and "Isopod 4."

Isopod Responses		
	Stimulus 1	Stimulus 2	Stimulus 3
Isopod 1			
Isopod 2			
Isopod 3			
Isopod 4			

DO NOT WRITE IN BOOK

 H.3.3.2 Knows that special care must be taken in using animals in scientific research

5. Place a layer of soil that is 1 cm or 2 cm deep in a small plastic container. Add a small slice of potato and a piece of chalk. Your isopods will eat these items.

6. Place four isopods in your container. Observe them for a minute or two before you perform your tests. Record your observations.

7. Decide which stimulus you want to test first. Carefully arrange the isopods at the "starting line." The starting line can be an imaginary line at one end of the container.

8. Gently stimulate each isopod at the same time and in the same way. In your data table, record the isopods' responses to the stimulus. Be sure to record the distance that each isopod travels. Don't forget to time the race.

9. Repeat steps 7–8 for each stimulus. Be sure to wait at least 2 min between trials.

Analyze the Results

1. **Describing Events** Describe the way that isopods move. Do their legs move together?

2. **Analyzing Results** Did your isopods move before or between the trials? Did the movement seem to have a purpose, or were the isopods responding to a stimulus? Explain.

Draw Conclusions

3. **Interpreting Information** Did any of the stimuli make the isopods move faster or go farther? Explain.

Applying Your Data

Like isopods and all other living things, humans react to stimuli. Describe three stimuli that might cause humans to run.

Chapter Review

USING KEY TERMS

Use a term from the chapter to complete each sentence below.

1 The process of maintaining a stable internal environment is known as __.

2 Offspring resemble their parents because of __.

3 A(n) __ obtains food by eating other organisms.

4 Starch is a(n) __ and is made up of sugars.

5 Fat is a(n) __ that stores energy for an organism.

UNDERSTANDING KEY IDEAS

Multiple Choice

6 Where do organisms store energy?
 a. in nucleic acids
 b. in phospholipids
 c. in lipids
 d. in water

7 All living things share six characteristics. One of these characteristics is that organisms need nutrients to fuel all of the activities that support life. Which of the following statements about this characteristic is true? G.1.3.3 CS *FCAT*
 a. Organisms do not use nutrients to grow.
 b. Organisms can respond to their environment without using energy.
 c. Nutrients are converted to ATP, which fuels all metabolic activity.
 d. Not all organisms need nutrients.

8 Which of the following statements about cells is true?
 a. Cells are the structures that contain all of the materials necessary for life.
 b. Cells are found in all organisms.
 c. Cells are sometimes specialized and have particular functions.
 d. All of the above

9 Which of the following statements about all living things is true? G.1.3.3 CS
 a. All living things reproduce sexually.
 b. All living things grow and develop.
 c. All living things make their food.
 d. All living things reproduce asexually.

10 How do organisms maintain a stable internal environment?
 a. through homeostasis
 b. through sexual reproduction
 c. through asexual reproduction
 d. through heredity

11 What is the term for a change in an organism's environment that affects the organism's activities?
 a. response
 b. stimulus
 c. metabolism
 d. producer

12 Similarities and differences in the characteristics of life can be used to classify organisms. Which of the following would help classify ants and spiders? G.1.3.3 CS *FCAT*
 a. studying ants
 b. growing ants and spiders
 c. comparing ants and spiders
 d. watching ants and spiders

Short Answer

13 What is the difference between asexual reproduction and sexual reproduction?

14 In one or two sentences, explain why living things must have air.

15 What is ATP, and why is it important to a cell?

The pictures below show the same plant over a period of 3 days. Use the pictures below to answer the questions that follow.

Day 1

Day 2

Day 3

CRITICAL THINKING

Extended Response

16 **Analyzing Ideas** A flame can move, grow larger, and give off heat. Is a flame alive? Explain. G.1.3.3 CS

17 **Applying Concepts** Based on what you know about carbohydrates, lipids, and proteins, why is it important for you to eat a balanced diet?

18 **Evaluating Hypotheses** Your friend tells you that frogs and toads are the same. How would you use the six characteristics of life to test your friend's claim? G.1.3.3 CS

Concept Mapping

19 Use the following terms to create a concept map: *cell, carbohydrate, protein, enzyme, DNA, sugar, lipid, nucleotide, amino acid,* and *nucleic acid.*

20 Explain what the plant is doing.

21 What characteristic(s) of living things is the plant exhibiting?

Standardized Test Preparation

For the following questions, write your answers on a separate sheet of paper.

1 Living things respond to changes in their internal and external environments. Mijin feels hungry during her math class, which is just before lunch. Which of the following is a true description of hunger?

    A.   Hunger is a stimulus.

    B.   DNA controls hunger.

    C.   Hunger requires energy.

    D.   Hunger results in homeostasis.

2 One way of classifying whether something is living or not is to see if it has all the characteristics of life. One of the charactaristics of life is that living things pass on characteristics from parents to offspring. Which of the following is responsible for carrying these characteristics?

    F.   DNA

    G.   enzymes

    H.   body cells

    I.   metabolism

3 Living things use energy to carry out various functions. Jonathan is going to run in a long race. Which of the following molecules stores the energy Jonathan will need for the race?

    A.   fats

    B.   proteins

    C.   enzymes

    D.   nucleic acids

4 Tina knows that all living things need water, air, and food to survive. She has a fish that lives on the bottom of her aquarium. How does Tina's fish get oxygen?

    F.   from light

    G.   from its food

    H.   from the water

    I.   from decomposers

5 Juan is studying four different organisms so that he can classify them according to how much each organism is like its parent. The chart below shows the characteristics of the four different organisms.

CHARACTERISTICS OF FOUR LIVING ORGANISMS

	Organism A	Organism B	Organism C	Organism D
Comparison to Parent	Different from parent	Similar to parent	Identical to parent	Similar to parent

Which of the organisms that Juan studied could have been produced from a single parent?

A.   Organism A
B.   Organism B
C.   Organism C
D.   Organism D

6 Lauren discovered something in her backyard that she thinks may be a living organism. She created a flowchart similar to the one shown below to describe the characteristics that would help her determine whether her discovery is living or nonliving.

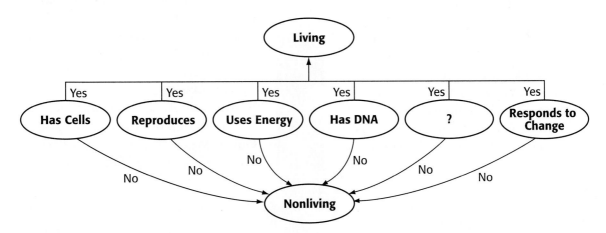

Which of the following traits would complete Lauren's flowchart?

F.   moves
G.   makes noises
H.   grows and develops
I.   changes shape and form

Science in Action

Science, Technology, and Society

Pushing the Boundaries of Life

Imagine that you are walking down the hall of a strange building. You turn the corner, and a dozen insectlike robots are in front of you! They move carefully and step over obstacles. Are you in a science fiction film? In fact, you could be in the University of Florida's Machine Intelligence Laboratory (MIL) in Gainesville, where scientists are building robots to assist in search-and-rescue missions. These robots might find people trapped in collapsed buildings or lost in the wilderness. Other robots might explore Mars. Because researchers are designing the robots to make simple decisions and to learn from experiences, this research may someday challenge the boundary between living things and machines.

Science Fiction

"They're Made Out of Meat" by Terry Bisson

Two space explorers millions of light-years from home are visiting an uncharted sector of the universe to find signs of life. Their mission is to contact, welcome, and log any and all beings in this part of the universe.

During their mission, they encounter a life-form quite unlike anything they have ever seen before. It looked too strange and, well, disgusting. The explorers have very strong doubts about adding this new organism to the list. But the explorers' official duty is to contact and welcome all life-forms no matter how ugly they are. Can the explorers bring themselves to perform their duty?

You'll find out by reading "They're Made Out of Meat," a short story by Terry Bisson. This story is in the **Holt** *Anthology of Science Fiction.*

Math ACTIVITY

If a robot can travel 10 cm in 5 min on flat ground and 5 cm in 5 min on a gentle slope, how long would it take the robot to move over 20 cm of flat ground and 30 cm of a gentle slope?

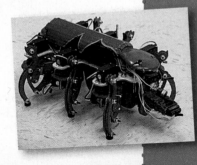

Language Arts ACTIVITY

WRITING SKILL Write a story about what happens when the explorers next meet the creatures on the star in G445 zone.

Janis Davis-Street

NASA Nutritionist Do astronauts eat shrimp cocktail in space? Yes, they do! Shrimp cocktail is nutritious and tastes so good that it is one of the most popular foods in the space program. And eating a proper diet helps astronauts stay healthy while they are in space.

But who figures out what astronauts need to eat? Janis Davis-Street is a nutritionist and laboratory supervisor for the Nutritional Biochemistry Laboratory at the Johnson Space Center in Houston, Texas. She was born in Georgetown, Guyana, on the northeastern coast of South America. She was educated in Canada.

Davis-Street is part of a team that uses their knowledge of nutrition, biology, and chemistry to figure out the nutritional requirements for spaceflight. For example, they determine how many calories and other nutrients each astronaut needs per day during spaceflight.

The Nutritional Biochemistry Laboratory's work on the space shuttle missions and *Mir* space station developed into tests that allow NASA to help ensure astronaut health before, during, and after flight. These tests are important for understanding how the human body adapts to long space missions, and for determining whether treatments for preventing bone and muscle loss during spaceflight are working.

Social Studies ACTiViTY

Scientists from more than 30 countries have been on space missions. Research which countries have provided astronauts or cosmonauts for space missions. Using a map, place self-stick notes on countries that have provided scientists for space missions. Write the names of the appropriate scientists on the self-stick notes.

To learn more about these Science in Action topics, visit go.hrw.com and type in the keyword **HT6FALFF.**

Current Science

Check out Current Science® articles related to this chapter by visiting go.hrw.com. Just type in the keyword HL5CS02.

Introduction to Cells

The Big Idea The levels of structural organization in organisms are cells, tissues, organs, and organ systems.

About the PHOTO

The rat snake must shed its skin to grow bigger. Its skin is one of the many organs that make up its body. Each organ is made up of many cells. Your skin is one of your organs, too. Why don't you shed your skin as you grow? Actually, your skin cells are flaking off all of the time. You just don't notice it because you don't shed all of your skin cells at once.

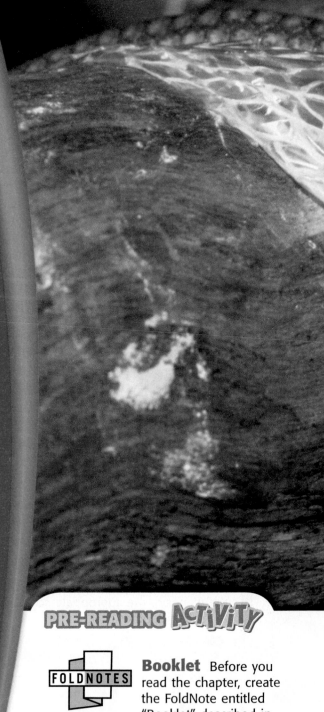

PRE-READING ACTIVITY

Booklet Before you read the chapter, create the FoldNote entitled "Booklet" described in the **Study Skills** section of the Appendix. Label each page of the booklet with a main idea from the chapter. As you read the chapter, write what you learn about each main idea on the appropriate page of the booklet.

START-UP ACTIVITY

Onion Skin F.1.3.2 CS

Cells are the basic structural unit of all living things. Do this activity to see what onion cells look like.

Procedure

1. Using **forceps**, choose a **piece of red onion** that has been soaking in **salty water** that your teacher prepared.

2. Place the piece of onion in a **small dish.** Using forceps, carefully separate the very thin inner onion layer from the thicker, fleshy onion layer.

3. Using forceps, place the thin onion layer flat on a **microscope slide,** and add a drop of water.

4. Without trapping air bubbles, gently place a **cover-slip** on top of the onion layer and water drop.

5. Place the slide on your **microscope.**

6. Using the lowest-powered lens first, find the onion cells. Once you can see the cells, switch to a higher-powered lens. If your microscope has a fine-adjustment knob, use it to focus properly.

7. Draw a picture of what you see.

Analysis

1. Describe the shape of the onion cells. Do the cells have different parts? If so, do the various parts have different colors?

2. Your body is also made up of cells. Do you think that any of your cells look like onion cells? Do you think that your cells contain water? Explain your answer.

Cells and Organisms

Microscopes are used to look at things that are too small to be seen with eyes alone. Scientists using the first microscopes to look at living things made an amazing discovery. What did the scientists see?

The scientists saw that living things were made of small boxes. Scientists called these boxes *cells*. A **cell** is the smallest unit that can do all of the activities needed for life.

Cells as Building Blocks

Cells are the basic structural units that make up all living things, or organisms (AWR guh NIZ uhmz). An **organism** is made up of one or more cells and carries out all of its own activities for life. Most organisms, such as amoebas, are made up of one cell. Other organisms, such as humans and the elephants in **Figure 1,** are made up of many cells that work together.

All cells do many activities, such as breaking down food, making proteins, and getting rid of wastes. Each cell has special parts that do these activities. These cell parts also help perform the life functions of the cell, such as growth.

Benchmark Check **What is the basic structural unit of all organisms?** F.1.3.2 CS

Figure 1 *Elephants are made up of trillions of cells that work together.*

F.1.3.2 CS knows that the structural basis of most organisms is the cell and most organisms are single cells, while some, including humans, are multicellular.

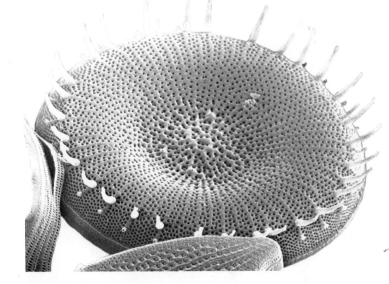

Figure 2 *The diatom on the left and the protozoans below are single-celled eukaryotes. They are called* eukaryotes *because they have a nucleus.*

Two Main Kinds of Cells

At some point in their life, all cells have **d**eoxyribo**n**ucleic **a**cid (dee AHKS uh RIE boh noo KLEE ik AS id), or DNA. DNA carries all of the instructions that a cell needs to live. There are two main kinds of cells. A *prokaryotic* (PROH kar ee AHT ik) cell has a single circular DNA molecule. An organism made up of a prokaryotic cell, such as a bacterium, is a **prokaryote.** A *eukaryotic* (yoo KAR ee AHT ik) cell has a part called a *nucleus*, which contains the DNA that controls the activities of the cell. An organism made up of one or more eukaryotic cells is a **eukaryote.**

✓ **Reading Check** Where is the DNA in a eukaryotic cell?

Single-Celled Organisms

A single-celled organism is made up of only one cell. This cell must be able to do all of the activities that the organism needs to live. All prokaryotes are single-celled organisms. Most single-celled eukaryotes, such as those in **Figure 2,** are called *protists*. Some of the features of protists are described below.

- Some protists have hard shells.
- Many protists have special structures for movement. Some protists cannot move at all.
- Some protists use a mouth-like opening to eat. Other protists absorb food through their cell membrane.
- Most protists live in water. Some protists live on land.
- Some protists live on their own. Other protists live on or inside other organisms.

Protists can be divided into groups based on how they get nutrients and how they move. Some protists engulf food particles from their surroundings. Other protists make their own food. Some protists do both. Many protists use special structures to move, and other protists cannot move at all.

cell the smallest unit that can perform all life processes; cells are covered by a membrane and contain DNA and cytoplasm

organism a living thing; anything that can carry out life processes independently

prokaryote a single-celled organism that does not have a nucleus or membrane-bound organelles; examples are archaea and bacteria

eukaryote an organism made up of cells that have a nucleus enclosed by a membrane; eukaryotes include protists, animals, plants, and fungi but not archaea or bacteria

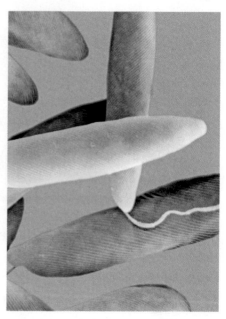

Figure 3 *Members of the genus* Ceratium *(left) and members of the genus* Euglena *(right) are examples of protists. They use special structures called* flagella *to move.*

A Pet Protist

Imagine that you have a tiny box-shaped protist for a pet. To care for your pet protist properly, you have to figure out how much to feed it. The dimensions of your protist are roughly 25 μm × 20 μm × 2 μm. If seven food particles per second can enter through each square micrometer of surface area, how many particles can your protist eat in 1 min?

Protozoans

Protozoans (PROHT oh ZOH uhns) make up one group of single-celled protists. Amoebas are protozoans. Amoebas move around to find food. They move by pushing out and pulling back a false foot, or *pseudopodium* (soo doh POH dee uhm) (plural, *pseudopodia*). Amoebas eat by surrounding a food particle and then digesting it. Amoebas do not have shells.

Diatoms

Diatoms make up another group of single-celled protists. Most diatoms cannot move on their own. Like plants, diatoms make their own food through photosynthesis. During photosynthesis (FOHT oh SIN thuh sis), diatoms use the sun's energy to make sugars. Diatoms have glassy shells and float in water.

Dinoflagellates

Dinoflagellates (DIE noh FLAJ uh lits) are also single-celled protists. Members of the genus *Ceratium,* shown in **Figure 3,** are dinoflagellates. Unlike diatoms, dinoflagellates move on their own by using two flagella (fluh JEL uh) (singular, *flagellum*), special structures that look like whips. Like diatoms, dinoflagellates perform photosynthesis and have hard shells.

Euglenoids

Euglenoids (yoo GLEE NOYDZ), members of the genus *Euglena,* make up a fourth group of single-celled protists. Euglenoids, shown in **Figure 3,** get food in two ways. Like diatoms, most euglenoids can perform photosynthesis. Like amoebas, some euglenoids can also surround and digest food particles. Euglenoids also use flagella to move.

Multicellular Organisms

There are many kinds of multicellular organisms. Some multicellular organisms, such as dust mites, are too small to see with your eyes alone. Other multicellular organisms are huge. For example, a fungus in Oregon covers more than 8.9 km^2.

Plants are multicellular organisms that perform photosynthesis to make their own food. Many multicellular organisms, such as humans, eat other organisms to get the nutrition that they need. A few multicellular organisms get their nutrition by performing photosynthesis and by eating other organisms. For example, the Pitcher plant can perform photosynthesis. The Pitcher plant also traps and digests insects for some kinds of nutrients.

There are many advantages of being multicellular. Multicellular organisms can be larger than single-celled organisms. Cells in a multicellular organism can be specialized. *Specialized cells* can do one specific job instead of doing all of the jobs that the cell of a single-celled organism does. Also, multicellular organisms generally live longer than single-celled organisms do.

Benchmark Check How does the cell of a multicellular organism differ from the cell of a single-celled organism? **F.1.3.2 CS**

Fungi

You have probably seen fungi before. Mushrooms, such as the ones shown in **Figure 4,** are examples of multicellular fungi. Some fungi, such as yeast, are single celled. Cells of a fungus have stiff cell walls that support the organism. Fungi get energy by absorbing nutrients from their environment.

CONNECTION TO Physics

Fly-Eating Robot Scientists in England are developing a robot that is powered by flies. The robot has special technology that uses bacteria to break down the flies. The breakdown of the flies generates electrical energy, which the robot can use to do work. Now it's your turn. Build or draw a model of a robot that you would like to make. Be sure to get your teacher's approval before building your model. What would the robot use as fuel?

ACTiViTY

Figure 4 *Fungi, such as mushrooms, are multicellular organisms. Unlike plants, mushrooms don't perform photosynthesis. Unlike animals, mushrooms don't move around on their own. Many mushrooms are poisonous. Never eat a mushroom from the wild.*

F.1.3.2 CS knows that the structural basis of most organisms is the cell and most organisms are single cells, while some, including humans, are multicellular.

F.1.3.2 CS knows that the structural basis of most organisms is the cell and most organisms are single cells, while some, including humans, are multicellular.

Animals

Animals, such as the Malachite butterfly in **Figure 5,** are multicellular organisms. Nearly all animals can move on their own. Animals must eat other organisms or materials to get the nutrition that they need. Animals can live on land, in water, or even in air. Animals can be as small as a fairy fly, which is less than 0.025 mm long (about half the length of a grain of salt). Animals can also be as large as a blue whale, which can grow to be as long as 30 m (or about the length of a standard basketball court).

Plants

Plants are another example of multicellular organisms. Unlike animals, plants generally cannot move from place to place. Most plants live on land, but some plants live partially or completely in water.

Unlike animals, most plants make their own food by performing photosynthesis. But some plants do not rely only on photosynthesis. Some orchids, such as the one shown in **Figure 5,** are called *air plants*. Many air plants live on trees and can perform photosynthesis. Air plants get water and nutrition from rain and plant matter that becomes trapped and decomposes in their roots. Other plants obtain some of their nutrition from other organisms. For example, mistletoe is a plant that grows on trees. Mistletoe can perform photosynthesis. But unlike the roots of an orchid, the roots of a mistletoe grow under the bark of the tree and absorb nutrition from the tree's tissues.

✓ **Reading Check** How do air plants get their nutrition?

Figure 5 *Both the Malachite butterfly and the Butterfly orchid found in Florida are multicellular organisms.*

Humans: Multicellular Organisms

Humans, such as the baby shown in **Figure 6,** are also multi-cellular. As a human develops, all of his or her cells develop from a single cell. Scientists estimate that the human body has trillions of cells. They also estimate that there are more than 200 kinds of cells in the human body. Different kinds of cells have different structures. Red blood cells are among the smallest cells in the human body. They are about 6 to 8 μm in diameter. On the other hand, nerve cells in the lower spine are some of the largest cells in the human body. One of these nerve cells stretches from the lower back to the toes.

✓ **Reading Check** How can you distinguish between different kinds of human cells?

Figure 6 *Even as babies, humans have trillions of cells.*

SECTION Review

Summary

- The cell is the basic unit of all living things. F.1.3.2 CS
- Prokaryotic cells have a single circular molecule of DNA. Eukaryotic cells have a nucleus, in which their DNA is stored.
- Single-celled eukaryotes, such as protozoans, diatoms, dinoflagellates, and euglenoids, have different structures, ways of obtaining energy, and ways of moving.
- Most organisms are single celled. Some organisms, such as humans, are multicellular. F.1.3.2 CS
- A single-celled organism's cell must perform all of the organism's life functions. Cells of a multicellular organism can specialize to do specific functions. F.1.3.2 CS

Using Key Terms

1. Write an original definition for *prokaryote* and *eukaryote.*

Understanding Key Ideas

2. Which of the following statements about a single-celled eukaryote is true?
   a. The organism is made up of many cells.
   b. The organism's DNA is contained in the nucleus of its cell.
   c. The organism does not have a nucleus.
   d. The organism does not have DNA.

3. What is the basic unit of all living things? F.1.3.2 CS

Critical Thinking

4. **Forming Hypotheses** You have noticed that a single-celled organism does not obtain food particles by surrounding them. How might this organism get the nutrition that it needs?

5. **Making Inferences** One protist has a long, whiplike structure, and another protist does not have this structure. Which protist can move on its own?

FCAT Preparation

6. The cell of a single-celled organism must do many jobs. Each cell in a multicellular organism can do one specific job. Which of the following statements comparing a human cell with the cell of a single-celled diatom is true? F.1.3.2 CS

   A. A human cell can perform photosynthesis; the cell of the diatom cannot.

   B. A human cell can move on its own; the cell of the diatom cannot.

   C. A human cell is specialized; the cell of the diatom is not.

   D. A human cell has a hard shell; the cell of the diatom does not.

SCiLINKS®

NSTA

Developed and maintained by the National Science Teachers Association

For a variety of links related to this chapter, go to www.scilinks.org

Topic: Eukaryotic Cells
SciLinks code: HSM0541

Inside a Cell

Different kinds of cells have different shapes and sizes. Although cells differ from each other, all cells must perform some similar life processes to survive. How do all of the different cells perform these life processes?

Each cell has parts that perform the life processes of the cell. Different cells can have similar parts that perform similar life processes for the cells. Some cell parts are called *organelles*. Each organelle performs a specific job for the cell.

Life Processes in Cells

The instructions for the life processes that take place in a cell are stored in a molecule called *deoxyribonucleic acid*, or DNA. DNA controls all of the life processes of the cell, including growth, reproduction, regulation, and maintenance. To perform their life processes, all cells need energy.

Energy

How do the cells of organisms get the energy that they need? Most cells have mitochondria. A *mitochondrion,* shown in **Figure 1,** is an organelle that helps break down sugars to make the chemical *adenosine* **tri***phosphate*, or ATP. Cells use ATP as a source of energy to power nearly all of their life processes.

Benchmark Check What cell part makes the ATP that an organism's cells use to power nearly all of their life processes? **F.I.3.5 CS**

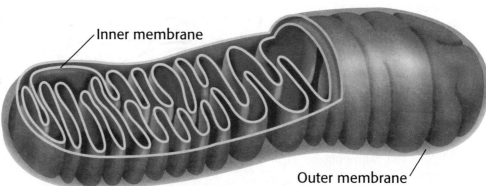

Inner membrane

Outer membrane

Figure 1 *In a eukaryotic cell, mitochondria break down sugars to get the energy that is needed for the cell's activities. Each mitochondrion has two membranes.*

Growth and Reproduction

Cells grow and reproduce to replace damaged cells and to allow the growth of the organism. When an animal cell reproduces, several steps take place. First, the cell makes copies of many of its cell parts and its DNA. Then, each copy of DNA moves to opposite sides of the cell. Finally, the cell pinches around the middle, as **Figure 2** shows, until two new, identical cells have formed. The DNA and cell parts found in each cell help each new cell live and develop.

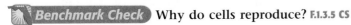 **Benchmark Check** Why do cells reproduce? F.1.3.5 CS

Regulation

The DNA in cells controls not only the development of cells but also the development of the whole organism. The processes that control development are called *regulation*. As the organism develops, other processes keep the organism healthy.

Maintenance

The processes that keep the cell and the organism healthy are called *maintenance*. Maintenance of the cell includes replacing damaged cell parts, taking in water and other nutrients, and getting rid of wastes. For the cell to be maintained, materials and cell parts inside the cell need to move to different places within the cell. Materials and cell parts move along the *cytoskeleton,* a cell part that is shown in **Figure 3.**

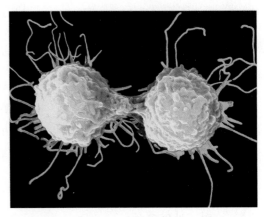

Figure 2 *This animal cell is dividing into two identical cells by pinching around the middle.*

Who Is Thirsty?

1. Use a **graduated cylinder** to measure out 5 mL of **water.**
2. Pour the water into a **test tube,** and insert a **plant cutting** into the test tube.
3. Set the test tube aside for 30 min.
4. Remove the plant cutting. How much water is left in the test tube?
5. Where did the water go? Explain your answer.

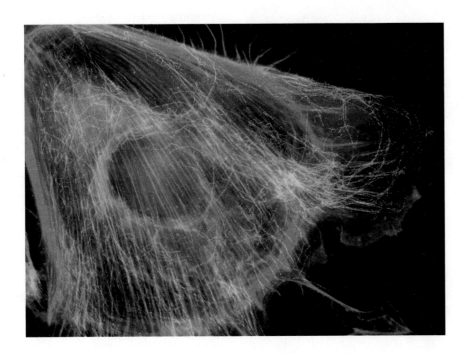

Figure 3 *The fibers that form the cytoskeleton of this hamster kidney cell are shown in green and red. The cytoskeleton supports the cell. Materials within the cell are also moved along the cytoskeleton.*

Parts of a Cell

Different kinds of cells, such as animal cells and plant cells, have many cell parts in common. But animal cells and plant cells also have cell parts that are different.

Parts of an Animal Cell

A typical animal cell, shown in **Figure 4,** has the following cell parts:

- **Cell Membrane** The cell membrane separates the cell from the surrounding environment. It also allows certain materials, such as gases, to move into and out of the cell.

- **Nucleus** The nucleus is the organelle that stores the cell's DNA. The nucleus also controls the activities of the cell.

- **Ribosomes** Ribosomes are organelles that make proteins for the cell.

- **Mitochondria** Mitochondria are organelles that break down food to make ATP.

- **Lysosomes** Lysosomes are organelles that have proteins that break down old organelles, wastes, and food.

- **Endoplasmic Reticulum** The endoplasmic reticulum is an organelle that transports proteins to the Golgi complex and breaks down toxic materials.

- **Golgi Complex** The Golgi complex is an organelle that changes proteins so that the proteins can function.

Figure 4 *Like all eukaryotic cells, animal cells contain a cell membrane, a nucleus, and other organelles for at least a part of their life.*

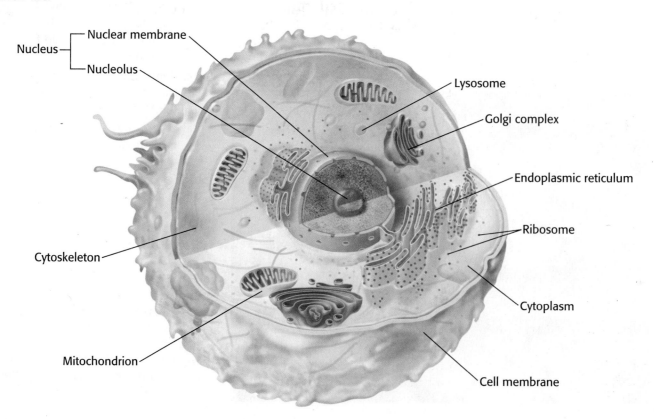

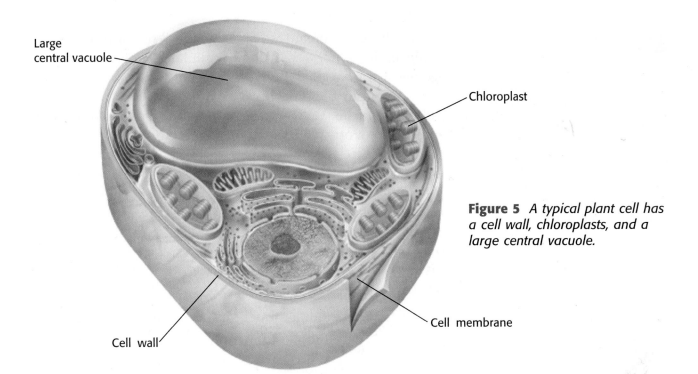

Large
central vacuole

Chloroplast

Figure 5 *A typical plant cell has a cell wall, chloroplasts, and a large central vacuole.*

Cell membrane

Cell wall

Parts of a Plant Cell

A typical plant cell has most of the kinds of organelles that an animal cell has. The reason is that plant cells need to perform the same activities that animal cells do.

Plant cells also have three parts that animal cells do not have. These cell parts, shown in **Figure 5,** perform specific activities for a plant. Listed below is the name of each of these cell parts, followed by a description of the cell part and its function.

- **Chloroplasts** Chloroplasts are organelles that trap light energy from the sun. Chloroplasts use light energy, carbon dioxide, and water to make sugars for the plant. The plant breaks down these sugars to release the energy needed to fuel the activities and life processes of its cells.

- **Large Central Vacuole** The large central vacuole is filled with liquid and is completely surrounded by a membrane. It can take up a lot of space in a cell. The large central vacuole helps the cell keep its shape. The large central vacuole also helps keep the plant upright.

- **Cell Wall** The tough, rigid cell wall surrounds the cell membrane. The cell wall helps support and protect the plant cell.

Benchmark Check What substance does a chloroplast make, and why is this substance important to the whole plant? **F.1.3.5 CS**

SCHOOL to HOME

The Model Cell

Build a model of either an animal cell or a plant cell. Use an old shoe box as the cell membrane. Use colored construction paper to make the different organelles. If you want to, label the organelles. Ask a parent or guardian to help you build your model.

ACTIVITY

F.1.3.5 CS explains how the life functions of organisms are related to what occurs within the cell.

function the special, normal, or proper activity of an organ or part

structure the arrangement of parts in an organism

Cell Function and Structure

In a single-celled organism, the cell must perform all of the organism's life processes. In a multicellular organism, cells work together to carry out the life processes of the entire organism. Each cell within a multicellular organism may not have every kind of organelle. Cells that do one job may have more of a certain kind of organelle than cells that perform another job do. These differences allow cells to specialize. Cells that *specialize* perform one job well. The cell's job is also called its **function.** To do its function, the cell may have a special shape and special properties. The shape and properties of the cell make up the cell's **structure.** Cells that are specialized often do not have to do all of the activities that the cell of a single-celled organism must do. Two general patterns between the functions of cells and the structures of cells are as follows:

1. Cells that have similar functions have similar structures.
2. Cells that have different functions have different structures.

Similar Functions, Similar Structures

In a multicellular organism, some cells look very similar. These cells likely have similar functions. Cells in many kinds of plants look like the cells from the plant leaf shown in **Figure 6.** These cells are specialized to perform photosynthesis, so they are packed with chloroplasts. Similarly, many animals, such as tigers and whales, have very similar red blood cells. These blood cells are full of the molecule that carries oxygen around the organism's body.

Benchmark Check Why do some cells from a plant leaf look similar? F.I.3.6 CS

Figure 6 *Many of the cells in a leaf carry out the same function, such as photosynthesis. Therefore, these cells have similar structures.*

F.I.3.6 CS knows that the cells with similar functions have similar structures, whereas those with different structures have different functions.

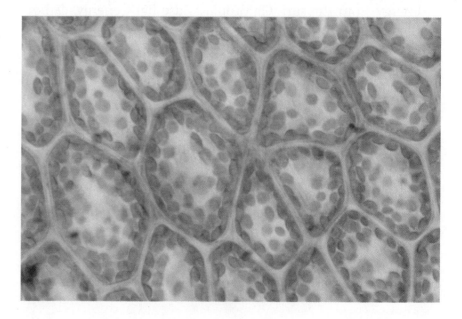

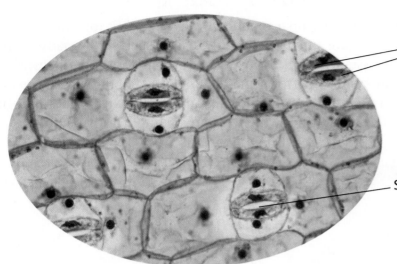

Guard cells

Figure 7 *In plants, the function of general epidermal cells differs from the function of guard cells. Thus, the structure of the general epidermal cells differs from the structure of the guard cells.*

Stoma

Different Functions, Different Structures

Generally, cells whose functions differ have structures that differ. For example, in a plant, the *epidermal cell layer* provides a barrier between the inside of the plant and the outside of the plant. Two kinds of epidermal (EP uh DUHR muhl) cells found in the epidermal cell layer are shown in **Figure 7.** Most general epidermal cells look like bricks and are packed closely together. *Guard cells* are sausage-shaped epidermal cells. Each pair of *guard cells* surround and control the size of a stoma (plural, *stomata*), an opening in the surface of a leaf. Stomata allow gases, such as carbon dioxide and oxygen, to move into and out of the leaf. What would happen if the guard cells had the same structure that the general epidermal cells have? The guard cells would fit together in the same way that the general epidermal cells do, so there would be no stomata.

Human blood cells provide another good example of how cells whose functions differ have structures that differ. Red blood cells (RBCs) carry oxygen from the lungs to all of the cells in the body. RBCs do not have a nucleus and look like flattened disks. This structure helps RBCs exchange oxygen with the body's cells and squeeze through the smallest blood vessels in the body efficiently.

White blood cells (WBCs) are responsible for destroying particles that do not belong in the body, such as viruses. Although there are different kinds of WBCs, each WBC has its own nucleus. The DNA in the nucleus of a WBC allows the WBC to respond efficiently to particles that do not belong in the body. **Figure 8** shows red blood cells and white blood cells. Notice how the structures of RBCs and WBCs differ.

Figure 8 *Red blood cells and white blood cells are shown by their colors. Their functions and structures differ.*

Benchmark Check Why does the structure of guard cells differ from the structure of general epidermal cells in plants? **F.1.3.6 CS**

Cell Function and Structure in Humans

Cells of multicellular organisms have to work together to perform the life functions of organisms, such as humans. Cells form tissues, which form organs, which form organ systems. Organ systems perform major functions for the whole organism. **Figure 9** shows how one kind of cell helps form a part of the small intestine, which is part of the digestive system.

F.1.3.4 CS knows that the levels of structural organization for function in living things include cells, tissues, organs, systems, and organisms.

F.1.3.6 CS knows that the cells with similar functions have similar structures, whereas those with different structures have different functions.

Figure 9 The Small Intestine

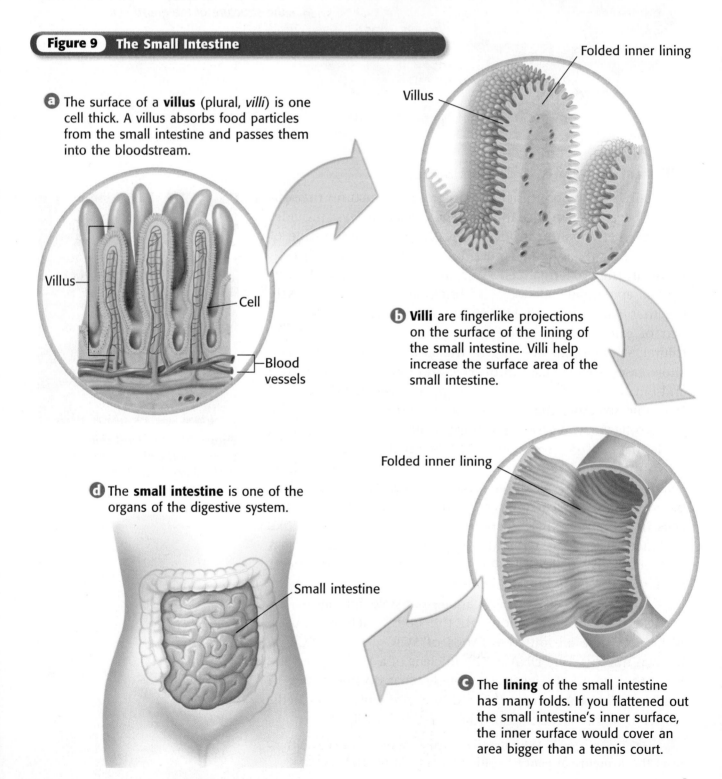

ⓐ The surface of a **villus** (plural, *villi*) is one cell thick. A villus absorbs food particles from the small intestine and passes them into the bloodstream.

Folded inner lining

Villus

Villus

Cell

Blood vessels

ⓑ **Villi** are fingerlike projections on the surface of the lining of the small intestine. Villi help increase the surface area of the small intestine.

ⓓ The **small intestine** is one of the organs of the digestive system.

Small intestine

Folded inner lining

ⓒ The **lining** of the small intestine has many folds. If you flattened out the small intestine's inner surface, the inner surface would cover an area bigger than a tennis court.

Summary

- All cells must carry out the same basic life processes for the cells and the organism to survive. **F.1.3.5 CS**
- Four basic life processes of single-celled and multicellular organisms are growth, reproduction, regulation, and maintenance.
- Animal cells and plant cells have many cell parts and organelles in common.

- Plant cells can have cell walls, large central vacuoles, and chloroplasts, that animal cells do not have.
- Cells in multicellular organisms are often specialized.
- Cells that have similar functions have similar structures, and cells that have different functions have different structures. **F.1.3.6 CS**

Using Key Terms

Use a term from the section to complete the sentence below.

1. Cells that have similar ___ have similar structures. **F.1.3.6 CS**

Understanding Key Ideas

2. Which of the following cell parts is found in both plant cells and animal cells?
   a. endoplasmic reticulum
   b. cell wall
   c. chloroplast
   d. large central vacuole

3. Name four main life processes that a cell needs to perform to survive.

4. Describe one activity that inlvolves transporting materials within the cell that a cell does to stay healthy or to maintain itself.

5. Describe a cell part that provides support for a plant cell and that an animal cell does not have.

Critical Thinking

6. **Making Inferences** A friend describes a cell that mainly makes proteins. Does this cell belong to a single-celled organism or to a multicellular organism? Explain your answer.

7. **Expressing Opinions** Animal cells do not have chloroplasts to make sugars. Plant cells do. In your opinion, do plant cells have an advantage over animal cells? Explain your position.

FCAT Preparation

8. Chloroplasts in plant cells make sugars for the plant. These sugars are broken down to release energy that the plant uses for many life functions. What would happen if the chloroplasts were destroyed by a disease and stopped working? **F.1.3.5 CS**
   A. The plant would produce more proteins.
   B. The plant would take up excess water.
   C. The plant would starve and die.
   D. The plant would grow quickly.

9. You are looking at the surface of a leaf under a microscope. You notice brick-shaped plant cells and sausage-shaped plant cells. From their shapes, what can you infer about these cells? **F.1.3.6 CS**
   F. These cells have the same structure.
   G. These cells have different functions.
   H. These cells have only chloroplasts.
   I. These cells do not have any organelles.

SCLINKS

NSTA
Developed and maintained by the
National Science Teachers Association

For a variety of links related to this chapter, go to www.scilinks.org

Topic: Cell Energy; Cell Structures
SciLinks code: HSM0237; HSM0240

Levels of Organization

A car engine is made of many different parts of varying shapes and sizes. These parts have to work together for the engine to run. Similarly, your body has many different cells of varying shapes and sizes. These cells work together to keep you healthy.

F.I.3.4 CS knows that the levels of structural organization for function in living things include cells, tissues, organs, systems, and organisms.

From Cells to Organisms

In a multicellular organism, such as a human, different kinds of cells perform different functions. These cells rely on each other and work together to do all of the activities needed for the organism to live. Such cells must be well organized in an organism. How are these cells organized?

There are five levels of structural organization: cells, tissues, organs, organ systems, and organisms. Therefore, a multicellular organism can have four levels of organization: cells, tissues, organs, and organ systems.

Cells: The Base

Unlike the cell of a single-celled organism, cells in a multicellular organism do not have to do everything that the organism needs to live. Cells in a multicellular organism can be specialized. A *specialized* cell performs a specific function. **Figure 1** shows one kind of cell in the gills of a shark. This type of cell is specialized to allow oxygen to move from the water, across the cell, and into the shark's blood as water flows over the gills.

Figure 1 *Multicellular organisms are made up of many specialized cells. Some cells in the gills of a shark are specialized to take in oxygen from the water.*

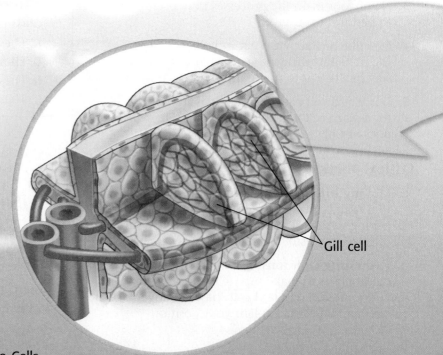

Gill cell

Tissues

Cells that have a similar function and a similar structure are organized into a **tissue.** The tissues that form a shark's gills are shown in **Figure 2.** In humans, there are four basic kinds of tissues:

- **Epithelial Tissues** Epithelial tissues form a barrier between you and the external environment. These tissues can be found in your stomach lining or in your skin.
- **Connective Tissues** Connective tissues connect and support other tissues. Blood is a connective tissue. It provides other tissues with oxygen.
- **Nervous Tissues** Nervous tissues help process information and send information around the body. Your brain is made up of nervous tissues.
- **Muscle Tissues** Muscle tissues contract and relax to produce movement. Muscle tissues in your legs help you walk.

Organs

Tissues that work together form an **organ.** An organ performs a specific function for an organism. For example, several kinds of tissues work together in the gill of a shark. The shark's gill is an organ that performs gas exchange. As the water flows into the shark's mouth and passes over the gill, oxygen diffuses into the cells of gill tissues. The cells in these tissues also release carbon dioxide as the water flows out of the gill.

Benchmark Check To which of the five levels of structural organization does a shark's gill belong? **F.1.3.4 CS**

tissue a group of similar cells that perform a common function

organ a collection of tissues that carry out a specialized function of the body

Figure 2 *The tissues in the gill of a shark are made up of similar cells. Cells of one of these kinds of tissues allow oxygen to move into the shark and allow carbon dioxide to move out of the shark.*

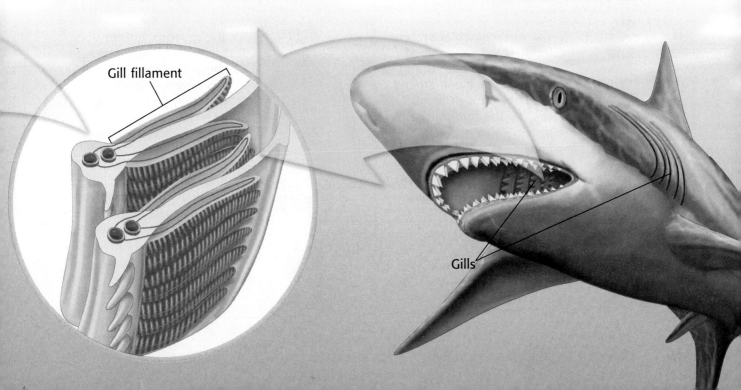

Gill fillament

Gills

Organ Systems

A group of organs that work together to perform a specific function for an organism is called an **organ system.** Organ systems can be placed into four major groups: systems for reproduction, systems for growth, systems for maintenance, and systems for regulation. Although more than one organ system is needed for each of these functions, **Figure 3** shows examples of an organ system for these four life functions in humans.

organ system a group of organs that work together to perform body functions

---

Figure 3 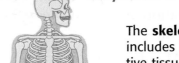 **Four Systems of the Human Body**

A System for Reproduction

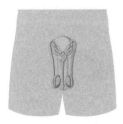

The **male reproductive system** produces and delivers the sperm necessary to fertilize an egg.

The **female reproductive system** produces eggs. An egg fertilized by a sperm usually develops into a fetus. The fetus grows in this system until it is born.

A System for Growth

The **skeletal system** includes bones and connective tissues that help support the body. The skeletal system is important in the growth of the organism. A skeleton supports the body and protects body parts as the body changes. The skeleton also provides places for muscles to attach so that the body can move.

A System for Maintenance

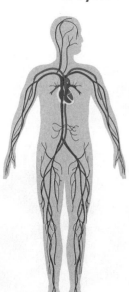

The **cardiovascular system** includes the heart, blood vessels, and blood. The heart pumps blood around the body through blood vessels. The cardiovascular system helps maintain the body by providing food and oxygen to cells. This system also helps remove waste and fight diseases.

A System for Regulation

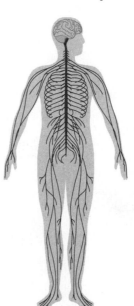

The **nervous system** is made up of nerves, the spinal cord, and the brain. The nervous system is important in regulating or controlling life functions, such as breathing. The brain processes information from inside the body and from outside the body. The brain then sends signals, which tell the body how to react.

Organisms

Multicellular organisms have many organ systems that perform life functions such as growth and regulation. Although one organ system may play a central role in a particular function, the system is supported by other organ systems. The same organ system also helps other organ systems perform other functions. Your organ systems work together to allow your body to do all of the activities that it must do for you to stay healthy.

Benchmark Check Name two life functions that organ systems perform for an organism. **F.1.3.1 AA**

How the Levels of Organization Work Together

Different levels of structural organization work together so that you can respond to and survive in changing surroundings.

Nerves and Muscles

The nervous system and muscles help the body react to stimuli. Nerves transmit signals to the spinal cord and to the brain. Then, the brain or spinal cord sends a signal to the body to respond. Reflex actions, such as the knee-jerk reflex shown in **Figure 4,** are responses that are signaled solely by the spinal cord. In the knee-jerk reflex, the spinal cord sends the signal to move the leg. This reaction happens so quickly that the brain becomes aware of the tap after the leg moves.

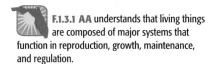
F.1.3.1 AA understands that living things are composed of major systems that function in reproduction, growth, maintenance, and regulation.

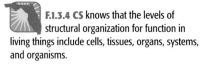
F.1.3.4 CS knows that the levels of structural organization for function in living things include cells, tissues, organs, systems, and organisms.

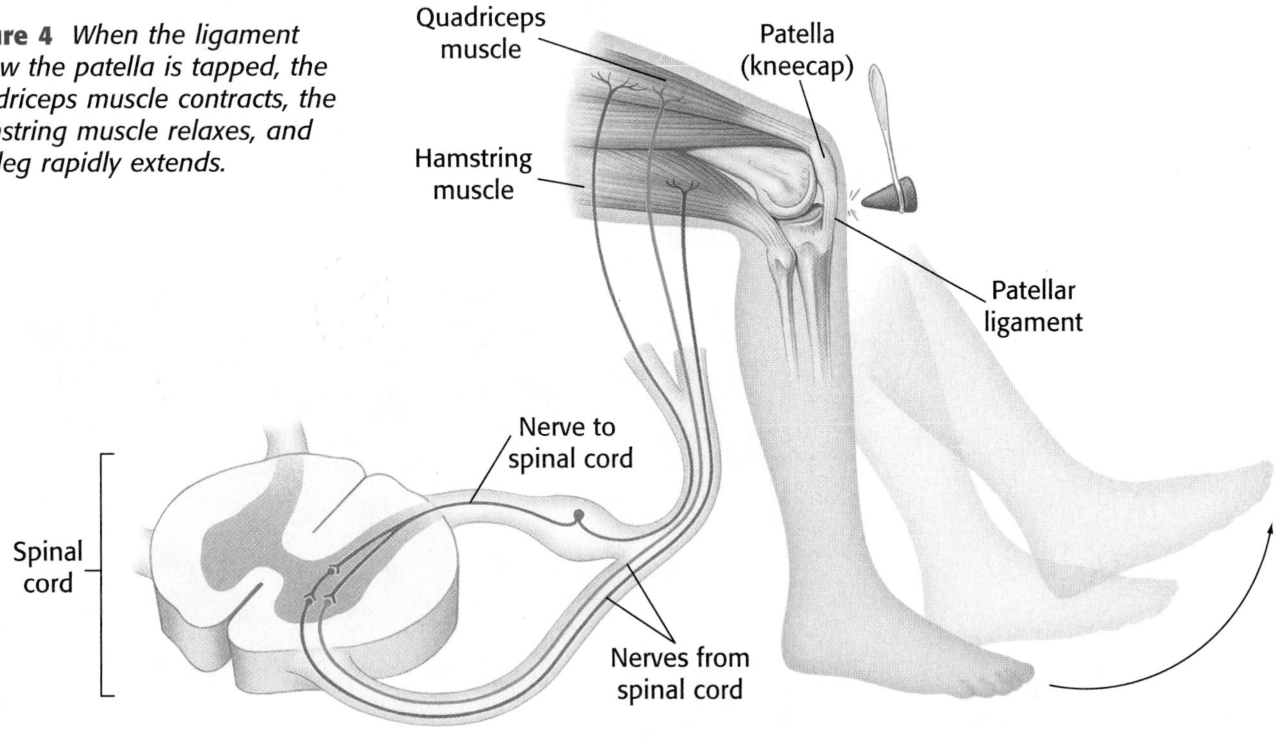

Figure 4 *When the ligament below the patella is tapped, the quadriceps muscle contracts, the hamstring muscle relaxes, and the leg rapidly extends.*

Quadriceps muscle

Patella (kneecap)

Hamstring muscle

Patellar ligament

Nerve to spinal cord

Spinal cord

Nerves from spinal cord

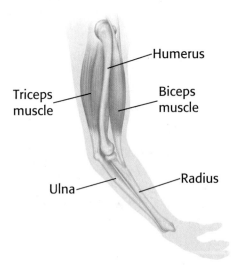

Figure 5 *Skeletal muscles work together on the bones of a human to allow movement.*

🌟 **F.1.3.1 AA** understands that living things are composed of major systems that function in reproduction, growth, maintenance, and regulation.

Muscles and Bones

Skeletal muscles allow humans to move their bodies. Skeletal muscles are muscles that are attached to the bones of the skeleton. Without skeletal muscles and bones, you would not be able to move.

Skeletal muscles must work together to move any part of an organism or an entire organism. For example, your biceps and triceps muscles work together to move your arm. Your biceps and triceps muscles are attached to the bones of your forearm, as **Figure 5** shows. Your biceps and triceps muscles work together to move your forearm. Nerves signal your biceps muscle to contract. As a result of this signal, your biceps muscle lifts your forearm. When another nerve signals your triceps muscle to contract, your triceps muscle lowers your forearm.

✓ *Reading Check* How do biceps and triceps muscles work together to move your forearm?

Bones and Blood Cells

Your bones are important organs that perform many functions for your body. Bones help support, protect, and move your body. Your bones also store calcium for your body. Calcium is an important chemical that is used by many cells in the body. Calcium found in dairy products plays a role in keeping your bones strong.

Red blood cells and white blood cells, as shown in **Figure 6,** are made by some of your bones. Your femur, the large bone in your upper leg, and your ribs are some of the bones that make blood cells for your body. On average, your bones make more than 170 billion new red blood cells each day.

✓ *Reading Check* What are three functions that your bones perform for you?

Figure 6 *Blood cells are made by your femur, your ribs, or other bones in your body.*

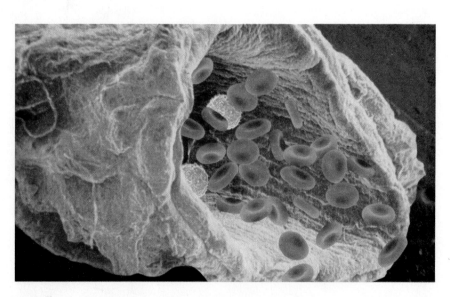

The Benefits of Organization

Specialized cells are organized into different levels of structural organization in the human body. These levels in the body must work well together. Through this organization, each cell in a person's body helps the person do many activities. For example, the girl shown in **Figure 7** is able to play softball because the cells in the various levels of structural organization of her body are working together. The cells in her eyes send signals to her brain. Her brain determines where the ball is and therefore how she should react. Her brain also signals her respiratory system to make any necessary changes in breathing. These examples are only a few of the many actions that the levels of structural organization allow the human body to do.

Figure 7 *Several levels of organization—from cells to organ systems—must work together to help a human function well.*

SECTION Review

Summary

- The levels of structural organization of many living things are cells, tissues, organs, organ systems, and organisms. **F.1.3.4 CS**

- Specialized cells perform specific functions.

- A tissue is made up of cells that have similar structures and similar functions. **F.1.3.4 CS**

- An organ is made up of a group of tissues. **F.1.3.4 CS**

- An organ system is made up of a group of organs. **F.1.3.4 CS**

- Organ systems perform the life functions of many multicellular organisms. **F.1.3.1 AA**

- The levels of structural organization help an organism do complex activities.

Using Key Terms

Use a term from the section to complete the sentence below.

1. Organs are made up of two or more ___ that work together.

Understanding Key Ideas

2. Which of the following lists all the levels of organization in a multicellular organism from the lowest level to the highest level? **F.1.3.4 CS**

   a. tissues and organ systems

   b. organ systems, tissues, organs, and cells

   c. tissues, cells, and organs

   d. cells, tissues, organs, and organ systems

Critical Thinking

3. **Expressing Opinions** Cells in multicellular organisms are specialized to do a specific function. In your opinion, what are the disadvantages of being specialized?

4. **Making Inferences** For you to move, your nerves must send signals to your skeletal muscles. How might nerve signals differ when you are walking from when you are running?

FCAT Preparation

5. Your organ systems help maintain your body. Choose an organ system that is responsible for providing the body with oxygen and nutrients. Explain how the organ system that you chose provides the cells in your body with oxygen and food. **F.1.3.1 AA**

6. Your small intestine helps you digest food. The small intestine is part of your digestive system. To which level of structural organization does your small intestine belong? **F.1.3.4 CS**

   A. cell

   B. tissue

   C. organ

   D. organ system

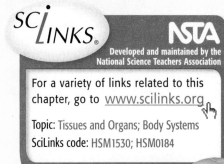

SCILINKS.

NSTA

Developed and maintained by the National Science Teachers Association

For a variety of links related to this chapter, go to www.scilinks.org

Topic: Tissues and Organs; Body Systems
SciLinks code: HSM1530; HSM0184

Skills Practice Lab

Name That Part!

Plant cells and animal cells have many organelles and other parts in common. For example, both plant cells and animal cells contain a nucleus and mitochondria. But plant cells and animal cells differ in several ways. In this exercise, you will identify cell structures that help support life. You will also investigate the similarities and differences between animal cells and plant cells.

Procedure

1. Using colored pencils or markers and white, unlined paper, trace or draw the plant cell and animal cell shown below. Draw each cell on a separate piece of paper. You may use a different color for each kind of organelle.

2. Label the parts of each cell. Do not write in your book.

3. On a separate piece of paper, draw a table like **Table 1,** and fill in the function of each structure for the animal cell and the plant cell. If a cell does not have a particular structure, simply draw a line through that box.

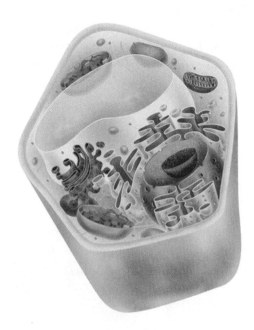

Plant cell

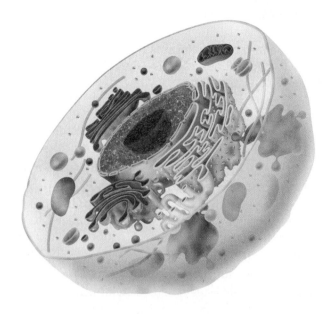

Animal cell

Table 1 Cell Structures and Functions		
Structure	Function of structure in plant cell	Function of structure in animal cell
Nucleus		
Lysosome		
Endoplasmic reticulum		
Golgi complex		
Mitochondrion		
Cell membrane		
Ribosome		
Cell wall		
Chloroplast		
Central vacuole		

DO NOT WRITE IN BOOK

Analyze the Results

1 List at least four structures that plant cells and animal cells have in common.

2 List three structures that plant cells have but that animal cells do not.

Draw Conclusions

3 **Interpreting Information** Choose two structures that an animal cell and a plant cell have in common. How is each structure important to the cell? How is each structure important to the organism?

4 **Interpreting Information** Choose one structure that a plant cell has but that an animal cell does not. Explain how you think the animal cell survives without this particular structure.

5 **Drawing Conclusions** Look through your table of structures and functions of animal cells and plant cells. Do you think that an animal cell could perform all of its life functions without any of its structures? Do you think that a plant cell could perform all of its life functions without any of its structures? Explain your answers.

Applying Your Data

Choose one of the following structures: a chloroplast, a large central vacuole, or a cell membrane. Write a short paragraph describing what would happen to the organism if the cell structure that you chose stopped working properly.

 F.1.3.5 CS explains how the life functions of organisms are related to what occurs within the cell.

Chapter Review

Short Answer

10 Describe one advantage that multi-cellular organisms have over single-celled organisms.

11 Most single-celled eukaryotic organisms are called *protists*. Protists can be divided into three smaller groups according to how they get their nutrition. What are the three groups?

12 Humans have many organ systems that perform various life functions. Name one organ system that is important in maintaining the human body.

F.1.3.1 AA

CRITICAL THINKING

Extended Response

13 **Making Inferences** At the hospital, you meet a patient who is anemic. She does not have enough red blood cells to carry oxygen. Why would the doctor test whether the patient's bones were functioning properly? F.1.3.1 AA *FCAT*

14 **Forming Hypotheses** You placed a white carnation in water that was mixed with blue food coloring. The next day, you notice that the edges of the flower's petals are turning blue. Form a hypothesis to explain what happened. F.1.3.5 CS

Concept Mapping

15 Use the following terms to create a concept map: *organism, single-celled, multicellular, cell, tissues, organs, ribosomes,* and *DNA.*

INTERPRETING GRAPHICS

Use the diagram of a cell below to answer the questions that follow.

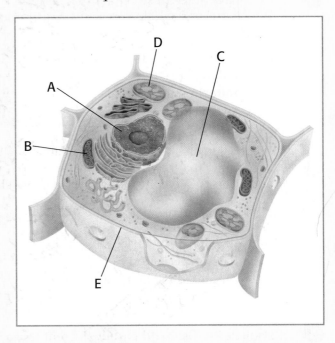

16 What is the name of structure A?

17 Why is structure A important to the cell?

18 What does structure B make?

19 What does this cell store in structure C?

20 Explain whether you think that this cell would be found in the leaf of a plant or in the bone of an animal.

21 Which structure makes sugars? What is the name of this structure?

22 Which structures provides support for the cell? What are the names of these structures?

For the following questions, write your answers on a separate sheet of paper.

1 Cells have different structures that perform specific functions for the cell and the organism. Which one of the following structures is found only in plants and performs the same function as the skeleton of an animal?

A. ribosomes
B. chloroplasts
C. mitochondria
D. large central vacuoles

2 Min knows that multicellular organisms are structurally more complex than single-celled organisms. Which one of the following is a characteristic of a multicellular orgranism but not of a single-celled organism?

F. having organelles
G. the ability to move
H. having specialized cells
I. the ability to obtain nutrition

3 Danielle knows that there are different levels of organization in plants and animals. She also knows that an organism must be able to perform all necessary life functions for itself. Which one of the following could be classified as an organism?

A. DNA
B. fungus
C. Golgi complex
D. mitochondrion

4 The inner lining of the small intestine has many folds. This greatly increases the surface area exposed to the food passing through the small intestine. Why is this structure important to the function of the digestive system?

F. It helps move food out of the stomach.
G. It allows the organism to regulate body temperature.
H. It makes it easier to absorb nutrients more efficiently.
I. It helps the digestive system structurally support other organ systems.

5 Luana is comparing an onion skin cell to a nerve cell under a microscope. Luana notices that the structure of an onion skin cell is very different from a nerve cell. What can she infer about cells that have different structures?

A. that they belong to different organisms
B. that these cells have different functions
C. that one cell is eukaryotic and the other cell is prokaryotic
D. that one cell is from a single-celled organism and the other cell is from a multicellular organism

6

Many of the actions that the human body performs daily are not consciously controlled. One of these actions is the knee-jerk reflex. When an object hits the kneecap, sensory neurons transmit that information to the spinal cord. The spinal cord responds by sending an impulse through motor neurons to the quadriceps muscle to contract. This reaction raises the leg. By the time the brain becomes aware of the tap on the knee, the leg has already moved.

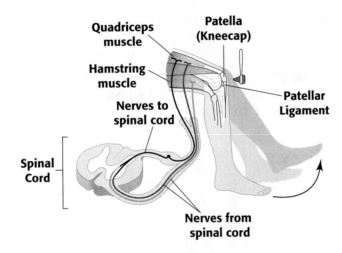

Other reflexes or involuntary actions include jerking away from things that are too hot or cause pain. Are reflexes important to the human body? Explain your answer.

Science in Action

Place to Visit

Welaka Fish Hatchery

Did you know that there is a place in Florida where nearly 5 million fish are grown from eggs and released into the wild every year? The Welaka Fish Hatchery in Putnam County is Florida's only fish hatchery. The fish grown at Welaka are released in Florida, Georgia, and Alabama. The scientists at Welaka are helping protect fish that are becoming increasingly threatened by overfishing and habitat loss. More than 35,000 visitors come each year to explore the hatchery and to learn about the science of raising fish. Come visit Welaka Hatchery, and find some fish tales of your own!

Language Arts ACTiViTY

WRITING SKILL Several kinds of fish are raised at Welaka. Pretend that you are one of the fish being raised at the hatchery. Write a short story about your life as a fish growing up in the hatchery.

Weird Science

Edible Vaccines

Vaccines protect you from life-threatening diseases. But vaccinations are expensive, and the people who give them must have extensive training. These and other factors often prevent people in developing countries from getting vaccinations. But help may be on the way. Scientists are developing edible vaccines. Imagine eating a banana and getting the same protection that you would get from several painful injections. These vaccines are made from DNA that resembles the DNA of specific parts of disease particles. This DNA is then inserted into the banana's genes. Researchers are still working on safe and effective edible vaccines.

Social Studies ACTiViTY

WRITING SKILL Do research to identify the childhood illnesses for which vaccines were not available 30 to 50 years ago. Then, interview a few older members of your family. Ask them if they had any of these illnesses when they were children because the vaccines were not available. Write a report on these interviews.

Jerry Yakel

Neuroscientist Jerry Yakel credits a sea slug for making him become a neuroscientist. While studying neurons, or nerve cells, in a college class, Yakel got to see first-hand how ions move across the cell membrane of *Aplysia californica,* also known as a *sea hare.* He says, "I was totally hooked. I knew that I wanted to be a neurophysiologist then and there. I haven't wavered since."

Today, Yakel is a senior investigator for the National Institutes of Environmental Health Sciences, which is part of the U.S. government's National Institutes of Health. "We try to understand how the normal brain works," Yakel says of his team. "Then, when we look at a diseased brain, we train to understand where the deficits are. Eventually, someone will have an idea about a drug that will tweak the system in this or that way."

Yakel studies the ways in which nicotine affects the human brain. "It is one of the most prevalent and potent neurotoxins in the environment," says Yakel. "I'm amazed that it isn't higher on the list of worries for the general public."

Math ACTIVITY

Smokers inhale 1 to 2 mg of nicotine from every cigarette that they smoke. Exposure to 2 to 5 mg of nicotine can cause nausea. How many cigarettes could make a smoker nauseous? Express your answer as a range.

To learn more about these Science in Action topics, visit go.hrw.com and type in the keyword **HT6FCF6F.**

Current Science

Check out Current Science® articles related to this chapter by visiting go.hrw.com. Just type in the keyword **HL5CS03.**

Living Things and the Environment

Throughout history, people have been trying to organize living things into groups, trying to understand plants, and trying to identify the interactions of living things in the environment. In this unit, you will join this effort. You will learn about plants, ecology, and the classification of living things. This timeline relates some of the important events that have occurred as scientists have learned more about living things and the interactions of living things.

Around 250

Mayan farmers build terraces to control the flow of water to crops.

1864

Louis Pasteur uses heat to eliminate microbes. This process is later called *pasteurization.*

1897

Beatrix Potter, the author of *The Tale of Peter Rabbit,* completes her collection of 270 watercolors of fungi. Today, she is considered an expert in mycology, the study of fungi.

1971

Ananda Chakrabarty uses genetics to design bacteria that can break down the oil in oil spills.

1580

Prospero Alpini discovers that plants have both male structures and female structures.

1683

Anton van Leeuwenhoek is the first person to describe bacteria.

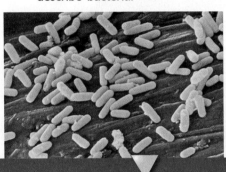

1760s

Joseph Kolreuter studies crosses of tobacco plants and discovers that both parent plants contribute traits to the offspring.

Escherichia coli under an electron microscope

1898

Martinus Beijerinck gives the name *virus* to infectious material that is smaller than a bacterium.

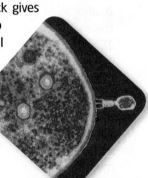

1928

Alexander Fleming observes that certain molds can eliminate bacterial growth. He also discovers penicillin.

1955

A vaccine for the polio virus developed by Dr. Jonas Salk becomes widely used.

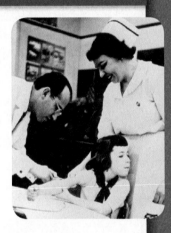

1983

HIV, the virus responsible for AIDS, is isolated.

1995

An outbreak of the deadly Ebola virus occurs in Zaire.

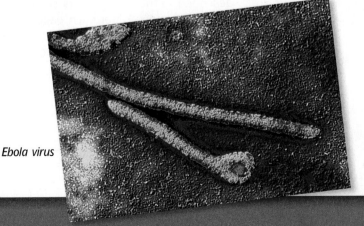

Ebola virus

2002

An international team decodes the DNA sequences of both the protist that causes malaria and the mosquito that carries this protist. As a result, the door to more-effective antimalarial drugs is opened.

Classification

The Big Idea Organisms can be classified into groups based on the organisms' characteristics.

About the PHOTO

Look at the katydids, grasshoppers, and mantids in the photo. A scientist is classifying these insects. Every insect has a label describing the insect. These descriptions will be used to help the scientist know if each insect has already been discovered and named. When scientists discover a new insect or another organism, they have to give the organism a name. The name chosen is unique and should help other scientists understand some basic facts about the organism.

PRE-READING ACTIVITY

Booklet Before you read the chapter, create the FoldNote entitled "Booklet" described in the **Study Skills** section of the Appendix. Label each page of the booklet with a main idea from the chapter. As you read the chapter, write what you learn about each main idea on the appropriate page of the booklet.

START-UP ACTIVITY

Classifying Shoes

In this group activity, each group will develop a system of classification for shoes.

Procedure

1. Gather **10 shoes.** Number **pieces of masking tape** from 1 to 10. Label the sole of each shoe with a numbered piece of tape.

2. Make a list of shoe features. Make a table that has a column for each feature. Complete the table by describing each shoe.

3. Use the data in the table to make a shoe identification key.

4. The key should be a list of steps. Each step should have two contrasting statements about the shoes. The statements will lead you either to the next step or to a specific shoe.

5. If your shoe is not identified in one step, go on to the next step or steps until the shoe is identified.

6. Trade keys with another group. How did the other group's key help you identify the shoes?

Analysis

1. How was listing the shoe features before making the key helpful?

2. Were you able to identify the shoes by using another group's key? Explain.

Sorting It All Out

Imagine that you live in a tropical rain forest and must get your own food, shelter, and clothing from the forest. What do you need to know to survive in the forest?

To survive in the rain forest, you need to know which plants are safe to eat and which are not. You need to know which animals you can eat and which might eat you. In other words, you need to study the living things around you and organize them into categories, or classify them. **Classification** is putting things into orderly groups based on similar characteristics.

Why Classify?

For thousands of years, humans have classified living things based on usefulness. The Chácabo people of Bolivia know of 360 types of plants that grow in the forest where they live. Of these 360 plant types, 305 are useful to the Chácabo.

Some biologists, such as those shown in **Figure 1,** classify living and extinct organisms. Scientists classify organisms to help make sense and order of the many kinds of living things in the world. Biologists use a system to classify living things. This system is a tool to group organisms according to the characteristics that they share. The classification of living things makes it easier for biologists to answer many important questions, such as the following:

- How many known species are there?
- What are the defining characteristics of each species?
- What are the relationships between these species?

Benchmark Check What are three questions that classifying organisms can help answer? G.1.3.3 CS

classification the division of organisms into groups, or classes, based on specific characteristics

Figure 1 *These biologists are sorting rain-forest plant material.*

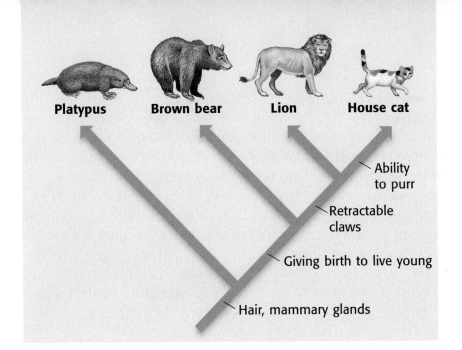

Figure 2 *This branching diagram shows the similarities and differences between four mammals.*

Ability to purr

Retractable claws

Giving birth to live young

Hair, mammary glands

How Do Scientists Classify Organisms?

Before the 1600s, many scientists divided organisms into two groups: plants and animals. But as more organisms were discovered, some did not fit into either group. In the 1700s, Carolus Linnaeus (KAR uh luhs li NAY uhs), a Swedish scientist, founded modern taxonomy. **Taxonomy** (taks AHN uh mee) is the science of describing, classifying, and naming living things. Linnaeus tried to classify all living things based on their shape and structure. Scientists today use a system of classification that is very similar to the one that Linnaeus developed.

Classification Today

Taxonomists use an eight-level system to classify living things based on shared characteristics. Scientists also use shared characteristics to hypothesize how closely related living things are. The more characteristics the organisms share, the more closely related the organisms may be. For example, the platypus, brown bear, lion, and house cat are thought to be related because they share many characteristics. These animals have hair and mammary glands, so they are grouped together as mammals. But they can be further classified into more-specific groups.

Branching Diagrams

Look at the branching diagram in **Figure 2.** Several characteristics are listed along the line that points to the right. Each characteristic is shared by the animals to the right of it. All of the animals shown have hair and mammary glands. But only the bear, lion, and house cat give birth to live young. The lion and the house cat have retractable claws, but the other animals do not. Thus, the lion and the house cat are more closely related to each other than to the other animals.

G.1.3.3 CS understands that the classification of living things is based on a given set of criteria and is a tool for understanding biodiversity and interrelationships.

taxonomy the science of describing, naming, and classifying organisms

WRITING SKILL A Branching Diagram

1. Construct a diagram similar to the one in **Figure 2,** using a frog, a snake, a kangaroo, and a rabbit.

2. Think of one major change that happened before the frog evolved.

3. For the last three organisms, write a change that happened between one of these organisms and the other two in your diagram.

4. Write a brief paragraph that describes how this diagram helps you understand how the organisms are related. **G.1.3.3 CS**

Levels of Classification

Every living thing is classified into one of three domains. Domains are the largest, most general groups. All living things in a domain are sorted into kingdoms. The members of one kingdom are more like each other than they are like the members of another kingdom. All living things in a kingdom are further sorted into phyla (singular, *phylum*). The members of a phylum are sorted into classes. Each class includes one or more orders. Orders are separated into families. Families are broken into genera (singular, *genus*). And genera are sorted into species. A species is a group of organisms that are closely related and that can mate to produce fertile offspring. **Figure 3** shows the classification of a house cat from the kingdom Animalia to the species *Felis domesticus*.

INTERNET ACTIVITY

Kingdom Competition! Choose a kingdom, and create an advertisement for it! Go to **go.hrw.com,** and type in the keyword **HL5CLSW.**

Scientific Names

By classifying organisms, biologists can give organisms scientific names. A scientific name remains the same for a specific kind of organism even if the organism has many common names. Before Linnaeus's time, scholars used names that were as long as 12 words to identify species. This system was hard to work with because the names were so long. The system was also hard to use because different scientists named organisms differently, so an organism could have more than one name.

G.1.3.3 CS understands that the classification of living things is based on a given set of criteria and is a tool for understanding biodiversity and interrelationships.

Figure 3 *Levels of classification include the kingdom, phylum, class, order, family, genus, and species.*

Kingdom Animalia	Phylum Chordata	Class Mammalia	Order Carnivora
All animals are in the **kingdom Animalia.**	All animals in the **phylum Chordata** have a hollow nerve cord. Most have a backbone.	Animals in the **class Mammalia** have a backbone. They also nurse their young.	Animals in the **order Carnivora** have a backbone and nurse their young. They also have special teeth for tearing meat.

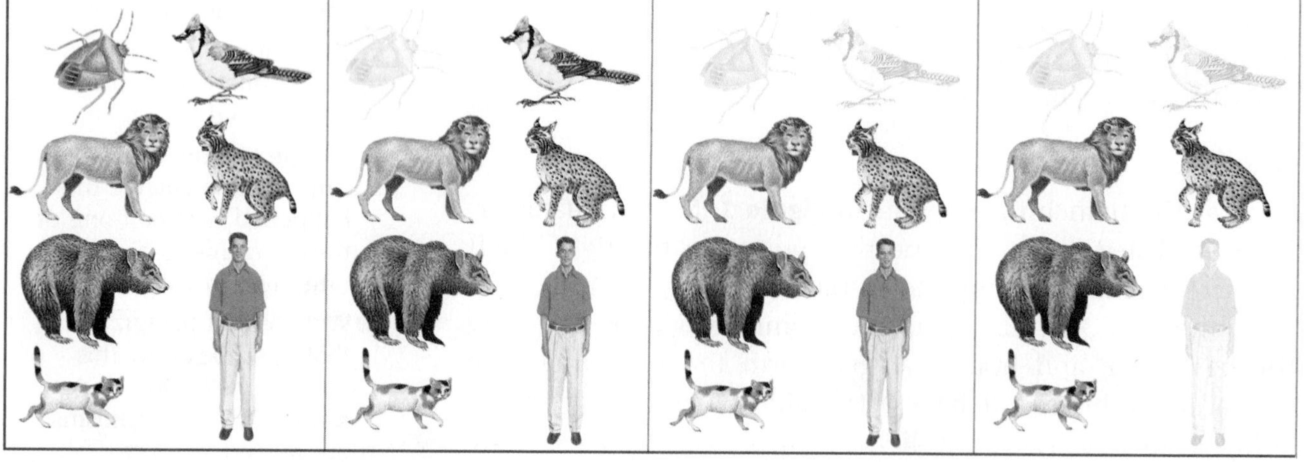

Two-Part Names

Linnaeus simplified the naming of living things by giving each species a two-part scientific name. For example, the scientific name for the Asian elephant is *Elephas maximus* (EL uh fuhs MAK suh muhs). The first part of the name, *Elephas,* is the genus name. The second part, *maximus,* is the specific name. No other species has the name *Elephas maximus.* Naming rules help scientists communicate clearly about living things.

All genus names begin with a capital letter. All specific names begin with a lowercase letter. Usually, both words are underlined or italicized. But if the surrounding text is italicized, the scientific name is not, as **Figure 4** shows. These printing styles show a reader which words are genus names and specific names.

Scientific names, which are usually Latin or Greek, contain information about an organism. The name of the animal shown in **Figure 4** is *Tyrannosaurus rex. Tyrannosaurus* is a combination of two Greek words and means "tyrant lizard." The word *rex* is Latin for "king." The name tells you that this animal was probably not a passive grass eater! Sometimes, *Tyrannosaurus rex* is referred to as *T. rex.* To be correct, the scientific name must consist of the genus name (or its abbreviation) and the specific name.

Figure 4 *You would never call* Tyrannosaurus rex *just* rex!

✓ Reading Check What are the two parts of a scientific name?

Family Felidae	Genus *Felis*	Species *Felis domesticus*
Animals in the **family Felidae** are cats. They have a backbone, nurse their young, have special teeth for tearing meat, and have retractable claws.	Animals in the **genus Felis** share traits with other animals in the same family. However, these cats cannot roar; they can only purr.	The **species Felis domesticus** is the common house cat. The house cat shares traits with all of the organisms in the levels above the species level, but it also has unique traits.

Dichotomous Keys

You might someday turn over a rock and find an organism that you don't recognize. How would you identify the organism? Taxonomists have developed special guides to help scientists identify organisms. A **dichotomous key** (die KAHT uh muhs KEE) is an identification aid that uses sequential pairs of descriptive statements. There are only two alternative responses for each statement. From each pair of statements, the person trying to identify the organism chooses the statement that describes the organism. Either the chosen statement identifies the organism or the person is directed to another pair of statements. By working through the statements in the key in order, the person can eventually identify the organism. Using the simple dichotomous key in **Figure 5,** try to identify the two animals shown.

dichotomous key an aid that is used to identify organisms and that consists of the answers to a series of questions

✔ **Reading Check** What is a dichotomous key?

Figure 5 *A dichotomous key can help you identify organisms.*

Dichotomous Key to 10 Common Mammals in the Eastern United States

1. a. This mammal flies. Its "hand" forms a wing. **b.** This mammal does not fly. Its "hand" does not form a wing.	**little brown bat** **Go to step 2.**
2. a. This mammal has no hair on its tail. **b.** This mammal has hair on its tail.	**Go to step 3.** **Go to step 4.**
3. a. This mammal has a short, naked tail. **b.** This mammal has a long, naked tail.	**eastern mole** **Go to step 5.**
4. a. This mammal has a black mask across its face. **b.** This mammal does not have a black mask across its face.	**raccoon** **Go to step 6.**
5. a. This mammal has a tail that is flat and paddle shaped. **b.** This mammal has a tail that is not flat or paddle shaped.	**beaver** **opossum**
6. a. This mammal is brown and has a white underbelly. **b.** This mammal is not brown and does not have a white underbelly.	**Go to step 7.** **Go to step 8.**
7. a. This mammal has a long, furry tail that is black on the tip. **b.** This mammal has a long tail that has little fur.	**longtail weasel** **white-footed mouse**
8. a. This mammal is black and has a narrow white stripe on its forehead and broad white stripes on its back. **b.** This mammal is not black and does not have white stripes.	**striped skunk** **Go to step 9.**
9. a. This mammal has long ears and a short, cottony tail. **b.** This mammal has short ears and a tail of medium length.	**eastern cottontail** **woodchuck**

A Growing System

You may think that all of the organisms on Earth have already been classified. But people are still discovering and classifying organisms. Some newly discovered organisms fit into existing categories. But sometimes, someone discovers a new organism that differs from other organisms so much that it does not fit into an existing category. For example, in 1995, scientists studied an organism named *Symbion pandora* (SIM bee AHN pan DAWR uh). *S. pandora* was living on lobster lips! Scientists learned that *S. pandora* had some characteristics that no other known organism had. In fact, scientists trying to classify *S. pandora* found that it didn't fit into any existing phylum. So, taxonomists created a new phylum for *S. pandora*.

G.1.3.3 CS understands that the classification of living things is based on a given set of criteria and is a tool for understanding biodiversity and interrelationships.

SECTION
Review

Summary

- Classification groups living things based on their similarities. **G.1.3.3 CS**
- A system of classification is a tool that helps us understand the relationships between organisms. **G.1.3.3 CS**
- The eight levels of organization of living things are the domain, kingdom, phylum, class, order, family, genus, and species.
- An organism has only one scientific name.
- Dichotomous keys are tools for identifying organisms.

Using Key Terms

1. Write an original definition for *classification* and *taxonomy*.

Understanding Key Ideas

2. The two parts of a scientific name are the genus name and the
   a. specific name.
   b. phylum name.
   c. family name.
   d. order name.

3. Why do scientists use scientific names for organisms?

4. List the eight levels of classification.

Critical Thinking

5. **Analyzing Processes** You have found an organism that has characteristics that have never been described before. What would you have to do to create a key to help others identify this organism?

6. **Applying Concepts** Both dolphins and sharks have a tail and fins. What tool can you use to determine if dolphins and sharks are closely related? **G.1.3.3 CS**

FCAT Preparation

7. Scientists use branching diagrams, like the one below, to identify organisms.

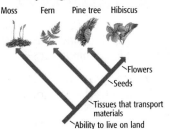

Moss   Fern   Pine tree   Hibiscus

Flowers
Seeds
Tissues that transport materials
Ability to live on land

How else do branching diagrams help us? **G.1.3.3 CS**

A. They show relationships between organisms.
B. They show all of the characteristics of an organism.
C. They show all organisms.
D. They show ages of organisms.

SCiLINKS®

NSTA

Developed and maintained by the National Science Teachers Association

For a variety of links related to this chapter, go to www.scilinks.org
Topic: Basis for Classification; Levels of Classification
SciLinks code: HSM0138; HSM0870

Domains and Kingdoms

What do you call an organism that is green, makes its own food, lives in pond water, and moves? Is it a plant, an animal, or something in between?

For hundreds of years, all living things were classified as either plants or animals. But over time, scientists discovered species that did not fit easily into these two kingdoms. For example, an organism of the genus *Euglena,* such as the one shown in **Figure 1,** has characteristics of both plants and animals. How would you classify such an organism?

What Is It?

Organisms are classified by their characteristics. For example, euglena, members of the genus *Euglena,*

- are single celled and live in pond water
- are green and perform photosynthesis

These characteristics might lead you to conclude that euglena are plants. However, before you form a conclusion, you should consider the following:

- Euglena move by whipping their "tails," which are called *flagella.*
- Euglena can feed on other organisms.

Plants do not move themselves around and usually do not eat other organisms. So, are euglena animals? As you can see, euglena do not fit into the plant or animal categories. Scientists solved this classification problem by adding another kingdom, the kingdom Protista, to classify organisms such as euglena.

As scientists learned about more living things, they had to adapt the classification system. Today, there are three domains in the classification system. Domains represent the largest differences between organisms. Currently, these domains are divided into several kingdoms.

Benchmark Check What do scientists use to classify organisms?
G.1.3.3 CS

G.1.3.3 CS understands that the classification of living things is based on a given set of criteria and is a tool for understanding biodiversity and interrelationships.

Figure 1 *How would you classify this member of the genus* Euglena, *which is highly magnified in this photo? This organism has characteristics of both plants and animals.*

Figure 2 *The Grand Prismatic Spring in Yellowstone National Park contains water that is about 90°C (194°F). The spring is home to archaea that thrive in its hot water.*

Archaea in a modern taxonomic system, a domain made up of pro-karyotes (most of which are known to live in extreme environments) that are distinguished from other prokary-otes by differences in their genetics and in the makeup of their cell wall; this domain aligns with the tradi-tional kingdom Archaebacteria

Bacteria in a modern taxonomic system, a domain made up of pro-karyotes that usually have a cell wall and that usually reproduce by cell division; this domain aligns with the traditional kingdom Eubacteria

Domain Archaea

The domain **Archaea** is made up entirely of archaea. Archaea (AHR kee uh) are one of two kinds of prokaryotes. *Prokaryotes* (proh KAR ee OHTS) are single-celled organisms that do not have a nucleus. Archaea were first discovered living in extreme envi-ronments, where other organisms could not survive. **Figure 2** shows a hot spring in Yellowstone National Park. The yellow and orange rings around the edge of the hot spring are made up of the billions of archaea that live there. Some archaea can also be found in more-moderate environments, such as the open ocean.

✔ **Reading Check** Describe one characteristic of an organism in the domain Archaea.

Figure 3 *Specimens of* E. coli *are shown on the point of a pin under a scanning electron microscope. These bacteria live in the intestines of animals and decompose undigested food.*

Domain Bacteria

All bacteria belong to the domain **Bacteria.** Bacteria (bak TEER ee uh), are another kind of prokaryote. Bacteria can be found in the soil, in water, and even on and inside the human body! For example, *Escherichia coli* (ESH uh RIK ee uh KOH LIE), pictured in **Figure 3,** is present in large numbers in human intestines, where it produces vitamin K. One kind of bacterium converts milk into yogurt. Some bacteria cause diseases, such as pneumonia. Other bacteria make chemicals that help us fight disease-causing bacteria.

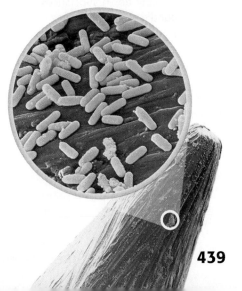

439

Figure 4 *This slime mold is a protist.*

Domain Eukarya

All organisms whose cells have a nucleus and membrane-bound organelles are called *eukaryotes*. Eukaryotes belong to the domain **Eukarya**. The four kingdoms within the domain Eukarya are Protista, Fungi, Plantae, and Animalia.

Kingdom Protista

Members of the kingdom **Protista** (proh TIST uh), commonly called *protists* (PROH tists), are single-celled or simple multicellular organisms. Scientists think that the first protists evolved from ancient bacteria about 2 billion years ago. Much later, protists gave rise to fungi, plants, and animals. The kingdom Protista contains many kinds of organisms. Animal-like protists are called *protozoans*. Plantlike protists are called *algae*. Slime molds, such as the one shown in **Figure 4,** and euglena also belong to the kingdom Protista.

Kingdom Fungi

Molds and mushrooms are examples of the complex, multicellular members of the kingdom **Fungi** (FUHN JIE). Unlike plants, fungi do not perform photosynthesis. Unlike animals, fungi do not eat food. Instead, fungi absorb nutrients from substances in their surroundings. They use digestive juices to break down the substances. **Figure 5** shows a very poisonous fungus. Never eat wild fungi.

Eukarya in a modern taxonomic system, a domain made up of all eukaryotes; this domain aligns with the traditional kingdoms Protista, Fungi, Plantae, and Animalia

Protista a kingdom of mostly one-celled eukaryotic organisms that are different from plants, animals, archaea, bacteria, and fungi

Fungi a kingdom made up of nongreen, eukaryotic organisms that have no means of movement, reproduce by using spores, and get food by breaking down substances in their surroundings and absorbing the nutrients

Figure 5 *This beautiful fungus of the genus* Amanita *is poisonous.*

G.1.3.3 CS understands that the classification of living things is based on a given set of criteria and is a tool for understanding biodiversity and interrelationships.

Figure 6 *Giant sequoias can measure 30 m around at the base and can grow to more than 91.5 m tall.*

Figure 7 *Plants such as these are common in the Tropics.*

Kingdom Plantae

Although plants vary remarkably in size and form, most people easily recognize the members of the kingdom Plantae. **Plantae** consists of organisms that are eukaryotic, have cell walls, and make food through photosynthesis. For photosynthesis to occur, plants must be exposed to sunlight. Plants can therefore be found on land and in water that light can penetrate.

The food that plants make is important not only for the plants but also for all of the organisms that get nutrients from plants. Most life on Earth is dependent on plants. For example, some fungi, protists, and bacteria consume plants. When these organisms digest the plant material, they get energy and nutrients made by the plants.

Plants also provide habitat for other organisms. The giant sequoias in **Figure 6** and the flowering plants in **Figure 7** provide birds, insects, and other animals with a place to live.

✓ Reading Check How do plants provide energy and nutrients to other organisms?

Plantae a kingdom made up of complex, multicellular organisms that are usually green, have cell walls made of cellulose, cannot move around, and use the sun's energy to make sugar by photosynthesis

Ring-Around-the-Sequoia
How many students would have to join hands to form a human chain around a giant sequoia that is 30 m in circumference? Assume for this calculation that the average student can extend his or her arms about 1.3 m.

Animalia a kingdom made up of complex, multicellular organisms that lack cell walls, can usually move around, and quickly respond to their environment

Kingdom Animalia

The kingdom **Animalia** contains complex, multicellular organisms that lack cell walls, are usually able to move around, and have specialized sense organs. These sense organs help most animals quickly respond to their environment. Organisms in the kingdom Animalia are commonly called *animals*. You probably recognize many of the organisms in the kingdom Animalia. All of the organisms in **Figure 8** are animals.

Animals depend on the organisms from other kingdoms. For example, animals depend on plants for food. Animals also depend on bacteria and fungi to recycle the nutrients found in dead organisms.

Figure 8 *The kingdom Animalia contains many different organisms, such as the bald eagle, the Florida mastiff bat and the Miami blue butterfly.*

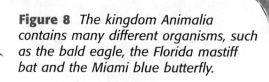

CONNECTION TO Social Studies

WRITING SKILL **Animals That Help** Humans have depended on animals for thousands of years. Many people around the world still use oxen to farm. Camels, horses, donkeys, goats, and llamas are still used as pack animals. Dogs still help herd sheep, protect property, and help people hunt. Scientists are even discovering new ways that animals can help us. For example, scientists are training bees to help find buried land mines. Using the library or the Internet, research an animal that helps people. Make a poster describing the animal and the animal's scientific name. The poster should show who uses the animal, how the animal is used, and how long people have depended on the animal. Find or draw pictures to put on your poster.

ACTiViTy

G.1.3.3 CS understands that the classification of living things is based on a given set of criteria and is a tool for understanding biodiversity and interrelationships.

Strange Organisms

Classifying organisms is often not easy. Like an animal, some plants can eat other organisms to obtain nutrition. Some protists can use photosynthesis as plants do and move around as animals do. The animal kingdom also includes some members that might surprise you, such as worms, insects, and corals.

The red cup sponge in **Figure 9** is also an animal. Sponges are usually considered the simplest animals. They lack sense organs, and most of them cannot move. Scientists used to classify sponges as plants. But sponges cannot make their own food. They must eat other organisms to get nutrients, which is one reason that sponges are classified as animals.

✓ Reading Check Why were sponges once thought to be plants?

Figure 9 *This red cup sponge is a simple animal.*

SECTION Review

Summary

- Most biologists recognize three domains: Archaea, Bacteria, and Eukarya.

- As scientists discover new organisms, classification systems are changed to include the characteristics of those new organisms. **G.1.3.3 CS**

- Archaea can live in extreme environments. Bacteria live almost everywhere else. All prokaryotes are members of the domain Archaea or the domain Bacteria.

- Eukarya is made up of four kingdoms: Protista, Fungi, Plantae, and Animalia. All members of Eukarya are eukaryotes.

Using Key Terms

1. Write an original definition for *Archaea* and *Bacteria*.

Understanding Key Ideas

2. Biological classification systems change **G.1.3.3 CS**
   a. as more kinds of organisms are discovered.
   b. every 100 years.
   c. when scientists disagree.
   d. only once.

3. Describe one characteristic of Eukarya and one characteristic of each kingdom in Eukarya.

Math Skills

4. If a certain bacterium divides every 30 min, when will there be more than 1,000 bacteria?

Critical Thinking

5. **Applying Concepts** To get nutrients, the Venus' flytrap uses photosynthesis and traps and digests insects. Its cells have cell walls. Into which kingdom would you place this organism? What makes this organism unusual in this kingdom?

FCAT Preparation

6. "Black smokers" are formations on the sea floor where very hot water gushes out. Scientists have discovered many new kinds of organisms around black smokers. Why are scientists using a classification system to group these organisms? **G.1.3.3 CS**

   A. to help us understand the relationships between organisms
   B. to help us collect organisms more easily
   C. to help us study what organisms eat
   D. to help us predict where organisms live

Skills Practice Lab

OBJECTIVES

Classify organisms.

Name organisms.

G.1.3.3 CS understands that the classification of living things is based on a given set of criteria and is a tool for understanding biodiversity and interrelationships.

Shape Island

You are a biologist exploring uncharted parts of the world to look for new animal species. You sailed for days across the ocean and finally found Shape Island hundreds of miles south of Hawaii. Shape Island has some very unusual organisms. The shape of each organism is a variation of a geometric shape. You have spent more than a year collecting and classifying specimens. You have been able to assign a two-part scientific name to most of the species that you have collected. Now, you must assign a two-part scientific name to each of the last 12 specimens collected before you begin your journey home.

Procedure

1 Draw each of the organisms pictured on the facing page. Beside each organism, draw a line for its name, as shown on the top left of the following page. The first organism pictured has already been named, but you must name the remaining 12. Use the glossary of Greek and Latin prefixes, suffixes, and root words in the table to help you name the organisms.

Greek and Latin roots, prefixes, and suffixes	Meaning
ankylos	angle
antennae	external sense organs
bi-	two
cyclo-	circular
macro-	large
micro-	small
mono-	one
peri-	around
-plast	body
-pod	foot
quad-	four
stoma	mouth
tri-	three
uro-	tail

Analyze Results

1 **Analyzing Results** If you gave species 1 a common name, such as *round-face-no-nose,* would other scientists know to which of the newly discovered organisms you were referring? Explain. How many other organisms have a round face and no nose? How does this information help you understand how these organisms might be related?

2 **Organizing Data** Describe two characteristics that all of your newly discovered specimens share.

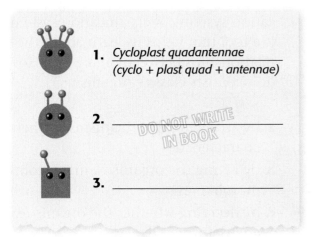

1. *Cycloplast quadantennae*
   (cyclo + plast quad + antennae)

2. _____
   DO NOT WRITE IN BOOK

3. _____

Draw Conclusions

3 **Applying Conclusions** One more organism exists on Shape Island, but you have not been able to capture it. However, your supplies are running out, and you must start sailing for home. You have had a good look at the unusual animal and can draw it in detail. Draw an animal that differs from all of the others, and give it a two-part scientific name.

Applying Your Data

Look up the scientific names *Mertensia virginica* and *Porcellio scaber*. Answer the following questions as they apply to each organism: Is the organism a plant or an animal? How many common names does the organism have? How many scientific names does it have?

Think of the name of your favorite fruit or vegetable. Find out if the fruit or vegetable has other common names, and find out its two-part scientific name.

Chapter Review

USING KEY TERMS

Use a term from the chapter to complete each sentence below.

1. Prokaryotes that live in extreme environments are in the domain ___.

2. Complex multicellular organisms that can usually move around and respond to their environment are in the kingdom ___.

3. A system of ___ can help scientists group animals into categories.

4. Prokaryotes that are not archaea are in the domain ___.

UNDERSTANDING KEY IDEAS

Multiple Choice

5. On an expedition in the Pacific ocean, you discovered three new prokaryotic organisms. You temporarily name the two that you found on the sea floor in extreme environments *Deep A* and *Deep B*. You call the third prokaryote, which you found in the surface waters, *Shallow A*. Which of the following statements about these organisms is most likely to be true? G.1.3.3 CS *FCAT*

   a. Deep A and Deep B are more closely related to each other than they are to Shallow A.

   b. Deep A is more closely related to Shallow A than to Deep B.

   c. Deep B is more closely related to Shallow A than to Deep A.

   d. The three organisms are equally related to each other.

6. Scientists are always improving classification systems. A classification system is a tool that helps us learn about the relationships between organisms. How do scientists classify organisms?

   G.1.3.3 CS *FCAT*

   a. by arranging the organisms by their characteristics

   b. by giving the organisms many common names

   c. by deciding whether the organisms are useful

   d. by using only existing categories of classification

7. When the eight levels of classification are listed from broadest to narrowest, which level is fifth in the list?

   a. class

   b. order

   c. genus

   d. family

8. The scientific name for the European white waterlily is *Nymphaea alba*. To which genus does this plant belong?

   a. *Nymphaea*

   b. *alba*

   c. water lily

   d. alba lily

9. *Animalia, Protista, Fungi,* and *Plantae* are the

   a. scientific names of different organisms.

   b. names of kingdoms.

   c. levels of classification.

   d. scientists who organized taxonomy.

Short Answer

10 Why is the use of scientific names important in biology?

11 What kind of evidence is used by modern taxonomists to classify organisms based on evolutionary relationships? G.1.3.3 CS

12 Is a bacterium a type of eukaryote? Explain your answer.

13 Scientists used to classify organisms as either plants or animals. Why doesn't that classification system work?

CRITICAL THINKING

Extended Response

14 Analyzing Methods Explain how the levels of classification depend on the similarities and differences between organisms. G.1.3.3 CS

15 Making Inferences Explain why two species that belong to the same genus, such as white oak (*Quercus alba*) and cork oak (*Quercus suber*), also belong to the same family. G.1.3.3 CS

16 Identifying Relationships What characteristic do the members of the four kingdoms in the domain Eukarya have in common? G.1.3.3 CS

Concept Mapping

17 Use the following terms to create a concept map: *kingdom, fern, lizard, Animalia, Fungi, algae, Protista, Plantae,* and *mushroom*.

INTERPRETING GRAPHICS

Use the branching diagram of selected primates below to answer the questions that follow.

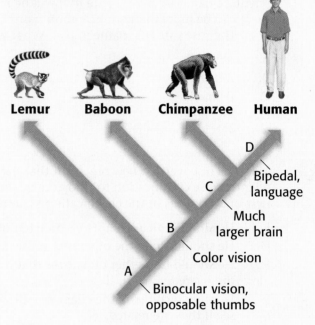

18 Which primate is the closest relative to the common ancestor of all primates?

19 Which primate shares the most traits with humans?

20 Do both lemurs and humans have the characteristics listed at point D? Explain your answer.

21 Name a characteristic that baboons have but that lemurs do not have. Explain your answer.

For the following questions, write your answers on a separate sheet of paper.

1 Ryan is looking for a rose for his grandmother at the local nursery. He knows that using the scientific name for her favorite rose will be more helpful than the common name because there can be more than one common name. The genus name of the rose he is looking for is *Rosa*. The rose's specific name is *alba*. What will it say on the tag identifying the plant?

A. *alba rosa*

B. *Alba rosa*

C. *Rosa alba*

D. *rosa alba*

2 Matt has discovered a new organism that has never been described before. He knows that scientists use classification to study organisms. What should he do to find out where this new organism fits in the classification system used today?

F. He should call a scientist to ask what to name the new organism.

G. He should study the organism on his own so that he can learn more about it.

H. He should find other organisms that live in the same area as the organism he discovered.

I. He should compare the characteristics between known organisms and the new one to see if they are related.

3 Classifying organisms can help us study the relationships between living things. Drea is comparing the characteristics of three organisms with each other. Two organisms have many of the same characteristics. However, these two organisms have very few characteristics in common with the third organism. What can Drea infer about the relatedness between these three organisms?

A. that the first two organisms were unrelated

B. that it depended on the characteristics the first two organisms shared

C. that the first two organisms were equally related to the third organism

D. that the first two organisms were more closely related to each other than to the third organism

4 Maria is collecting different types of plants and insects for her aquarium. She just found a strange organism that she has never seen before. She knows that it has many cells, but it cannot move. She has never seen it eat food, but she does not think that it can perform photosynthesis either. What kingdom do you think the mystery organism belongs to?

F. Kingdom Animalia

G. Kingdom Fungi

H. Kingdom Plantae

I. Kingdom Protista

5 In the woods, Chen saw an interesting animal that was brown, with white on its belly. It also had a long furry tail with a black tip. Chen used this dichotomous key to figure out what he saw.

DICHOTOMOUS KEY TO 10 COMMON MAMMALS IN THE EASTERN UNITED STATES

1. a. This mammal flies. Its "hand" forms a wing. **b.** This mammal does not fly. Its "hand" does not form a wing.	**Little Brown Bat** **Go to step 2.**
2. a. This mammal has no hair on its tail. **b.** This mammal has hair on its tail.	**Go to step 3.** **Go to step 4.**
3. a. This mammal has a short, naked tail. **b.** This mammal has a long, naked tail.	**Eastern Mole** **Go to step 5.**
4. a. This mammal has a black mask across its face. **b.** This mammal does not have a black mask across its face.	**Raccoon** **Go to step 6.**
5. a. This mammal has a tail that is flat and paddle shaped. **b.** This mammal has a tail that is not flat or paddle shaped.	**Beaver** **Opossum**
6. a. This mammal is brown and has a white underbelly. **b.** This mammal is not brown and does not have a white underbelly.	**Go to step 7.** **Striped Skunk**
7. a. This mammal has a long, furry tail that is black on the tip. **b.** This mammal has a long tail that has little fur.	**Longtail Weasel** **White-Footed Mouse**

Which of the following animals do you think Chen saw?

A. a striped skunk

B. a little brown bat

C. a long-tail weasel

D. a white-footed mouse

6 Scientists use diagrams of how organisms are classified to study the similarities and differences between organisms. One way is with a branching diagram, such as the one below.

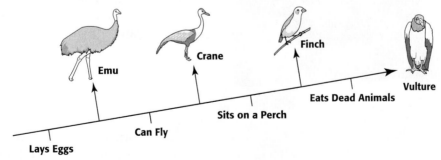

Which bird can fly but does not perch on trees or roost?

F. the crane

G. the emu

H. the finch

I. the vulture

Science in Action

A Place to Visit

The Monkey Jungle

Have you ever heard of a monkey that dives in the water for its food? The Java monkey eats crabs and shellfish as well as fruits. You won't want to miss the Java monkeys feeding or the orangutans playing at the Monkey Jungle, a wilderness park in Miami, Florida. The Monkey Jungle is home to over 30 species of primates. In this park, learning about primates can be more fun than a barrel of monkeys! Some of the park's louder residents include the red howler monkeys, such as the one in this photo. The red howler monkey can be heard nearly 8.5 km away. You can also learn how the park helps protect endangered primates. Come and see the experts monkey around at the Monkey Jungle.

Math ACTIVITY

Crab-eating macaques also live at the Monkey Jungle. The average mass of male crab-eating macaques is 6.45 kg. The average mass of female crab-eating macaques is 4 kg. How much smaller than the average male is the average female? Express your answer as a percentage.

Scientific Discoveries

A New Insect Order

In 2001, Oliver Zompro was studying an insect fossilized in amber. The insect resembled a grasshopper and a walking stick. But it was unique and could not be classified into either the group that includes grasshoppers or the group that includes walking sticks. Zompro wondered if he was seeing a new type of insect or an insect thought to be extinct. The insect was less than 4 cm long. Because of its spiny appearance, the insect earned the nickname "gladiator." The gladiator bug is so unusual that it cannot be classified into any of the 30 existing orders of insects. Instead, the gladiator bug constitutes its own new order, which has been named *Mantophasmatodea*.

Language Arts ACTIVITY

WRITING SKILL Give the gladiator bug a new nickname. Write a short essay describing why you chose that particular name for the insect.

Michael Fay

Crossing Africa Finding and classifying wild animals takes a great deal of perseverance. Just ask Michael Fay, who spent 15 months crossing 2,000 miles of uninhabited rain forest in the Congo River Basin of West Africa. He used video, photography, and old-fashioned note taking to record the types of animals and vegetation that he encountered along the way.

To find and classify wild animals, Fay often had to think like an animal. When coming across a group of monkeys swinging high above him in the emerald green canopy, Fay would greet the monkeys with his imitation of the crowned eagle's high-pitched, whistling cry. When the monkeys responded with their own distinctive call, Fay could identify exactly what species they were and would jot it down in one of his 87 waterproof notebooks. Fay also learned other tricks, such as staying downwind of an elephant to get as close to the elephant as possible. He could then identify its size, its age, and the length of its tusks.

Social Studies ACTIVITY

WRITING SKILL Many organizations around the world are committed to helping preserve biodiversity. Conduct some Internet and library research to find out about an organization that works to keep species safe from extinction. Create a poster that describes the organization and some of the species that the organization protects.

To learn more about these Science in Action topics, visit go.hrw.com and type in the keyword HT6FCSFF.

Current Science

Check out Current Science® articles related to this chapter by visiting go.hrw.com. Just type in the keyword HL5CS09.

15

Introduction to Plants

The Big Idea Plants can be classified by their structures.

About the

In Costa Rica's Monteverde Cloud Forest Preserve, a green coil begins to unfold. It is hidden from all but the most careful observer. The coil looks alien, but it is very much of this Earth. The coil is the leaf of a fern, a plant that grows in moist areas. Soon, the coil will unfold into a lacy, delicate frond.

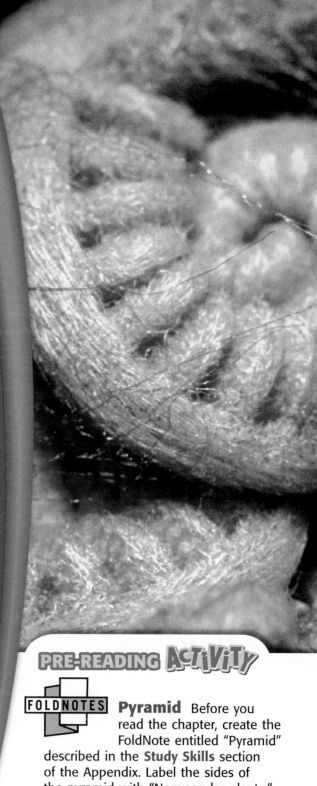

PRE-READING ACTIVITY

FOLDNOTES **Pyramid** Before you read the chapter, create the FoldNote entitled "Pyramid" described in the **Study Skills** section of the Appendix. Label the sides of the pyramid with "Nonvascular plants," "Seedless vascular plants," and "Seed plants." As you read the chapter, define each kind of plant, and write characteristics of each kind of plant on the appropriate pyramid side.

Observing Plant Growth

When planting a garden, you bury seeds and water them. What happens to the seeds below the soil? How do seeds grow into plants?

Procedure

1. Fill a clear **2 L soda bottle** to within 8 cm of the top with **moist potting soil.** Your teacher will have already cut off the neck of the bottle.

2. Press **three or four bean seeds** into the soil and against the wall of the bottle. Add enough additional potting soil to increase the depth by 5 cm.

3. Cover the sides of the bottle with **aluminum foil** to keep out light. Leave the top of the bottle uncovered.

4. Water the seeds with about **60 mL of water,** or water them until the soil is moist. Add more water when the soil dries out.

5. Place the bottle in an area that receives sunshine. Check on your seeds each day, and record your observations.

Analysis

1. How many seeds grew?

2. How long did the seeds take to start growing?

3. From where did the seeds most likely get the energy to grow?

What Is a Plant?

Imagine spending a day without plants. What would you eat? It would be impossible to make chocolate chip cookies and many other foods.

Without plants, you couldn't eat much. Almost all food is made from plants or from animals that eat plants. Life would be very different without plants!

Plant Characteristics

Plants come in many shapes and sizes. So, what do cactuses, water lilies, ferns, and all other plants have in common? One plant may seem very different from another. But most plants share certain characteristics.

Photosynthesis

Take a look at **Figure 1.** Do you know why this plant is green? Plant cells contain chlorophyll (KLAWR uh FIL). *Chlorophyll* is a green pigment that captures energy from sunlight. Chlorophyll is found in chloroplasts (KLAWR uh PLASTS). Chloroplasts are organelles found in many plant cells and in some protists. Plants use energy from sunlight to make food from carbon dioxide and water. This process is called *photosynthesis* (FOHT oh SIN thuh sis). Because plants make their own food, they are called *producers.*

Cuticles

Most plants live on dry land and need sunlight to live. But why don't plants dry out? Plants don't dry out because they are protected by a cuticle. A *cuticle* is a waxy layer that coats most of the surfaces of plants that are exposed to air.

Figure 1 *Chlorophyll makes the leaves of this plant green. Chlorophyll helps plants make their own food by capturing energy from sunlight.*

Figure 2 Some Structures of a Photosynthetic Plant Cell

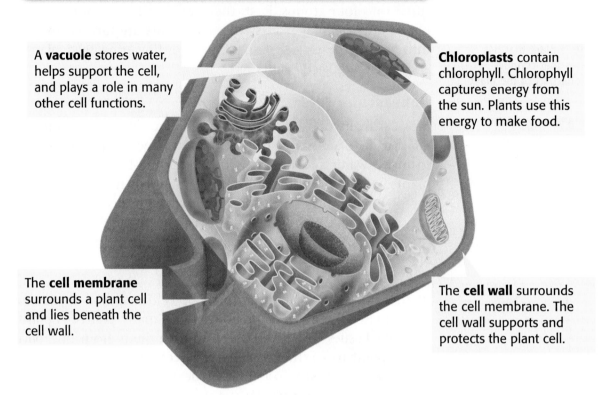

A **vacuole** stores water, helps support the cell, and plays a role in many other cell functions.

Chloroplasts contain chlorophyll. Chlorophyll captures energy from the sun. Plants use this energy to make food.

The **cell membrane** surrounds a plant cell and lies beneath the cell wall.

The **cell wall** surrounds the cell membrane. The cell wall supports and protects the plant cell.

Cell Walls

How do plants stay upright? Unlike animals, plants do not have skeletons. Instead, plant cells are surrounded by a rigid cell wall. The cell wall lies outside the cell membrane, as shown in **Figure 2.** Carbohydrates and proteins in the cell wall form a hard material. Cell walls support and protect the plant cell. Some plant cells also have a secondary cell wall that forms after the cell is mature. When this wall has formed, a plant cell cannot grow larger.

Reproduction

Plants have two stages in their life cycle—the sporophyte (SPAWR uh FIET) stage and the gametophyte (guh MEET uh FIET) stage. In the sporophyte stage, plants make spores. In a suitable environment, such as damp soil, the spores of some plants grow. These new plants are called *gametophytes*.

During the gametophyte stage, female gametophytes produce eggs. Male gametophytes produce sperm. Eggs and sperm are sex cells. For a new plant to be produced, a sperm must fertilize an egg. This type of reproduction is called *sexual reproduction* because two parent cells unite to produce offspring. The fertilized egg will eventually grow into a sporophyte, and the cycle will begin again.

Benchmark Check How do plants reproduce sexually? F.2.3.1 CS

CONNECTION TO Social Studies

Countries and Crops
Without plants, most life on land couldn't survive. But plants are important for more than the survival of living things. Many countries rely on plants for income. Identify five major food crops. Then, find out which countries are the main producers of these crops and how much the countries produce each year. Make a table to show your findings.

F.2.3.1 CS (partial) knows the patterns and advantages of sexual and asexual reproduction in plants and animals.

Plant Classification

nonvascular plant a plant that lacks specialized conducting tissues and true roots, stems, and leaves

vascular plant a plant that has specialized tissues that conduct materials from one part of the plant to another

gymnosperm a woody, vascular seed plant whose seeds are not enclosed by an ovary or fruit

angiosperm a flowering plant that produces seeds within a fruit

tropism growth of all or part of an organism in response to an external stimulus, such as light *FCAT VOCAB*

Although all plants share basic characteristics, they can be classified into four groups. First, they are classified as nonvascular plants and vascular plants. Vascular plants are further divided into three groups—seedless plants, nonflowering seed plants, and flowering seed plants.

Nonvascular Plants

Mosses, liverworts, and hornworts are nonvascular plants. A **nonvascular plant** is a plant that doesn't have specialized tissues to move water and nutrients through the plant. Nonvascular plants depend on diffusion to move materials from one part of the plant to another. Diffusion is possible because nonvascular plants are small. If nonvascular plants were large, the cells of the plants would not get enough water and nutrients.

Vascular Plants

In the same way that the human body has special tissues to move materials through the body, so do many plants. A plant that has tissues to deliver water and nutrients from one part of the plant to another is called a **vascular plant.** Its tissues are called *vascular tissues*. Vascular tissues can move water to any part of a plant. So, vascular plants can be almost any size.

Vascular plants are divided into three groups—seedless plants and two types of seed plants. Seedless vascular plants include ferns, horsetails, and club mosses. Nonflowering seed plants are called **gymnosperms** (JIM noh SPUHRMZ). Flowering seed plants are called **angiosperms** (AN jee oh SPUHRMZ). The four main groups of plants are shown in **Figure 3.**

F.1.3.7 CS (partial) knows that behavior is a response to the environment and influences growth, development, maintenance, and reproduction.

G.1.3.3 CS understands that the classification of living things is based on a given set of criteria and is a tool for understanding biodiversity and interrelationships.

Benchmark Check Describe how plants are classified. **G.1.3.3 CS**

Figure 3 The Main Groups of Plants

Nonvascular Plants	Vascular Plants		
Mosses, liverworts, and hornworts	Seedless plants	Seed plants	
	Ferns, horsetails, and club mosses	Nonflowering	Flowering
		Gymnosperms	Angiosperms

How Plants Respond to Stimuli

Plants respond to stimuli such as touch, light, and gravity. Plants sense stimuli by using chemicals inside their cells. Stimuli change the chemistry of cells. As a result, those cells grow differently or change the chemistry of other cells.

Plant growth in response to an external stimulus is called a **tropism** (TROH PIZ uhm). There are several specific kinds of tropisms. All are responses to different kinds of stimuli. For example, the vine in **Figure 4** has tendrils that respond to touch. This kind of tropism is called *thigmotropism*. When the tendrils sense pressure on one side, they grow toward the pressure. As a result, the tendrils wrap around the supports. Two other kinds of tropisms are *phototropism* and *gravitropism*. Phototropism is a change in the growth of a plant in response to the direction of light. Gravitropism is a change in a plant's direction of growth due to the effect of gravity.

Figure 4 *This vine has tendrils that are sensitive to touch. Thigmotropism is a plant's response to touch.*

SECTION Review

Summary

- All plants make their own food and have cuticles, cells walls, and a two-stage life cycle.

- Gametophytes produce eggs and sperm. When a sperm fertilizes an egg, the egg can grow into a sporophyte. F.2.3.1 CS

- Plants are classified into two groups: nonvascular plants and vascular plants. G.1.3.3 CS

- Thigmotropism is a plant's response to touch. Phototropism is a plant's response to light. F.1.3.7 CS

Using Key Terms

1. Write an original definition for *nonvascular plant, vascular plant,* and *tropism*. FCAT VOCAB

Understanding Key Ideas

2. What are four characteristics that all plants share?

3. How are vascular plants classified? G.1.3.3 CS

4. Describe the pattern of sexual reproduction in plants. F.2.3.1 CS

Critical Thinking

5. **Analyzing Ideas** What are the benefits for a plant's shoots to have phototropism? F.1.3.7 CS

6. **Applying Concepts** Imagine an environment that is very dry and receives a lot of sunlight. Water is found deep below the soil. Which of the four groups of plants could survive in this environment? Explain your answer.

FCAT Preparation

7. A vascular plant has tissues that deliver water and nutrients from one part of the plant to another. Which of the following is a characteristic of vascular plants? G.1.3.3 CS

   A. They can be almost any size.

   B. They depend on diffusion to move materials.

   C. They do not have flowers.

   D. Mosses are vascular plants.

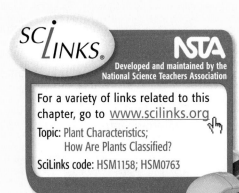

Developed and maintained by the National Science Teachers Association

For a variety of links related to this chapter, go to www.scilinks.org

Topic: Plant Characteristics; How Are Plants Classified?

SciLinks code: HSM1158; HSM0763

Seedless Plants

When you think of plants, you probably think of plants that make seeds, such as trees and flowers. But two groups of plants don't make seeds.

One group of seedless plants is made up of nonvascular plants, such as mosses, liverworts, and hornworts. The other group is made up of seedless vascular plants, such as ferns, horsetails, and club mosses.

Nonvascular Plants

Mosses, liverworts, and hornworts are small. They grow on soil, the bark of trees, and rocks. These plants don't have vascular tissue. So, nonvascular plants usually live in places that are damp. Each cell of a nonvascular plant must get water from the environment or from a nearby cell.

Mosses, liverworts, and hornworts don't have true stems, roots, or leaves. However, they do have structures that carry out the activities of stems, roots, and leaves.

Mosses

Mosses often live together in large groups. They cover soil or rocks in the form of a mat made up of tiny green plants. Mosses have leafy stalks and rhizoids (RIE ZOYDZ). A **rhizoid** is a rootlike structure that holds nonvascular plants in place. Rhizoids help the plants get water and nutrients. As **Figure 1** shows, mosses have two stages in their life cycle.

Figure 1 **Moss Life Cycle**

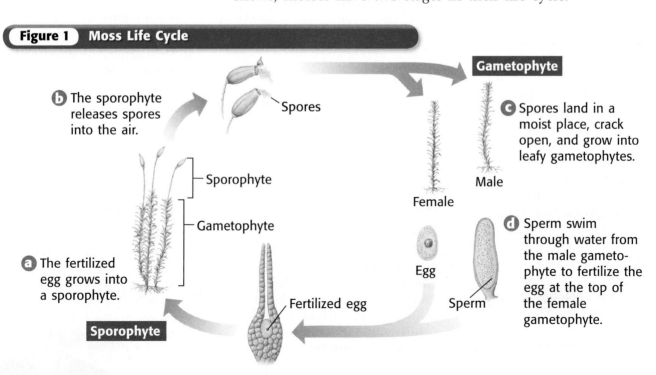

b The sporophyte releases spores into the air.

Spores

Gametophyte

c Spores land in a moist place, crack open, and grow into leafy gametophytes.

Sporophyte

Male

Female

Gametophyte

d Sperm swim through water from the male gametophyte to fertilize the egg at the top of the female gametophyte.

Egg

a The fertilized egg grows into a sporophyte.

Sperm

Fertilized egg

Sporophyte

Liverworts and Hornworts

Like mosses, liverworts and hornworts are small, nonvascular plants that usually live in damp places. The life cycles of liverworts and hornworts are similar to the life cycle of mosses. The gametophytes of liverworts can be leafy and mosslike or broad and flattened. Hornworts also have broad, flattened gametophytes. Both liverworts and hornworts have rhizoids.

The Importance of Nonvascular Plants

Nonvascular plants play an important role in the environment. They are usually the first plants to live in a new environment, such as newly exposed rock. When these nonvascular plants die, they form a thin layer of soil. New plants can grow in this soil. More nonvascular plants may grow and hold the soil in place. This reduces soil erosion. Some animals eat nonvascular plants. Other animals use these plants for nesting material.

Peat mosses are important to humans. Peat mosses grow in bogs and other wet places. In some places, dead peat mosses have built up over time. This peat can be dried and burned as a fuel. Peat mosses are also used in potting soil.

Benchmark Check How do nonvascular plants prevent soil erosion? **D.1.3.4 AA**

Seedless Vascular Plants

Ancient ferns, horsetails, and club mosses grew very tall. Club mosses grew to 40 m tall in ancient forests. Horsetails once grew to 18 m tall. Some ferns grew to 8 m tall. Today, ferns, horsetails, and club mosses are usually much smaller. But because they have vascular tissue, they are often larger than nonvascular plants. **Figure 2** shows club mosses and horsetails.

rhizoid a rootlike structure in nonvascular plants that holds the plants in place and helps plants get water and nutrients

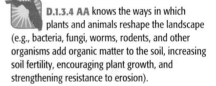
D.1.3.4 AA knows the ways in which plants and animals reshape the landscape (e.g., bacteria, fungi, worms, rodents, and other organisms add organic matter to the soil, increasing soil fertility, encouraging plant growth, and strengthening resistance to erosion).

F.2.3.1 CS (partial) knows the patterns and advantages of sexual and asexual reproduction in plants and animals.

Figure 2 *Seedless vascular plants include club mosses (left) and horsetails (right).*

Ferns

Ferns grow in many places, from the cold Arctic to warm, humid tropical forests. Many ferns are small plants. But some tropical tree ferns grow as tall as 24 m. Most ferns have a rhizome (RIE zohm). A **rhizome** is an underground stem from which new leaves and roots grow. At first, fern leaves, or fronds, are tightly coiled. These fronds look like the end of a violin, or fiddle. So, they are called *fiddleheads*. You are probably most familiar with the leafy fern sporophyte. The fern gametophyte is a tiny plant about half the size of one of your fingernails. The fern gametophyte is green and flat. It is usually shaped like a tiny heart. The life cycle of ferns is shown in **Figure 3.**

rhizome a horizontal, underground stem that produces new leaves, shoots, and roots

Horsetails and Club Mosses

Modern horsetails can be as tall as 8 m. But many horsetails are smaller. They usually grow in wet, marshy places. Their stems are hollow and contain silica. The silica gives horsetails a gritty texture. In fact, early American pioneers referred to horsetails as *scouring rushes*. They used horsetails to scrub pots and pans. Horsetails and ferns have similar life cycles.

Club mosses are often about 20 cm tall. They grow in woodlands. Club mosses are not actually mosses. Unlike mosses, club mosses have vascular tissue. The life cycle of club mosses is similar to the life cycle of ferns.

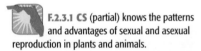 **F.2.3.1 CS** (partial) knows the patterns and advantages of sexual and asexual reproduction in plants and animals.

Figure 3   Fern Life Cycle

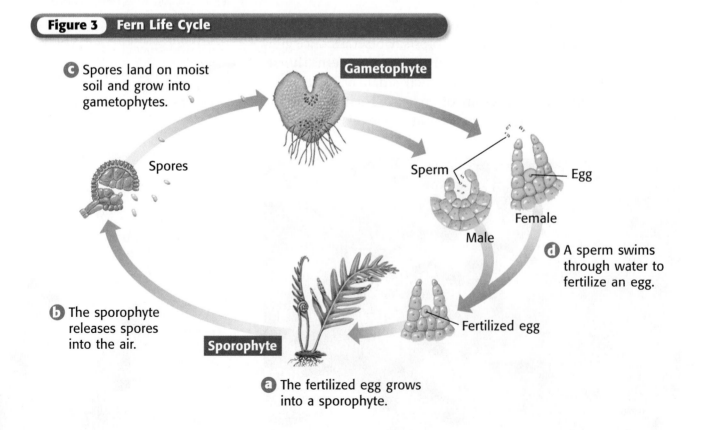

c Spores land on moist soil and grow into gametophytes.

Gametophyte

Spores

Sperm

Egg

Female

Male

d A sperm swims through water to fertilize an egg.

b The sporophyte releases spores into the air.

Sporophyte

Fertilized egg

a The fertilized egg grows into a sporophyte.

The Importance of Seedless Vascular Plants

Seedless vascular plants play important roles in the environment. Ferns, horsetails, and club mosses help form soil. They also help prevent soil erosion. In rocky areas, ferns can play a role in the formation of communities. After lichens and mosses create a layer of soil, ferns may take over. Ferns add to soil depth, which allows other plants to grow.

Ferns and some club mosses are popular houseplants. The fiddleheads of some ferns can be cooked and eaten. The shoots and roots of young horsetails are also edible. Horsetails are used in some dietary supplements, shampoos, and skin-care products.

Seedless vascular plants that lived and died about 300 million years ago are among the most important to humans. The remains of these ancient ferns, horsetails, and club mosses formed coal. Coal is a fossil fuel that humans mine from Earth's crust. Humans rely on coal for energy.

Benchmark Check How are seedless vascular plants important to the environment? D.1.3.4 AA

D.1.3.4 AA knows the ways in which plants and animals reshape the landscape (e.g., bacteria, fungi, worms, rodents, and other organisms add organic matter to the soil, increasing soil fertility, encouraging plant growth, and strengthening resistance to erosion).

SECTION Review

Summary

- Seedless nonvascular plants include mosses, liverworts, and hornworts.
- Seedless vascular plants include ferns, horsetails, and club mosses.
- Seedless nonvascular plants prevent erosion by holding soil in place. **D.1.3.4 AA**
- Seedless vascular plants help form soil and prevent erosion. They also form coal, a fossil fuel, over a long period of time. **D.1.3.4 AA**

Understanding Key Ideas

1. Describe two ways in which seedless nonvascular plants are important to the environment. **D.1.3.4 AA**

2. Describe six kinds of seedless plants.

3. What is the relationship between coal and seedless vascular plants? **D.1.3.4 AA**

Critical Thinking

4. **Making Inferences** Imagine a very damp area. Mosses cover the rocks and trees in this area. Liverworts and hornworts are also very abundant. What might happen if the area dries out? Explain your answer.

5. **Applying Concepts** Modern ferns, horsetails, and club mosses are smaller than they were millions of years ago. Why might these plants be smaller?

FCAT Preparation

6. Seedless plants play an important role in the environment. Which of the following statements best describes the role of seedless plants? **D.1.3.4 AA**

A. They decompose dead organisms.

B. They provide fruit for other organisms.

C. They protect young plants.

D. They help form soil.

SCILINKS. **NSTA** Developed and maintained by the National Science Teachers Association

For a variety of links related to this chapter, go to www.scilinks.org

Topic: Seedless Plants
SciLinks code: HSM1368

Seed Plants

Think about the seed plants that you use during the day. You likely use dozens of seed plants, from the food you eat to the paper you write on.

The two groups of vascular plants that produce seeds are gymnosperms and angiosperms. Gymnosperms are trees and shrubs that do not have flowers or fruit. Angiosperms have flowers and seeds that are protected by fruit.

Characteristics of Seed Plants

Like seedless plants, seed plants have a life cycle that alternates between two stages. But seed plants, such as the plant in **Figure 1,** differ from seedless plants in three ways:

- Seed plants produce seeds. Seeds nourish and protect young sporophytes.
- Unlike the gametophytes of seedless plants, the gametophytes of seed plants do not live independently of the sporophyte. The gametophytes of seed plants are tiny. They form within the reproductive structures of the sporophyte.
- The sperm of seedless plants need water to swim to the eggs of female gametophytes. The sperm of seed plants do not need water to reach an egg. Sperm form inside tiny structures called **pollen.** Pollen can be transported by wind or by animals.

These three characteristics allow seed plants to live just about anywhere. For this reason, seed plants are the most common plants on Earth today.

Benchmark Check Describe three ways in which seed plants differ from seedless plants. **F.2.3.1 CS**

READING WARM-UP

Objectives

- Describe how the pattern of sexual reproduction in seed plants differs from the pattern of sexual reproduction in seedless plants. **F.2.3.1 CS**
- Describe the structure and function of seeds. **F.1.3.1 AA**
- Identify two advantages of seed plants. **F.2.3.1 CS**
- Describe the life cycle of gymnosperms. **F.2.3.1 CS**
- Describe reproduction in angiosperms. **F.2.3.1 CS**

Terms to Learn

pollen
pollination

READING STRATEGY

Reading Organizer As you read this section, make a table comparing angiosperms and gymnosperms.

pollen the tiny granules that contain the male gametophyte of seed plants

Figure 1 *Dandelion fruits, which each contain a seed, are spread by wind.*

F.2.3.1 CS (partial) knows the patterns and advantages of sexual and asexual reproduction in plants and animals.

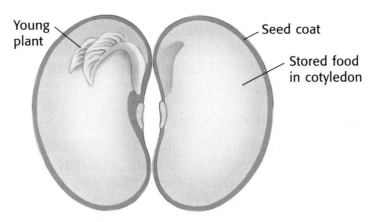

Young plant

Seed coat

Stored food in cotyledon

Figure 2 *A seed contains stored food and a young plant, or sporophyte. A seed is surrounded and protected by a seed coat.*

The Structure of Seeds

A seed forms after fertilization, when sperm and eggs are joined. A seed is made up of three parts, as shown in **Figure 2.** The first part is a young plant, or the sporophyte. The second part is stored food. It is often found in the cotyledons (KAHT uh LEED uhnz), or the seed leaves of the young plant. Finally, a seed coat surrounds and protects the young plant.

Benchmark Check What are the three parts of a seed? F.1.3.1 AA

Advantages of Seed Plants

Seed plants have some advantages over seedless plants. For example, when a seed begins to grow, the young plant uses the food stored in the seed. The spores of seedless plants don't have stored food to help a new plant grow. Another advantage of seed plants is that seeds can be spread by animals. The spores of seedless plants are usually spread by wind. Animals spread seeds more efficiently than the wind spreads spores.

CONNECTION TO Environmental Science

WRITING SKILL **Animals That Help Plants** Animals need plants in order to live, but some plants benefit from animals, too. These plants produce seeds with tough seed coats. An animal's digestive system can wear down these seed coats and speed the growth of a seed. Identify a plant that animals help in this way. Then, find out how it is possible for seeds to grow after animals eat the plant identified. Write your findings in your **science journal.**

Benchmark Activity

Dissecting Seeds

1. Soak a **lima bean seed** in **water** overnight. Draw the seed before placing it in the water.

2. Remove the seed from the water. Draw what you see.

3. The seed will likely look wrinkly. The wrinkly, outer layer of the seed is the seed coat. Use a **toothpick** to gently remove the seed coat from the lima bean seed.

4. Gently separate the halves of the lima bean seed. Draw what you see.

5. What did you see after you split the lima bean seed in half?

6. What part of the seed do you think provides the lima bean plant with the energy to grow?

F.1.3.1 AA

F.1.3.1 AA understands that living things are composed of major systems that function in reproduction, growth, maintenance, and regulation.

Gymnosperms

Seed plants that do not have flowers or fruit are called *gymnosperms*. Gymnosperm seeds are usually protected by a cone. The four groups of gymnosperms are conifers, ginkgoes, cycads, and gnetophytes (NEE toh FIETS). You can see some gymnosperms in **Figure 3.**

The Importance of Gymnosperms

Conifers are the most economically important gymnosperms. People use conifer wood for building materials and paper products. Pine trees produce a sticky fluid called *resin*. Resin is used to make soap, turpentine, paint, and ink. Some conifers produce an important anticancer drug. Some gnetophytes produce anti-allergy drugs. Conifers, cycads, and ginkgoes are popular in gardens and parks.

Figure 3 Examples of Gymnosperms

Conifers Conifers, such as this ponderosa pine, make up the largest group of gymnosperms. There are about 550 species of conifers. Most conifers are evergreens that keep their needle-shaped leaves all year. Conifer seeds develop in cones.

Ginkgoes Today, the only living species of ginkgoes is the ginkgo tree. Ginkgo seeds are not produced in cones. The seeds have fleshy seed coats and are attached directly to the branches of the tree.

Cycads The cycads were more common millions of years ago. Today, there are only about 140 species of cycads. These plants grow in the Tropics. Like conifer seeds, cycad seeds develop in cones.

Gnetophytes About 70 species of gnetophytes, such as this joint fir, exist today. Many gnetophytes are shrubs that grow in dry areas. The seeds of most gnetophytes develop in cones.

Figure 4 The Life Cycle of a Pine Tree

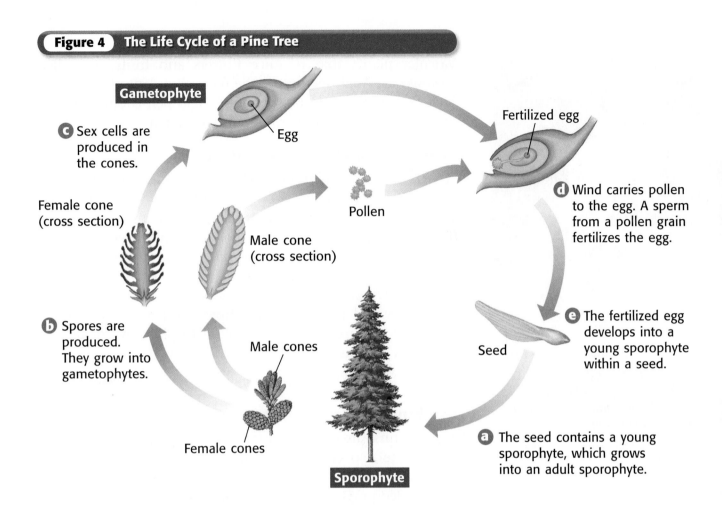

Gametophyte

c Sex cells are produced in the cones.

Egg

Fertilized egg

d Wind carries pollen to the egg. A sperm from a pollen grain fertilizes the egg.

Female cone (cross section)

Pollen

Male cone (cross section)

b Spores are produced. They grow into gametophytes.

Male cones

Seed

e The fertilized egg develops into a young sporophyte within a seed.

Female cones

Sporophyte

a The seed contains a young sporophyte, which grows into an adult sporophyte.

Life Cycle of Gymnosperms

The gymnosperms that are most familiar to you are probably the conifers. The word *conifer* comes from two words that mean "cone-bearing." Conifers have two kinds of cones—male cones and female cones. The spores of each kind of cone become tiny gametophytes.

The male gametophytes of gymnosperms are found in pollen. Pollen contain sperm. The female gametophytes produce eggs. Wind carries pollen from the male cones to the female cones. This transfer of pollen from the male cones to the female cones is called **pollination.** The female cones can be on the same plant or on another plant of the same species.

Sperm from pollen fertilize the eggs of a female cones. A fertilized egg develops into a young sporophyte within the female cone. The sporophyte is surrounded by a seed. Eventually, the seed is released. Some cones release seeds right away. Other cones release seeds under special circumstances, such as after forest fires. If conditions are right, the seed will grow. The life cycle of a pine tree is shown in **Figure 4.**

Benchmark Check Describe the life cycle of gymnosperms.

F.2.3.1 CS

pollination the transfer of pollen from the male reproductive structures to the female structures of seed plants

F.2.3.1 CS (partial) knows the patterns and advantages of sexual and asexual reproduction in plants and animals.

Angiosperms

Vascular plants that produce flowers and fruits are called *angiosperms*. Angiosperms are the most abundant plants today. There are at least 235,000 species of angiosperms. Angiosperms can be found in almost every land ecosystem.

Reproduction in Angiosperms

Flowers help angiosperms reproduce. Some angiosperms depend on the wind for pollination. But others have flowers that attract animals. As **Figure 5** shows, when animals visit different flowers, the animals may carry pollen from flower to flower.

Fruits surround and protect seeds. Some fruits and seeds have structures that help the wind carry them short or long distances. Other fruits attract animals that eat the fruits. The animals discard the seeds away from the plant. Some fruits, such as burrs, are carried from place to place by sticking to the fur of animals.

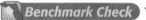 **Benchmark Check** Why do angiosperms have flowers? F.2.3.1 CS

Two Kinds of Angiosperms

Angiosperms are divided into two classes—monocots and dicots. The two classes differ in the number of cotyledons, or seed leaves, that their seeds have. Monocot seeds have one cotyledon. Grasses, orchids, onions, lilies, and palms are monocots. Dicot seeds have two cotyledons. Dicots include roses, cactuses, sunflowers, peanuts, and peas. Other differences between monocots and dicots are shown in **Figure 6.**

Figure 5 *This bee is on its way to another squash flower, where it will leave some of the pollen that it is carrying.*

F.2.3.1 CS (partial) knows the patterns and advantages of sexual and asexual reproduction in plants and animals.

Figure 6 **Two Classes of Angiosperms**

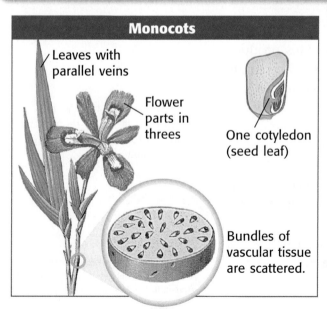

Monocots

Leaves with parallel veins

Flower parts in threes

One cotyledon (seed leaf)

Bundles of vascular tissue are scattered.

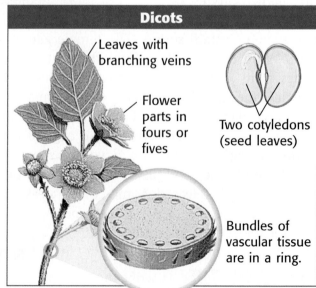

Dicots

Leaves with branching veins

Flower parts in fours or fives

Two cotyledons (seed leaves)

Bundles of vascular tissue are in a ring.

The Importance of Angiosperms

Flowering plants provide many land animals with the food that they need to survive. A field mouse that eats seeds and berries is using flowering plants directly as food. An owl that eats a field mouse is using flowering plants indirectly as food.

People use flowering plants in many ways. Major food crops, such as corn, wheat, and rice, are flowering plants. Some flowering plants, such as oak trees, are used for building materials. Flowering plants such as cotton and flax are used to make clothing and rope. Flowering plants are also used to make medicines, rubber, and perfume oils.

Reading Check How are flowering plants important to humans?

INTERNET ACTIVITY

Weird and Wonderful Plants What's your favorite plant? Tell your classmates all about it. Go to **go.hrw.com**, and type in the keyword **HL5PL1W.**

SECTION Review

Summary

- Seeds nourish the young sporophyte of seed plants. Gametophytes rely on the sporophyte and do not need water for fertilization. **F.2.3.1 CS**

- A seed has a sporophyte, cotyledons, and a seed coat. Seeds nourish a young plant. **F.1.3.1 AA**

- Two advantages of seed plants are that seeds have stored food and seeds can be spread by animals. **F.2.3.1 CS**

- In gymnosperms, sperm from the male cone fertilizes the eggs of the female cone. The egg develops within the female cone, which then releases seeds. **F.2.3.1 CS**

- Flowers, fruit, wind, and animals help angiosperms reproduce. **F.2.3.1 CS**

Using Key Terms

1. Write an original definition for *pollen* and *pollination*.

Understanding Key Ideas

2. Describe the structure of seeds. **F.1.3.1 AA**

3. Briefly describe the four groups of gymnosperms. Which group is the largest and most economically important?

4. Compare angiosperms and gymnosperms.

5. How are angiosperms important to organisms?

Critical Thinking

6. **Applying Concepts** An angiosperm lives in a dense rain forest, close to the ground. It receives little wind. Several herbivores live in this area of the rain forest. What are some ways that the plant can ensure that its seeds are carried throughout the forest? **F.2.3.1 CS**

7. **Making Inferences** In what ways are flowers and fruits adaptations that help angiosperms reproduce? **F.2.3.1 CS**

FCAT Preparation

8. Seed plants produce seeds. Seeds have three parts: a sporophyte, cotyledons, and a seed coat. Which of the following is an advantage of seed plants? **F.2.3.1 CS**

   A. Seed plants grow in few places.

   B. Seed plants can begin photosynthesis as soon as they begin to grow.

   C. Seed plants need water for fertilization.

   D. Young plants are nourished by food stored in the seed.

SCILINKS

NSTA

Developed and maintained by the National Science Teachers Association

For a variety of links related to this chapter, go to www.scilinks.org

Topic: Plants with Seeds
SciLinks code: HSM1168

Structures of Seed Plants

You have different body systems that carry out many functions. Plants also have systems—a root system, a shoot system, and a reproductive system.

A plant's root system and shoot system help perform life functions of the plant, such as maintenance and growth. These systems supply the plant with what it needs to survive.

The vascular tissues of the root and shoot systems are connected. There are two kinds of vascular tissue: xylem (ZIE luhm) and phloem (FLOH EM). **Xylem** is vascular tissue that transports water and minerals through the plant. Xylem moves materials from the roots to the shoots. **Phloem** is vascular tissue that transports food molecules to all parts of a plant. Xylem and phloem are found in all parts of vascular plants.

Roots

Root systems are made of roots. Most roots are underground, as shown in **Figure 1.** Root systems can be extensive. For example, a corn plant that is 2.5 m tall can have roots that grow 2.5 m deep and 1.2 m out and away from the stem!

Root Functions

Roots have three main functions:

- Roots supply a plant with water and dissolved minerals absorbed from the soil. The water and minerals are transported to the shoots in the xylem.

- Roots hold a plant securely in the soil.

- Roots store surplus food made during photosynthesis as sugar or starch. The food is produced in the leaves. Then, it is transported in the phloem to the roots.

Benchmark Check Describe three functions of roots. F.1.3.1 AA

READING WARM-UP

Objectives

- Describe the structure and functions of roots and stems. F.1.3.1 AA
- Describe the structure and functions of a leaf. F.1.3.1 AA
- Identify the parts of a flower, and explain their functions. F.1.3.1 AA

Terms to Learn

xylem	stamen
phloem	pistil
sepal	ovary
petal	

READING STRATEGY

Mnemonics As you read this section, create a mnemonic device to help you remember the parts of a plant.

xylem the type of tissue in vascular plants that provides support and conducts water and nutrients from the roots

phloem the tissue that conducts food in vascular plants

Figure 1 *The roots of these plants provide the plants with water and minerals.*

F.1.3.1 AA understands that living things are composed of major systems that function in reproduction, growth, maintenance, and regulation.

Onion   **Dandelion**   **Carrots**

Root Structure

The structures of a root are shown in **Figure 2.** The layer of cells that covers the surface of a root is called the *epidermis*. Some cells of the epidermis extend from the root. These cells, or root hairs, increase the surface area of the root. This surface area helps the root absorb enough water and minerals. After water and minerals are absorbed by the epidermis, they diffuse into the center of the root, where the vascular tissue is located.

Roots grow longer at their tips. A group of cells called the *root cap* protects the tip of a root. The root cap produces a slimy substance. This substance makes it easier for the root to push through soil as it grows.

Benchmark Check How does the structure of a root help the root grow? F.1.3.1 AA

Root Systems

There are two kinds of root systems: taproot systems and fibrous root systems. A taproot system has one main root, or a taproot. The taproot grows downward. Many smaller roots branch from the taproot. Taproots can reach water deep underground. Dicots and gymnosperms usually have taproot systems.

A fibrous root system has several roots that spread out from the base of a plant's stem. The roots usually are of similar size. Fibrous roots usually get water from close to the soil surface. Monocots usually have fibrous roots.

Practice with Percentages

The following table gives an estimate of the number of species in each plant group. What percentage of plants do not produce seeds?

Plant Species	
Plant group	**Number of species**
Mosses, liverworts, and hornworts	15,600
Ferns, horsetails, and club mosses	12,000
Gymnosperms	760
Angiosperms	235,000

Figure 2   **The Structures of a Root**

A root absorbs water and minerals, which move into the xylem. Growth occurs at the tip of a root. The root cap releases a slimy substance that helps the root grow through soil.

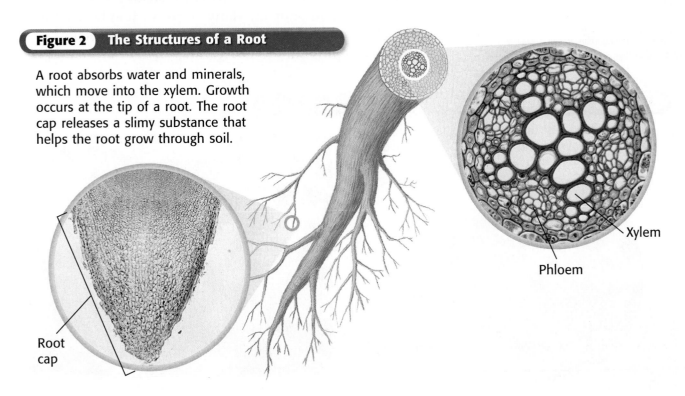

Root cap

Xylem

Phloem

Stems

Stems vary greatly in shape and size. Stems are usually located above the ground. However, many plants have underground stems. The trunk of the valley oak in **Figure 3** is a stem.

Stem Functions

Stems and leaves make up the shoot system. Stems connect a plant's roots to its leaves and flowers. A stem also has the following functions:

- Stems support the plant body. Leaves are arranged along stems or on the ends of stems. This arrangement helps leaves get sunlight for photosynthesis. Stems hold up flowers, which helps pollinators, such as bees, see the flowers.
- Stems transport materials between the root system and the shoot system. Xylem carries water and dissolved minerals from the roots to the leaves and other shoot parts. Phloem carries the food made during photosynthesis to roots and other parts of the plant.
- Some stems store materials. For example, the stems of cactuses and some trees are adapted for water storage.

Benchmark Check Describe three functions of stems. F.1.3.1 AA

Figure 3 *The stem, or trunk, of this valley oak keeps the tree upright, which helps leaves get sunlight for photosynthesis.*

F.1.3.1 AA understands that living things are composed of major systems that function in reproduction, growth, maintenance, and regulation.

Herbaceous Stems

Many plants have stems that are soft, thin, and flexible. These stems are called *herbaceous stems* (huhr BAY shuhs STEMZ). Examples of plants that have herbaceous stems are wildflowers, such as clovers and poppies. Many crops, such as beans, tomatoes, and corn, have herbaceous stems. A cross section of a herbaceous stem is shown in **Figure 4.**

Figure 4 **Cross Section of a Herbaceous Stem**

Buttercups are just one plant that has herbaceous stems. Wildflowers and many vegetables have soft, thin, and flexible stems.

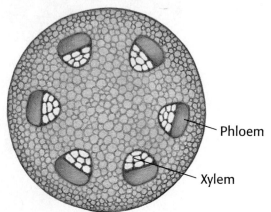

Phloem

Xylem

Figure 5 Cross Section of a Woody Stem

Some plants, such as these trees, have woody stems. Plants that have woody stems usually live for many years. People can use growth rings to estimate the age of a plant.

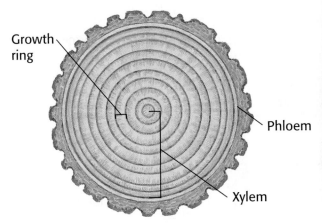

Growth ring

Phloem

Xylem

Woody Stems

Trees and shrubs have rigid stems made of wood and bark. These stems are called *woody stems*. **Figure 5** shows a cross section of a woody stem. Trees or shrubs that live in areas with cold winters have a growing period during the spring and summer. These plants have a dormant period during the winter. At the beginning of each growing period, large xylem cells are produced. As fall approaches, the plants produce smaller xylem cells, which appear darker. In the fall and winter, the plants stop producing new cells. The next spring, the cycle begins again. A ring of dark cells surrounding a ring of light cells makes up a growth ring.

Leaves

Leaves vary greatly in shape. They may be round, narrow, heart shaped, or fan shaped. Leaves also vary in size. Raffia palm leaves may be 6 times as long as you are tall. The leaves of duckweed, an aquatic plant, are so small that several leaves can fit on your fingernail. **Figure 6** shows a poison ivy leaf.

Leaf Functions

The main function of leaves is to make food for the plant. Chloroplasts in the cells of leaves capture energy from sunlight. The leaves also absorb carbon dioxide from the air. The leaves use the captured energy to make food, or sugar and oxygen, from carbon dioxide and water during photosynthesis.

Figure 6 *The leaves of poison ivy are very distinctive. They make food to help the plant survive.*

 **Benchmark Check** What is the function of leaf cells? **F.1.3.1 AA**

F.1.3.5 CS explains how the life functions of organisms are related to what occurs within the cell.

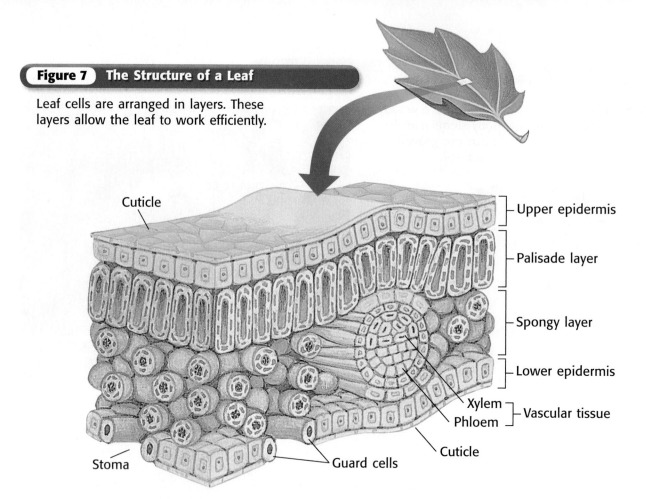

Figure 7 The Structure of a Leaf

Leaf cells are arranged in layers. These layers allow the leaf to work efficiently.

Cuticle

Upper epidermis

Palisade layer

Spongy layer

Lower epidermis

Xylem
Phloem — Vascular tissue

Cuticle

Guard cells

Stoma

Looking at Leaves

Leaves are many shapes and sizes and are arranged on a stem in many ways. Walk around your home. In your **science journal,** sketch the leaves of the plants that you see. Notice the arrangement of the leaves on the stem, the shapes of the leaves, and the veins in the leaves. Use a ruler to measure the size of the leaves.

ACTIVITY

F.1.3.1 AA understands that living things are composed of major systems that function in reproduction, growth, maintenance, and regulation.

F.1.3.5 CS explains how the life functions of organisms are related to what occurs within the cell.

Leaf Structure

The structure of leaves, shown in **Figure 7,** is related to the main function of leaves, photosynthesis. The outer surfaces of a leaf are covered by a cuticle. The cuticle is a waxy layer that prevents the leaf from losing water. A single layer of cells, the epidermis, lies beneath the cuticle. Light can pass through the epidermis. *Stomata* (singular, *stoma*)—tiny openings between guard cells in the epidermis—let carbon dioxide enter the leaf. Guard cells open and close the stomata.

Most photosynthesis takes place in the middle of a leaf. This part of a leaf often has two layers. Cells in the upper layer, the palisade layer, contain many chloroplasts. Photosynthesis takes place in the chloroplasts. Carbon dioxide moves freely in the space between the cells of the second layer, the spongy layer. Xylem and phloem are also found in the spongy layer.

Leaf Adaptations

Some leaves have functions other than photosynthesis. For example, the leaves of many cactuses are modified as spines. These spines keep animals from eating the cactuses. The leaves of another plant, the sundew, are modified to catch insects. Sundews grow in soil that does not contain enough nitrogen to meet the plants' needs. By catching and digesting insects, a sundew is able to get the nitrogen that it needs.

Flowers

Most people admire the beauty of flowers, such as the wild-flowers in **Figure 8.** But why do plants have flowers? Flowers are adaptations for sexual reproduction.

Flowers come in many shapes, colors, and fragrances. Brightly colored and fragrant flowers usually rely on animals for pollination. For example, some flowers look and smell like rotting meat. These flowers attract flies. The flies pollinate the flowers. Plants that lack brightly colored flowers and fragrances, such as grasses, depend on the wind to spread pollen.

Many flowers also produce nectar. Nectar is a fluid that contains sugar. Nectar attracts birds and insects. These animals move from flower to flower and drink the nectar. As they do so, they often carry pollen between the flowers.

Benchmark Check What function does a flower perform for a plant? Give an example. **F.1.3.1 AA**

Sepals and Petals

Flowers usually have the following basic parts: sepals, petals, stamens, and one or more pistils. The flower parts are usually arranged in rings around the central pistil.

Sepals are modified leaves that make up the outermost ring of flower parts. Like other leaves, sepals are often green. Sepals cover and protect a flower while it is a bud. As the blossom opens, the sepals fold back. Then, the petals can unfold and become visible. **Petals** are broad, flat, and thin leaflike parts of a flower. Petals vary greatly in color and shape. Petals attract insects or other animals to the flower. These animals help plants reproduce by carrying pollen from flower to flower.

sepal in a flower, one of the outermost rings of modified leaves that protect the flower bud

petal one of the usually brightly colored, leaf-shaped parts that make up one of the rings of a flower

Figure 8 *Many flowers help the plants reproduce by attracting pollinators with bright petals and strong fragrances.*

Figure 9 The Structure of a Flower

The stamens, which produce pollen, and the pistil, which produces eggs, are surrounded by the petals and the sepals.

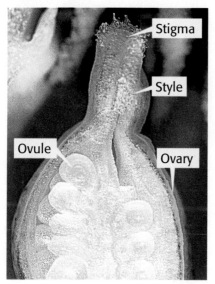

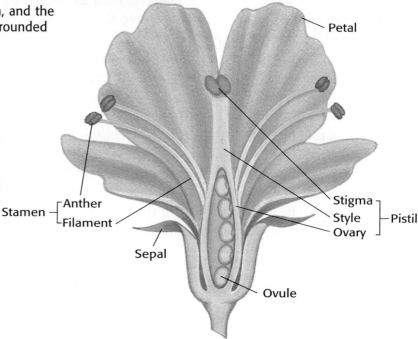

Stamens and Pistils

As **Figure 9** shows, the stamens of flowers are usually found just above the petals. A **stamen** is the male reproductive structure of flowers. Each stamen has a thin stalk called a *filament*. The filament is topped by an anther. Anthers are saclike structures that produce pollen.

The center of most flowers contains one or more pistils. A **pistil** is the female reproductive structure of flowers. The tip of the pistil is called the *stigma*. Pollen grains collect on stigmas, which are often sticky or feathery. The long, slender part of the pistil is the style. The rounded base of a pistil that contains one or more ovules is called the **ovary.** Each ovule contains an egg. When the egg is fertilized, the ovule develops into a seed. The ovary develops into a fruit.

Benchmark Check Describe the female and male parts of a flower. F.I.3.1 AA

The Importance of Flowers

Flowers help plants reproduce. Humans also use flowers for many things. Roses and many other flowers are used for floral arrangements. Some flowers, such as artichokes, broccoli, and cauliflower, can be eaten. Other flowers, such as hibiscus and chamomile flowers, are used to make tea. Flowers used as spices include cloves and saffron. Flowers are also used in perfumes, lotions, and shampoos.

stamen the male reproductive structure of a flower that produces pollen and consists of an anther at the tip of a filament

pistil the female reproductive part of a flower that produces seeds and consists of an ovary, style, and stigma

ovary in flowering plants, the lower part of a pistil that produces eggs in ovules

F.I.3.1 AA understands that living things are composed of major systems that function in reproduction, growth, maintenance, and regulation.

Summary

- Roots supply plants with water and dissolved minerals. They support and anchor plants. Roots also store surplus food made during photosynthesis. **F.1.3.1 AA**

- Stems support the body of a plant. They allow transport of material between the root system and shoot system. Some stems store materials, such as water. **F.1.3.1 AA**

- A leaf has a thin epidermis on its upper and lower surfaces. The epidermis allows sunlight to pass through to the center of the leaf. **F.1.3.1 AA**

- Most photosynthesis occurs in the cells in a leaf's palisade layer. The leaf's spongy layer contains xylem and phloem and allows the movement of carbon dioxide. **F.1.3.5 CS**

- The four main parts of a flower are the sepals, the petals, the stamens, and one or more pistils.

- Flowers are usually arranged around the pistil. The ovary of a pistil contains ovules. When the eggs are fertilized, ovules develop into seeds and the ovary becomes a fruit. **F.1.3.1 AA**

Using Key Terms

1. Write an original definition for *xylem, phloem, stamen,* and *pistil.*

2. Use *sepal, petal,* and *ovary* in separate sentences.

Understanding Key Ideas

3. Which of the following flower structures produces pollen?

   a. pistil   **c.** anther

   b. filament   **d.** stigma

4. Compare the function of xylem with the function of phloem.

5. How are the cells in the palisade layer of a leaf important to a plant? **F.1.3.5 CS**

6. What are the functions of stems? **F.1.3.1 AA**

7. Identify the two types of stems, and briefly describe each type.

8. How do flowers attract pollinators? **F.1.3.1 AA**

Critical Thinking

9. **Making Inferences** Describe two kinds of root systems. How does the structure of each system help the roots perform their three functions? **F.1.3.1 AA**

10. **Making Inferences** Describe a leaf adaptation other than photosynthesis. Why do you think this adaptation evolved?

FCAT Preparation

11. Pollinators are attracted to flowers by bright colors, fragrances, and nectar. Pampas grass flowers are found at the top of tall stems, are light colored, and are unscented. Explain how pampas grass flowers are most likely pollinated. **F.1.3.1 AA**

12. You are looking at the cells in the palisade layer of a leaf of a diseased plant under a microscope. You notice that some of the cells are yellow instead of green. How will the plant's disease affect the plant? **F.1.3.5 CS**

    A. The cells will make too much food for the plant.

    B. The cells will not make enough food for the plant.

    C. The cells will make too much carbon dioxide for the plant.

    D. The cells will not make enough oxygen for the plant.

SCiLINKS

NSTA

Developed and maintained by the
National Science Teachers Association

For a variety of links related to this chapter, go to www.scilinks.org

Topic: Structure of Seed Plants
SciLinks code: HSM1467

Model-Making Lab

Build a Flower

Scientists often make models in the laboratory. Models help scientists understand processes and structures. Models are especially useful when scientists are trying to understand processes that are too small to be seen easily, such as pollination, or processes that are too large to be examined in a laboratory, such as the growth of a tree. Models also make it possible to examine the structures of objects, such as flowers.

In this activity, you will use your creativity and your understanding of the structure of a flower to make a model of a flower from recycled materials and art supplies.

Build a model of a flower.

Explain how the model represents an actual flower.

Describe the basic parts of a flower.

MATERIALS

- art materials such as colored paper, pipe cleaners, beads, and yarn
- card, index, 3 in. × 5 in.
- glue
- recycled items such as paper plates and cups, yogurt containers, wire, string, buttons, cardboard, and bottles
- scissors
- tape

SAFETY

Procedure

1. Draw a flower similar to the one shown in the figure below. This flower has both male and female parts. Not all flowers have this structure. The flowers of many species of plants have only male parts or only female parts, not both.

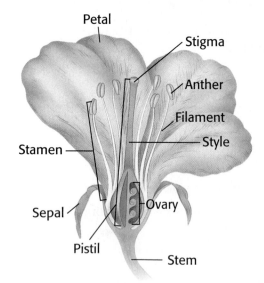

2. Decide which materials you will use to represent each flower part. Then, build a three-dimensional model of a flower that looks like one of the flowers on the next page. Your model should contain the following parts: stem, sepals, petals, stamens (anther and filament), and pistil (stigma, style, and ovary).

F.1.3.1 AA understands that living things are composed of major systems that function in reproduction, growth, maintenance, and regulation.

Lily

Tulip

Hibiscus

3 After you build your model, draw a key for your flower model on an index card. Label each of the structures represented on your flower.

Analyze the Results

1 **Organizing Data** List the structures of a flower, and explain the function of each structure.

2 **Identifying Patterns** What is the outermost part of your flower? What is the innermost part of your flower?

3 **Analyzing Data** How are your flower model and an actual flower alike? How are they different?

Draw Conclusions

4 **Drawing Conclusions** How might your flower attract pollinators? What modifications could you make to your flower to attract a greater number of pollinators?

5 **Evaluating Models** Is your model an accurate representation of a flower? Why or why not?

6 **Making Predictions** If you based your flower model on a plant species that had flowers that did not have both male and female parts, how would that model differ from your current model?

Applying Your Data

Research flowering plants whose flowers do not have both male and female reproductive parts. Build models of the male flower and the female flower for one of these flowering plants. Then, compare the new models with your original model, which includes both male and female reproductive parts.

Chapter Review

USING KEY TERMS

1 Use *tropism*, *pollen*, and *pollination* in separate sentences. **FCAT VOCAB**

For each pair of terms, explain how the meanings of the terms differ.

2 *pistil* and *stamen*

3 *xylem* and *phloem*

4 *rhizome* and *rhizoid*

5 *vascular plant* and *nonvascular plant*

UNDERSTANDING KEY IDEAS

Multiple Choice

6 Which of the following statements about angiosperms is NOT true?

a. Their seeds are protected by cones.

b. They produce seeds.

c. They provide animals with food.

d. They have flowers.

7 Roots **F.1.3.1 AA**

a. supply water and nutrients.

b. anchor and support a plant.

c. store surplus food.

d. All of the above

8 Mosses are small and often live in groups in damp places. Each cell of a moss must get water from the environment or a nearby cell. In which group would you classify mosses? **G.1.3.3 CS FCAT**

a. angiosperms

b. seed plants

c. seedless nonvascular plants

d. gymnosperms

9 Chloroplasts are located within leaf cells. Chloroplasts capture energy from sunlight. How does the function of chloroplasts affect a plant? **F.1.3.5 CS FCAT**

a. The function of chloroplasts does not affect a plant.

b. Chloroplasts capture energy so that leaves can produce seeds.

c. Chloroplasts capture energy so that leaves can carry water and dissolved minerals from the roots to the shoots.

d. Chloroplasts capture energy so that leaves can perform photosynthesis.

Short Answer

10 Describe the pattern of sexual reproduction in plants. **F.2.3.1 CS**

11 List the four main groups of plants. **G.1.3.3 CS**

12 Name three nonvascular plants and three seedless vascular plants.

13 Describe three kinds of tropisms. **F.1.3.7 CS**

14 How are seedless plants, gymnosperms, and angiosperms important to the environment? **D.1.3.4 AA**

15 What are two advantages that seeds have over spores? **F.2.3.1 CS**

Extended Response

16 **Making Comparisons** Imagine that a seed and a spore are beginning to grow in a deep, dark crack in a rock. Which of the two is more likely to grow into an adult plant? Explain your answer. F.1.3.1 AA, F.2.3.1 CS

17 **Identifying Relationships** Grass flowers do not have strong fragrances or bright colors. How might these characteristics be related to the way in which grass flowers are pollinated? F.2.3.1 CS

18 **Analyzing Ideas** Plants that are pollinated by wind produce more pollen than plants pollinated by animals do. Why might wind-pollinated plants produce more pollen? F.2.3.1 CS

19 **Applying Concepts** A scientist discovered a new plant. The plant has vascular tissue and produces seeds. It has brightly colored and strongly scented flowers. It also has sweet fruits. Based on this information, which of the four main types of plants did the scientist discover? How is the plant most likely pollinated? How does the plant most likely spread its seeds?
G.1.3.3 CS

Concept Mapping

20 Use the following terms to create a concept map: *flowers, pollen, stamens, ovaries, pistils, stigmas, filaments, anthers, ovules, petals,* and *sepals.*

21 Look at the cross section of a woody stem below. Based on the diagram, how old is the tree?

Use the diagram of the flower below to answer the questions that follow.

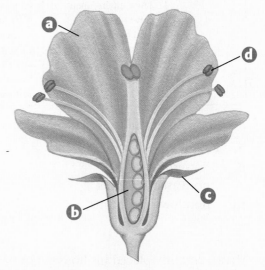

22 Which letter corresponds to the structure in which pollen is produced? What is the name of this structure? F.1.3.1 AA

23 Which letter corresponds to the structure that contains the ovules? What is the name of this structure? F.1.3.1 AA

24 Which letter corresponds to the structure that protects the flower bud? What is the name of this structure?
F.1.3.1 AA

For the following questions, write your answers on a separate sheet of paper.

1 The table below shows how plants are classified.

TYPES OF PLANTS

	Nonvascular Plants	Vascular Plants		
		Seedless Plants	Seed Plants	
			Nonflowering Plants	Flowering Plants
Nutrition	Obtain nutrients through diffusion	Obtain nutrients through roots and stems	Obtain nutrients through roots and stems	Obtain nutrients through roots and stems
Size	Small size	Any size	Any size	Any size
Importance	First plants to live in a new environment; prevent erosion; used by animals for food and nesting material	Help form soil, prevent erosion; some used for houseplants; some eaten for food; ancient seedless vascular plants formed coal	Provide building materials; produce resin; some produce antiallergy or anticancer drugs	Major food source for animals and humans; provide building materials, clothing, and medicines

According to the table, in which of the following groups would orange trees be classified?

A. seedless plants
B. flowering plants
C. nonvascular plants
D. nonflowering plants

2 Shawn recently placed his houseplant next to a window. After a week, Shawn noticed that the shoot tips of the plant started to bend toward the light coming from the window. What kind of tropism does Shawn's plant have?

F. gravitropism
G. phototropism
H. thigmotropism
I. seasonal tropism

3 All plants have a life cycle that alternates between two stages. What are the two stages of the plant life cycle?

A. phloem and xylem
B. vascular and nonvascular
C. gametophyte and sporophyte
D. angiosperm and gymnosperm

4 Stems vary greatly in shape and size. Stems are usually located above the ground. However, some plants have underground stems. Which of the following **best** describes the function of stems?

F. Stems make food for plants.

G. Stems are the female reproductive part of plants.

H. Stems supply plants with water and dissolved minerals absorbed from the soil.

I. Stems support the plant body and transport material between the root system and the shoot system.

5 Lamont lives near a river bed. During the summer, the river began to dry up, which exposed many large rocks. When Lamont went to look at the river bed he found some plants growing on the rocks. Which plants did Lamont **most** likely find in the river bed?

A. club mosses

B. ginkgoes

C. hornworts

D. monocots

6 Kiesha is studying the different ways plants reproduce. She knows that pollen is produced by the male reproductive structures and that eggs are produced by the female reproductive structures. She also knows that the egg must be fertilized for a new plant to form. Kiesha made a diagram of the life cycle of a pine tree similar to the one shown below.

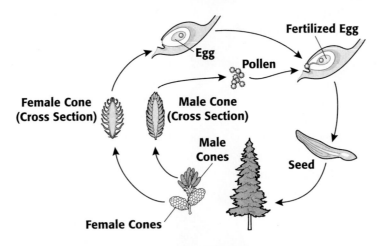

Pine Life Cycle

Which of the following **most** likely carries pollen from the male cones to the female cones during the life cycle of a pine tree?

F. bees

G. birds

H. water

I. wind

Science in Action

Place to Visit

The Botanical Gardens at the University of South Florida

Where can you go to see butterfly gardens, plants from a rain forest, and a bog full of carnivorous plants all in one place? At the Botanical Gardens at the University of South Florida (USF) in Tampa, researchers are growing more than 3,000 kinds of plants from all over the world. The gardens are also home to many animals, such as gopher tortoises, butterflies, and more than 60 species of birds. On a visit to the Botanical Gardens at USF, you can explore different habitats and can observe the interactions between many species of plants and animals.

Social Studies ACTiViTY

Many different groups of people rely on the Amazon rain forest. Research how different groups of people use the Amazon rain forest, and create a poster that illustrates your findings.

Science, Technology, and Society

Plant Poachers

Imagine that you are walking through a swamp. The swamp is full of life. You are surrounded by trees, vines, and waterlilies. You can hear frogs singing and mosquitoes buzzing. Then, you notice a ghost orchid hanging from a tree branch. The flower of this orchid looks like a ghost or like a white frog leaping. For some people, this orchid is worth stealing. These people, called *plant poachers*, steal orchids and other plants from the wild. Many plant species and natural areas are threatened by plant theft.

Math ACTiViTY

A plant poacher stole 100 plants from a nature preserve. He planned on selling each plant for $50, but he was caught and was fined $300 for each stolen plant. What is the difference between the total fine and the total amount of money that the poacher hoped to make by selling the plants?

Paul Cox

Ethnobotanist Paul Cox is an ethnobotanist. He travels to remote places to look for plants that can help treat diseases. He seeks the advice of native healers in his search. In Samoan cultures, the healer is one of the most valued members of the community. In 1984, Cox met a 78-year-old Samoan healer named Epenesa. Epenesa understood human anatomy, and she dispensed medicines with great accuracy.

After Cox spent months observing Epenesa, Epenesa gave Cox her treatment for yellow fever. Cox brought the yellow-fever remedy to the United States. In 1986, researchers at the National Cancer Institute found that the plant contains prostratin, a virus-fighting chemical that may have potential as a treatment for AIDS.

When two of the Samoan healers that Cox observed died in 1993, medical knowledge spanning several generations was lost with them. The healers' deaths show the urgency of recording this knowledge before all of the healers are gone. Cox and other ethnobotanists are working hard to gather knowledge from healers before their knowledge is lost.

Language Arts ACTiViTY

WRITING SKILL Imagine that you are a healer. In a letter to an ethnobotanist, describe some of the plants that you use to treat diseases.

To learn more about these Science in Action topics, visit go.hrw.com and type in the keyword **HT6FPLFF.**

Current Science

Check out Current Science® articles related to this chapter by visiting go.hrw.com. Just type in the keyword **HL5CS12.**

16

Introduction to Ecology

Ecology is the study of the interactions of living things with their environment.

About the PHOTO

Dragonflies are scrumptious! Well, at least they are to green frogs. Every living thing in the environment depends on other living things in order to survive. For example, by eating the dragonfly, the green frog is getting energy that it needs to survive.

PRE-READING ACTIVITY

Graphic Organizer

Comparison Table Before you read the chapter, create the graphic organizer entitled "Comparison Table" described in the **Study Skills** section of the Appendix. Label the columns with "Producer," "Consumer," and "Decomposer." Label the rows with "Definition" and "Examples." As you read the chapter, fill in the table with details about the different groups of living things that live in an environment.

START-UP ACTiViTY

A Classroom Aquarium

Did you know that an aquarium is a small environment that contains a community of organisms? In this activity, each group will put an aquarium together. As your group plans the aquarium, think about how all of the parts are connected.

Procedure

1. Get a **tank** from your teacher. Check the Internet, your library, or a pet store to find instructions on the proper way to clean and prepare an aquarium. **Caution:** Handle animals only as your teacher directs. Also, do not release animals purchased at a pet store into the wild.

2. Find out about the kinds of **plants** and **animals** that you can put in your aquarium.

3. Choose a place to put the tank, and tell your teacher the plan. Then, set up the aquarium.

Analysis

1. Compare the environment your group created with one that is familiar to you. How are they similar? How are they different? Identify the limitations of your group's model.

2. After you read the chapter, take another look at the aquarium. See if you can name all of the parts of this environment. Then, see if you can define the role that each living thing plays in this environment.

Environmental Organization

Imagine that you are walking along a beach. You smell salt in the air and see sandpipers pecking at the sand. On the sand dunes, you see sparrows sitting on sea oats. Coquina shells tickle your feet as the tide washes in and out.

In the beach environment described above, many interactions are taking place between organisms and their physical environment. For example, the sea oats provide shelter for many small animals such as sparrows and lizards, and the roots of the sea oats help hold the sand dunes in place. Each of these interactions is connected and is a part of a larger environment.

The Science of Ecology

The study of the interactions of living organisms with each other and with their environment is called **ecology.** Scientists who study ecology are called *ecologists*. As we learn more about the environment, we can better protect, manage, and restore the environments in which we live.

Parts of an Environment

An organism's environment is all of the things outside the organism that affect the organism's life, development, and survival. Things in an organism's environment can be grouped into two categories: living and nonliving. All of the living organisms in an environment are **biotic** (bie AHT ik) factors. The flamingos and plants in **Figure 1** are biotic factors. **Abiotic** (AY bie AHT ik) factors are the nonliving things in an environment. Abiotic factors include water, soil, light, and temperature.

ecology the study of the interactions of living organisms with one another and with their environment

biotic describes living factors in the environment *FCAT VOCAB*

abiotic describes the nonliving part of the environment, including water, rocks, light, and temperature *FCAT VOCAB*

Figure 1 *Flamingos and plants are examples of biotic factors. Water and soil are examples of abiotic factors.*

Figure 2 *The group of sea oats (left) is a population. The Great Egret and turtle (right) are part of a community in Everglades National Park, Florida.*

Organisms, Populations, and Communities

Most environments are complex places. To understand how an environment works, ecologists categorize all of the factors in the environment into distinct levels of organization. The smallest level of organization is an organism. An *organism* is any individual living thing.

A **population** is the second level of organization and is made up of a group of organisms of the same species that live in the same area. The group of sea oats growing in the dune in **Figure 2** is a population. The next level of organization is a community. A **community** is all of the populations of species that live in the same area and interact with each other. Communities are made up of several populations, each of which represents a species of animals or plants. The Great Egret and the turtle in **Figure 2** are part of a community.

✓ *Reading Check* How is a population a part of a community?

Ecosystems and the Biosphere

The fourth level of organization is an ecosystem. An **ecosystem** is a community of organisms and their abiotic environment. An ecosystem can include several populations as well as several communities. There are many ecosystems on Earth. For example, an ocean ecosystem includes several coastal communities, such as sea grass meadows, coral reefs, and estuaries. The fifth and largest level of organization is the biosphere. The **biosphere** is the part of Earth where life exists. It includes the air, land, and all bodies of water on Earth.

population a group of organisms of the same species that live in a specific geographical area

community all of the populations of species that live in the same habitat and interact with each other

ecosystem a community of organisms and their abiotic, or nonliving, environment *FCAT VOCAB*

biosphere the part of Earth where life exists

The Five Levels of Organization

Every ecosystem on Earth can be described in terms of the five levels of environmental organization. **Figure 3** shows five levels of a mangrove forest. Notice that the ecosystem level shows a view of almost all of the mangrove forest, which includes multiple coastal communities. Notice that the community level shows several types of organisms, including mangrove trees, roseate spoonbills, brown pelicans, snails, and frogs.

Figure 3 The Five Levels of Environmental Organization

Biosphere

Ecosystem

Community

Population

Organism

G.2.3.4 AA (partial) understands that humans are a part of an ecosystem and their activities may deliberately or inadvertently alter the equilibrium in ecosystems.

The Role of Humans in an Ecosystem

Like other organisms, humans are a part of each level of environmental organization, including the ecosystem level. Humans depend on the biotic and abiotic factors in an ecosystem to survive. These factors provide humans with air, food, and a stable atmosphere. The role that humans play in an ecosystem, however, can affect an ecosystem positively and negatively.

Human activities, such as fishing, lawn and car maintenance, construction, and agriculture, can affect ecosystems in many ways. For example, recreational fishing, shown in **Figure 4,** usually does not have a big impact on fish populations. However, if overfishing occurs, fish populations can decrease. To keep Earth and its ecosystems healthy, humans have to consider the environment when they plan activities and when they make decisions.

Benchmark Check Give two examples of how humans interact with an ecosystem. **G.2.3.4 AA**

Figure 4 *Fishing is one way humans interact with the environment.*

SECTION Review

Summary

- Ecology is the study of the interactions within the environment.

- Examples of biotic factors are plants and animals. Examples of abiotic factors are water, soil, and light.

- The five levels of environmental organization are an organism, population, community, ecosystem, and biosphere.

- Humans are a part of an ecosystem. They interact with that ecosystem in many ways. **G.2.3.4 AA**

Using Key Terms

1. Write an original definition for *ecology, biotic,* and *abiotic.* **FCAT VOCAB**

Understanding Key Ideas

2. List the five levels of environmental organization.

3. Differentiate between a population and a community.

Critical Thinking

4. **Applying Ideas** In **Figure 3,** a mangrove forest ecosystem is organized into levels. Classify as many things from the figure as you can as either biotic or abiotic factors.

5. **Identifying Relationships** Every human is a part of an ecosystem. In what ways do you interact with the ecosystem in which you live? **G.2.3.4 AA**

FCAT Preparation

6. Imagine that you make your living catching fish from the ocean. In the past year, three fishing boats have started fishing in the same area where you usually fish. How might this competition affect your catch size next year? **G.2.3.4 AA**

A. Catch size will increase.

B. Catch size will stay the same.

C. Catch size will decrease.

D. Catch size will double.

Developed and maintained by the National Science Teachers Association

For a variety of links related to this chapter, go to www.scilinks.org

Topic: Biotic and Abiotic Factors; Florida's Environment

SciLinks code: HSM0164; HSMF06

Energy in Ecosystems

Just as a car cannot run without fuel, organisms cannot survive without a constant supply of energy. But how does an organism get its energy?

Almost all organisms get their energy directly or indirectly from the sun. For example, tiny plants in the ocean called *phytoplankton* take in energy from the sun to make food. Then, tiny animals called *zooplankton* eat the phytoplankton to get the energy that they need. In turn, zooplankton are eaten by and provide energy for larger animals such as fish, crabs, and shrimp.

The Transfer of Energy

Each organism in the ocean ecosystem described above contains energy that is transferred to another organism. Every organism plays a role in energy transfer and is either a producer, consumer, or decomposer.

Producers and Consumers

A **producer** can make its own food by using the energy from its surroundings. During *photosynthesis,* producers use carbon dioxide from the environment and energy from sunlight to make food. Producers provide food for the entire community. An example of a producer in Florida is sea grass. A **consumer** is an organism that eats other organisms. Consumers cannot make their own food and must depend on other plants and animals for energy. An example of a consumer in Florida is a green sea turtle. Other examples of producers and consumers that live in and around Florida are shown in **Table 1.**

READING WARM-UP

Objectives

● Define the roles of producers, consumers, and decomposers in an ecosystem.

● Describe how the interactions between organisms in food chains and food webs result in the flow of energy. G.1.3.4 AA

● Give examples of how human actions can alter the balance of ecosystems. G.2.3.4 AA, D.2.3.2

● Describe how the availability of a resource can affect a population. G.2.3.3 CS

Terms to Learn

producer   omnivore
consumer   food chain
herbivore   food web
carnivore   energy pyramid

READING STRATEGY

Discussion Read this section silently. Write down questions that you have about this section. Discuss your questions in a small group.

producer an organism that can make its own food by using energy from its surroundings

consumer an organism that eats other organisms or organic matter

Table 1 Producers and Consumers		
Organism	**Energy source**	**Examples**
Producer	makes its own food through photosynthesis	mangrove tree, cypress tree, salt marsh grass, phytoplankton
Consumer	gets its energy by eating other producers or other consumers	manatee, shark, dolphin, human, deer, woodpecker, panther, spider, zooplankton

Figure 1 Energy Transfer

Energy from the sun

Producer

Herbivore

Carnivore

Types of Consumers

The four types of consumers in ecosystems are herbivores, carnivores, omnivores, and decomposers. A **herbivore** is an organism that eats only plants. Examples of herbivores include manatees, deer, and green sea turtles. A **carnivore** is an organism that eats animals. Carnivores eat herbivores as well as other carnivores. Examples of carnivores include panthers, hawks, snakes, and spiders. An **omnivore** is an organism that eats both plants and animals. Humans, fish, seabirds, bears, pigs, and lobsters are examples of omnivores. Some omnivores are called *scavengers*. Scavengers, such as vultures, hyenas, and sea gulls, eat dead plant and animal matter.

The transfer of energy between the sun and a producer and the producer and a consumer is shown in **Figure 1.** In the figure, the clover is the producer, and both the rabbit and the coyote are consumers. Furthermore, the rabbit is a herbivore, and the coyote is a carnivore.

Benchmark Check How is energy transferred when a rabbit eats the leaves of a clover plant? **G.1.3.4 AA**

Decomposers

Decomposers are consumers that get their energy by breaking down dead organisms. Decomposers are essential to ecosystems because as matter is broken down, important nutrients are returned to the soil, water, and the atmosphere. These nutrients then become available for other organisms to use. Examples of decomposers include bacteria and fungi.

herbivore an organism that eats only plants

carnivore an organism that eats animals

omnivore an organism that eats both plants and animals

G.1.3.4 AA knows that the interactions of organisms with each other and with the nonliving parts of their environments result in the flow of energy and the cycling of matter throughout the system.

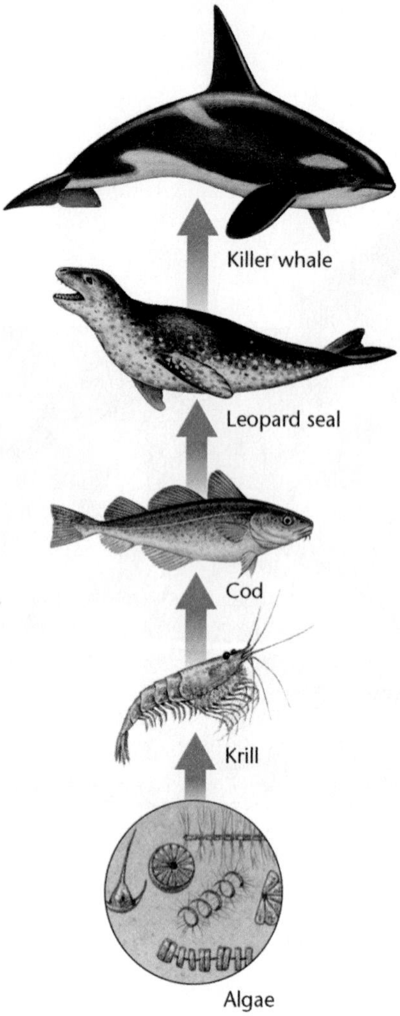

The Flow of Energy in Food Chains

Figure 2 shows a simple aquatic food chain. A **food chain** is a diagram that shows how energy in food flows from one organism to another. In the figure, algae are eaten by krill (shrimplike organisms), which are eaten by cod. The cod are eaten by leopard seals, which are eaten by killer whales.

The Flow of Energy in Food Webs

Because few organisms eat only one kind of food, the energy connections in nature are more accurately shown by a food web than by a food chain. A **food web** is a diagram that shows the feeding relationships between organisms in an ecosystem. Notice that the food chain in **Figure 2** is part of the larger food web in **Figure 3.** All organisms in a food web depend on producers, which are at the bottom of the food web. For example, the algae in **Figure 3** are the producers in the food web. Without algae, the food web could not function and energy could not be transferred.

Energy in a food chain or a food web moves from one organism to the next in a one-way direction. Any energy that is not immediately used by an organism is stored in the organism's tissues. Only the energy stored in an organism's tissues can be used by the next consumer.

Figure 2 *This food chain shows that energy is transferred from one organism to another.*

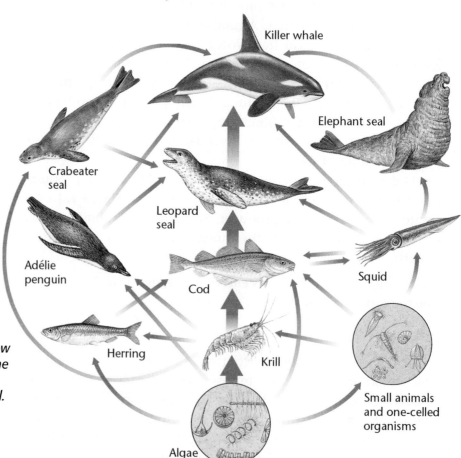

Figure 3 *In this food web, the arrow going from the Adélie penguin to the leopard seal shows that the Adélie penguin is food for the leopard seal. The Adélie penguin is also food for the killer whale.*

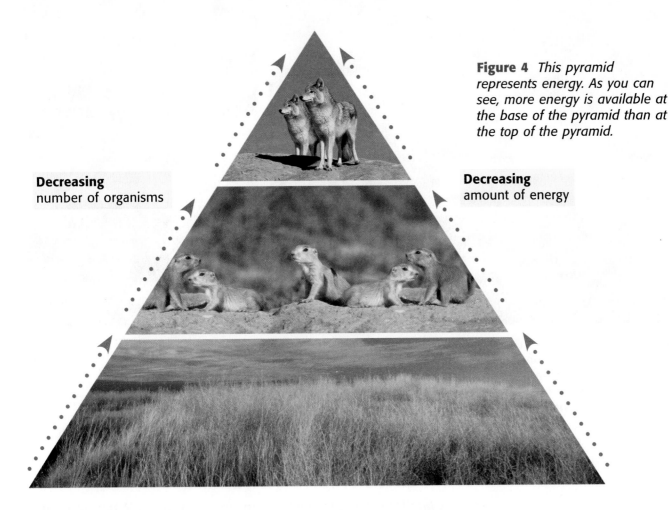

Decreasing number of organisms

Decreasing amount of energy

Figure 4 *This pyramid represents energy. As you can see, more energy is available at the base of the pyramid than at the top of the pyramid.*

Energy Pyramids

One way to diagram the loss of energy in a food chain or food web is through an **energy pyramid.** An example of an energy pyramid is shown in **Figure 4.**

The base and largest level of a pyramid is usually made up of producers. Producers provide most of the energy for a community and have the largest population. The grass uses most of the energy that it gets from the sun for its own life processes. However, some of the energy is stored in its tissues. This energy is used by the prairie dogs and other animals that eat the grass. Prairie dogs use most of the energy that they get from the grass and store only a little in their tissues. The population of prairie dogs can support only a few coyotes, because one coyote needs to eat several prairie dogs to get enough energy to survive. Therefore, the top level of a pyramid usually represents the top consumer, which has the smallest population size. For energy to be balanced in this community, there must be more grass than prairie dogs and more prairie dogs than coyotes.

Benchmark Check How does an energy pyramid show the loss of energy in a community? **G.1.3.4 AA**

food chain the pathway of energy transfer through various stages as a result of the feeding patterns of a series of organisms

food web a diagram that shows the feeding relationships between organisms in an ecosystem

energy pyramid a triangular diagram that shows an ecosystem's loss of energy, which results as energy passes through the ecosystem's food chain

G.1.3.4 AA knows that the interactions of organisms with each other and with the nonliving parts of their environments result in the flow of energy and the cycling of matter throughout the system.

Figure 5 *The manatee on the left was injured by boat propellers. The manatee on the right is being rehabilitated at a manatee rescue center.*

Humans and the Balance of Ecosystems

Plant and animal communities depend on each other and the stability of their ecosystem for survival. Because humans are a part of ecosystems, human activities can alter the balance of an organism's ecosystem.

The Effects of Habitat Destruction

A *habitat* is the place where an organism lives. When land and coastal areas are cleared or developed, an organism's habitat can be destroyed. This situation can be devastating for an organism that cannot adapt to a nearby habitat. One example of such an organism is the Florida manatee. Manatees are large, slow-swimming marine mammals that feed primarily on sea grass in coastal areas. Human activities, such as the development of land and an increase in recreational boating, have decreased the population of sea grass. Because sea grass is the main food source for manatees, the manatee population has also decreased. In addition, many manatees have been injured by boat propellers, as **Figure 5** shows. Manatees are endangered, and only an estimated 3,000 remain in Florida waters.

Benchmark Check How is the population of sea grass affecting the manatee population? **G.2.3.3 CS**

Saving the Manatee

Increased boater safety and awareness can help save manatees. Boaters should move at slow speeds to avoid manatees and prevent habitat destruction. Rehabilitation centers, such as the one shown in **Figure 5,** can also help save manatees. Rehabilitation centers rescue injured manatees, nurse them back to health, and try to release them back into the wild.

G.2.3.3 CS knows that a brief change in the limited resources of an ecosystem may alter the size of a population or the average size of individual organisms and that long-term change may result in the elimination of animal and plant populations inhabiting the Earth.

G.2.3.4 AA understands that humans are a part of an ecosystem and their activities may deliberately or inadvertently alter the equilibrium in ecosystems.

D.2.3.2 knows the positive and negative consequences of human action on the Earth's systems.

Other Human Actions and Ecosystems

The use of pesticides can also affect an ecosystem. Some pesticides become more concentrated in the tissues of organisms higher up in a food chain. For example, a top consumer such as a bald eagle, needs to eat a large amount of lower consumers, such as fish, in order to survive. Thus, if a bald eagle eats a large amount of fish that contain pesticide, the concentration of pesticide in the bald eagle will be much larger than it is in a single fish. High levels of poison may kill the bird or affect its ability to reproduce. As a result, the bald eagle population may decrease, and the population of fish may increase.

Benchmark Check Describe how the use of a pesticide can affect an aquatic ecosystem. **G.2.3.4 AA, D.2.3.2**

SECTION
Review

Summary

- In an ecosystem, producers make their own food, consumers eat other organisms, and decomposers break down dead organisms.

- Some interactions between organisms in food chains and food webs result in the flow of energy. **G.1.3.4 AA**

- Human actions, such as habitat destruction, can alter the balance of an ecosystem. **G.2.3.4 AA, D.2.3.2**

- The availability of a resource can affect the population of a species. **G.2.3.3 CS**

Using Key Terms

1. Use *food chain, food web,* and *energy pyramid* in separate sentences.

2. Use *herbivore* and *carnivore* in the same sentence.

Understanding Key Ideas

3. List the four types of consumers in an ecosystem.

4. Describe how producers, consumers, and decomposers interact in an ecosystem.

5. Why is the smallest population of organisms at the top of an energy pyramid?

6. How could a pesticide that washed into a lake affect the size of the population of fish that lives in the lake? **G.2.3.3 CS**

Critical Thinking

7. **Identifying Relationships** Why do producers usually make up the largest population in a food web? **G.1.3.4 AA**

8. **Evaluating Data** In what ways are human actions positively and negatively affecting the Florida manatee? **G.2.3.4 AA, D.2.3.2**

FCAT Preparation

9. A dock was built over a large bed of sea grass in a manatee habitat. The dock shaded the bed of sea grass from the sun. The population of manatees decreased in the area even though the manatees could still swim under the dock. Why did the population of manatees decrease? **G.2.3.3 CS**

   A. The sea grass grew too thick.

   B. The manatees swam to another area to eat sea grass.

   C. The sea grass was poisoned.

   D. The sea grass died because the dock shaded it from the sun.

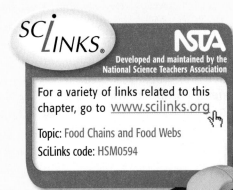

Developed and maintained by the
National Science Teachers Association

For a variety of links related to this chapter, go to www.scilinks.org

Topic: Food Chains and Food Webs
SciLinks code: HSM0594

Cycles in Nature

Did you know that you could not enjoy a glass of fresh water or a warm campfire without the cycling of Earth's natural resources? Earth recycles its resources in the same way that we recycle aluminum cans, glass, and paper.

A *natural resource* is any natural material that is used by humans. Earth is made up of many natural resources. Some of Earth's natural resources are water, minerals, forests, and animals. These and other resources are cycled in nature through the water cycle, carbon cycle, and nitrogen cycle.

Renewable Resources

A **renewable resource** is a natural resource that can be replaced at the same rate at which the resource is used. The water being used in **Figure 1** is an example of a renewable resource. Other examples of renewable resources are trees and fish. Although these resources are renewable, some forests can be used up before they are renewed. And if too many fish of the same species are killed, the species may not survive.

Nonrenewable Resources

A **nonrenewable resource** is a resource that forms at a rate that is much slower than the rate at which the resource is used. Coal, petroleum, and minerals, such as phosphate, are examples of nonrenewable resources. The phosphate mine in **Figure 1** is located near Tampa, Florida.

Benchmark Check Give one example of a renewable resource and one example of a nonrenewable resource. G.2.3.1 CS

READING WARM-UP

Objectives

- Differentiate between renewable resources and nonrenewable resources. G.2.3.1 CS
- Explain how the interactions between organisms and nonliving parts of the environment result in the cycling of water, carbon, and nitrogen. G.1.3.4 AA
- Describe how changes in nature's cycles can result in positive and negative consequences.
- Describe how human activities may deliberately or inadvertently alter ecosystems. G.2.3.4 AA, D.2.3.2

Terms to Learn

renewable resource
nonrenewable resource
evaporation
condensation
precipitation

READING STRATEGY

Prediction Guide Before reading this section, write the title of each heading in this section. Next, under each heading, write what you think you will learn.

Figure 1 *Water is an example of a renewable resource (left). Phosphate (right) is a nonrenewable resource. Florida produces 25% of the world's phosphate.*

Figure 2 The Water Cycle

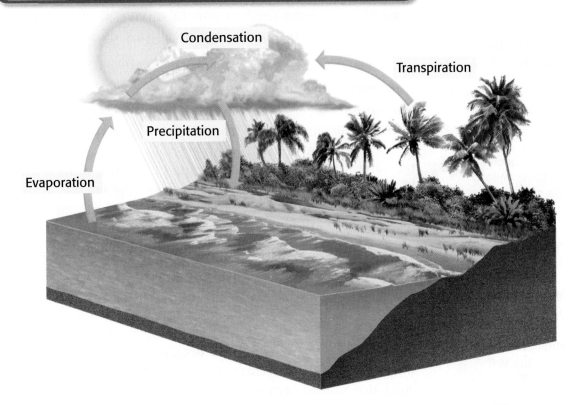

Condensation

Transpiration

Precipitation

Evaporation

The Water Cycle

Water on Earth never stops moving through the *water cycle.* Water constantly cycles between the oceans, atmosphere, land, and organisms, as illustrated in **Figure 2.**

The Parts of the Water Cycle

The water cycle could not occur without the sun. The sun's heat causes water to change from liquid to vapor during **evaporation.** During **condensation,** the water vapor in the air cools and changes back into a liquid. This water then falls back to Earth's surface as **precipitation.** Precipitation can be in the form of rain, hail, sleet, or snow. Most precipitation falls into the ocean, but some falls into lakes, into rivers, and on land. Precipitation is important because it can carry nutrients to other areas and can help wash away wastes.

The Water Cycle and Organisms

Water is necessary for life, and all organisms depend on water to survive. For example, up to 60% of your body is water. Without water, your cells could not function and your body temperature could not be regulated. Plants also interact with the water cycle. Plants need water to grow, but they also release large amounts of water vapor into the environment through a process called *transpiration.*

renewable resource a natural resource that can be replaced at the same rate at which the resource is consumed

nonrenewable resource a resource that forms at a rate that is much slower than the rate at which the resource is consumed

evaporation the change of state from a liquid to a gas

condensation the change of state from a gas to a liquid

precipitation any form of water that falls to Earth's surface from the clouds

 G.2.3.1 CS knows that some resources are renewable and others are nonrenewable.

 G.1.3.4 AA knows that the interactions of organisms with each other and with the nonliving parts of their environments result in the flow of energy and the cycling of matter throughout the system.

![Benchmark Activity]

The Carbon Cycle

1. Pour **100 mL of water** from a **graduated cylinder** into a **250 mL beaker.** Add several drops of **bromthymol blue** to the beaker of water.

2. Exhale through a **straw** into the solution until the solution turns yellow. (Caution: Be sure not to inhale or ingest the solution.)

3. Pour the yellow solution into a large **test tube** that contains a **sprig of an Elodea** plant.

4. Put a **stopper** in the test tube, and place it in a sunny location. Observe the solution in the test tube after 15 min.

5. What do you think happened to the carbon dioxide that you exhaled into the solution?

6. What can you infer about plants and their role in the carbon cycle?

G.1.3.4 AA

The Carbon Cycle

The second most abundant atom found in organisms is carbon. All organisms need carbon to survive. Carbon is cycled between the environment and organisms during the *carbon cycle*, which is shown in **Figure 3.**

Photosynthesis and Respiration

Carbon dioxide is a form of carbon. Plants use carbon dioxide from the air and energy from the sun to make sugars (molecules containing carbon) during photosynthesis. Animals get the carbon that they need by eating plants and other animals. Plants and animals break down carbon for energy during a process called *respiration*. During respiration, plants and animals release carbon dioxide back into the atmosphere.

Benchmark Check What is the relationship between animals and the carbon cycle? G.1.3.4 AA

Decomposition and Combustion

Carbon is also returned to the atmosphere during decomposition. *Decomposition* is the breakdown of substances into simpler molecules. Decomposers, such as bacteria and fungi, break down dead organisms into other forms of carbon. These molecules can form coal, oil, and natural gas underground. These materials are known as *fossil fuels*. The carbon in fossil fuels can be released during *combustion*, the process of burning a substance.

Figure 3 The Carbon Cycle

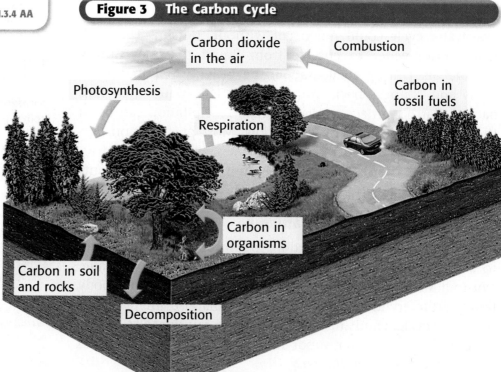

Carbon dioxide in the air

Combustion

Photosynthesis

Respiration

Carbon in fossil fuels

Carbon in organisms

Carbon in soil and rocks

Decomposition

G.1.3.4 AA knows that the interactions of organisms with each other and with the nonliving parts of their environments result in the flow of energy and the cycling of matter throughout the system.

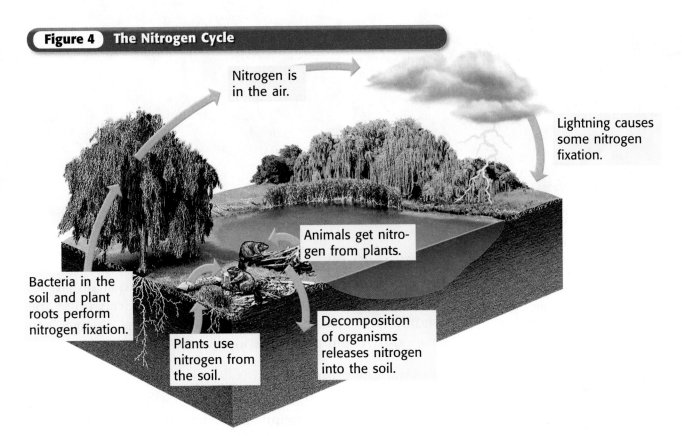

Figure 4 **The Nitrogen Cycle**

Nitrogen is in the air.

Lightning causes some nitrogen fixation.

Animals get nitrogen from plants.

Bacteria in the soil and plant roots perform nitrogen fixation.

Plants use nitrogen from the soil.

Decomposition of organisms releases nitrogen into the soil.

The Nitrogen Cycle

Nitrogen is an essential nutrient that all organisms need to survive. Organisms need nitrogen to build proteins, which are used to build new cells. Most of the nitrogen in Earth's atmosphere exists as nitrogen gas. The cycling of nitrogen between the environment and organisms is called the *nitrogen cycle*. The nitrogen cycle is shown in **Figure 4.**

Nitrogen Fixation

Nitrogen is abundant in the atmosphere as nitrogen gas. But most organisms cannot use nitrogen in this form. Only a few species of bacteria can change nitrogen gas into a usable form. These bacteria often live in the roots of plants. The bacteria combine nitrogen with other elements and release the compounds into the soil. These compounds can then be used by plants. Animals get the nitrogen that they need by eating plants or other animals.

Decomposers and the Nitrogen Cycle

After organisms obtain and use the nitrogen that they need, decomposers eventually return the nitrogen to the atmosphere. After plants and animals die, decomposers in the soil break down the organisms into a form of nitrogen that plants can use. Decomposers also change a small amount of nitrogen from dead organisms into nitrogen gas, which cycles back to the atmosphere.

CONNECTION TO Environmental Science

WRITING SKILL **Humans and the Nitrogen Cycle**

Humans are a regular part of the nitrogen cycle. However, some human activities can alter parts of the cycle, which in turn can affect ecosystems. Using nitrogen fertilizers on land, burning fossil fuels for energy, and operating power plants can alter the nitrogen cycle. These activities increase the amount of nitrogen in the atmosphere. As a result, air pollution, the loss of soil nutrients, and the overgrowth of algae in aquatic ecosystems may occur. Do research on the Internet or at the library to learn about how each of these changes can affect an ecosystem. Summarize your findings in an essay.

Figure 5 *This fire in Flagler County, Florida, was started by lightning. About 1,000 fires caused by lightning occur in Florida each year. On the right, a farmer is using fertilizer to promote the growth of crops. Excess fertilizer can wash into aquatic ecosystems and cause an overgrowth of algae.*

INTERNET ACTIVITY

Renewable Energy Resources
Write a persuasive essay about the use of renewable energy resources. Go to **go.hrw.com,** and type in the keyword **HZ5ENRW.**

G.2.3.4 AA understands that humans are a part of an ecosystem and their activities may deliberately or inadvertently alter the equilibrium in ecosystems.

D.2.3.2 knows the positive and negative consequences of human action on the Earth's systems.

Changes in Nature's Cycles

The cycles in nature are essential for Earth to maintain its natural resources. However, certain influences can cause the conditions in nature's cycles to change. These changes can have positive and negative consequences in ecosystems.

Positive Consequences

Fires caused by lightning, such as the fire shown in **Figure 5,** can have positive consequences. Fires break down molecules and release nutrients, such as nitrogen, into the soil. These changes promote plant growth and a healthy ecosystem. Fires can clear away dead and dying vegetation, which helps return nutrients to the soil. Flooding from rain can also have positive consequences. Flooding often deposits nutrient-rich soil from areas upstream, which creates fertile soil. Floods can also wash away wastes from rivers and streams, which can improve long-term water quality.

Negative Consequences

The amount of carbon dioxide in the atmosphere is increasing. The reason is that carbon dioxide is released when fossil fuels are burned. Humans burn fossil fuels to operate cars, factories, and power plants. Some scientists think that the increase of carbon dioxide in the carbon cycle is causing Earth's temperature to rise. This concept is known as *global warming.*

Fertilizer promotes the growth of plants and crops, as shown in **Figure 5.** However, the excess use of fertilizer can have negative consequences in an ecosystem. Fertilizer from farms, houses, and cities can wash into nearby rivers and lakes and can overwhelm these bodies of water with nitrogen. This may cause an overgrowth of algae to occur. As a result, the algae can use up the oxygen and nutrients that other organisms need to survive.

Benchmark Check Describe a negative consequence of human action on Earth. **D.2.3.2**

Protecting Earth

There are many ways to help manage and protect Earth's cycles, resources, and ecosystems. For example, you can help aquatic ecosystems by participating in a cleanup to remove garbage and other debris from local waterways. You can also volunteer at a wildlife rehabilitation center to help return wildlife to their natural habitats, as shown in **Figure 6.** Recycling and turning off appliances when they are not in use can also help protect Earth and prevent changes in its cycles.

✓ **Reading Check** List one thing that you can do to protect Earth's cycles, resources, or ecosystems.

Figure 6 *This volunteer is returning a rehabilitated sea turtle to the Atlantic Ocean, off the coast of Florida.*

SECTION Review

Summary

● Renewable resources include water and animals. Nonrenewable resources include coal and phosphate. **G.2.3.1 CS**

● Interactions between organisms and the non-living parts of their environment result in the cycling of water, carbon, and nitrogen. **G.1.3.4 AA**

● Changes in nature's cycles can result in positive and negative consequences.

● Human activities may deliberately or inadvertently alter ecosystems. **G.2.3.4 AA**

● There are positive and negative consequences of human action on Earth's systems. **D.2.3.2**

Using Key Terms

For each pair of terms, explain how the meanings of the terms differ.

1. *renewable resource* and *nonrenewable resource* **G.2.3.1 CS**

2. *condensation* and *evaporation*

Understanding Key Ideas

3. Describe the process of the water cycle. Be sure to include how plants and animals interact with the cycle. **G.1.3.4 AA**

4. Give an example of one renewable resource and one nonrenewable resource that you used today. **G.2.3.1 CS**

Critical Thinking

5. **Identifying Relationships** How can fires help an ecosystem? **G.2.3.4 AA, D.2.3.2**

6. **Analyzing Processes** Draw a simple diagram of each of the cycles discussed in this section. Draw lines between the cycles to show how the parts of each cycle are related.

FCAT Preparation

7. Bacteria and fungi are examples of decomposers. What is the relationship between decomposers and the nitrogen cycle? **G.1.3.4 AA**

A. Decomposers break down dead organisms into nitrogen that plants can use.

B. Decomposers break down dead organisms into other forms of carbon.

C. Decomposers are not part of the nitrogen cycle.

D. Decomposers consume nitrogen.

8. Carbon dioxide is released when fossil fuels are burned. How does this affect the carbon cycle? **G.2.3.4 AA**

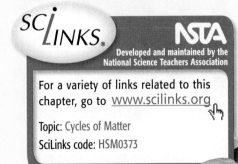

SCiLINKS®

NSTA
Developed and maintained by the National Science Teachers Association

For a variety of links related to this chapter, go to www.scilinks.org

Topic: Cycles of Matter
SciLinks code: HSM0373

Skills Practice Lab

OBJECTIVES

Observe the behavior of a frog in a dry container and in water.

Compile your observations in a written report.

MATERIALS

- beaker, 600 mL
- container half-filled with dechlorinated water
- crickets, live
- frog, live, in a dry container
- gloves, protective
- rock, large (optional)

SAFETY

F.1.3.7 CS (partial) knows that behavior is a response to the environment and influences growth, development, maintenance, and reproduction.

A Prince of a Frog

Imagine that you are a scientist interested in amphibians. You have heard in the news that amphibians are disappearing all over the world. What a great loss it will be to the environment if all amphibians become extinct! Your job is to learn as much as possible about how frogs normally behave so that you can act as a resource for other scientists who are studying the problem. In this activity, you will observe a normal frog in a dry container and in water.

Procedure

1. Make a table similar to the one below to note all of your observations of the frog in this investigation.

Observations of a Live Frog

Characteristic	Observation
Breathing	
Eyes	
Legs	*DO NOT WRITE IN BOOK*
Response to food	
Skin texture	
Swimming behavior	
Skin coloration	

2. Observe a live frog in a dry container. Draw a picture of the frog. Label the eyes, nostrils, front legs, and hind legs.

3. Watch the movements of the frog as it breathes air with its lungs. Write a description of the frog's breathing.

4. Look closely at the frog's eyes, and note their location. Examine the upper and lower eyelids as well as the transparent third eyelid. Which of these three eyelids actually moves over the eye?

5. Study the frog's legs. Note in your data table the difference between the front and hind legs.

6. Place a live insect, such as a cricket, in the container. Observe and record how the frog reacts.

7. Carefully pick up the frog, and examine its skin. How does its skin feel? **Caution:** Remember that a frog is a living thing and deserves to be handled gently and respectfully.

8. Place a 600 mL beaker in the container. Place the frog in the beaker. Cover the beaker with your hand, and carry it to a container of dechlorinated water. Tilt the beaker, and gently submerge it in the water until the frog swims out of the beaker.

9. Watch the frog float and swim in the water. How does the frog use its legs to swim? Notice the position of the frog's head.

10. As the frog swims, bend down and look up into the water so that you can see the underside of the frog. Then, look down on the frog from above. Compare the color on the top and underside of the frog. Record your observations in your data table.

Analyze the Results

1. **Analyzing Data** From the position of the frog's eyes, what can you infer about its field of vision? How might the position of its eyes benefit the frog while it is swimming?

2. **Explaining Events** How can a frog "breathe" while it is swimming in water?

3. **Examining Data** How are the hind legs of a frog adapted for life on land and in water?

4. **Analyzing Data** How does the coloration on the frog's top side and underside differ? What advantage might these color differences provide?

5. **Examining Data** How does the frog eat? What senses help the frog catch its prey?

Draw Conclusions

6. **Interpreting Information** Compile your observations in a written report about frog behavior.

Chapter Review

USING KEY TERMS

1 Write an original definition for *renewable resource* and *nonrenewable resource*.

2 Use *population, community, ecosystem,* and *biosphere* in separate sentences. **FCAT VOCAB**

3 Use *producer* and *consumer* in the same sentence.

UNDERSTANDING KEY IDEAS

Multiple Choice

4 Humans use nonrenewable resources to operate electrical appliances. Which of the following is an example of a nonrenewable resource? **G.2.3.1 CS FCAT**

a. water
b. trees
c. sunlight
d. coal

5 Bacteria are decomposers. Bacteria are very important recyclers of which of the following elements? **G.1.3.4 AA FCAT**

a. carbon
b. water
c. nitrogen
d. carbon and nitrogen

6 What type of consumer would eat only living sea grass in a coastal ecosystem?

a. a producer
b. a herbivore
c. a carnivore
d. a scavenger

7 Which of the following processes occurs when the sun's heat causes water to change from liquid to vapor?

a. decomposition
b. precipitation
c. evaporation
d. condensation

8 An organism uses 90% of the energy that it consumes to produce new cells, regulate body temperature, and move from one place to another. What percentage of the total energy is available for the organism in the next level of the energy pyramid? **G.1.3.4 AA FCAT**

a. 5%
b. 10%
c. 90%
d. 100%

9 The process in which carbon is returned to the atmosphere by burning wood or fossil fuels is called **G.1.3.4 AA**

a. combustion.
b. photosynthesis.
c. nitrogen fixation.
d. respiration.

Short Answer

10 A prairie dog gets energy by eating grass. A coyote gets energy by eating a prairie dog. Explain how energy flows through this food chain. **G.1.3.4 AA FCAT**

11 List two examples of biotic factors in a mangrove forest ecosystem.

12 How can a fire be good for an ecosystem? **D.2.3.2**

Extended Response

13 Identifying Relationships Describe the five levels of environmental organization, and indicate how each level is related to the others.

14 Predicting Consequences Sometimes, human activities affect one species or one level of an energy pyramid. For example, imagine that sardines (bait-fish) in an ocean community were overfished. Predict what might happen to other organisms, such as trout or dolphins, if the sardines were not available anymore. **G.2.3.4 AA** *FCAT*

15 Forming Hypotheses Imagine that you are a plankton ecologist. An overgrowth of plankton has occurred along the southwestern coast of Florida. Several major river systems drain into the Gulf of Mexico, which is in this region. A phosphate mine and farms are located upstream from these rivers. Form several hypotheses about what is contributing to this major and persistent overgrowth of plankton.
G.2.3.4 AA *FCAT*

Concept Mapping

16 Use the following terms to create a concept map: *natural resources, carbon cycle, nature's cycles, water cycle, nitrogen cycle, nonrenewable resources,* and *renewable resources*.

Use the diagram below to answer the questions that follow.

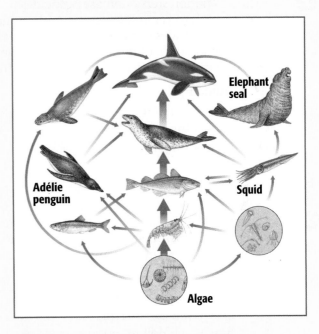

17 How many organisms depend on the squid as a source of food?

18 What effect would a drastic decrease in the population of Adélie penguins in this ecosystem have on the population of elephant seals? **G.2.3.3 CS**

19 What role do algae play in this food web?

20 List three consumers shown in the food web.

21 Which type of consumer is the elephant seal?

Standardized
Test Preparation

For the following questions, write your answers on a separate sheet of paper.

1 Farmers and foresters often use pesticides to control insect populations that destroy crops and trees. However, pesticides can be harmful to people and other organisms. Runoff that contains pesticides can affect organisms in an aquatic ecosystem as well as the organisms that depend on them for food. Which of the following organisms would have the **highest** concentration of pesticides in their tissues from runoff into a lake?

    A.   human
    B.   phytoplankton
    C.   fish-eating bird
    D.   plant-eating fish

2 Jayden knows that a resource can be classified as either a renewable resource or a nonrenewable resource. Which one of the following characteristics is the **most** important to know about a resource when trying to find out if it is considered renewable?

    F.   how combustible it is
    G.   how easily it decomposes
    H.   how fast it can be replaced
    I.   how much pollution it causes

3 Ants and aphids are a part of most ecosystems. Ants are attracted to foods that contain sugar. Sugar supplies ants with the energy they need to survive. Aphids are insects that excrete a sweet nectar. Ants feed on the aphids to get the energy they need. How would the aphid population change if the ants were all killed?

    A.   The aphid population would decrease rapidly.
    B.   The aphid population would decrease gradually.
    C.   There would be no change in the aphid population.
    D.   There would be an increase in the aphid population.

4 In many parts of the country, wildlife management officials conduct planned burning of forests. This is done to prevent a massive and destructive forest fire. While a forest fire is a tragic event for an ecosystem, there are positive outcomes. List one negative and one positive consequence of a forest fire. Explain why these consequences harm and help the environment.

5 Food webs show the flow of energy from producers to consumers in an ecosystem. The food web below shows a typical lake community.

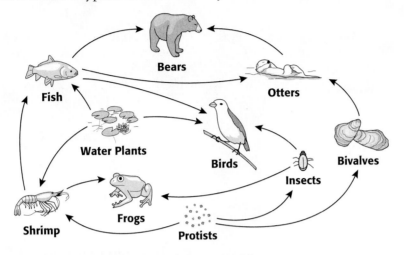

How many producers are there in this foodweb?

F. 0
G. 1
H. 2
I. 3

  6 All organisms need nitrogen to build their body cells. Nitrogen exists in the atmosphere as a gas. Most organisms cannot use nitrogen in this form. The diagram below shows the nitrogen cycle.

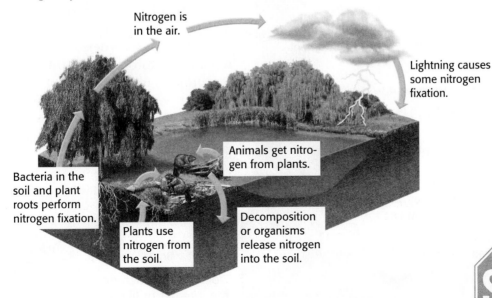

How do bacteria release nitrogen in a form that plants can use?
How does an animal get the nitrogen it needs so that it can produce new body cells?

Science in Action

Weird Science

Attack of an Exotic Species: Lionfish

The lionfish uses its pectoral fins to herd prey into a corner before it swallows them whole. Lionfish have red and golden bands that cover their entire bodies and have strange horns above their eyes and gills. Lionfish usually live in the tropical waters around Australia and Asia. However, lionfish recently have been spotted in the Atlantic coastal waters around Florida. Because lionfish are near the top of the food chain and are not native to Florida, they have upset food chains in some of Florida's coral reef environments. So, how did the lionfish get so far from home? No one knows for sure, but one possibility is that lionfish larvae hitched a ride on transport ships. It is also possible that some owners of exotic fish tired of their pets or wanted to set them free and dropped them off in local waters.

Math ActiVity

You spotted a total of 10 lionfish in one week. You saw 1 on Sunday, 3 on Monday, none on Tuesday or Wednesday, the same number on Thursday and Friday, and 2 on Saturday. On which day did you see the largest number of lionfish?

Science, Technology, and Society

Restoration of Molasses Reef

You might not realize how sensitive some ecosystems actually are. Molasses Reef, a barrier reef located near Key Largo, Florida, was once covered with colorful living coral. It was also home to millions of other tropical organisms. However, much of this situation changed on August 4, 1984, when the *Wellwood,* a cargo ship measuring more than 111 m long, grounded on the reef.

After the ship was finally removed, nearly 1 km² of the reef was completely devastated, and over 9 km² of the reef were damaged. The owners of the *Wellwood* funded the restoration of the reef. Restoration projects included transplanting species of living coral from nearby reef sites and building 22 structures to restore the shape of the reef. More than 20 years later, marine biologists have seen the regrowth of many coral species. But despite efforts, not all of the original coral species have returned.

Social Studies ActiVity

Do some research on Molasses Reef. Using the Internet or library resources, find out how the U.S. Coast Guard and National Oceanic Atmospheric Administration are working together to protect Molasses Reef.

Nalini Nadkarni

Canopy Scientist As a child, Nalini Nadkarni loved to climb trees. She still does. Nadkarni is a biologist who studies the forest canopy. The canopy is the uppermost layer of the trees. It includes leaves, twigs, and branches and the air between them. Far above the ground, the canopy is home to many types of plants, birds, insects, and other animals.

Canopy science was a new field of study when Nadkarni started her research 20 years ago. Because most canopies are tall, few scientists visited them. Most field biologists did their research with both feet planted firmly on the ground. Today, scientists know that the canopy is an important habitat for wildlife.

Nadkarni tells others about the importance of forests. As she puts it, "I can have a real impact in raising public awareness of the need to save forests." Nadkarni has invited artists and musicians to visit the canopy. "In my job, I try to understand the science of the canopy, but artists and musicians help capture the aesthetic value of the canopy."

Language Arts ACTiViTY

WRITING SKILL Imagine that you are a canopy scientist. Then, write a creative story about something that you would like to study in the canopy.

go.hrw.com

To learn more about these Science in Action topics, visit go.hrw.com and type in the keyword **HT6FEF6F**.

Current Science

Check out Current Science® articles related to this chapter by visiting go.hrw.com. Just type in the keyword **HL5CS18**.

UNIT 7

TIMELINE

Matter, Motion, and Energy

Can you imagine a world without rocks, water, or air? Try to imagine a world without light bulbs and computers. All of these items are made up of matter. Matter is anything that has mass and takes up space. Everything that you can see is made up of matter! Many things that you cannot see, such as air, are also made up of matter.

In this unit, you will learn about matter, the motion of matter, and energy. This timeline describes some of the events that have helped people better understand matter and energy.

1751

Benjamin Franklin attaches a key to a kite and flies the kite in a thunderstorm to demonstrate that lightning is a form of electricity.

1903

Willem Einthoven, a Dutch physician, develops the first electrocardiograph machine to record the tiny electric currents in the body's tissues.

1947

The transistor is invented.

1958

The invention of the integrated circuit, which uses millions of transistors, revolutionizes electronic technology.

1773

American colonists hold the Boston Tea Party and dump 342 chests of British tea into Boston Harbor.

1831

Michael Faraday, a British scientist, and Joseph Henry, an American physicist, separately demonstrate the principle of electromagnetic induction, in which magnetism is used to generate electricity.

1876

Alexander Graham Bell officially invents the telephone when he beats Elisha Gray to the patent office by only a few hours.

1911

Superconductivity is discovered. Superconductivity is the ability of some metals and alloys to carry electric current without resistance under certain conditions.

1945

Grace Murray Hopper, a pioneer in computers and computer languages, coins the phrase "debugging the computer" after removing a moth from the wiring of her computer. The moth had caused the computer to fail.

1984

The first portable CD player is introduced.

1997

Garry Kasparov, reigning world chess champion, loses a historic match to a computer named Deep Blue.

2003

One of the largest electricity blackouts in North American history started in the afternoon on August 14, 2003. The blackout left several large cities—including New York City; Detroit, Michigan; and Toronto, Canada—in the dark. Several days passed before electrical energy was fully restored to the millions of people affected in eight U.S. states and Canada.

Introduction to Matter

The Big Idea Matter has properties that are observable and measurable.

About the

Matter is all around you. Everything you can hold in your hand is made of matter. In fact, everything in this picture is made of matter. Even the air that fills the hot air balloon is made of matter. But what is matter? In this chapter, you will learn that matter is anything that has mass and volume.

PRE-READING ACTIVITY

Booklet Before you read the chapter, create the FoldNote entitled "Booklet" described in the **Study Skills** section of the Appendix. Label each page of the booklet with a main idea from the chapter. As you read the chapter, write what you learn about each main idea on the appropriate page of the booklet.

START-UP ACTIVITY

What's the Matter? A.1.3.1 AA

In this activity, you will test your ability to identify a substance based on its properties and its ability to change.

Procedure

1. Your teacher will give your group a **sealed box.** Do not open the box.

2. When instructed to do so, have one member of your group open the box and follow the directions written on the lid.

3. Only one person should see what the substance is and how it changes. The rest of the group will need to determine what the substance is from the observer's verbal clues.

4. Record important clues that might help you identify the substance.

Analysis

1. Spend three minutes comparing notes with the other members of your group.

2. Make a single list of all of the properties of this substance.

3. With your group, develop a hypothesis about the identity of the substance.

4. Look at the substance. Did you correctly identify the substance? What other observations were needed to correctly identify the substance? Record your answers.

What Is Matter?

Look around you. What do you see? Do you see a window, a tree, a book, or your classmates? What do these things have in common? Everything that you see has at least one thing in common. Even the objects that you can't see have the same thing in common.

Every object that you can think of, including you, is made of matter. **Matter** is anything that has mass and takes up space.

Common Properties of All Matter

The food you eat, the liquid you drink, and the air you breathe are examples of matter. These things seem so different. For example, you can't see the air you breathe because it is not visible. But all matter shares two properties. First, all matter has mass. **Mass** is a measure of the amount of matter in an object. Second, all matter has volume. **Volume** is a measure of the amount of space that an object takes up.

Both mass and volume are measurable and observable properties. **Figure 1** shows how the mass and volume of a balloon change when the balloon is filled with matter in the form of air. Mass and volume can also be used to distinguish one substance from another.

Benchmark Check What are two properties of all matter?
A.1.3.1 AA

READING WARM-UP

Objectives

- Define *matter*.
- Describe the two common properties of all matter.
- Compare mass and weight. **A.1.3.2**
- Describe density as the relationship between mass and volume.
- Identify ways in which substances differ. **A.1.3.1 AA, A.1.3.6**

Terms to Learn

matter
mass *FCAT VOCAB*
volume
weight
density

READING STRATEGY

Prediction Guide Before reading this section, write the title of each heading in this section. Next, under each heading, write what you think you will learn.

matter anything that has mass and takes up space

mass a measure of the amount of matter in an object *FCAT VOCAB*

volume a measure of the size of a body or region in three-dimensional space

Figure 1 *When the balloon is filled with air, the mass and volume of the balloon change because air takes up space and consists of matter.*

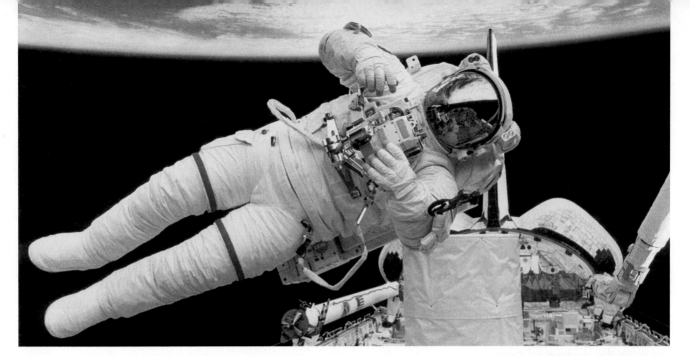

Figure 2 *The amount of matter making up this astronaut is the same on Earth and in space, but his weight is different.*

Mass

Looking at an object is not a reliable way to measure how much matter is in the object. Sometimes, very large objects can be made of a small amount of matter. For example, even large sponges have little mass. This is true because sponges are made of matter that is not packed very closely together. Also, it is possible for small objects, such as lead fishing sinkers, to be made up of a great deal of matter. Scientists often measure an object's mass by using a balance. A balance compares an object's mass to known standards of mass. The mass of an object remains the same regardless of where the object is located in the universe.

Mass, Not Weight

You probably do not know your mass. On the other hand, you have been weighed many times over the course of your life. Are mass and weight two ways to measure how heavy something is? No, mass and weight measure two different things.

Weight is a measure of the gravitational force on an object. An object feels heavy because of the force of gravity. Because the force of gravity changes based on an object's location, the object's weight also changes based on the object's location. For example, the weight of the astronaut in **Figure 2** changed when the astronaut left Earth and went into space. If this astronaut landed on the moon, he would weigh less than he did on Earth. This is true because the gravitational force of the moon is smaller than the gravitational force on Earth. But the astronaut has the same mass on Earth as he does in space.

weight a measure of the gravitational force exerted on an object; its value can change with the location of the object in the universe

A.1.3.1 AA identifies various ways in which substances differ (e.g., mass, volume, shape, density, texture, and reaction to temperature and light).

A.1.3.2 understands the difference between weight and mass.

 Benchmark Check How are weight and mass different? **A.1.3.2**

Figure 3 *These students are using three different methods to measure the volumes of three different objects.*

Volume

The way in which you measure volume depends on the kind of matter you are measuring. The volume of a regularly shaped solid, such as a cube or rectangular block, can be measured by using a ruler. The student on the left in **Figure 3** is finding the volume of a regularly shaped solid. She is measuring the length, width, and height of the object. By multiplying these measurements, she will find the volume of the block.

$$length \times width \times height = volume$$

Volume of Liquids

Can you imagine using a ruler to measure the volume of a liquid? Instead of using a ruler, you measure the volume of a liquid by using a graduated cylinder. A graduated cylinder is a measuring device that is specifically designed for measuring liquids. When poured into a graduated cylinder, a liquid often forms a *meniscus,* or curve, at its surface. When you use a graduated cylinder, the liquid's volume is read by finding the mark that is closest to the bottom of the meniscus. The middle student in **Figure 3** is measuring the volume of a liquid.

Volume of Irregularly Shaped Solids

Think about all of the solid objects that have odd shapes. How do you find the volume of a rock, a coin, or a marble? A graduated cylinder comes in handy in these situations, too. Look at **Figure 3.** The student on the right is measuring the volume of a marble. He has placed the marble in a graduated cylinder that contains a known volume of water. The marble's volume is equal to the amount that the volume of the water increased when the marble was placed in the graduated cylinder.

Calculating Volume

A regularly shaped block of cheese is measured. Its height is 12 cm. Its width is 10 cm, and its length is 8 cm. What is the volume of this cheese? To answer the question, use the following equation:

$$volume = length \times width \times height$$

A.1.3.1 AA identifies various ways in which substances differ (e.g., mass, volume, shape, density, texture, and reaction to temperature and light).

A.1.3.6 knows that equal volumes of different substances may have different masses.

Density: Relating Mass and Volume

You have learned that mass and volume are important properties that all matter possesses. Another property of all matter is density. **Density** is a measure of the amount of matter in a given amount of space. You can calculate density by dividing the mass of an object by the volume of the object.

Two different objects that have the same volume may have different masses. For example, the ducks in **Figure 4** have roughly the same volume. But, the duckling has more mass than the rubber duck has. Because the duckling has more matter packed into about the same amount of space, the duckling has a greater density than the rubber duck has. Density is an important way in which substances can differ. Scientists often use density calculations to determine the kind of substance with which they are dealing. The reason is that the density of most substances differs from the density of other substances.

Figure 4 *These ducks have similar volumes, but their densities are very different.*

Benchmark Check Describe how you can tell the difference between two substances if they have the same volume. A.1.3.1 AA, A.1.3.6

density the ratio of the mass of a substance to the volume of the substance

SECTION Review

Summary

- Matter is anything that has mass and volume.
- Mass is the amount of matter in an object.
- Volume is the space that matter occupies.
- Weight is a measure of the gravitational pull on an object. Mass does not depend on gravity. A.1.3.2
- Density measures how closely particles in an object are packed. Density is the ratio of mass to volume.
- Mass, volume, and density can be used to distinguish between various kinds of matter.
  A.1.3.1 AA, A.1.3.6

Using Key Terms

1. Write an original definition for *matter, weight,* and *volume.*

Understanding Key Ideas

2. Why can mass be used to distinguish between equal volumes of two substances? A.1.3.1 AA, A.1.3.6

3. List the three ways in which volume can be measured.

Math Skills

4. Density is calculated by dividing an object's mass by the object's volume. What is the density of a 5 g piece of metal that has a volume of 2 cm³?

Critical Thinking

5. **Applying Ideas** What happens to an astronaut's weight and mass when the astronaut leaves Earth and travels to the moon? A.1.3.2

FCAT Preparation

6. Tyrone is determining the volume of an S-shaped metal bar.

   Part A Describe the equipment that Tyrone should use.

   Part B Explain what Tyrone should do to measure the volume of the metal bar. A.1.3.1 AA

Developed and maintained by the National Science Teachers Association

For a variety of links related to this chapter, go to www.scilinks.org

Topic: What Is Matter?
SciLinks code: HSM1662

Particles of Matter

An orange appears to be a solid object. But when you eat an orange, you're able to see that it is composed of many smaller parts. Did you know that a single drop of orange juice can be broken down into smaller particles?

All matter—regardless of what it is or where it comes from—is made of very small particles called atoms. An **atom** is the smallest unit of an element that maintains the properties of that element. **Figure 1** shows that citric acid, one of the substances in orange juice, is made of several kinds of atoms.

Atoms Forming Matter

All matter is made of a unique combination of one or more atoms. Just as combinations of different letters of the alphabet make different words, combinations of different atoms yield substances that have different properties. There are roughly 100 kinds of atoms that occur naturally on Earth. Each kind of atom makes up a substance called an element. An **element** is a pure substance that cannot be broken into simpler substances.

All atoms in an element are alike. However, the properties of atoms of one element differ from the properties of atoms of any other element. The properties of an atom are determined by the particles that compose the atom. For example, every atom of the element gold is composed of 78 positively charged particles. Atoms from no other element have exactly the same properties as atoms of gold.

atom the smallest unit of an element that maintains the properties of that element

element a substance that cannot be separated or broken down into simpler substances by chemical means

Figure 1 *Every substance that you can think of is composed of atoms. Citric acid is just one kind of substance in orange juice. Citric acid is made of three kinds of atoms.*

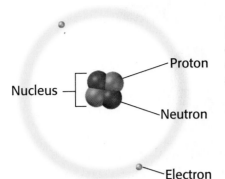

Figure 2 *A helium atom is composed of two protons, two neutrons, and two electrons. Each subatomic particle has a special place in the atom.*

Proton

Nucleus

Neutron

Electron

Structure of the Atom

Atoms are so small that even the most powerful microscope cannot look inside them. What we know about atoms has been determined through experimentation over several centuries. While there is still much to learn, we know that all atoms have some features in common. For example, all atoms are made of the same three particles. These particles are called *subatomic particles* because they are smaller than atoms. The subatomic particles that make up atoms are protons, neutrons, and electrons. The particles each play a special role in determining the properties and behavior of the atoms that they compose.

 **Benchmark Check** What particles make up an atom? A.2.3.2 CS

Protons and Neutrons

Protons and neutrons make up the nucleus of an atom, as shown in **Figure 2.** A **proton** is a subatomic particle of an atom and has a positive charge. Protons are important for several reasons. Scientists use the number of protons in an atom to identify what kind of atom they are working with. For example, all atoms that have one proton are hydrogen atoms. The number of protons in an atom is called the *atomic number*. Protons are massive, at least by subatomic standards. The mass of a proton is 1 atomic mass unit (amu). A **neutron** is a subatomic particle with no charge. Like protons, neutrons form the nucleus and have a mass of 1 amu.

Electrons

Electrons are found in the area surrounding the nucleus. An **electron** is a subatomic particle with a negative charge. Because opposite charges attract, electrons are attracted to protons in the nucleus. When two atoms come in contact with one another, the electrons of each atom interact first. The mass of an electron is so much smaller than the mass of a proton or neutron that an electron is said to have a mass of 0 amu. For this reason, electrons are not considered when calculating the mass of an atom.

proton a subatomic particle that has a positive charge and that is located in the nucleus of an atom; the number of protons in the nucleus is the atomic number, which determines the identity of an element **FCAT VOCAB**

neutron a subatomic particle that has no charge and that is located in the nucleus of an atom **FCAT VOCAB**

electron a subatomic particle that has a negative charge **FCAT VOCAB**

A.2.3.2 CS knows the general properties of the atom (a massive nucleus of neutral neutrons and positive protons surrounded by a cloud of negative electrons) and accepts that single atoms are not visible.

Figure 3 The Nucleus

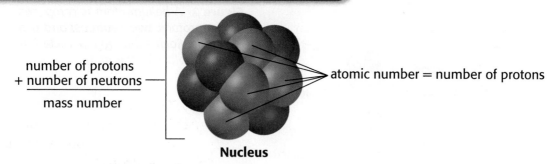

number of protons
+ number of neutrons
mass number

atomic number = number of protons

Nucleus

The Nucleus

nucleus in physical science, an atom's central region, which is made up of protons and neutrons
FCAT VOCAB

The **nucleus** is the dense center of an atom and is made up of neutrons and protons. Even though most of an atom's mass is located in the nucleus, the nucleus is very small. The nucleus is so small that if an atom were the size of your classroom, the atom's nucleus would be the size of a small dust particle! So, most of the atom is empty space. Because protons are part of the nucleus, the nucleus has a positive charge. And because opposite charges attract, electrons are attracted to the nucleus. Atoms of different elements have different numbers of protons in their nuclei. Also, atoms of different elements are different in size. So, the attraction of electrons to the nucleus of each atom is different. Both the number of protons and the strength of the attractions of electrons to the nucleus influence the properties of the atom.

Benchmark Check Why is the charge of the nucleus important?
A.2.3.2 CS

Atoms and Isotopes

Because neutrons have no charge, it is possible for atoms of a single element to have different numbers of neutrons. *Isotopes* are atoms that have the same number of protons but different numbers of neutrons. A single element can have many isotopes. Isotopes of an element have different masses because each isotope contains a different number of neutrons. As **Figure 3** shows, the mass number of an atom is calculated by adding the number of protons and the number of neutrons. Isotopes of an element appear identical in most physical and chemical properties. However, each isotope of an element has some unique properties.

For example, carbon has several isotopes. Carbon-12 is an isotope of carbon that has six neutrons in its nucleus. Carbon-14 is an isotope of carbon that has eight neutrons in its nucleus. Both of these isotopes react with oxygen to form identical compounds. However, carbon-14 is a radioactive isotope and will undergo radioactive decay over time.

A.2.3.2 CS knows the general properties of the atom (a massive nucleus of neutral neutrons and positive protons surrounded by a cloud of negative electrons) and accepts that single atoms are not visible.

Mass Number An atom of chlorine has 17 protons, 18 neutrons, and 17 electrons. What is the mass number of this atom?

Step 1: Identify the number of protons and the number of neutrons in the atom. Electrons are not counted because they have very little mass.

protons = 17; neutrons = 18

Step 2: Add these numbers to find the mass number of the atom.

17 + 18 = 35

Now It's Your Turn

1. What is the mass number of an iodine atom that has 53 protons, 53 electrons, and 74 neutrons?

Atoms: Neutral Particles

Atoms have no overall charge because the number of protons is always equal to the number of electrons in an atom. **Figure 4** calculates the overall charge for atoms of two elements. The atom on the left is lithium. It has three protons and three electrons. Finding the overall charge of the atom is as simple as adding the total charge of the protons to the total charge of the electrons. For lithium, the sum of 3+ and 3– is 0. Because neutrons have no charge, they do not change the overall charge of the atom. In the same way, you can find the charge of the oxygen atom on the right in **Figure 4.** Oxygen has eight positive protons and eight negative electrons. When you add the charges of the protons and electrons, you find that the oxygen atom has an overall charge of 0. The atom is neutral.

Figure 4 **Calculating an Atom's Charge**

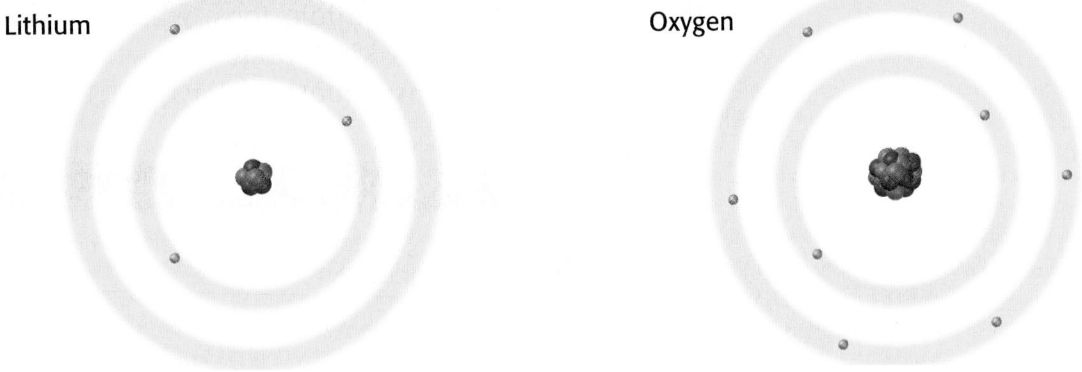

Lithium

Oxygen

charge of	=
3 protons	3+
3 neutrons	0
3 electrons	3–
overall	0

charge of	=
8 protons	8+
8 neutrons	0
8 electrons	8–
overall	0

Figure 5 The Formation of a Positive Ion

A lithium atom will lose an electron in certain circumstances. As a result, a positive lithium ion forms.

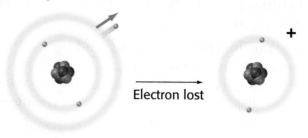

Lithium atom   Lithium ion

Atoms Losing, Gaining, or Sharing Electrons

Atoms are always neutral. However, sometimes atoms can lose or gain electrons to become more stable. Because electrons are charged particles, when the number of electrons in an atom changes, the overall charge of the atom changes, too. An **ion** forms when an atom gains or loses one or more electrons. **Figure 5** shows that a positive ion forms when an electron is lost. **Figure 6** shows that a negative ion forms when an electron is gained. Notice the *-ide* ending that is used for the name of the negative ion that forms.

ion a charged particle that forms when an atom or group of atoms gains or loses one or more electrons

Ionic Bonds

The same force that causes protons and electrons to be attracted to one another causes positive ions to be attracted to negative ions. Ions that have opposite charges are attracted to each other. The attraction between oppositely charged ions is called an *ionic bond*. A substance that has ionic bonds, such as table salt, is composed of ions in a specific ratio based on the charges of the ions. For example, lithium ions, which have a charge of 1+, form a compound with fluoride ions, which have a charge of 1–. The ions in this compound have a 1:1 ratio.

Figure 6 The Formation of a Negative Ion

A fluorine atom will gain an electron in certain circumstances. As a result, a negative fluoride ion forms.

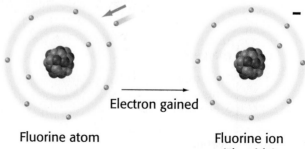

Fluorine atom   Fluorine ion
                                 (Fluoride)

Covalent Bonds

Ions are not the only particles that combine to form substances. Many atoms are able to combine to form more complex substances. When atoms share electrons, a bond that holds the atoms together forms. This type of bond is called a *covalent bond*. Covalent bonds can form between similar atoms. Sometimes, covalent bonds can form between two atoms of the same element. Covalent bonds are in particles called *molecules*. For example, hydrogen and oxygen atoms share electrons and form water molecules, such as the molecule in **Figure 7**.

✓ Reading Check How do atoms form substances?

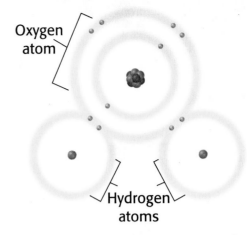

Figure 7 *Two hydrogen atoms and one oxygen atom are held together by covalent bonds to form water.*

SECTION Review

Summary

- All matter is composed of atoms. **A.2.3.2 CS**
- Atoms are made of protons, neutrons, and electrons. The nucleus of an atom contains protons and neutrons. **A.2.3.2 CS**
- The atomic number of an atom is the number of protons in the atom.
- The mass number of an atom is the sum of the number of protons and the number of neutrons.
- All atoms are neutral because they have equal numbers of protons and electrons.
- One force that holds atoms together is the attraction between the oppositely charged protons and electrons.
- Atoms gain or lose electrons to become ions.

Understanding Key Ideas

1. How are protons and neutrons alike? How are they different?

2. A carbon atom has six protons and six neutrons. Determine its atomic number.

3. An element whose mass number is 9 has four protons. The element also has
   a. nine neutrons.
   b. five neutrons.
   c. four neutrons.
   d. no neutrons.

4. The smallest piece of an element that maintains the properties of that element is a(n) **A.2.3.2 CS**
   a. particle.
   b. piece.
   c. atom.
   d. fragment.

Critical Thinking

5. **Identifying Relationships** How would an atom be different if its nucleus had a negative charge? **A.2.3.2 CS**

6. **Applying Concepts** Explain why almost the entire mass of an atom is in the nucleus.

FCAT Preparation

7. Carissa is studying the elements helium and hydrogen. She notices the following things. Helium does not react in the presence of oxygen or fluorine. Helium does not form ions. Hydrogen reacts in the presence of oxygen. Also, hydrogen forms a positive ion in the presence of fluorine. Which statement best describes what is happening? **A.2.3.2 CS**

   A. The hydrogen atom is losing an electron to become an ion.
   B. The neutrons of hydrogen are interacting with the neutrons of oxygen.
   C. Helium is gaining protons.
   D. Hydrogen is losing a proton to form an ion.

SCI **LINKS**.

Developed and maintained by the
National Science Teachers Association

For a variety of links related to this chapter, go to www.scilinks.org

Topic: Inside an Atom
SciLinks code: HSM0799

Three States of Matter

You have just walked home on one of the hottest days of the year. The air conditioner is on full blast. And there is a pitcher of lemonade on the kitchen table.

You pour yourself a glass of lemonade and add ice cubes to your glass. You take the lemonade out to the front porch to drink. After you have been on the porch for a short time, you notice drops of water forming on the outside of your glass. The scene described above has examples of the three most familiar states of matter: solid, liquid, and gas.

States of Matter

The **states of matter** are the physical forms in which a substance can exist. For example, water exists in three states of matter: solid (ice), liquid (water), and gas (steam). The state of matter is determined by the motion and position of the atoms or molecules in a substance. **Figure 1** shows matter in different states. Atoms or molecules in a solid have a fixed position. Atoms or molecules in a liquid or a gas do not have a fixed position and thus are free to move around. Atoms or molecules in a solid move more slowly than the atoms or molecules in a liquid or gas of the same substance. In fact, atoms or molecules in a solid are able only to vibrate and rotate in place.

 **Benchmark Check** Describe the three states of matter. A.1.3.4 CS

Figure 1 Models of a Solid, a Liquid, and a Gas

Particles of a solid do not move fast enough to overcome the strong attraction between them. So, they are close together and vibrate and rotate in place.

Particles of a liquid move fast enough to overcome some of the attraction between them. The particles are close together but can slide past one another.

Particles of a gas move fast enough to overcome almost all of the attraction between them. The particles are far apart and move independently of one another.

Solids

Imagine dropping a marble into a bottle. Would anything happen to the shape or size of the marble? If you put the marble in a larger bottle, would its shape or size change?

Definite Shape and Volume

Even in a bottle, a marble keeps its original shape and volume. Because the marble is a solid, its shape and volume stay the same no matter how big the bottle into which you drop the marble is. A **solid** is the state of matter that has a fixed shape and volume.

The particles of a substance in a solid are very close together. The attraction between them is stronger than the attraction between the particles of the same substance in a liquid or gas. The particles in a solid move, but they do not move fast enough to overcome the attraction between them. Each particle is locked in place by the particles around it. Therefore, each particle in a solid vibrates and rotates in place.

Two Kinds of Solids

There are two kinds of solids—*crystalline* (KRIS tuhl in) and *amorphous* (uh MAWR fuhs). Crystalline solids have a very orderly, three-dimensional arrangement of particles. The particles of crystalline solids are in a repeating pattern of rows. Iron, diamond, and ice are examples of crystalline solids.

Amorphous solids are made of particles that do not have a special arrangement. So, each particle is in one place, but the particles are not arranged in a pattern. Examples of amorphous solids are glass, rubber, and wax. **Figure 2** shows a photo of quartz (a crystalline solid) and glass (an amorphous solid).

✓ **Reading Check** How are the particles in a crystalline solid arranged?

CONNECTION TO Physics

Is Glass a Liquid? At one time, there was a theory that glass was a liquid. This theory came about because of the observation that ancient windowpanes were often thicker at the bottom than at the top. People thought that glass flowed to the bottom of the pane and so must be a liquid. Research this theory. Present your research to your class in an oral presentation.

ACTIVITY

states of matter the physical forms of matter, which include solid, liquid, and gas

solid the state of matter in which the volume and shape of a substance are fixed

A.1.3.4 CS knows that atoms in solids are close together and do not move around easily; in liquids, atoms tend to move farther apart; in gas, atoms are quite far apart and move around freely.

Figure 2 Crystalline and Amorphous Solids

The particles of crystalline solids, such as this quartz crystal, have an orderly, three-dimensional pattern.

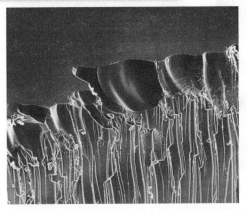

Glass, an amorphous solid, is made of particles that are not arranged in any particular pattern.

Figure 3 *Although their shapes are different, the beaker and the graduated cylinder each contain 350 mL of juice.*

Liquids

How does orange juice change if you pour the juice from a can into a glass? Is the volume of juice different? Does the shape of the juice change?

A Change in Shape but Not in Volume

The only thing that changes when you pour the juice into the glass is the shape of the juice. The shape changes because juice is a liquid. A **liquid** is the state of matter that has a definite volume but that takes the shape of its container. The particles in a liquid move fast enough to overcome some of the attractions between them. The particles slide past each other until the liquid takes the shape of its container.

Although liquids change shape, they do not easily change volume. A can of juice contains a certain volume of liquid. That volume stays the same whether you pour the juice into a large container or a small one. **Figure 3** shows the same volume of liquid in two different containers.

Unique Characteristics of Liquids

A special property of liquids is surface tension. *Surface tension* is a force that acts on the particles at the surface of a liquid. Surface tension causes some liquids to form spherical drops, such as the beads of water shown in **Figure 4.** Different liquids have different surface tensions. For example, gasoline has a very low surface tension and forms flat drops. Water forms spherical drops because it has a high surface tension.

Another important property of liquids is viscosity. *Viscosity* is a liquid's resistance to flow. Usually, the stronger the attractions between the molecules of a liquid, the more viscous the liquid is. For example, honey flows more slowly than water does. So, honey has a higher viscosity than water does.

✓ Reading Check What is viscosity?

liquid the state of matter that has a definite volume but not a definite shape

gas a form of matter that does not have a definite volume or shape

change of state the change of a substance from one physical state to another

Figure 4 *Water forms spherical drops as a result of surface tension.*

Gases

Would you believe that one small tank of helium can fill almost 700 balloons? How is this possible? After all, the volume of a tank is equal to the volume of only about 5 filled balloons. The answer has to do with helium's state of matter.

A Change in Both Shape and Volume

The helium in a balloon is a gas. A **gas** is the state of matter that has no fixed shape or volume. The particles of a gas move quickly. So, they can break away from one another completely. The particles of a gas are less attracted to each other than particles of the same substance in the solid or liquid state are.

The amount of empty space between gas particles can change. Look at **Figure 5.** The particles of helium in the balloons are farther apart than the particles of helium in the tank. The particles spread out as helium fills the balloon. So, the amount of empty space between the gas particles increases.

Benchmark Check How does the motion and position of the atoms or molecules in a gas differ from the motion and position of the atoms or molecules in a liquid? **A.1.3.4 CS**

Changes of State

A **change of state** occurs when a substance changes from one physical state to another. This change happens when the attraction between the particles of a substance is overcome. The motion of the particles in a substance affects the attraction between the particles. For the motion and position of atoms and molecules in a substance to change, the amount of energy that the atoms and molecules have has to change.

Melting and Freezing

Melting and freezing describe the changes of state that occur between solids and liquids. *Melting* is the change of state in which a solid becomes a liquid when energy is added to the substance. The amount of energy required to melt a solid depends on the attraction between the atoms or molecules in the substance. Some substances, such as water, melt below room temperature. Other substances, such as table salt, melt at much higher temperatures.

Freezing is the change of state in which a liquid becomes a solid when energy is removed. For example, you make ice by placing liquid water in a freezer, which draws energy away from the water. Because water freezes at 0°C, you may associate freezing with cold temperatures. But some substances freeze at fairly high temperatures. For example, lead changes into a solid at 379°C.

Figure 5 *Many balloons can be filled from one tank of helium because the particles of helium gas in the balloons are far apart.*

A.1.3.4 CS knows that atoms in solids are close together and do not move around easily; in liquids, atoms tend to move farther apart; in gas, atoms are quite far apart and move around freely.

Quick Lab

Boiling Water Is Cool

1. Remove the cap from a **syringe.**
2. Place the tip of the syringe in the **warm water** that is provided by your teacher. Pull the plunger out until you have 10 mL of water in the syringe.
3. Tighten the cap on the syringe.
4. Hold the syringe, and slowly pull the plunger out.
5. Observe any changes that you see in the water. Record your observations.
6. Why doesn't the water in the syringe burn you?

Evaporation, Boiling, and Condensation

Three changes of state may occur between a liquid and a gas. *Evaporation* (ee VAP uh RAY shuhn) happens when a substance changes from a liquid to a gas. Evaporation can occur at the surface of a liquid that is below its boiling point. *Boiling* occurs when a substance changes from a liquid to a gas throughout the entire substance. Boiling happens in a liquid at its boiling point. As energy is added to the liquid, particles throughout the liquid move faster until they evaporate and become a gas.

Condensation is the reverse of evaporation and boiling. As the middle image of **Figure 6** shows, *condensation* happens when a substance changes from a gas to a liquid. Gas condenses when it comes in contact with a cooler surface. The gas, whose particles are far apart, loses energy and changes into a liquid, whose particles are closer together.

✓ **Reading Check** Give an example of condensation.

Figure 6 **Three Common Changes of State**

Solid ice melts as its thermal energy increases. This change of state will result in a liquid.

Water vapor in the air condenses as its thermal energy transfers to the cool glass.

Water evaporates as its thermal energy increases. This change of state results in a gas.

Sublimation: Solid to Gas

The fog effect in **Figure 7** is made with dry ice. Dry ice is carbon dioxide in a solid state. It is called *dry ice* because instead of melting into a liquid, it goes through sublimation. *Sublimation* is the change of state in which a solid changes directly into a gas. Dry ice is much colder than ice made from water.

For a solid to change directly into a gas, the particles of the substance must change from being very tightly packed to being spread far apart. So, the attractions between the particles must be overcome completely. The substance must gain energy for the particles to overcome their attractions. You might have experienced sublimation in your freezer. Ice that is left for a long time seems to disappear as a result of sublimation.

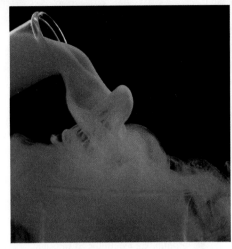

Figure 7 *The dry ice in the beaker changes directly from a solid to a gas as water is poured onto the ice.*

SECTION Review

Summary

- The three most familiar states of matter are solid, liquid, and gas.
- The physical state of matter is determined by the arrangement and movement of the particles of matter. **A.1.3.4 CS**
- A solid has a definite shape and volume. **A.1.3.4 CS**
- A liquid has a definite volume, but not a definite shape. **A.1.3.4 CS**
- A gas does not have a definite shape or volume. **A.1.3.4 CS**
- A change of state happens when a substance changes from one physical form to another.

Understanding Key Ideas

1. How does melting differ from freezing? Give an example to support your answer.

2. How do condensation and evaporation differ? Give an example to support your answer.

3. What is one property that all particles of matter in a substance share? **A.1.3.4 CS**
   a. They never move in solids.
   b. They move only in gases.
   c. They move constantly.
   d. None of the above

4. Use shape and volume to describe solids, liquids, and gases. **A.1.3.4 CS**

Critical Thinking

5. **Identifying Relationships** The volume of a gas can change, but the volume of a solid cannot change. Explain why this statement is true.

6. **Applying Concepts** Drops of moisture appear on the outside of a cold soda can. Explain why.

7. **Making Comparisons** How does the movement of the atoms or molecules in a substance determine the state of matter of that substance?

FCAT Preparation

8. The image below is a model of the particles in a solid. Which statement best describes this substance? **A.1.3.4 CS**

A. Particles in the solid move faster than particles in the gas would.

B. Particles in the solid move faster than particles in the liquid would.

C. Particles in the solid move slower than particles in the liquid would.

D. Particles in the solid move at the same rate that particles in the liquid would.

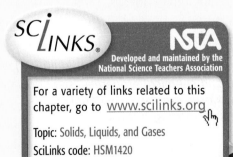

Developed and maintained by the National Science Teachers Association

For a variety of links related to this chapter, go to www.scilinks.org

Topic: Solids, Liquids, and Gases
SciLinks code: HSM1420

Matter and Its Properties

Think about all of the cars that you've seen today. They all have some features in common. But in many ways, they are very different. How are they the same? How do they differ?

Just as cars have certain features that distinguish them from other cars, different kinds of matter have distinguishing features, or properties.

Chemical and Physical Properties

Would you make a truck out of paper? Of course not! Paper is not strong enough. The burning of gasoline that powers most trucks would cause the paper truck to catch on fire! The substances used to make a truck must be strong and unreactive. The steel and plastic used to make the truck in **Figure 1** have the right properties for their purposes.

All matter has physical and chemical properties that distinguish it from other kinds of matter. **Physical properties** are characteristics of a substance that can be observed without changing the substance. **Chemical properties** are properties of matter that describe a substance's ability to change into a new substance. Chemical properties describe how and under what circumstances a particular substance will change into a new substance. Generally, chemical properties describe how a substance is able to interact with other substances.

Benchmark Check Distinguish between physical and chemical properties. A.1.3.1 AA

physical property a characteristic of a substance that does not involve a chemical change, such as density, color, or hardness

chemical property a property of matter that describes a substance's ability to participate in chemical reactions

Figure 1 *Because of their physical and chemical properties, steel and plastic are useful materials for constructing a truck.*

Steel
bumper

Plastic
shield

Figure 2 *Steel nails are attracted to this magnet because of the physical property of magnetism.*

Physical Properties

The metal magnet in **Figure 2** has many of the physical properties that the steel used in trucks does. Both the material in the magnet and steel are solid, dense substances. Both substances can be shaped and bent. On the other hand, each object has unique physical properties. Each has a different shape and size. And the object in **Figure 2** is magnetic. You can observe physical properties, such as magnetism, without changing the substance.

Measuring and Observing Physical Properties

Your senses are helpful in identifying the properties of substances. For example, even your sense of smell can identify a physical property—odor. There are many other ways to detect and measure physical properties. Tools, such as rulers and graduated cylinders, extend our ability to measure and record the physical properties of a substance. No matter how you measure and observe properties, the identity of a substance does not change when a physical property is observed.

Common Physical Properties

Length, height, width, mass, shape, and state are familiar physical properties. Yet there are many other physical properties. The most useful physical properties are characteristic properties. *Characteristic properties* are properties that do not change when the amount of the substance changes. Characteristic properties are most useful in identifying an unknown substance because even the smallest sample will have the same characteristic properties that the whole has.

There are many examples of characteristic properties. *Thermal conductivity* is the rate at which a substance transfers heat. *Solubility* is the ability of a substance to dissolve in another substance. *Ductility* is the ability of a substance to be pulled into a wire. *Malleability* is the ability of a substance to be rolled or pounded into sheets.

A.1.3.1 AA identifies various ways in which substances differ (e.g., mass, volume, shape, density, texture, and reaction to temperature and light).

MATH FOCUS

Calculating Density What is the density of a liquid that has a mass of 25 g and a volume of 50 mL?

Step 1: Write the equation for density.

$$D = m \div V$$

Step 2: Replace m and V with the measurements given in the problem, and solve.

$$D = 25 \text{ g} \div 50 \text{ mL} = 0.5 \text{ g/mL}$$

Now It's Your Turn

1. Find the density of a marble that has a mass of 52 g and a volume of 25 cm^3. If water has a density of 1.0 g/mL, will the marble float or sink?
2. Find the density of a book that has a mass of 502 g and a volume of 250 mL.
3. Platinum has a density of 21.5 g/cm^3. What is the mass of 10 cm^3 of platinum?

Density

Density is another characteristic property. You calculate density by dividing the mass of a substance by the volume of the substance. A substance's density is the same no matter how much of the substance is being measured. Density is very useful in determining whether a substance will float or sink in water. If a substance is less dense than water, the substance will float. If a substance is denser than water, the substance will sink.

Chemical Properties

Chemical properties, such as those in **Figure 3,** describe how a substance changes into new substances. To observe chemical properties, you must observe a substance when it might change into new substances. For example, substances in your saliva have chemical properties that allow these substances to react with and change food you eat as soon as you start chewing. You can experience this chemical property in action if you chew a saltine cracker for 60 seconds or more. The salty cracker will start to taste sweet as the chemical reaction occurs.

Figure 3 **Examples of Chemical Properties**

Reactivity Baking soda reacts with vinegar.

Decay Compounds in the food react with oxygen.

Reactivity Aluminum and iron(III) oxide react violently.

Observing Chemical Properties

Because chemical properties must be observed while a substance might change into new substances, they are not as easy to observe with your senses as physical properties are. But as the reactions in **Figure 3** show, there are many signs that indicate that new substances might be forming. For example, if you were exploring the chemical properties of an unknown solid, you might start by testing a small amount of this substance with water. You might observe the formation of bubbles, a change in color, or an increase in temperature. If one or more of these changes occur, you might be observing a chemical property. However, even if no change happens, you are still observing a chemical property of the substance—the substance does not react with water!

Reactivity

Reactivity is an example of a chemical property. *Reactivity* is the ability of two or more substances to combine and form one or more new substances. When baking soda and vinegar are combined, as **Figure 3** shows, a chemical reaction occurs and new substances form. A chemical property of baking soda is that baking soda reacts with vinegar and forms carbon dioxide.

Flammability

A chemical property that you may be familiar with is flammability. *Flammability* is the ability of a substance to burn. Flammable materials, such as wood, burn in the presence of oxygen. The wood reacts with oxygen in the air to produce water, carbon dioxide, and ash. These new substances have different chemical and physical properties than the wood had.

Benchmark Check What are two chemical properties that can be used to tell one substance from another? **A.1.3.1 AA**

A.1.3.1 AA identifies various ways in which substances differ (e.g., mass, volume, shape, density, texture, and reaction to temperature and light).

Rusting Iron reacts with oxygen and water.

Reactivity Sodium sulfide and cadmium nitrate react.

Digestion Chemicals in your body break down food.

Comparing Physical and Chemical Properties

Physical and chemical properties both describe matter. Observing physical properties does not change the identity of the substance. For example, when you observe the malleability of an object by pounding on the object with a hammer, you are changing the shape of the object. The composition of the substance does not change. It is important to remember that when you observe a substance's chemical properties, the substance can be changed. As a result of observing chemical properties, new substances whose structure differs from the structure of the original substance or substances can form.

Using Properties to Identify Substances

A scientist uses both physical and chemical properties to identify matter. The student in **Figure 4** has an unknown white powder. She uses the powder's physical properties to create a list of substances that the powder could be. Her list might include sugar, salt, baking soda, and powdered sugar, all of which are white powders. She can now test the powder to see if it has the chemical properties of any of the substances on her list. She begins testing the powder's chemical properties by mixing the powder with vinegar because she knows that only one of the four substances on her list reacts with vinegar. When the powder reacts with vinegar to form bubbles of carbon dioxide, she is able to confirm that the powder has the physical and chemical properties of baking soda. Both chemical and physical properties were used to identify the substance.

Benchmark Check How are physical and chemical properties used to find the identity of a substance? A.1.3.1 AA

A.1.3.1 AA identifies various ways in which substances differ (e.g., mass, volume, shape, density, texture, and reaction to temperature and light).

Figure 4 *In this experiment, a student is using both physical properties and chemical properties to determine the identity of a substance.*

Using Properties to Help Determine Use

You use physical and chemical properties every day. Physical properties are useful when you are deciding what clothes to wear. For example, the physical properties of wool make wool ideal for cold, wet weather. You use chemical properties when you decide how to remove a stain from your clothes. Suppose that you want to build a bridge. You would want to use a metal that could be shaped into beams but that was strong enough to support a lot of weight. You might select iron because it has these physical properties. But iron rusts when it comes in contact with moisture. Because you know these chemical properties, you might decide to paint the bridge to protect it from rusting.

INTERNET ACTIVITY

My New Material Create a new substance, and describe its properties. Go to **go.hrw.com,** and type in the keyword **HP5MATW.**

SECTION Review

Summary

- Matter has physical and chemical properties. **A.1.3.1 AA**

- Physical properties can be determined without changing the composition of matter.

- Density is the mass of a substance per unit volume.

- Chemical properties can be determined only by trying to change the composition of matter.

- Properties can be used to identify matter. **A.1.3.1 AA**

Understanding Key Ideas

1. Flammability of a substance is
   a. a physical property.
   b. a chemical property.
   c. not a property.
   d. Both (a) and (b)

2. For each statement, identify whether the statement describes a physical property or a chemical property. **A.1.3.1 AA**
   a. A substance bubbles when placed in water.
   b. A substance has a boiling point of 100°C.
   c. A substance is bright green.
   d. A substance dissolves in water.
   e. A substance is very hard.

Math Skills

3. Calculate the density of a liquid that has a mass of 20 g and a volume of 56 mL.

Critical Thinking

4. **Applying Concepts** Why is the melting point of a substance not a chemical property?

5. **Analyzing Processes** What physical properties would you use to find the right materials to build a birdhouse? **A.1.3.1 AA**

FCAT Preparation

6. Irene has been given a sample of an unknown liquid. She has been asked to observe the physical and chemical properties of the substance to identify the substance. She knows that it is best to test for chemical properties after observing physical properties. Which of the following properties will Irene test last? **A.1.3.1 AA**
   A. mass
   B. density
   C. malleability
   D. flammability

SCI LINKS.

NSTA Developed and maintained by the National Science Teachers Association

For a variety of links related to this chapter, go to www.scilinks.org

Topic: Describing Matter
SciLinks code: HSM0391

Matter and Change

You're helping your parent prepare dinner. You chop vegetables and put them on the grill. As the vegetables cook, you notice the difference in how they smell and the way they slowly brown. When they are finished, you eat!

The vegetables undergo the physical change of being cut into smaller pieces. And the vegetables undergo the chemical changes of cooking and digestion. Those vegetables, like all of the food in **Figure 1,** are going through dramatic changes!

Kinds of Change

Matter is constantly changing. If you think carefully about your day, you may have seen ice melting, water boiling, and food being eaten. Most changes that matter undergoes can be classified as either physical changes or chemical changes.

A **physical change** occurs when matter changes from one physical form to another. The chemical properties of matter do not change during a physical change. The melting of ice and the boiling of water are physical changes. In both cases, the properties of water remain the same.

A **chemical change** is a change that occurs when one or more substances change into entirely new substances. The properties of the new substances differ from the properties of the original substances. Many of the changes that food undergoes as it is eaten and digested are examples of chemical changes.

Benchmark Check How does a physical change differ from a chemical change? **A.1.3.5 CS**

READING WARM-UP

Objectives

- Describe two ways that matter can change. **A.1.3.5 CS**
- Explain what happens during a physical change.
- Explain what happens during a chemical change.
- Compare physical and chemical changes. **A.1.3.5 CS**

Terms to Learn

physical change
chemical change

READING STRATEGY

Reading Organizer As you read this section, make a table comparing physical changes with chemical changes.

Figure 1 *Preparing food involves physical changes, such as cutting vegetables and meat, and chemical changes, such as cooking.*

A.1.3.5 CS knows the difference between a physical change in a substance (i.e., altering the shape, form, volume, or density) and a chemical change (i.e., producing new substances with different characteristics).

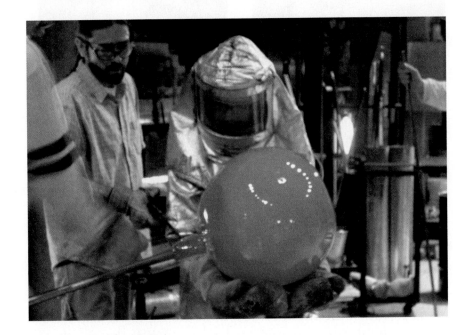

Figure 2 *This piece of glass art has been formed through a series of physical changes.*

Physical Changes

Many things happen during a physical change. The appearance, shape, size, or other physical properties of a substance may be altered during a physical change. However, the chemical properties of a substance are never altered during a physical change. No new substances are formed during a physical change.

Figure 2 shows an example of a physical change. Artists are creating a piece of glass by physically altering a few substances. Silica, in the form of sand, is one of these substances. Sand exists as many small particles that are not held together. After being heated to very high temperatures, the sand forms molten glass. Even though the appearance of the beginning substance has changed dramatically, no new substance has been formed. If examined chemically, the glass that was formed would have the same chemical properties that the original silica did.

Signs of a Physical Change

Physical changes take many forms. Some physical changes, such as rolling metal into a sheet, are easy to see. The metal has changed shape but keeps many of the same characteristics that first allowed you to identify it. Other physical changes are more difficult to see. For example, dissolving salt in water is a physical change. It would be difficult to see that a physical change has occurred if you compared a glass of water with a glass of salt water. But several physical properties of the salt water differ from the properties of pure water. Salt water is denser than pure water. Salt water also has a higher boiling point than pure water does. But the identity of the water has not changed, so these changes are merely signs of a physical change.

physical change a change of matter from one form to another without a change in chemical properties

chemical change a change that occurs when one or more substances change into entirely new substances with different properties

CONNECTION TO Geology

Igneous Rock Igneous rock forms when magma cools and hardens. This process can happen below the surface of Earth or at Earth's surface. When magma cools at Earth's surface, the magma is called *lava*. Research where active lava flows occur on Earth, and describe how the lava is changing physically.

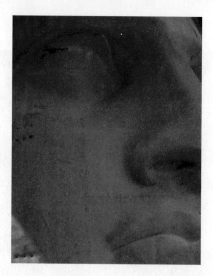

Figure 3 *The copper used to form the Statue of Liberty has changed chemically as it has been exposed to water and air.*

Chemical Changes

Chemical changes, sometimes called *chemical reactions,* take many forms. Some chemical reactions are explosive and release heat and light. Some chemical reactions, such as the one shown in **Figure 3,** are visible but do not release energy explosively. Other chemical reactions, such as the chemical reaction that occurs between aluminum and oxygen, are not easily noticed. The substance that forms during the reaction between aluminum and oxygen looks like pure aluminum.

What Happens During a Chemical Change?

Even though chemical reactions appear different, all chemical reactions have one thing in common. They all result in the formation of one or more new substances. All matter is made of atoms. During a chemical change, the atoms of a substance are rearranged to form new substances. For example, when a chemical reaction between oxygen gas and hydrogen gas occurs, atoms in both substances are rearranged to form water. Because the atoms have been rearranged, the substance formed during the chemical reaction has new chemical properties.

Benchmark Check What event happens during a chemical change but does not happen during a physical change? A.1.3.5 CS

Physical and Chemical Changes Together

Often, a combination of chemical and physical changes are used to complete a task. For example, the welder in **Figure 4** has physically changed the steel by cutting it. Then, the welder uses a welding tool to cause a chemical reaction that bonds the two pieces of metal. When you cook, you also use a combination of physical and chemical changes. When you bake cookies, you physically change the ingredients by mixing them together. Then, you change the mixture chemically as a result of the high temperature in the oven.

A.1.3.5 CS knows the difference between a physical change in a substance (i.e., altering the shape, form, volume, or density) and a chemical change (i.e., producing new substances with different characteristics).

Figure 4 *A welder uses both physical and chemical changes to form metal.*

When the welder cuts the steel, a physical change happens.

A chemical change occurs during welding.

Summary

- Physical changes do not alter the chemical properties of matter. A.1.3.5 CS

- Chemical changes alter the chemical properties of matter. A.1.3.5 CS

- Chemical changes always result in new substances.

- Chemical changes result in the rearrangement of atoms in a substance.

- Physical and chemical changes are used together in art and industry.

Using Key Terms

1. Write an original definition for *physical change* and *chemical change*.

Understanding Key Ideas

2. A change occurs, but the chemical properties of the substance are not altered. What kind of change has occurred? A.1.3.5 CS

   a. a chemical change
   b. a physical change
   c. a chemical reaction
   d. an ionic change

Critical Thinking

3. **Applying Concepts** How could you prove that grinding a bar of iron into a powder is not a chemical change?

4. **Analyzing Ideas** The boiling point of water changes when salt is dissolved in water. Explain if a chemical change occurs.

FCAT Preparation

5. When two liquids are mixed, heat is generated and a new substance forms. What kind of change occurred? A.1.3.5 CS

   A. a chemical change
   B. a physical change
   C. a nuclear change
   D. an endothermic change

SCI LINKS **NSTA**
Developed and maintained by the
National Science Teachers Association

For a variety of links related to this chapter, go to www.scilinks.org

Topic: Physical Changes; Chemical Changes
SciLinks code: HSM1142; HSM0266

Skills Practice Lab

Volumania!

You have learned how to measure the volume of a solid object that has square or rectangular sides. But there are many objects in the world that have irregular shapes. In this lab activity, you'll learn some ways to find the volume of objects that have irregular shapes.

Part A: Finding the Volume of Small Objects

Procedure

1. Fill a graduated cylinder half full with water. Read and record the volume of the water. Be sure to look at the surface of the water at eye level and to read the volume at the bottom of the meniscus, as shown below.

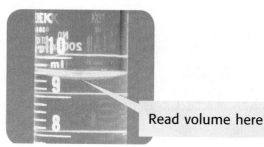

Read volume here

2. Carefully slide one of the objects into the tilted graduated cylinder, as shown below.

3. Read the new volume, and record it.

4. Subtract the original volume from the new volume. The resulting amount is equal to the volume of the solid object.

5. Use the same method to find the volume of the other objects. Record your results.

Analyze the Results

1. What changes do you have to make to the volumes that you determine in order to express the volumes correctly?

2. Do the heaviest objects have the largest volumes? Why or why not?

Part B: Finding the Volume of Your Hand

Procedure

1. Completely fill the container with water. Put the container in the center of the pie pan. Be sure not to spill any of the water into the pie pan.

2. Make a fist, and put your hand into the container up to your wrist.

3. Remove your hand, and let the excess water drip into the container, not the pie pan. Dry your hand with a paper towel.

4. Use the funnel to pour the overflow water into the graduated cylinder. Measure the volume. This measurement is the volume of your hand. Record the volume. (Remember to use the correct unit of volume for a solid object.)

5. Repeat this procedure with your other hand.

Analyze the Results

1. Did your hands have the same volume? If not, were you surprised? What might be the reason that a person's hands have different volumes?

2. Would placing your open hand instead of your fist into the container change the results? Explain your reasoning.

3. Compare the volume of your right hand with the volume of every classmates' right hand. Create a class graph that shows the volume of each student's right hand. What is the average volume for your class?

Applying Your Data

Design an experiment to determine the volume of a person's body. In your plans, be sure to include the materials needed for the experiment and the procedures that must be followed. Include a sketch that shows how your materials and methods would be used in this experiment.

Using an encyclopedia, the Internet, or other reference materials, find out how the volumes of very large samples of matter—such as an entire planet—are determined.

Chapter Review

USING KEY TERMS

① Use each of the following terms in a separate sentence: *matter*, *element*, *states of matter*, and *physical property*.

For each pair of terms, explain how the meanings of the terms differ.

② *volume* and *mass* **FCAT VOCAB**

③ *atom* and *ion*

④ *liquid* and *gas*

UNDERSTANDING KEY IDEAS

Multiple Choice

⑤ Maria and Gretchen have entered a science fair. They are exploring ways that sugar undergoes change. Which of the following actions changes sugar's identity? **A.1.3.5 CS FCAT**

   a. dissolving sugar in water
   b. mixing salt and sugar
   c. forming small sugar cubes
   d. burning sugar

⑥ Atoms are the smallest particles of matter to have distinct properties. They are composed of three subatomic particles: electrons, neutrons, and protons. Which particles make up the nucleus? **A.2.3.2 CS FCAT**

   a. protons and electrons
   b. protons and neutrons
   c. only protons
   d. neutrons and electrons

⑦ Two substances are placed side by side on a lab table. Substance A is a flammable, clear liquid. Substance B is a nonflammable, clear liquid. Which of the following is true? **A.1.3.1 AA FCAT**

   a. Substances A and B are identical.
   b. Substance A would be useful in starting a campfire.
   c. Substance B is safe to drink.
   d. Substance A takes the shape and volume of its container.

⑧ Which of the following is a characteristic property?

   a. density
   b. mass
   c. volume
   d. height

Short Answer

⑨ Jonathan has been asked to develop a model that illustrates how mass and weight differ. Propose an argument that he can use to demonstrate this difference. **A.1.3.1 AA FCAT**

⑩ What happens to a liquid when it evaporates?

⑪ Describe the difference between melting and freezing.

⑫ What is the difference between a physical change and a chemical change? **A.1.3.5 CS**

Math Skills

⑬ What is the density of a liquid that has a mass of 206 g and a volume of 321 mL?

14 Calculate the mass number of an atom that has 92 protons and 108 neutrons.

15 What is the charge of an atom that has 15 protons, 16 neutrons, and 15 electrons?

CRITICAL THINKING

Extended Response

16 Identifying Relationships The three most common physical states of matter are solid, liquid, and gas. Devise a way to distinguish between each state by using the movement and spacing of a substance's particles. **A.1.3.4 CS**

17 Applying Concepts Shari dissolves a cup of sugar in a liter of water. Explain why this change is not a chemical change. **A.1.3.5 CS**

18 Analyzing Processes Explain how physical and chemical properties are used to distinguish between different substances. Use at least one example. **A.1.3.1 AA**

19 Analyzing Ideas Describe the importance of the following statement: "All matter is composed of atoms." How do you think the study of matter changed as this statement gained support? **A.2.3.2 CS**

Concept Mapping

20 Use the following terms to create a concept map: *matter, volume, mass, density, physical property, chemical property, solid, liquid,* and *gas.*

INTERPRETING GRAPHICS

Use the photographs below to answer the questions that follow.

21 List three physical properties of the balloon.

22 What kind of change in the balloon occurred from picture A to picture B? Describe the change.

23 What two properties of this balloon changed from picture A to picture B?

24 What caused the balloon to change from picture A to picture B?

25 How do picture A and picture B prove that air is made up of matter?

For the following questions, write your answers on a separate sheet of paper.

1 In his physical science class, Arturo is learning about three different states of matter. He knows that, for most substances, particles in a solid are packed closely together and that particles in a liquid are spaced a little farther apart. He also knows that particles in a gas are spaced very far apart from each other. His teacher has explained that each of these different physical states of matter results from the speed at which the particles move and the attraction among the particles. Which one of the following would have the **fastest** moving particles?

   A. paper
   B. steam
   C. milk shake
   D. soda water

2 Ms. Wilson is teaching her class about the differences between physical and chemical changes. She wants to give an example of a physical change from daily life. Which one of the following could she give as an example?

   F. growing a plant
   G. freezing a chicken
   H. spoiling orange juice
   I. burning a hamburger

3 The dimensions in centimeters (cm) of three different blocks are shown in the table below.

DIMENSIONS OF DIFFERENT BLOCKS

	Length (cm)	Width (cm)	Height (cm)
Block A	3.0	1.0	1.5
Block B	2.0	2.5	1.5
Block C	2.0	1.0	4.5

Calculate the volume of each block in cubic centimeters (cm^3) and record the average volume in the grid.

4 Kendra wants to find out whether a can of spaghetti sauce or a can of soup has greater mass. She thinks that the can of spaghetti sauce has a greater mass because it feels heavier. Describe the process that Kendra should use to measure the mass of each can. Explain the difference between mass and weight and how this difference affects Kendra's process.

5 Dr. Huynh's class is studying the properties of matter. He has given the class information on the mass and volume of four different types of balls. The data is shown in the table below. Dr. Huynh has told the class that density is determined by dividing the mass of the object by the volume.

$$\text{density} = \frac{\text{mass}}{\text{volume}}$$

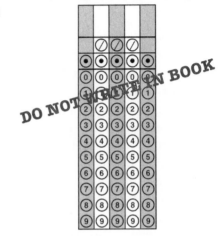

MASS AND VOLUME OF VARIOUS SPORTS BALLS

	Mass in Grams (g)	Volume in Cubic Centimeters (cm^3)
Golf Ball	45	41
Tennis Ball	57	69
Baseball	145	209
Soccer Ball	400	14 827

Calculate the density in grams per cubic centimeter (g/cm^3) of the ball with the greatest volume and record the density of this ball in the grid.

6 Ethan knows that atoms are the smallest particles of matter and that there are only about 100 different kinds of atoms. Different kinds of atoms vary by their chemical properties. Also, different atoms combine to form all of the substances found on Earth. What subatomic particle participates in chemical bonds with other atoms?

    A.   electron

    B.   ion

    C.   neutron

    D.   proton

Science in Action

The UNIVERSE of SCIENCE

FOCUS ON FLORIDA

Science Fiction

"There Will Come Soft Rains" by Ray Bradbury

Ticktock, seven o'clock, time to get up, seven o'clock. The voice clock in the living room sent out the wake-up message, gently calling to the family to get up and begin the new day. A few minutes later, the automatic stove in the kitchen began the family breakfast. A soft rain was falling outside, so the weather box by the front door suggested that raincoats were necessary today.

But no family sounds come from the house. The house goes on talking to itself as if it were keeping itself company. Why doesn't anyone answer? Find out when you read Ray Bradbury's "There Will Come Soft Rains" in the *Holt Anthology of Science Fiction*.

Language Arts ACTIVITY

WRITING SKILL The story described above takes place in 2026. The author has imagined how the future world might be. Write a short story about how you think life will be different in the year 2050.

Place to Visit

Museum of Science and History in Jacksonville, Florida

Why do you look funny in a fun-house mirror? How low does a musical note have to be for you to be unable to hear it? In its Universe of Science exhibit, the Museum of Science and History in Jacksonville, Florida, has answers to these questions and more. The exhibit is divided into eight categories: magnetism, gravity, sound, mechanics, light, energy, pendulums, and buoyancy. At the exhibit, you can launch a rocket, explore the physics of helicopter blades, observe ferrofluids in action, and perform many other hands-on demonstrations.

Social Studies ACTIVITY

Pick one of the categories of science featured in the Universe of Science exhibit. Research the life of an important scientist in the field that you chose. Prepare a timeline of the scientist's life and discoveries.

Aundra Nix

Metallurgist Aundra Nix is a chief metallurgist for a copper mine in Sahuarita, Arizona, where she supervises laboratories and other engineers. "To be able to look at rock in the ground and follow it through a process of drilling, blasting, hauling, crushing, grinding, and finally mineral separation—where you can hold a mineral that is one-third copper in your hand—is exciting."

Although she is a supervisor, Nix enjoys the flexible nature of her job. "My work environment includes office and computer work, plant work, and outdoor work. In this field you can 'get your hands into it,' which I always prefer," says Nix. "I did not want a career where it may be years before you see the results of your work." Aundra Nix enjoyed math and science, "so engineering seemed to be a natural area to study," she says. Nix's advice to students planning their own career is to learn all that they can in science and technology, because that is the future.

Math ACTIVITY

A large copper-mining company employed about 2,300 people at three locations in New Mexico. Because of an increase in demand for copper, 570 of these employees were hired over a period of a year. Of the 570 new employees, 115 employees were hired within a three-week period. What percentage of the total work force do the newly hired employees represent? What percentage of the new employees were hired during the three-week hiring period?

18

Matter in Motion

The Big Idea Motion may be described, measured, and predicted.

About the PHOTO

Speed skaters are fast. In fact, some skaters can skate at a rate of 12 m/s! That rate is equal to a speed of 27 mi/h. To reach such a speed, skaters must exert large forces. Skaters must also use friction to turn corners on the slippery surface of the ice.

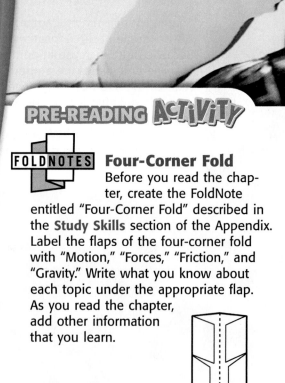

PRE-READING ACTIVITY

FOLDNOTES **Four-Corner Fold**
Before you read the chapter, create the FoldNote entitled "Four-Corner Fold" described in the **Study Skills** section of the Appendix. Label the flaps of the four-corner fold with "Motion," "Forces," "Friction," and "Gravity." Write what you know about each topic under the appropriate flap. As you read the chapter, add other information that you learn.

START-UP ACTIVITY

The Domino Derby C.1.3.1 CS, H.1.3.5 AA

Speed is the distance that an object travels in a certain amount of time. In this activity, you will observe one factor that affects the speed of falling dominoes.

Procedure

1. Set up **25 dominoes** in a straight line. Try to keep an equal distance between each domino.

2. Use a **meterstick** to measure the total length of your row of dominoes, and record the length.

3. Use a **stopwatch** to time how long the dominoes take to fall. Record this measurement.

4. Predict what will happen to that amount of time if you change the distance between the dominoes. Write your predictions.

5. Repeat steps 2 and 3 several times, but change the distance between the dominoes so that it is smaller and larger than the distance used in your first setup. Use the same number of dominoes in each trial.

Analysis

1. Calculate the average speed for each trial by dividing the total distance (the length of the domino row) by the time the dominoes take to fall.

2. How did the spacing between the dominoes affect the average speed? Is this result what you expected? If it is not, explain why.

Measuring Motion

If you look around, you will likely see something in motion. Your teacher may be walking across the room, or perhaps your friend is writing with a pencil.

Even if you do not see anything moving, motion is still occurring all around you. Air particles are moving. Earth is circling the sun. And blood is traveling through your blood vessels.

Observing Motion by Using a Reference Point

You may think that you only have to watch an object to detect its motion. But you are actually watching the object in relation to another object that appears to stay in place. The object that appears to stay in place is a *reference point*. When an object changes position over time relative to a reference point, the object is in **motion.** You can use a reference direction—such as north, south, east, west, up, or down—to describe the direction of the object's motion.

Benchmark Check What two pieces of information can you use to describe the motion of an object? C.1.3.1 CS

Common Reference Points

Earth's surface is a common reference point for determining motion, as shown in **Figure 1.** Nonmoving objects, such as trees and buildings, are also useful reference points.

A moving object can also be used as a reference point. For example, if you were on the hot-air balloon shown in **Figure 1,** you could watch a bird fly by and see that the bird was changing position in relation to your moving balloon.

motion an object's change in position relative to a reference point

Figure 1 *In the interval between the times that these pictures were taken, the hot-air balloon changed position relative to a reference point— the mountain.*

Speed's Dependence on Distance and Time

Speed is the distance that an object travels divided by the time the object takes to travel that distance. The motion of any object can be fully described by the object's position, direction of motion, and speed. So, if the balloon in **Figure 1** is traveling at 5 m/s, you can say that relative to the mountain, the balloon is moving up and to the right at a speed of 5 m/s.

The SI unit for speed is meters per second (m/s). Other units that are often used to express speed are kilometers per hour (km/h), feet per second (ft/s), and miles per hour (mi/h).

Determining Average Speed

Most of the time, objects do not travel at a constant speed. For example, you probably do not walk at a constant speed from one class to the next. So, the following equation for calculating *average speed* can be very useful:

$$average\ speed = \frac{total\ distance}{total\ time}$$

Recognizing Speed on a Graph

Suppose a person drove from one city to another. The blue line in the graph in **Figure 2** shows the total distance that this person drove in 4 h. Notice that the distance traveled during each hour is different. The distance varies because the speed is not constant. The driver may have changed speed because of weather, traffic, or varying speed limits. The average speed for the entire trip can be calculated as follows:

$$average\ speed = \frac{360\ km}{4\ h} = 90\ km/h$$

The red line on the graph shows how far the driver must travel each hour to reach the same city if he or she moves at a constant speed. The slope of this line is the average speed.

Benchmark Activity

Where Are You Going?

With a partner, measure a distance of 5 m or a distance of 25 ft. Use a stopwatch or a watch to time your partner as he or she travels the distance you measured. In your **science journal,** write 2–3 sentences using position, direction, and speed to describe your partner's motion. After you finish, switch roles. **C.1.3.1 CS**

speed the distance traveled divided by the time interval during which the motion occurred **FCAT VOCAB**

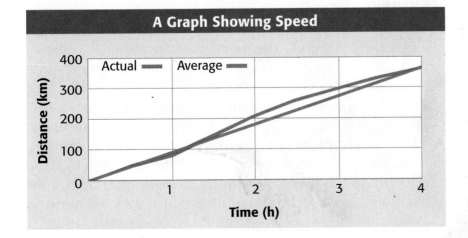

A Graph Showing Speed

Figure 2 *Speed can be shown on a graph of distance versus time.*

C.1.3.1 CS knows that the motion of an object can be described by its position, direction of motion, and speed.

Calculating Average Speed An athlete swims a distance of 50 m from one end of a pool to the other end in a time of 25 s. What is the athlete's average speed?

Step 1: Write the equation for average speed.

$$average\ speed = \frac{total\ distance}{total\ time}$$

Step 2: Replace the total distance and total time with the values given, and solve.

$$average\ speed = \frac{50\ m}{25\ s} = 2\ m/s$$

Now It's Your Turn

1. Kira jogs to a store 72 m away in a time of 36 s. What is Kira's average speed?
2. If you travel 7.5 km and walk for 1.5 h, what is your average speed?
3. An airplane traveling from San Francisco to Chicago travels 1,260 km in 3.5 h. What is the airplane's average speed?
4. A bird flies at a speed of 15 m/s for 10 s, 20 m/s for 10 s, and 25 m/s for 5 s. What is the bird's average speed?

Velocity: Direction Matters

Imagine that two birds leave the same tree at the same time. They both fly at 10 km/h for 5 min, 12 km/h for 8 min, and 5 km/h for 10 min. Why don't they end up at the same place?

Figure 3 *The speeds of these cars may be similar, but the velocities of the cars differ because the cars are going in different directions.*

Have you figured out the answer? The birds went in different directions. Their speeds were the same, but they had different velocities. **Velocity** (vuh LAHS uh tee) is the speed of an object in a particular direction.

Be careful not to confuse the terms *speed* and *velocity*. They do not have the same meaning. Velocity must include a reference direction. If you say that an airplane's velocity is 600 km/h, you are not correct. But you can say that the plane's velocity is 600 km/h south. **Figure 3** shows an example of the difference between speed and velocity.

Benchmark Check How does velocity describe the motion of an object? **C.1.3.1 CS**

Changing Velocity

Velocity can be thought of as the rate at which an object changes its position. The velocity of an object is constant only if the speed and direction of the object do not change. So, constant velocity is always motion along a straight line. The velocity of an object changes if either the speed or direction of the object changes. For example, as a bus traveling at 15 m/s south speeds up to 20 m/s south, its velocity changes. If the bus continues to travel at the same speed but changes direction to travel east, its velocity changes again. And if the bus slows down at the same time that it swerves north to avoid a cat, the velocity of the bus changes yet again.

Figure 4 Finding Resultant Velocity

15 m/s east

1 m/s east

When you combine two veloc-ities that are **in the same direction,** add them together to find the resultant velocity.

Person's resultant velocity
15 m/s east + 1 m/s east = 16 m/s east

1 m/s west

15 m/s east

When you combine two velocities that are **in opposite directions,** subtract the smaller velocity from the larger veloc-ity to find the resultant velocity. The resultant velocity is in the direction of the larger velocity.

Person's resultant velocity
15 m/s east − 1 m/s west = 14 m/s east

Combining Velocities

Imagine that you are riding in a bus that is traveling east at 15 m/s. You and the other passengers are also traveling at a velocity of 15 m/s east. But suppose you stand up and walk down the bus's aisle while the bus is moving. Are you still moving at the same velocity that the bus is? No, you are not. **Figure 4** shows how you can combine velocities to find the *resultant velocity.*

Acceleration

Although the word *accelerate* is commonly used to mean "speed up," the word means something else in science. **Acceleration** (ak SEL uhr AY shuhn) is the rate at which velocity changes. Velocity changes if speed, direction, or both change. So, an object accelerates if its speed, direction, or both change.

An increase in velocity is often called *positive acceleration.* A decrease in velocity is often called *negative acceleration,* or *deceleration.* Keep in mind that acceleration is not only how much velocity changes but also how fast velocity changes. The faster the velocity changes, the greater the acceleration is.

velocity the speed of an object in a particular direction *FCAT VOCAB*

acceleration the rate at which velocity changes over time; an object accelerates if its speed, direction, or both change *FCAT VOCAB*

C.1.3.1 CS knows that the motion of an object can be described by its position, direction of motion, and speed.

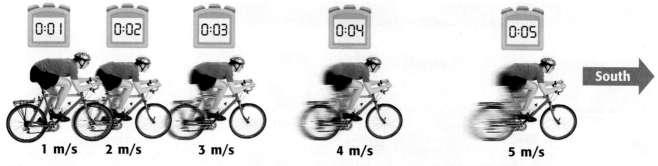

Figure 5 *This cyclist is accelerating at 1 m/s² south.*

Calculating Average Acceleration

The following equation is used to find average acceleration:

$$average\ acceleration = \frac{final\ velocity - starting\ velocity}{time\ it\ takes\ to\ change\ velocity}$$

Velocity is expressed in meters per second (m/s), and time is expressed in seconds (s). So, acceleration is expressed in meters per second per second, or (m/s)/s, which is written as m/s². For example, the southward velocity of the cyclist in **Figure 5** increases by 1 m/s every second. His average acceleration can be calculated as follows:

$$average\ acceleration = \frac{5\ m/s - 1\ m/s}{4\ s} = 1\ m/s^2\ south$$

✓ Reading Check Compare the units of velocity and acceleration.

Recognizing Acceleration on a Graph

Suppose that you are riding a roller coaster. The roller coaster car moves up a hill and stops at the top. Then, you are off! The graph in **Figure 6** shows the next 10 s of your acceleration. During the first 8 s, you move down the hill. You can tell from the graph that your acceleration is positive for the first 8 s because your velocity increases as time passes. During the last 2 s, your car starts climbing the next hill. Your acceleration is negative because your velocity decreases as time passes.

Calculating Acceleration

Use the equation for average acceleration to do the following problem: A plane passes over point A at a velocity of 240 m/s north. Forty seconds later, the plane passes over point B at a velocity of 260 m/s north. What is the average acceleration of the plane?

Figure 6 *Acceleration can be shown on a graph of velocity versus time.*

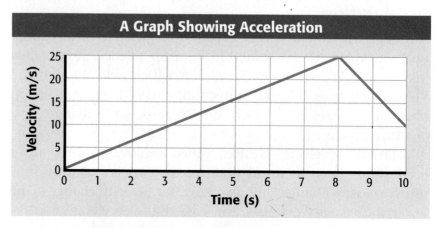

Circular Motion: Continuous Acceleration

You may be surprised to know that even when you are completely still, you are experiencing acceleration. You may not seem to be changing speed or direction, but you are! You are traveling in a circle as Earth rotates. An object traveling in a circular motion is always changing direction. Therefore, the object's velocity is always changing. So, the object is accelerating. The acceleration that occurs in circular motion is known as *centripetal acceleration* (sen TRIP uht uhl ak SEL uhr AY shuhn). Centripetal acceleration occurs as a Ferris wheel turns at an amusement park or as the moon orbits Earth. **Figure 7** shows another example of centripetal acceleration.

Figure 7 *The blades of these windmills are constantly changing direction. Thus, centripetal acceleration is occurring.*

SECTION Review

Summary

- An object is in motion if it changes position over time in relation to a reference point. **C.1.3.1 CS**
- Speed is the distance that an object travels divided by the time that the object takes to travel that distance. **C.1.3.1 CS**
- Speed can be represented on a graph of distance versus time.
- Velocity is speed in a given direction. **C.1.3.1 CS**
- Acceleration is the rate at which velocity changes.
- An object can accelerate by changing speed, direction, or both.
- Acceleration can be represented by graphing velocity versus time.

Understanding Key Ideas

1. Which of the following is NOT an example of acceleration?
   a. a person jogging at 3 m/s along a winding path
   b. a car stopping at a stop sign
   c. a cheetah running 27 m/s east
   d. a plane taking off

2. Explain the difference between speed and velocity.

3. What two things must you know to determine speed?

4. How are velocity and acceleration related?

Critical Thinking

5. **Applying Concepts** Look around you to find an object in motion. Describe the object's motion by discussing its position and direction of motion in relation to a reference point. Then, describe how to determine the object's speed. **C.1.3.1 CS**

6. **Evaluating Data** A wolf is chasing a rabbit. Use the following data to graph the wolf's motion: 15 m/s at 0 s, 10 m/s at 1 s, 5 m/s at 2 s, 2.5 m/s at 3 s, 1 m/s at 4 s, and 0 m/s at 5 s. What does the graph tell you?

FCAT Preparation

7. You see a dog in a park. Which of the following reference points will best determine if the dog is in motion? **C.1.3.1 CS**
   A. a tree in the park
   B. the dog's collar
   C. a dog that is running
   D. a jogger in the park

8. A swimmer travels the length of a pool twice in 80 s. The length of the pool is 50 m. Which of the following equations will determine the speed of the swimmer? **C.1.3.1 CS**
   F. 80 s ÷ 50 m
   G. 50 m ÷ 80 s
   H. 80 s ÷ 100 m
   I. 100 m ÷ 80 s

SCiLINKS®

NSTA
Developed and maintained by the National Science Teachers Association

For a variety of links related to this chapter, go to www.scilinks.org

Topic: Measuring Motion
SciLinks code: HSM0927

What Is a Force?

You have probably heard the word force *in everyday conversation. People say things such as "That storm had a lot of force" or "Our football team is a force to be reckoned with." But what exactly is a force?*

In science, a **force** is simply a push or a pull. All forces have both size and direction. A force can change the acceleration of an object. This acceleration can be a change in the speed or direction of the object. In fact, anytime you see a change in an object's motion, you can be sure that the change in motion was created by a force. Scientists express force by using a unit called the **newton** (N).

Forces Acting on Objects

All forces act on objects. For any push to occur, something has to receive the push. You cannot push nothing! The same is true for any pull. When doing schoolwork, you use your fingers to pull open books or to push the buttons on a computer keyboard. In these examples, your fingers are exerting forces on the books and the keys. So, the forces act on the books and keys. Another example of a force acting on an object is shown in **Figure 1**.

A force can act on an object without causing the object to be set in motion. For example, you are probably sitting on a chair. But the force you are exerting on the chair does not cause the chair to move. The chair does not move because the floor is also exerting a force on the chair.

Figure 1 *The bulldozer is exerting a force on the pile of soil. But the pile of soil is also exerting a force by simply sitting on the ground!*

Unseen Sources and Receivers of Forces

It is not always easy to tell what is exerting a force or what is receiving a force, as shown in **Figure 2.** You cannot see what exerts the force that pulls magnets to refrigerators. And you cannot see that the air around you is held near Earth's surface by a force called *gravity*.

Determining Net Force

Usually, more than one force is acting on an object. The **net force** is the combination of all of the forces acting on an object. So, how do you determine the net force? The answer depends on the directions of the forces.

Forces in the Same Direction

Suppose the music teacher asks you and a friend to move a piano. You pull on one end, and your friend pushes on the other end, as **Figure 3** shows. The forces that you and your friend exert on the piano act in the same direction. Because the forces are in the same direction, they reinforce each other. So, the two forces are added to determine the net force. In this case, the net force is 45 N. This net force is large enough to move the piano—that is, if the piano is on wheels!

Benchmark Check When do the forces acting on an object reinforce each other? C.2.3.3, C.2.3.6 AA

Figure 2 *Something that you cannot see exerts a force that makes this cat's fur stand up.*

force a push or a pull exerted on an object in order to change the motion of the object; force has size and direction

newton the SI unit for force (symbol, N)

net force the combination of all of the forces acting on an object

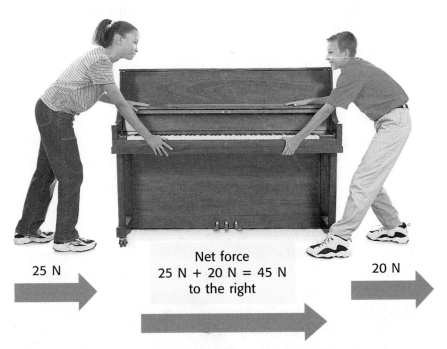

25 N

Net force
25 N + 20 N = 45 N
to the right

20 N

Figure 3 *When forces act in the same direction, you add the forces to determine the net force. The net force will be in the same direction as the individual forces.*

C.2.3.3 knows that if more than one force acts on an object, then the forces can reinforce or cancel each other, depending on their direction and magnitude.

C.2.3.6 AA explains and shows the ways in which a net force (i.e., the sum of all acting forces) can act on an object.

10 N

Net force
12 N − 10 N = 2 N
to the right

12 N

Figure 4 *When two forces act in opposite directions, you subtract the smaller force from the larger force to determine the net force. The net force will be in the same direction as the larger force.*

Figure 5 *Because all of the forces on this house of cards are balanced, none of the cards move.*

C.2.3.3 knows that if more than one force acts on an object, then the forces can reinforce or cancel each other, depending on their direction and magnitude.

C.2.3.6 AA explains and shows the ways in which a net force (i.e., the sum of all acting forces) can act on an object.

Forces in Different Directions

Look at the dogs in **Figure 4.** Each dog is exerting a force on the rope. But the forces are in opposite directions. Which dog will win the tug of war? Because the forces are in opposite directions, the net force on the rope is found by subtracting the smaller force from the larger one. In this case, the net force is 2 N in the direction of the dog on the right.

What will happen if each dog pulls on the rope with a force of 10 N? Because the forces are the same size and are in opposite directions, the forces will cancel each other.

Benchmark Check When do the forces acting on an object cancel each other? **C.2.3.3, C.2.3.6 AA**

Balanced and Unbalanced Forces

If you know the net force on an object, you can determine the effect of the net force on the object's motion. Why? The net force tells you whether the forces on the object are balanced or unbalanced.

Balanced Forces

When the forces on an object produce a net force of 0 N, the forces are *balanced*. Balanced forces will not cause a change in the motion of a moving object. And balanced forces do not cause a nonmoving object to start moving.

Many objects around you have only balanced forces acting on them. For example, a light hanging from the ceiling does not move because the force of gravity pulling down on the light is balanced by the force of the cord pulling upward. **Figure 5** shows another example of balanced forces.

Unbalanced Forces

When the net force on an object is not 0 N, the forces on the object are *unbalanced*. Unbalanced forces produce a change in motion, such as a change in speed or a change in direction. Unbalanced forces are necessary to cause a nonmoving object to start moving.

Unbalanced forces are also necessary to change the motion of moving objects. For example, consider a soccer game, such as the one shown in **Figure 6.** The soccer ball is already moving when it is passed from one player to another. When the ball reaches another player, that player exerts an unbalanced force—a kick—on the ball. After the kick, the ball moves in a new direction and at a new speed.

An object can continue to move when the unbalanced forces are removed. For example, when it is kicked, a soccer ball receives an unbalanced force. The ball continues to roll on the ground long after the force of the kick has ended.

Figure 6 *The soccer ball moves because the players exert an unbalanced force on the ball each time they kick it.*

SECTION Review

Summary

- A force is a push or a pull. Forces have size and direction and are expressed in newtons.

- Force is always exerted by one object on another object.

- Net force is found by combining forces. Forces in the same direction are added. Forces in opposite directions are subtracted. **C.2.3.3, C.2.3.6 AA**

- Balanced forces produce no change in motion. Unbalanced forces produce a change in motion. **C.2.3.6 AA**

Understanding Key Ideas

1. Explain the difference between balanced and unbalanced forces.

2. Give an example of an unbalanced force causing a change in motion. **C.2.3.6 AA**

3. Give an example of forces that reinforce each other. **C.2.3.3, C.2.3.6 AA**

4. What is a force? Why do all forces have to act on objects?

Critical Thinking

5. **Making Inferences** When finding net force, why must you know the directions of the forces acting on an object? **C.2.3.3**

6. **Predicting Consequences** You push a book toward your friend with a force of 5 N. At the same time, your friend pushes the book back to you with a force of 5 N. Explain how the book will move. **C.2.3.3, C.2.3.6 AA**

FCAT Preparation

7. A boy pulls a wagon with a force of 6 N east while another boy pushes the wagon with a force of 4 N east. What is the net force? How will the wagon move? **C.2.3.6 AA**

   A. 10 N east; It will move east.

   B. 2 N east; It will move east.

   C. 10 N east; It will not move.

   D. 2 N east; It will not move.

Friction and Gravity

While playing ball, your friend throws the ball out of your reach. Rather than running for the ball, you walk after it. You know that the ball will stop. But do you know why?

You know that the ball is slowing down. An unbalanced force is needed to change the speed of a moving object. So, what force is stopping the ball? The ball is stopped by friction. **Friction** is a force that opposes motion between two surfaces that are in contact. Friction happens only between objects that are touching. But other forces, such as gravity, act at a distance.

The Source of Friction

Friction occurs because the surface of any object is rough. Even surfaces that feel smooth are covered with microscopic hills and valleys. When two surfaces are in contact, the hills and valleys of one surface stick to the hills and valleys of the other surface. This contact causes friction.

The amount of friction between two surfaces depends on many factors. One factor is the roughness of the surfaces that are in contact. The rougher the surface, the greater the friction. Another factor is the force pushing the surfaces together. If this force increases, friction also increases. Objects that weigh less exert less downward force than objects that weigh more do. So, lighter objects experience less friction than heavier objects do, as shown in **Figure 1.** But the amount of surface that comes in contact with another surface does not affect the amount of friction.

Figure 1 Force and Friction

ⓐ The friction between the heavier book and the table is greater than the friction between the lighter book and the table. A harder push is needed to move the heavier book.

ⓑ Turning a book on its edge does not change the amount of friction between the table and the book.

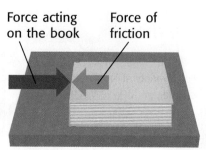

Force acting on the book   Force of friction

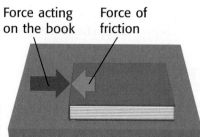

Force acting on the book   Force of friction

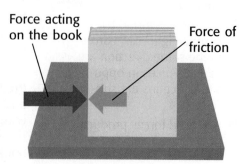

Force acting on the book   Force of friction

Figure 2 Comparing Kinetic Friction

ⓐ Moving a heavy piece of furniture in your room can be hard work because **the force of sliding kinetic friction is large.**

ⓑ Moving a heavy piece of furniture is easier if you put it on wheels. **The force of rolling kinetic friction is smaller** and easier to overcome.

Types of Friction

There are two types of friction. The friction observed when you slide books across a tabletop is *kinetic friction*. The other type of friction is *static friction*. You observe static friction when you push on a piece of furniture that you cannot move.

Benchmark Check What are two types of friction? C.2.3.2

Kinetic Friction

The word *kinetic* means "moving." So, kinetic friction is friction between moving surfaces. The amount of kinetic friction between two surfaces depends in part on how the surfaces move. Surfaces can slide past each other. Or a surface can roll over another surface. Usually, the force of sliding kinetic friction is greater than the force of rolling kinetic friction. Thus, it is usually easier to move objects on wheels than to slide the objects along the floor, as shown in **Figure 2.**

Kinetic friction is very useful in everyday life. You use sliding kinetic friction when you apply the brakes on a bicycle and when you write with a pencil or a piece of chalk. You also use sliding kinetic friction when you scratch a bug bite!

Rolling kinetic friction is an important part of many forms of transportation. Anything that has wheels—bicycles, in-line skates, cars, trains, and planes—uses rolling kinetic friction.

SCHOOL to HOME

Comparing Friction

WRITING SKILL Ask an adult at home to sit on the floor. Try to push the adult across the room. Next, ask the adult to sit on a chair that has wheels and to keep his or her feet off the floor. Try pushing the adult and the chair across the room. In your **science journal,** explain why there was a difference between the two trials.

ACTIVITY

 C.2.3.2 knows common contact forces.

Figure 3 Static Friction

ⓐ There is no friction between the block and the table when no force is applied to the block.

ⓑ If a small force (purple arrow) is exerted on the block, the block does not move. The force of static friction (green arrow) balances the force applied.

ⓒ When the force exerted on the block is greater than the force of static friction, the block starts moving. When the block starts moving, all static friction is gone, and only kinetic friction (green arrow) opposes the force applied.

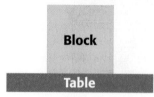

Block

Table

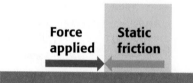

Force applied   **Static friction**

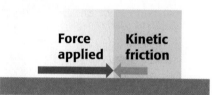

Force applied   **Kinetic friction**

Static Friction

When a force is applied to an object but does not cause the object to move, *static friction* occurs. The word *static* means "not moving." The object does not move because the force of static friction balances the force applied. Static friction can be overcome by applying a large enough force. Static friction disappears as soon as an object starts moving, and then kinetic friction immediately occurs. **Figure 3** explains under what conditions static friction affects an object.

Friction: Harmful and Helpful

Friction is both harmful and helpful. Friction can cause holes in the knees of your jeans. Friction by wind and water can cause erosion of the topsoil that nourishes plants. On the other hand, friction between your pencil and your paper is needed to allow the pencil to leave a mark. Without friction, you would slip and fall when you tried to walk. Because friction can be both harmful and helpful, it should sometimes be decreased or increased.

✓ Reading Check When is friction helpful? When is it harmful?

Reducing and Increasing Friction

One way to reduce friction is to use lubricants (LOO bri kuhnts). Lubricants are substances that are applied to surfaces to reduce the friction between the surfaces. Some examples of common lubricants are motor oil, wax, and grease. Friction can also be reduced by switching from sliding friction to rolling friction.

One way to increase friction is to make surfaces rougher. For example, sand scattered on icy roads keeps cars from skidding. Sometimes, baseball players wear textured batting gloves to increase the friction between their hands and the bat. The increased friction helps stop the bat from flying out of their hands. **Figure 4** shows another way to increase friction.

Figure 4 *No one likes cleaning dirty pans. To get this chore done quickly, press down with the scrubber to increase friction.*

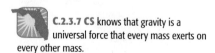

C.2.3.1 CS knows that many forces (e.g., gravitational, electrical, and magnetic) act at a distance (i.e., without contact).

C.2.3.7 CS knows that gravity is a universal force that every mass exerts on every other mass.

H.1.3.6 recognizes the scientific contributions that are made by individuals of diverse backgrounds, interests, talents, and motivations.

Quick Lab

Reducing Friction

1. Stack **two heavy books** on a table. Use one finger to push the books across the table.

2. Place **five round pens or pencils** under the books, and push the books again.

3. Compare the force used in step 1 with the force used in step 2. Explain your observations.

4. Open a **jar** with your hands, and close it again.

5. Spread a **small amount of liquid soap** on your hands. Try to open the jar again.

6. Did the soap make the jar easier or harder to open? Explain your answer.

7. In which situation was friction helpful? In which situation was friction harmful?

Gravity: Force at a Distance

Two questions puzzled people for thousands of years. Why do objects fall toward Earth, and what keeps the planets moving in the sky? The two questions were treated separately until 1665, when Sir Isaac Newton, a British scientist, realized that they were two parts of the same question.

The Core of an Idea

The legend is that Newton made the connection between the two questions when he watched a falling apple, as shown in **Figure 5.** He knew that unbalanced forces are needed to change the motion of objects. He concluded that an unbalanced force on the apple made the apple fall. And he reasoned that an unbalanced force pulling on the moon kept the moon moving circularly around Earth. He proposed that these two forces are actually the same force—a force he called gravity. **Gravity** is a force of attraction between objects that is due to their masses. Unlike friction, gravity can act between objects that are not touching. In other words, gravity acts at a distance.

Benchmark Check How does gravity differ from friction? C.2.3.1 CS

The Birth of a Law

Newton summarized his ideas about gravity in a law now known as the *law of universal gravitation*. This law describes the relationships between gravitational force, mass, and distance. The law is called *universal* because the law applies to all objects in the universe.

Figure 5 *Sir Isaac Newton realized that the same unbalanced force affected the motions of the apple and the moon.*

gravity a force of attraction between objects that is due to their masses

The Law of Universal Gravitation

The law of universal gravitation states that all objects in the universe attract each other through gravitational force. The size of the force depends on the masses of the objects and the distance between the objects. Understanding the law is easier if you consider it in two parts.

Part 1: Gravitational Force Increases As Mass Increases

Imagine an elephant and a cat. Because an elephant has a larger mass than a cat does, the amount of gravity between an elephant and Earth is greater than the amount of gravity between a cat and Earth. So, a cat is much easier to pick up than an elephant is! There is also gravity between the cat and the elephant. But that force is very small because the cat's mass and the elephant's mass are so much smaller than Earth's mass. **Figure 6** shows the relationship between mass and gravitational force.

This part of the law of universal gravitation also explains why the astronauts on the moon bounce when they walk. The moon has less mass than Earth does. Therefore, the moon's gravitational force is less than Earth's. The astronauts bounce around on the moon because the moon's gravitational force does not pull down on them as much as Earth's does.

✓ **Reading Check** How does mass affect gravitational force?

C.2.3.1 CS knows that many forces (e.g., gravitational, electrical, and magnetic) act at a distance (i.e., without contact).

C.2.3.7 CS knows that gravity is a universal force that every mass exerts on every other mass.

Figure 6 **How Mass Affects Gravitational Force**

The gravitational force between objects increases as the masses of the objects increase. The arrows indicate the gravitational force between two objects. The length of the arrows indicates the strength of the force.

ⓐ Gravitational force is small between objects that have small masses.

ⓑ Gravitational force is large when the mass of one or both objects is large.

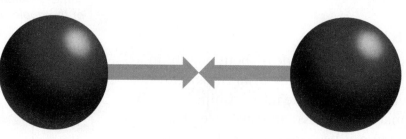

Figure 7 How Distance Affects Gravitational Force

The gravitational force between objects decreases as the distance between the objects increases. The length of the arrows indicates the strength of the gravitational force between two objects.

a Gravitational force is strong when the distance between two objects is small.

b If the distance between two objects increases, the gravitational force pulling them together decreases rapidly.

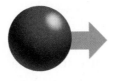

Part 2: Gravitational Force Decreases As Distance Increases

The gravitational force between you and Earth is large. Whenever you jump up, you are pulled back down by Earth's gravitational force. On the other hand, the sun is more than 300,000 times as massive as Earth. So, why doesn't the sun's gravitational force affect you more than Earth's does? The reason is that the sun is so far away.

You are about 150 million kilometers (93 million miles) away from the sun. At this distance, the gravitational force between you and the sun is very small. But if you stood on the sun, you would not be able to move. The gravitational force acting on you would be so great that you could not move any part of your body!

Although the sun's gravitational force on your body is very small, the sun's gravitational force on Earth and on the other planets is very large. The gravity between the sun and the planets is large because, unlike people, the planets have large masses. If the sun's gravitational force did not have such an effect on the planets, the planets would not stay in orbit around the sun. **Figure 7** will help you understand the relationship between gravitational force and distance.

The gravitational force between the sun and the planets is an example of gravity acting at a distance. The force of gravity attracts the sun and the planets to each other even though only empty space exists between them.

CONNECTION TO Astronomy

WRITING SKILL **Black Holes** The gravitational effects around a black hole are very large. The gravitational force of a black hole is so large that objects that enter a black hole can never get out. Even light cannot escape from a black hole. Because black holes do not emit light, they cannot be seen. Research how astronomers can detect black holes without seeing them. Write a one-page paper that details the results of your research.

Figure 8 Electric Force and Magnetic Force

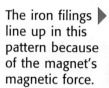

The iron filings line up in this pattern because of the magnet's magnetic force.

▲ The stream of water is attracted to the charged balloon because of an electric force.

Other Forces Acting at a Distance

Gravity is not the only force that can act at a distance. Two other forces that can act at a distance are electric force and magnetic force.

Electric Force

Charge is a physical property. An object can have a positive charge, a negative charge, or no charge. You can best understand charge by learning how charged objects interact. Charged objects exert a force on other charged objects. The force between charged objects is an *electric force.*

An electric force pulls together objects that have opposite charges and pushes apart objects that have the same charge. You can see the effect of an electric force whenever you see objects stuck together by static electricity. But electric force can also act at a distance, as shown on the left in **Figure 8.**

Magnetic Force

When you bring two magnets close together, each magnet exerts a *magnetic force* on the other magnet. Think of the last time that you worked with magnets. If you held two magnets in a certain way, they pulled together. When you turned one of the magnets around, the magnets pushed apart. The force that is pulling or pushing the magnets is the magnetic force.

Every magnet has two kinds of magnetic poles. The magnetic poles are the points on a magnet that have opposite magnetic qualities. The magnetic force between magnets depends on how the poles of the magnets line up. Like poles repel, and opposite poles attract. Like gravity and electric force, magnetic force can act at a distance, as shown on the right in **Figure 8.**

C.2.3.1 CS knows that many forces (e.g., gravitational, electrical, and magnetic) act at a distance (i.e., without contact).

Benchmark Check Name two forces that act at a distance.
C.2.3.1 CS

Summary

- Friction is a force that opposes motion. **C.2.3.2**

- Friction is caused by hills and valleys on surfaces that are touching each other.

- The amount of friction depends on many factors, such as the roughness of surfaces and the force pushing surfaces together.

- Two kinds of friction are kinetic friction and static friction. **C.2.3.2**

- Friction can be harmful or helpful.

- Gravity is a force of attraction between objects that is due to their masses. **C.2.3.7 CS**

- The law of universal gravitation states that all objects in the universe attract each other through gravitational force. **C.2.3.7 CS**

- Gravitational force increases as mass increases. Gravitational force decreases as distance increases. **C.2.3.7 CS**

- Gravity, electric force, and magnetic force are forces that act at a distance. **C.2.3.1 CS**

Using Key Terms

1. Write an original definition for *friction* and *gravity*.

Understanding Key Ideas

2. Explain why friction occurs.

3. What is the law of universal gravitation? **C.2.3.7 CS**

4. How does the mass of an object relate to the gravitational force that the object exerts on other objects? **C.2.3.7 CS**

5. Explain how friction can be both helpful and harmful. **C.2.3.2**

6. How does the distance between objects affect the gravitational force between them?

7. List the two types of friction, and give an example of each.

8. Describe three forces that act at a distance. **C.2.3.1 CS**

Critical Thinking

9. **Applying Concepts** Your friend says that astronauts float in spacecrafts because there is no gravity in space. How can you explain to your friend that there must be gravity in space? **C.2.3.7 CS**

10. **Analyzing Processes** Name two ways that friction is harmful and two ways that friction is helpful when you are riding a bicycle.

FCAT Preparation

11. Some forces, such as friction, are contact forces. Contact forces can act only between objects that are touching. Other forces, such as gravity, can act at a distance. Which of the following is an example of gravity acting at a distance? **C.2.3.1 CS**

    A. Your feet touch the ground while walking.

    B. Balls eventually stop rolling.

    C. Clothes stick together by static electricity.

    D. The planets orbit the sun.

12. Gravity is a force of attraction between objects that is due to their masses. Which of the following is true about gravity? **C.2.3.7 CS**

    F. It exists only between Earth and the sun.

    G. It exists between all objects in the universe.

    H. It affects only objects that touch.

    I. It affects only large objects in space.

SCi LINKS®

NSTA

Developed and maintained by the National Science Teachers Association

For a variety of links related to this chapter, go to www.scilinks.org

Topic: Force and Friction; Matter and Gravity

SciLinks code: HSM0601; HSM0922

Skills Practice Lab

Detecting Acceleration

Have you ever noticed that you can "feel" acceleration? In a car or in an elevator, you may notice changes in speed or direction—even with your eyes closed! You are able to sense these changes because of tiny hair cells in your ears. These cells detect the movement of fluid in your inner ear. The fluid accelerates when you do, and the hair cells send a message about the acceleration to your brain. This message allows you to sense the acceleration. In this activity, you will build a device that detects acceleration. This device is called an *accelerometer* (ak SEL uhr AHM uht uhr).

Procedure

1. Cut a piece of string that reaches three-quarters of the way into the container.

2. Use a pushpin to attach one end of the string to the cork or plastic-foam ball.

3. Use modeling clay to attach the other end of the string to the center of the inside of the container lid. The cork or ball should hang no farther than three-quarters of the way into the container.

4. Fill the container with water.

5. Tightly close the lid on the container. The string and cork should be inside the container.

6. Turn the container upside down. The cork should float about three-quarters of the way up inside the container, as shown at left. You are now ready to detect acceleration by using your accelerometer and completing the following steps.

7. Put the accelerometer on a tabletop. The container lid should touch the tabletop. Notice that the cork floats straight up in the water.

8. Now, gently push the accelerometer across the table at a constant speed. Notice that the cork quickly moves in the direction you are pushing and then swings backward. If you did not see this motion, repeat this step until you are sure that you can see the first movement of the cork.

OBJECTIVES

Build an accelerometer.

Explain how an accelerometer works.

MATERIALS

- container, 1 L, with watertight lid
- cork or plastic-foam ball, small
- modeling clay
- pushpin
- scissors
- string
- water

SAFETY

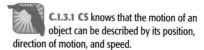
C.1.3.1 CS knows that the motion of an object can be described by its position, direction of motion, and speed.

9 After you are familiar with how to use your accelerometer, try the following changes in motion. For each change, record your observations of the cork's first motion.

a. As you move the accelerometer across the table, gradually increase its speed.

b. As you move the accelerometer across the table, gradually decrease its speed.

c. While moving the accelerometer across the table, change the direction in which you are pushing.

d. Make any other changes in motion that you can think of. You should make only one change to the motion for each trial.

Analyze the Results

1 **Analyzing Results** When you move the bottle at a constant speed, why does the cork quickly swing backward after it moves in the direction of acceleration?

2 **Explaining Events** The cork moves forward (in the direction you were moving the bottle) when you speed up but moves backward when you slow down. Explain why the cork moves this way. (Hint: Think about the direction of acceleration.)

Draw Conclusions

3 **Making Predictions** Imagine you are standing on a corner and watching a car that is waiting at a stoplight. A passenger inside the car is holding some helium balloons. Use what you observed with your accelerometer to predict what will happen to the balloons when the car begins moving.

Applying Your Data

What do you predict the cork will do if you move the bottle in a circle at a constant speed? Try it, and check your answer.

Chapter Review

USING KEY TERMS

Use a term from the chapter to complete each sentence below.

1 ___ opposes motion between surfaces that are touching. **C.2.3.2**

2 The ___ is the unit of force.

3 ___ is determined by combining forces. **C.2.3.3, C.2.3.6 AA**

4 Acceleration is the rate at which ___ changes.

UNDERSTANDING KEY IDEAS

Multiple Choice

5 If a student rides her bicycle on a straight road and does not speed up or slow down, she is traveling with a

a. constant acceleration.

b. constant velocity.

c. positive acceleration.

d. negative acceleration.

6 A magnet can exert a magnetic force on materials containing iron. Which of the following is an example of a magnetic force acting at a distance? **C.2.3.1 CS FCAT**

a. Opposite poles of magnets stick together.

b. Magnets stick on refrigerator doors.

c. Magnets hold papers on refrigerator doors.

d. A paper clip sticks to a magnet.

7 A hurricane is heading toward Florida. What information do you need to determine when the hurricane will strike the coast? **C.1.3.1 CS FCAT**

a. the hurricane's speed and position

b. the hurricane's position and direction of motion

c. the hurricane's speed and direction of motion

d. the hurricane's position, speed, and direction of motion

8 The gravitational force between 1 kg of lead and Earth is ___ the gravitational force between 1 kg of marshmallows and Earth. **C.2.3.7 CS**

a. greater than

b. less than

c. equal to

d. None of the above

9 Which of the following is a measurement of velocity?

a. 16 m east

b. 25 m/s²

c. 55 m/h south

d. 60 km/h

Short Answer

10 Describe the relationship between motion and a reference point. **C.1.3.1 CS**

11 How is it possible to be accelerating and traveling at a constant speed?

Math Skills

12 A kangaroo hops 60 m to the east in 5 s. Use this information to answer the following questions:

   a. What is the kangaroo's average speed? **C.1.3.1 CS**

   b. The kangaroo stops at a lake for a drink of water and then starts hopping again to the south. Each second, the kangaroo's velocity increases 2.5 m/s. What is the kangaroo's acceleration after 5 s?

CRITICAL THINKING

Extended Response

13 **Applying Concepts** Your friend asks to help move some boxes. One box is so heavy that you must push it across the room rather than lift it. How could you reduce friction to make moving the box easier? **C.2.3.6 AA** *FCAT*

14 **Analyzing Ideas** Consider the scientific meaning of the word *acceleration* and the use of the term *accelerator* when talking about a car's gas pedal. How can these meanings lead to confusion?

15 **Identifying Relationships** Explain why airplane pilots should know wind velocity as well as wind speed during a flight.

Concept Mapping

16 Use the following terms to create a concept map: *speed, velocity, force, acceleration, direction,* and *motion.*

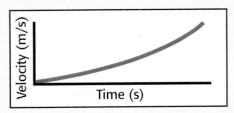

INTERPRETING GRAPHICS

Use the appropriate figure to answer the following questions.

17 Is the graph below showing positive acceleration or negative acceleration? How can you tell?

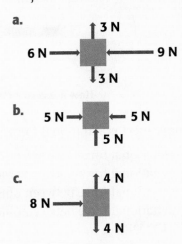

18 You know how to combine two forces that act in one or two directions. The same method can be used to combine several forces acting in several directions. Look at the diagrams, and calculate the net force in each diagram. Predict the direction in which each object will move. **C.2.3.3, C.2.3.6 AA**

   a.

   3 N ↑   6 N → ← 9 N   ↓ 3 N

   b.

   5 N → ← 5 N   ↑ 5 N

   c.

   4 N ↑   8 N →   ↓ 4 N

For the following questions, write your answers on a separate sheet of paper.

1

Two balls are on a billiards table. Ball B is at rest. Ball A hits Ball B and both balls bounce around until each eventually rolls to a stop.

Part A Are the forces that act on Ball B balanced or unbalanced? Explain.

Part B What force acts on the billiard balls to bring them to a stop? Explain.

2

At a picnic, Sheila and three of her friends challenge four other girls to a tug-of-war with a long rope. On Sheila's team, each girl except Sheila is able to pull with a force of 140 newtons (N). Sheila can pull with a force of 160 N. On the other team, one girl can pull with a force of 120 N, one can pull with a force of 130 N, and two can each pull with a force of 140 N. Sheila's team wins the tug-of-war. Calculate the net force on the rope in newtons.

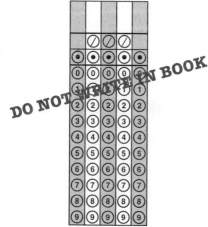

DO NOT WRITE IN BOOK

3

Gravity is a force that acts at a distance between objects. The mass of objects affects gravitational force. Look at the image below. The length of the arrows indicates the size of the gravitational force. The larger spheres represent objects with larger masses.

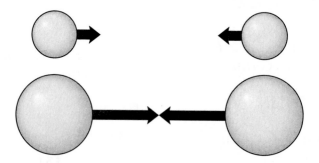

How Mass Affects Gravitational Force

How does mass affect gravitational force?

A. The gravitational force between objects decreases as the masses of the objects increase.

B. The gravitational force between objects increases as the masses of the objects increase.

C. The gravitational force between objects increases as the masses of the objects decrease.

D. The gravitational force between objects increases even when the masses of the objects remain the same.

4 Acceleration has a particular meaning in science. What is the meaning of acceleration as it is used in science?

    F.   An object accelerates if its speed increases.

    G.   An object accelerates if its speed increases or decreases.

    H.   An object accelerates if its speed and/or direction change.

    I.   An object accelerates if its speed increases or its direction changes.

5 Since most objects do not travel at a constant speed, average speed is often used to calculate speed. Yesterday Kyra traveled 30 kilometers. She drove 16 kilometers in 20 minutes, walked 4 kilometers in 1 hour, then rode a bus going 10 kilometers in 10 minutes. Calculate her average speed in kilometers per hour.

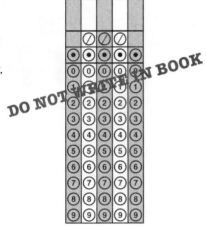

DO NOT WRITE IN BOOK

6 Of the following forces, which two act at a distance between objects?

    A.   friction and kinetic force

    B.   visible force and unseen force

    C.   magnetic force and electric force

    D.   balanced force and unbalanced force

Science in Action

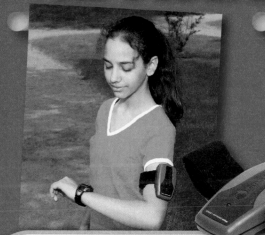

Science, Technology, and Society

GPS Watch System

Some athletes are concerned about knowing their speed during training. To calculate speed, they need to know distance and time. Using a watch to measure time is easy. But determining distance is more difficult. However, a GPS watch system is now available to help with this problem. *GPS* stands for *global positioning system*. A GPS unit, which is worn on an athlete's upper arm, monitors the athlete's position by using signals from satellites. As the athlete moves, the GPS unit calculates the distance traveled. The GPS unit sends a signal to the watch, which keeps the athlete's time, and the watch displays the athlete's speed.

Math ACTIVITY

Suppose an athlete wishes to finish a 5 K race in under 25 min. A distance of 5 K is 5 km. (Remember that 1 km = 1,000 m.) If the athlete runs the race at a constant speed of 3.4 m/s, will she meet her goal?

Weird Science

Jai Alai: The World's Fastest Sport

Imagine catching a ball that is traveling at a speed of more than 240 km/h (150 mi/h)! If you ever play the sport of jai alai, you may have to catch this ball. Some people think that jai alai is the world's fastest sport. Because the jai alai ball, called a *pelota,* can move so fast, players catch and throw it with a curved device called a *cesta*. The cesta protects a player's hand and allows the player to throw the pelota with great force.

Jai alai is very popular in Florida but is not very well known elsewhere in the United States. Jai alai teams are found in many major cities in Florida, including Miami, Orlando, Fort Pierce, and Ocala. In fact, the jai alai stadium (called a *fronton*) in Miami is the world's largest jai alai fronton.

Language Arts ACTIVITY

WRITING SKILL Do research to find out how the game of jai alai is played. Then, write a short instruction manual that explains the rules of the game to someone who does not know how to play it.

Victor Petrenko

Snowboard and Ski Brakes Have you ever wished for emergency brakes on your snowboard or skis? Thanks to Victor Petrenko and the Ice Research Lab of Dartmouth College, snowboards and skis that have braking systems may soon be available.

Few people know more about the properties of ice and ice-related technologies than Petrenko does. He has spent most of his career researching the electrical and mechanical properties of ice. Through his research, Petrenko learned that ice can hold an electric charge. He used this property to design a braking system for snowboards. The system is a form of electric friction control.

The power source for the brakes is a battery. The battery is connected to a network of wires embedded on the bottom surface of a snowboard. When the battery is activated, the bottom of the snowboard gains a negative charge. This negative charge creates a positive charge on the surface of the snow. Because opposite charges attract, the snowboard and the snow are pulled together. The force that pulls the surfaces together increases friction, and the snowboard slows down.

Social Studies
ACTIVITY

Research the history of skiing. Make a poster that includes a timeline of significant dates in the history of skiing. Illustrate your poster with photos or drawings.

go.hrw.com

To learn more about these Science in Action topics, visit go.hrw.com and type in the keyword **HT6FMTFF**.

Current Science

Check out Current Science® articles related to this chapter by visiting go.hrw.com. Just type in the keyword **HP5CS05**.

Introduction to Energy

The Big Idea Energy cannot be created or destroyed but can be changed from one form to another.

About the

Imagine that you are a driver in a race. Your car needs a lot of energy to finish. So, it probably needs a lot of gasoline, right? No, it just needs a lot of sunshine! The car shown runs on solar energy. Solar energy is one of many forms of energy. Energy is needed to drive a car, turn on a light bulb, play sports, and walk to school. Energy is always being changed into different forms for different uses.

PRE-READING ACTIVITY

FOLDNOTES **Layered Book** Before you read the chapter, create the FoldNote entitled "Layered Book" described in the **Study Skills** section of the Appendix. Label the tabs of the layered book with "Types of energy," "Wave energy," "Energy conversion and transfer," and "Energy uses." As you read the chapter, write information you learn about each category under the appropriate tab.

START-UP ACTIVITY

Energy Swings! B.1.3.2

In this activity, you'll observe a moving pendulum to learn about energy.

Procedure

1. Make a pendulum by tying a **string** that is 50 cm long around the hook of a **100 g hooked mass.**

2. Hold the string with one hand. Pull the mass slightly to the side, and let go of the mass without pushing it. Watch it swing at least 10 times.

3. Record your observations. Note how fast and how high the pendulum swings.

4. Repeat step 2, but pull the mass farther to the side.

5. Record your observations. Note how fast and how high the pendulum swings.

Analysis

1. Does the pendulum have energy? Explain your answer.

2. What causes the pendulum to move?

3. Do you think that the pendulum had energy before you let go of the mass? Explain your answer.

What Is Energy?

The tennis player tosses the ball into the air and slams it with her racket. The ball flies toward her opponent, who swings her racket at the ball. THWOOSH! The ball goes into the net and causes the net to shake. The player scores—game, set, and match!

The tennis player needs energy to slam the ball with her racket. And the ball must have energy to cause the net to shake. Energy is around you all of the time. But what is energy?

Energy and Work: Working Together

In science, **energy** is the ability to do work. Work is done when a force causes an object to move in the direction of the force. How do energy and work help you play tennis? The tennis player in **Figure 1** does work on her racket by exerting a force on it. The racket does work on the ball. And if it hits the net, the ball does work on the net. When one object does work on another, energy is transferred from the first object to the second object. This energy allows the second object to do work. So, work is a transfer of energy. Like work, energy is expressed in units of joules (J). There are many different forms of energy, such as kinetic energy and potential energy. All forms of energy can be measured and compared.

✓ **Reading Check** What is energy?

energy the capacity to do work

Figure 1 *This tennis player does work and transfers energy to the racket. With this energy, the racket can then do work on the ball.*

B.1.3.1 AA identifies forms of energy and explains that they can be measured and compared.

Kinetic Energy

In tennis, energy is transferred from the racket to the ball. As it flies over the net, the ball has kinetic (ki NET ik) energy. **Kinetic energy** is the energy of motion. All moving objects have kinetic energy. Like all forms of energy, kinetic energy can be used to do work. For example, kinetic energy allows a hammer to do work on a nail, as shown in **Figure 2.**

Figure 2 *When you swing a hammer, you give it kinetic energy, which does work on the nail.*

Mass and Speed

The amount of kinetic energy that a moving object has depends on the object's mass and speed. The faster an object is moving, the more kinetic energy it has. Also, the more mass a moving object has, the greater its kinetic energy is.

But, mass and speed do not contribute equally to kinetic energy. Speed has a greater effect on kinetic energy than mass does. For example, a truck that has twice the mass of a car moving at the same speed as the truck is moving has 2 times the amount of kinetic energy that the car has. But if the speed of the car doubles, the car's kinetic energy increases by *4 times*! For this reason, car crashes are much more dangerous at high speeds than at low speeds.

kinetic energy the energy of an object that is due to the object's motion

potential energy the energy that an object has because of the position, shape, or condition of the object **FCAT***VOCAB*

Potential Energy

Not all energy has to do with motion. **Potential energy** is the energy an object has because of its position. For example, the stretched bow shown in **Figure 3** has potential energy. The bow has energy because work has been done to change its shape. The energy of that work is turned into potential energy.

Gravitational Potential Energy

When you lift an object, you do work on it. You use a force that is working against the force of gravity. When you lift an object, you transfer energy to the object and give the object *gravitational potential energy.* Books on a shelf have gravitational potential energy, and so does your backpack after you lift it onto your back. The amount of gravitational potential energy that an object has depends on its weight and its height.

Figure 3 *The stored potential energy of the bow and string allows them to do work on the arrow when the string is released.*

Mechanical Energy

mechanical energy the amount of work an object can do because of the object's kinetic and potential energies

How would you describe the energy of a cat walking along the top of a fence? To describe the cat's total energy, you would state the cat's mechanical energy. **Mechanical energy** is the total energy of motion and position of an object. Both potential energy and kinetic energy are types of mechanical energy. Mechanical energy can be made up of only potential energy, only kinetic energy, or some of each.

thermal energy the kinetic energy of a substance's atoms *FCAT VOCAB*

Other Forms of Energy

Energy can come in other forms besides mechanical energy. These forms of energy include thermal, chemical, electrical, sound, light, and nuclear energy.

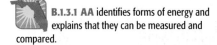

B.1.3.1 AA identifies forms of energy and explains that they can be measured and compared.

Thermal Energy and Chemical Energy

All matter is made of particles that are always in random motion. Because the particles are moving, they have kinetic energy. **Thermal energy** is all of the kinetic energy due to the random motion of the particles that make up an object. Thermal energy is often measured by measuring temperature.

All matter also has chemical energy. *Chemical energy* is energy stored in chemical bonds. The energy in food is stored as chemical energy. Chemical energy is a form of potential energy.

Electrical Energy and Sound Energy

The electrical outlets in your home allow you to use electrical energy. *Electrical energy* is the energy of moving electrons. The singer in **Figure 4** is using an electric amplifier. The amplifier uses electrical energy to produce a louder sound.

You can hear a song because of sound energy. *Sound energy* is energy that is created by an object's vibrations. Inside an amplifier is a cone that vibrates. The cone's vibrations cause the air particles around the cone to vibrate. The vibration of the air particles transmits sound energy to your ear. When the energy reaches your ear, you hear the singer's voice.

Benchmark Check Identify and describe four different forms of energy. B.1.3.1 AA

Figure 4 *The movement of electrons provides the electrical energy that an amplifier and a microphone use to produce sound.*

Light Energy

Light allows you to see, but not all light can be seen. For example, microwaves in a microwave oven and ultraviolet light from the sun are kinds of light energy that you cannot see. *Light energy* travels in waves called *electromagnetic waves*. Electromagnetic waves can be produced by the vibration of electrically charged particles.

Nuclear Energy

Nuclear (NOO klee uhr) *energy* is the energy that comes from changes in the nucleus (NOO klee uhs) of an atom. The energy given off by the sun comes from nuclear energy. In the sun, shown in **Figure 5,** hydrogen nuclei join to make a helium nucleus. This reaction, called *fusion,* gives off a huge amount of energy. The sun's light and heat come from these reactions. Without nuclear energy from the sun, life would not exist on Earth.

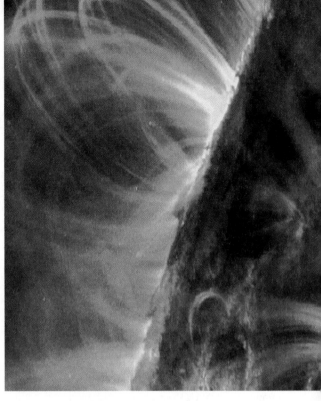

Figure 5 *Solar flares on the surface of the sun release energy produced by fusion reactions.*

SECTION Review

Summary

- Energy is the ability to do work.
- Kinetic energy is energy of motion and depends on speed and mass. **B.1.3.1 AA**
- Potential energy is energy of position. **B.1.3.1 AA**
- Mechanical energy is the sum of kinetic energy and potential energy.
- Other forms of energy are thermal, chemical, electrical, sound, light, and nuclear energy. **B.1.3.1 AA**

Understanding Key Ideas

1. What is the relationship between energy and work?

2. What two factors determine gravitational potential energy? **B.1.3.1 AA**

3. Describe the difference between nuclear energy and light energy. **B.1.3.1 AA**

Critical Thinking

4. **Identifying Relationships** When you hit a nail into a board by using a hammer, the head of the nail gets warm. In terms of kinetic and thermal energy, describe why you think the nail head becomes warm.

5. **Making Inferences** Why is chemical energy a form of potential energy? **B.1.3.1 AA**

6. **Making Comparisons** Compare kinetic, potential, and mechanical energy. **B.1.3.1 AA**

FCAT Preparation

7. The kinetic energy of an object depends on the object's mass and speed. As the object's mass or speed increases, its kinetic energy also increases. Which of the following has the most kinetic energy? **B.1.3.1 AA**

   A. a truck parked in a lot

   B. a kitten running in a room

   C. a jet airplane flying in the air

   D. a car driving on a highway

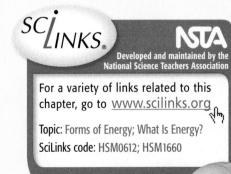

SCILINKS.

NSTA
Developed and maintained by the National Science Teachers Association

For a variety of links related to this chapter, go to www.scilinks.org

Topic: Forms of Energy; What Is Energy?
SciLinks code: HSM0612; HSM1660

Wave Energy: Sound and Light

You're waiting in a darkened concert hall. Suddenly, the spotlights come on, music starts playing, and your favorite band members run onstage singing their newest hit song.

You may not realize it, but you can enjoy all the sights and sounds of a concert because of waves. When you hear the word *wave*, you may think only of water waves. But there are many other kinds of waves, such as light waves and sound waves.

What Is a Wave?

Throw a pebble into a puddle, and you will see waves spread outward from where the pebble entered the water. A **wave** is a periodic motion that carries energy through matter and space. The energy from the pebble causes the water to vibrate up and down. These vibrations set up wave disturbances that move outward and toward the edges of the puddle. Waves always spread away from the source of vibration.

Energy is carried along with the wave as the wave moves outward. In fact, the energy carried by a water wave is what causes floating objects to move up and down, or bob, as the wave passes by. However, the wave will not carry the objects along with it, as shown in **Figure 1.** Why? Objects do not travel with a wave because the water does not move outward with the energy.

Benchmark Check What happens when you throw a pebble into a puddle? **C.1.3.2**

wave a periodic disturbance in a solid, liquid, or gas as energy is transmitted through a medium

Figure 1 *A boogie boarder bobs up and down on ocean waves but does not move toward the shore.*

Figure 2 *The light that makes up this rainbow is just one kind of electromagnetic wave.*

Waves Traveling Through a Medium

Many kinds of waves travel as vibrations through matter. The matter through which a wave travels is called the *medium* (plural, *media*). The medium can be a liquid, a gas, or a solid. Water is the medium for waves in ponds, lakes, or oceans. Air is the medium for the sound waves you hear at a concert. On a violin, the media that vibrate are the strings and the wooden body of the instrument.

Waves Traveling Without a Medium

Not all waves travel through a medium. Light waves travel from the sun to Earth through the emptiness of space. The rainbow in **Figure 2** is formed by light waves from the sun. Light waves are rapid vibrations of both magnetic and electric fields. So, light is also called *electromagnetic radiation* or *electromagnetic waves* (EM waves).

Visible light, the light that forms rainbows, is one kind of EM wave that reaches Earth from the sun. Radio waves are another kind of EM wave that comes from the sun. Radio waves are the kind of EM waves used to transmit radio and television signals. Other examples of EM waves that come from the sun include microwaves, infrared waves, and ultraviolet light.

Benchmark Check Name five forms in which energy comes to Earth from the sun. **B.1.3.3**

Making Waves

1. Fill a **shallow pan** halfway with **water**. When the surface of the water is smooth, drop a **pebble** into the pan. Describe what you see.

2. Place a **small cork** in the water. Drop **another pebble** into the pan. Describe the motion of the cork.

3. Which direction did the waves travel? Which direction did the cork move? Will the cork move in different directions if you drop pebbles in different spots in the pan? **C.1.3.2**

crest the highest point of a wave *FCAT VOCAB*

trough the lowest point of a wave *FCAT VOCAB*

B.1.3.6 AA knows the properties of waves (e.g., frequency, wavelength, and amplitude); that each wave consists of a number of crests and troughs; and the effects of different media on waves.

Parts of Waves

A wave is a periodic motion. So, a wave moves in the same way over and over again. Because waves have a repetitive motion, they are made of a series of repeating parts. Some waves are a series of crests and troughs, and other waves are a series of compressions and rarefactions.

Crests and Troughs

Imagine that you photographed a water wave as it moved on the surface of the pond. The photograph of the wave would show that part of the wave is slightly above the surface of the pond and that part is slightly below. The photograph would also show that the wave changes smoothly between the high points and the low points.

The high points on a wave are called **crests.** The low points are called **troughs. Figure 3** shows a rope wave that has its crests and troughs labeled. The crests and troughs of a wave form when the particles of the medium vibrate perpendicularly to the direction that the wave is traveling. *Perpendicular* means "at right angles."

Waves in which the particles move perpendicularly are called *transverse waves*. All transverse waves consist of a series of crests and troughs. Water waves and waves on a violin string are examples of transverse waves. Although electromagnetic waves do not always travel in a medium, all electromagnetic waves are considered to be transverse waves.

Benchmark Check Draw a transverse wave, and label its crests and troughs. B.1.3.6 AA

Figure 3 **Parts of a Transverse Wave**

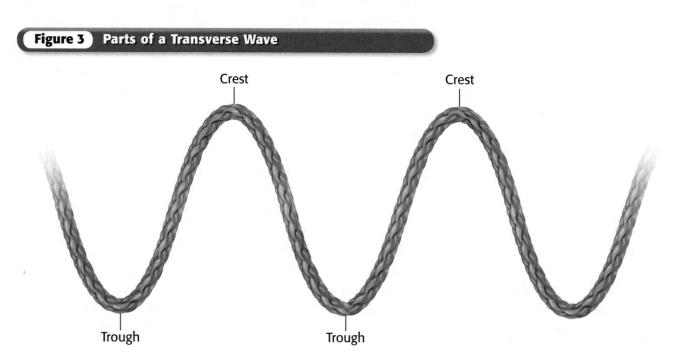

Crest

Crest

Trough

Trough

Figure 4 Forming a Longitudinal Wave

When the drumhead moves out after being hit, a compression is created in the air particles.

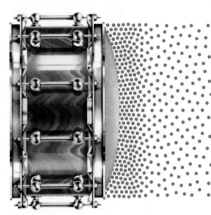

When the drumhead moves back in, a rarefaction is created.

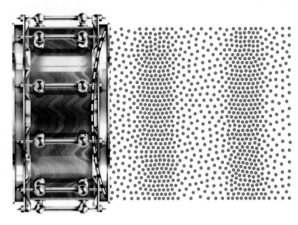

Compressions and Rarefactions

Sound waves display another kind of wave motion. In a sound wave, air particles move back and forth in the same direction that the wave moves. Waves in which particles move back and forth are called *longitudinal waves*. Longitudinal waves consist of particles that are squeezed together and then spread apart. Areas where particles are squeezed together are called *compressions*. Areas where particles are spread apart are called *rarefactions*. **Figure 4** shows how compressions and rarefactions can be formed. In sound waves, air particles are compressed and spread apart hundreds or thousands of times each second.

Waves and Particles

Although many waves consist of vibrating particles, waves and particles have different properties. For example, particles, such as atoms and molecules, are made of matter and have mass and volume. Waves do not have mass or volume. Waves, such as water waves, may look like they have mass and volume. But the particles of the medium through which the wave is traveling have mass and volume—not the wave itself.

However, in more advanced physics, the distinction between particles and waves is blurred. Scientists study matter and light as both particles and waves. Neither matter nor light can be described as only particles or only waves. For example, some properties of light are best understood if light is thought of as an EM wave. But other properties are best understood if light is thought of as consisting of particles called *photons*.

What's Your Frequency?
Create a brochure helping soon-to-propagate waves decide on a frequency to meet their personal goals. Go to **go.hrw.com,** and type in the keyword **HP5LGTW.**

Benchmark Check What is the difference between particles and waves? A.2.3.1 CS

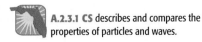

A.2.3.1 CS describes and compares the properties of particles and waves.

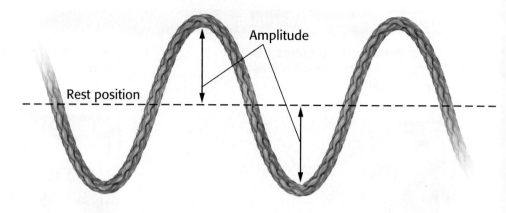

Amplitude

Rest position

Properties of Waves

The devastating damage that ocean waves can cause during a hurricane is a result of the amount of energy carried by the waves. A wave's energy depends on the properties of the wave, such as its amplitude, wavelength, frequency, and speed.

Amplitude

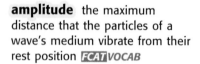

amplitude the maximum distance that the particles of a wave's medium vibrate from their rest position *FCAT VOCAB*

B.1.3.6 AA knows the properties of waves (e.g., frequency, wavelength, and amplitude); that each wave consists of a number of crests and troughs; and the effects of different media on waves.

The amplitude of a wave is a measure of how much the wave disturbs the medium. A wave's **amplitude** is the maximum distance that the particles of a medium vibrate from their rest position. For a water wave, the amplitude is how high the wave rises above the surface of the water. The amplitude is also how low the wave dips below the surface of the water.

Figure 5 shows a rope wave with its amplitude labeled. Creating a rope wave that has a large amplitude requires more energy than creating a rope wave that has a small amplitude. So, a wave that has a large amplitude carries more energy than a wave that has a small amplitude carries.

The amplitude of sound waves is related to the loudness of the sound. Loud sounds have large amplitudes. So, an amplifier, such as the one in **Figure 6,** increases amplitude. Human ears are able to detect a wide range of sound amplitudes. Loudness is often measured in units called *decibels.*

Benchmark Check How is the amplitude of a wave related to the energy carried by the wave? B.1.3.6 AA

Figure 6 *An amplifier increases the amplitude of sound waves. As a result, you hear a louder sound.*

Longitudinal wave

Wavelength

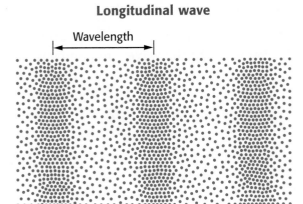

Wavelength

Transverse wave

Wavelength

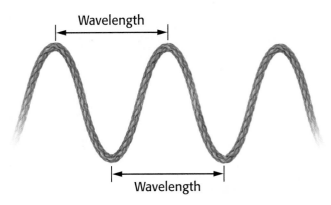

Wavelength

Figure 7 *Wavelength can be measured from different points on a wave. But, the wavelength of the wave is always the same.*

Wavelength

Another property of waves is wavelength. A **wavelength** is the distance from any point on a wave to an identical point on the next wave. **Figure 7** shows how wavelength may be measured on a longitudinal wave and a transverse wave.

Imagine making waves on a rope. The rate at which you shake the rope determines whether the wavelength is short or long. If you shake the rope rapidly back and forth, the wavelength will be short. The more rapidly you shake the rope, the more energy you are using to shake it. So, a wave that has a shorter wavelength carries more energy than a wave that has a longer wavelength does.

The wavelengths of electromagnetic waves have a very wide range. EM waves that have the longest wavelengths are radio waves. Their wavelengths are longer than 30 cm. EM waves that have the shortest wavelengths are gamma rays. Gamma rays have wavelengths that are shorter than 0.1 nanometer, or 0.1 nm. A nanometer is equal to 0.000000001 m. More than 100 million gamma-ray waves can fit in 1 cm.

Visible light waves have wavelengths between those of radio waves and gamma rays. The wavelengths of visible light range from about 400 nm to about 700 nm. The different wavelengths of visible light are seen as different colors. Red light has the longest wavelength, and violet light has the shortest wavelength. The range of colors that humans can see is shown in **Figure 8** and is called the *visible spectrum.*

Benchmark Check How can you measure the wavelength of a wave? **B.1.3.6 AA**

wavelength the distance from any point on a wave to an identical point on the next wave **FCAT VOCAB**

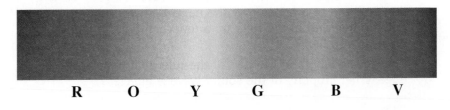

R   O   Y   G   B   V

Figure 8 *The visible spectrum contains all colors of light.*

Figure 9 *Frequency can be measured by counting how many waves pass a point in a certain amount of time. Here, two waves go by in 10 s, so the frequency is 2/10 s = 0.2 Hz.*

frequency the number of waves produced in a given amount of time
FCAT *VOCAB*

Frequency

The number of waves produced in a given amount of time is the **frequency** of the wave. Frequency is often expressed in hertz (Hz). For waves, one hertz equals one wave per second (1 Hz = 1/s). **Figure 9** shows a wave with a frequency of 0.2 Hz. Like amplitude and wavelength, frequency is related to the amount of energy carried by a wave. High-frequency waves carry more energy than low-frequency waves do.

Humans can hear sound waves that have frequencies between 20 Hz and 20,000 Hz. Lower frequencies are heard as low pitches, and higher frequencies are heard as high pitches.

Some sound waves cannot be heard by humans. For example, ultrasound machines used for medical imaging use sound waves that have frequencies too high for humans to hear. In fact, the prefix *ultra-* means "beyond." So, the word *ultrasound* means "beyond sound" or "beyond hearing."

Wave Speed

Waves travel in a large variety of speeds. The fastest speed of any wave is the speed of light. The speed of light is 300,000,000 m/s. All EM waves travel at this speed through the vacuum of space. The average speed of light is slightly slower in a medium, such as in air, water, or glass.

Sound waves traveling in air move at about 350 m/s. The difference between the speed of light and the speed of sound causes you to hear thunder several seconds after you see lightning. Sound travels much faster through liquids and solids than through air. These waves travel about 10 to 20 times faster in solids than they do in air.

Benchmark Check What relationship exists between wave speed and the medium through which a wave is traveling? **B.1.3.6 AA**

Sounding Board

1. With one hand, hold a **metal or plastic ruler** on your **desk** so that one end of it hangs over the edge. With your other hand, pull the free end of the ruler up a few centimeters, and let go. What do you hear?

2. Change the length of the part of the ruler that hangs over the edge. What property of the sound wave is affected?

B.1.3.6 AA knows the properties of waves (e.g., frequency, wavelength, and amplitude); that each wave consists of a number of crests and troughs; and the effects of different media on waves.

Summary

- Vibrations in materials set up periodic disturbances called waves. Waves travel in all directions away from their source. **C.1.3.2**

- Most waves travel through a medium, but electromagnetic waves do not need a medium through which to travel.

- Transverse waves are made of crests and troughs. Longitudinal waves are made of compressions and rarefactions. **B.1.3.6 AA**

- Waves and particles have different properties. Particles have mass and volume, but waves do not. **A.2.3.1 CS**

- Four properties of waves are amplitude, wavelength, frequency, and wave speed. **B.1.3.6 AA**

- Wave speed changes based on the medium through which a wave is traveling. **B.1.3.6 AA**

Using Key Terms

Use a term from the section to complete each sentence below.

1. The brightness of light depends on the ___ of the light waves.

2. The pitch of a sound wave depends on the sound wave's ___.

Understanding Key Ideas

3. What property of waves determines the color of a light? **B.1.3.6 AA**

   a. amplitude

   b. mass

   c. wavelength

   d. wave speed

4. Explain how waves are formed, and describe how they travel. **C.1.3.2**

5. Name the parts of a transverse wave. Name the parts of a longitudinal wave. **B.1.3.6 AA**

6. What are two properties that particles have that waves do not have? **A.2.3.1 CS**

7. Describe the four properties of waves. **B.1.3.6 AA**

Critical Thinking

8. **Applying Concepts** A drum is struck gently and then is struck harder. What will be the difference in the amplitude of the sounds made?

9. **Making Comparisons** Compare transverse waves and longitudinal waves. Give an example of each kind of wave.

FCAT Preparation

10. Sound waves consist of compressions and rarefactions of particles in a medium, such as air. Which of the following is a property of sound waves? **A.2.3.1 CS**

    A. amplitude

    B. charge

    C. mass

    D. volume

11. Although light can pass through different media, it does not need a medium through which to travel. The speed of light waves depends on the medium through which the waves are traveling. How does the speed of light in glass compare to the speed of light in a vacuum? **B.1.3.6 AA**

    F. It is less than the speed in a vacuum.

    G. It is greater than the speed in a vacuum.

    H. It is equal to the speed in a vacuum.

    I. It is half of the speed in a vacuum.

Developed and maintained by the National Science Teachers Association

For a variety of links related to this chapter, go to www.scilinks.org

Topic: What Is Sound?; Light Energy

SciLinks code: HSM1663; HSM0880

Energy Conversion and Transfer

Imagine that you are finishing a clay mug in art class. You turn around, and your elbow knocks the mug off the table. Luckily, you catch the mug before it hits the ground.

The mug has potential energy while it is on the table. As the mug falls, its potential energy changes into kinetic energy. This change is an example of an energy conversion. An **energy conversion** is a change from one form of energy to another. Any form of energy can change into any other form of energy. Often, one form of energy changes into more than one other form.

Kinetic and Potential Energy Conversions

Look at **Figure 1.** At the instant this picture was taken, the skateboarder on the left side of the picture was hardly moving. How did he get up so high in the air? As you might guess, he was moving at a high speed on his way up the half pipe. So, he had a lot of kinetic energy. What happened to that energy? His kinetic energy changed into potential energy. Immediately after this picture was taken, his potential energy became kinetic energy once again as he zipped down the side of the half pipe.

Benchmark Check What is an energy conversion? B.1.3.2

READING WARM-UP

Objectives

● Describe and give examples of energy conversions. B.1.3.2

● Explain how friction affects energy conversions.

● Explain how energy is conserved within a closed system. B.1.3.2

● Describe three events that involve energy transfers. B.2.3.1 AA

Terms to Learn

energy conversion
friction
law of conservation of energy
FCAT VOCAB

READING STRATEGY

Brainstorming The key idea of this section is energy conversion. Brainstorm words and phrases related to energy conversion.

energy conversion a change from one form of energy to another

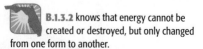

B.1.3.1 AA (partial) identifies forms of energy and explains that they can be measured and compared.

B.1.3.2 knows that energy cannot be created or destroyed, but only changed from one form to another.

Figure 1 **Potential Energy and Kinetic Energy**

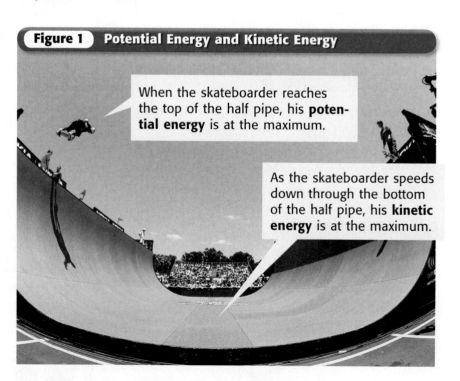

When the skateboarder reaches the top of the half pipe, his **potential energy** is at the maximum.

As the skateboarder speeds down through the bottom of the half pipe, his **kinetic energy** is at the maximum.

Energy Conversions in a Rubber Band

Did you know that energy can be stored in a rubber band? Look at **Figure 2.** The wound-up rubber band in the toy airplane has stored potential energy. This stored energy can also be converted into other forms of energy. When the rubber band is let go, the stored potential energy becomes kinetic energy, spins the propeller, and makes the airplane fly.

You can change the shape of a rubber band by stretching it. Stretching the rubber band takes a little effort. The energy you put into stretching it is converted to potential energy. The potential energy in the rubber band is similar to the potential energy of the skateboarder at the top of the half pipe. When you let the rubber band go, it goes back to its original shape. And as the rubber band returns to its original shape, it releases its stored potential energy—as you know if you have ever snapped a rubber band against your skin!

Figure 2 *The wound-up rubber band in this model airplane has potential energy because its shape has been changed.*

Conversions Involving Chemical Energy

You may have heard someone say that breakfast is the most important meal of the day. But why is eating breakfast so important? As shown in **Figure 3,** chemical energy comes from the food you eat. Your body uses chemical energy to function. The food you eat during breakfast gives your body the energy needed to help you start the day.

Figure 3 *Some of the chemical energy of food is converted into kinetic energy when you are active. Some of it is also converted into thermal energy to maintain body temperature.*

Figure 4 From Light Energy to Chemical Energy

Light energy

Chlorophyll in green leaves

Photosynthesis

carbon dioxide + water $\xrightarrow[\text{chlorophyll}]{\text{light energy}}$ sugar + oxygen

Carbon dioxide in the air

Sugar in food

Water in the soil

Energy Conversions in Plants

Did you know that the chemical energy in the food you eat comes from the sun's energy? As shown in **Figure 4,** plants use photosynthesis (FOHT oh SIN thuh sis) and light energy from the sun to make new substances that have chemical energy. When you eat fruits, vegetables, or grains, you are taking in chemical energy that was converted from the sun's energy. When you eat meat from animals that ate plants, you are also taking in energy that first came from the sun.

The chemical energy stored in plants can also be converted to other forms of energy. For example, burning wood from a tree converts chemical energy into thermal energy. So, if you follow the conversion of energy back far enough, the energy from a wood fire actually comes from the sun!

Benchmark Check Where does the chemical energy that is stored in fruits, vegetables, and grains come from? **B.1.3.2**

Continuation of the Process

Let's trace where the energy goes. Plants change light energy into chemical energy. The chemical energy in the food you eat is changed into another kind of chemical energy that your body can use. Your body then uses that energy to give you the kinetic energy that you use in everything you do. The process is endless—energy is always going somewhere!

Energy Conversions and Friction

Roller coasters have a mechanism that pulls the cars up to the top of the first hill. But the cars are on their own for the rest of the ride. As the cars go up and down the hills on the track, their potential energy is converted into kinetic energy and back to potential energy again. But the cars never return to the height at which they started. Does the energy get lost somewhere? No, it is converted into other forms of energy.

Friction and Thermal Energy

To find out where a roller coaster's original potential energy goes, you have to think about more than just the hills of the roller coaster. Friction plays a part, too. **Friction** is a force that opposes motion between two surfaces that are touching. There is friction between the cars' wheels and the track and between the cars and the air around them. Because of friction, some energy is always converted to thermal energy. As a result, not all of the potential energy of the cars changes into kinetic energy as the cars go down the first hill. Likewise, as you can see in **Figure 5,** not all of the kinetic energy of the cars changes back into potential energy.

friction a force that opposes motion between two surfaces that are in contact

B.1.3.1 AA (partial) identifies forms of energy and explains that they can be measured and compared.

B.1.3.2 knows that energy cannot be created or destroyed, but only changed from one form to another.

Figure 5   **Energy Conversions in a Roller Coaster**

Not all of the cars' potential energy (*PE*) is converted into kinetic energy (*KE*) as the cars go down the first hill. In addition, not all of the cars' kinetic energy is converted into potential energy as the cars go up the second hill. Some of it is changed into thermal energy because of friction.

a The *PE* is greatest at the top of the first hill.

b The *KE* at the bottom of the first hill is less than the *PE* at the top was.

c The *PE* at the top of the second hill is less than *KE* and *PE* from the first hill.

Energy in a Closed System

A *closed system* is a group of objects that transfer energy only to each other. For example, the closed system of a roller coaster consists of the track, the cars, and the air around them. On a roller coaster, some mechanical energy (the sum of kinetic and potential energy) is always converted into thermal energy because of friction. Sound energy also comes from the energy conversions in a roller coaster. If you combine the cars' kinetic energy at the bottom of the first hill, the thermal energy due to friction, and the sound energy, the total amount of energy is the same as the original amount of potential energy. So, energy is conserved and not lost.

Law of Conservation of Energy

Energy is always conserved. Because no exception to this rule has been found, this rule is described as a law. The **law of conservation of energy** states that energy cannot be created or destroyed. The total amount of energy in a closed system is always the same. As **Figure 6** shows, energy can change from one form to another. But all of the different forms of energy in a system always have the same total amount of energy. The total is the same no matter how many energy conversions take place.

Benchmark Check What does the law of conservation of energy state? B.1.3.2

law of conservation of energy
the law that states that energy cannot be created or destroyed but can be changed from one form to another FCAT VOCAB

B.1.3.2 knows that energy cannot be created or destroyed, but only changed from one form to another.

Figure 6 **Energy Conservation in a Light Bulb**

Some energy is converted into thermal energy, which makes the bulb feel warm.

Some electrical energy is converted into light energy.

As electrical energy is carried through the wire, some of it is converted into thermal energy.

Figure 7 *Hurricane Floyd was a powerful category 4 hurricane. It had maximum wind speeds of more than 225 km/h and traveled parallel to the Florida coast before hitting land in North Carolina.*

Energy Transfers

Energy transfers are a useful way to describe changes in the world. But in all energy transfers, some useful energy is lost, and the disorder of the system and its surroundings increases. Increased disorder means that energy is converted to other forms, causing changes to the system or the surroundings. Most events in the universe, such as weather changes, moving cars, and nerve impulses, involve some form of energy transfer.

Energy Transfers and Weather Changes

The energy transfers involved in weather have many forms. For example, thermal energy from the sun evaporates water on Earth. This water vapor forms clouds. The water can return to the ground as the gravitational potential energy of the water in the clouds is converted into the kinetic energy of falling water drops. This process is the scientific explanation of rain.

A hurricane is a very dramatic form of weather-related energy transfers. The energy of the warm ocean waters allows the formation of vast storms that may become hurricanes. The kinetic energy of hurricane winds can cause billions of dollars in damages. Hurricanes may extend over hundreds of kilometers, as shown in the satellite image in **Figure 7.** Luckily, hurricanes die down because they lose energy over time.

Benchmark Check Describe the energy transfers that cause rain to fall. **B.2.3.1 AA**

B.2.3.1 AA knows that most events in the universe involve some form of energy transfer and that these changes almost always increase the total disorder of the system and its surroundings, reducing the amount of useful energy.

Figure 8 How Energy Makes a Car Move

a Gasoline stores chemical energy, which is converted to thermal energy when the gasoline is burned.

b The engine changes thermal energy to kinetic energy as the pistons move up and down. The kinetic energy of the pistons turns the crankshaft.

c The kinetic energy of the crankshaft turns the wheels. The kinetic energy of the turning wheels helps move the car down the road.

Energy Transfers and Moving Cars

A car is a good example of how energy changes forms. **Figure 8** explains how the chemical energy of gasoline undergoes energy transfers to move a car. But not all of the gasoline's energy makes a car move. In every energy transfer, some of the original energy is changed into thermal energy because of friction. As in all energy transfers, this thermal energy is lost to the surroundings. You can feel some of the lost thermal energy if you hold your hand above the hood of a recently driven car.

Benchmark Check Why does the hood of a recently driven car feel warm? B.2.3.1 AA

Energy Transfers and Nerve Impulses

Imagine stepping on a shell at the beach. You pull your foot away almost instantly. How is energy involved in the reflex action of pulling your foot away? After you step on the shell, pain receptors on the bottom of your foot trigger chemical reactions. The chemical energy released in these reactions is converted into electrical energy. This electrical energy is sent as impulses to the spinal cord and then through nerves to the muscles in your leg and foot. The impulses cause chemical energy to convert into kinetic energy as you lift your foot. Amazingly, the reflex happens even faster than the electrical impulses can travel through your nerves to your brain. So, you move your foot before you know that you are injured.

B.2.3.1 AA knows that most events in the universe involve some form of energy transfer and that these changes almost always increase the total disorder of the system and its surroundings, reducing the amount of useful energy.

Summary

- An energy conversion is a change from one form of energy to another. **B.1.3.2**

- Examples of energy conversions happen in your body, in plants, in roller coasters, and in falling objects. **B.1.3.2**

- Because of friction, some energy is always converted into thermal energy during an energy conversion.

- Energy is conserved within a closed system because energy cannot be created or destroyed. **B.1.3.2**

- The loss of useful energy from a system to its surroundings causes the amount of disorder to increase. **B.2.3.1 AA**

- Weather changes, moving cars, and the transmission of nerve impulse are events that involve energy transfers. **B.2.3.1 AA**

Using Key Terms

1. Write an original definition for *energy conversion*. **B.1.3.2**

2. Use the *law of conservation of energy* and *friction* in the same sentence. **FCAT VOCAB**

Understanding Key Ideas

3. Why is energy conserved within a closed system? **B.1.3.2**

4. Give three examples of energy conversions. **B.1.3.2**

5. What is the relationship between friction and energy conversions?

6. Describe a case in which electrical energy is converted into thermal energy.

7. Describe three events that involve energy transfers. **B.2.3.1 AA**

8. What happens to a system and its surroundings when useful energy is lost? **B.2.3.1 AA**

Critical Thinking

9. **Analyzing Ideas** Consider the statement, "You can move parts of your body because of energy from the sun." Describe a series of energy conversions that prove that this idea is true. **B.1.3.2**

10. **Making Inferences** A car that brakes suddenly comes to a screeching halt. Is the sound energy produced in this conversion a useful form of energy? Explain your answer.

FCAT Preparation

11. As a pendulum swings, energy is converted back and forth between potential energy and kinetic energy. But a pendulum will eventually stop swinging. Why will it stop swinging? **B.2.3.1 AA**

    A. Gravity destroys kinetic energy.

    B. The motion of the pendulum destroys potential energy.

    C. Friction causes some energy to convert into chemical energy.

    D. Friction causes some energy to convert into thermal energy.

12. Identify the forms of energy associated with a bouncing ball. Explain how the forms of energy are changed from one form to another form. **B.1.3.1 AA**

SCI LINKS.

NSTA
Developed and maintained by the
National Science Teachers Association

For a variety of links related to this chapter, go to www.scilinks.org

Topic: Energy Conversions
SciLinks code: HSM0511

Uses of Energy

Energy makes the world work. Without energy, you could not ride a bike, use a computer, or read a book at night. In the modern world, people use large quantities of energy.

There are many useful forms of energy. For example, televisions, hair dryers, and lamps use electrical energy. And sound energy allows you to talk to others and listen to music. But one of the most useful forms of energy is radiation.

What Is Radiation?

The transfer of energy as electromagnetic waves is called **radiation.** Radiation is one of the primary ways energy can be transferred from place to place.

As you have learned, there are many kinds of electromagnetic waves. Every kind of EM wave can transfer energy as radiation. The entire range of electromagnetic waves is called the *electromagnetic spectrum*, which is shown in **Figure 1.**

Radiation from each part of the electromagnetic spectrum is useful to people. For example, infrared waves from space heaters keep you warm on chilly evenings. Visible light allows you to see things, and ultraviolet light can be used to kill bacteria that cause food to spoil. You can communicate by using the radio waves of walkie-talkies or by using the microwaves of cellular phones. There are many other ways that radiation can be used.

Benchmark Check List four ways in which radiation is used.
A.2.3.3

radiation the transfer of energy as electromagnetic waves *FCAT VOCAB*

Figure 1 The Electromagnetic Spectrum

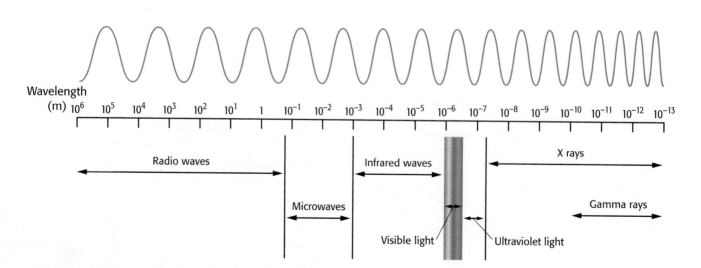

Wavelength
(m)

Radio waves   Microwaves   Infrared waves   Visible light   Ultraviolet light   X rays   Gamma rays

Cooking Food

The modern kitchen is filled with different appliances for cooking. These appliances make cooking easy and enjoyable. And all of these appliances use forms of radiation.

Conventional Ovens and Stoves

Radiation is used in a conventional oven and stove in many ways. The use that is easiest to understand is baking. Imagine putting bread dough in a hot oven. Thermal energy in the oven bakes the bread. This energy arrives at the dough from the movement of hot air and from infrared radiation.

A conventional stove cooks by a process called conduction. *Conduction* is the transfer of thermal energy through direct contact. Thermal energy from the gas or electric burners is conducted through a cooking pan to the food. Thermal energy is also transferred from the burners as infrared waves.

Microwave Ovens

You have probably used a microwave oven to reheat leftover pizza. **Figure 2** explains how microwave ovens use microwave radiation to warm and cook foods.

Microwave ovens can cook foods more quickly than conventional ovens and stoves can. However, microwave ovens have a few drawbacks. For example, microwave ovens tend to heat food unevenly unless the food is turned by a turntable or by hand. Also, the surface of food cooked in a microwave oven does not become very hot, so the food does not brown.

Figure 2 How a Microwave Oven Works

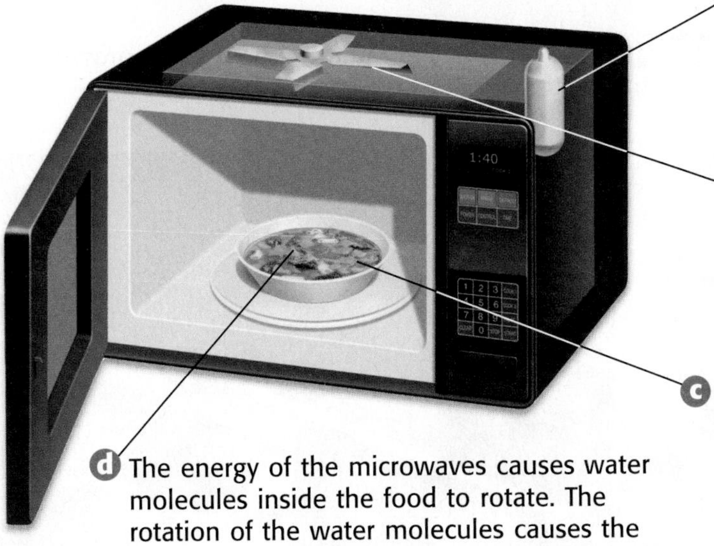

a A device called a *magnetron* produces microwaves by accelerating charged particles.

b The microwaves reflect off a metal fan and are directed into the cooking chamber.

c Microwaves can penetrate several centimeters into the food.

d The energy of the microwaves causes water molecules inside the food to rotate. The rotation of the water molecules causes the temperature of the food to increase.

Speed-Cook Ovens

Speed-cook ovens, such as the one shown in **Figure 3,** are a new kind of cooking appliance. A speed-cook oven is a combination of a microwave oven and a conventional oven. Advanced technology is used to combine the two cooking methods because they cook food at different rates. But the result is food that is cooked rapidly and browned at the same time. In fact, a speed-cook oven can roast a chicken in just 25 minutes while making the skin brown and crisp! The same chicken would take more than an hour to cook in a conventional oven. The speed-cook method combines the best of both cooking methods.

Providing Energy

People consume large amounts of energy in their everyday lives. Much of the energy needed in homes, schools, and businesses is used in the form of electrical energy. Providing electrical energy is a major industry. Traditionally, electrical energy is generated by burning fossil fuels. But fossil fuels are a nonrenewable resource. Fortunately, electrical energy can also be generated by collecting solar energy.

Solar Energy

Solar energy is the energy received by Earth from the sun in the form of radiation. Solar energy in the form of visible light can be changed into electrical energy through solar cells. As shown in **Figure 4,** solar cells can be placed near a house to provide the house with electrical energy. Solar energy can also be used instead of fossil fuels or electrical energy to heat homes.

As fossil fuels become scarce, solar radiation may become an important source of energy. Today, scientists and engineers are trying to find better ways to harness this renewable source of energy.

Benchmark Check How can radiation be used to provide energy to a house? A.2.3.3

Figure 3 *This speed-cook oven can bake delicious food up to 50% faster than a conventional oven can.*

Figure 4 *This University of Florida researcher inspects the solar cells that collect energy to provide the house in the background with electrical energy.*

A.2.3.3 knows that radiation, light, and heat are forms of energy used to cook food, treat diseases, and provide energy.

Treating Disease

Electromagnetic radiation is frequently used to treat many diseases. For example, electromagnetic radiation from lasers is often used to treat tumors, eye diseases, and other medical problems. Another important source of radiation for medical treatments is a device called a *particle accelerator*. These devices produce high-energy X rays and gamma rays that are used to treat some forms of cancer. Doctors focus the rays on tumors inside a patient's body to kill the cancer cells. Today, many hospitals have their own particle accelerators. **Figure 5** shows a particle accelerator in use.

A more familiar use of radiation in medicine is the use of X rays to make images of teeth and bones. X rays have been used in this way since they were discovered by Wilhelm Roentgen in 1895. In fact, Roentgen made images of the bones in his wife's hands during his discovery.

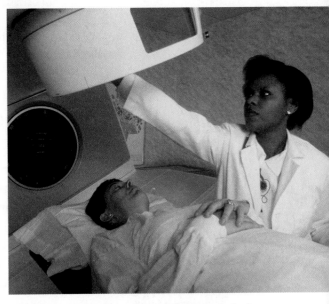

Figure 5 *This particle accelerator is being used to kill cancer cells.*

SECTION Review

Summary

- Radiation is the transfer of energy as electromagnetic waves.

- Infrared radiation, microwaves, and thermal energy are used in different appliances to cook food. A.2.3.3

- Solar energy in the form of visible light can be changed into usable electrical energy. A.2.3.3

- Radiation in the form of laser light, X rays, and gamma rays is used to treat diseases. A.2.3.3

Using Key Terms

1. Write an original definition for *radiation*. FCAT VOCAB

Understanding Key Ideas

2. How are radiation and thermal energy used to cook foods? A.2.3.3

3. Explain how visible light from the sun can be used to provide energy. A.2.3.3

4. Describe how electromagnetic radiation is used in medicine. A.2.3.3

Critical Thinking

5. **Applying Concepts** Describe how three different kinds of radiation have been useful to you today.

6. **Making Inferences** Using what you have learned, describe situations in which you would use a conventional oven, a microwave oven, and a speed-cook oven.

FCAT Preparation

7. Conventional ovens cook food by heating the food to high temperatures. What kinds of energy do ovens use to cook food? B.1.3.1 AA
   A. thermal and electrical energy
   B. thermal energy and microwaves
   C. thermal and chemical energy
   D. thermal energy and infrared radiation

Developed and maintained by the National Science Teachers Association

For a variety of links related to this chapter, go to www.scilinks.org

Topic: Electromagnetic Spectrum
SciLinks code: HSM0482

Skills Practice Lab

Finding Energy

When you coast down a hill on a bike or skateboard, you may notice that you pick up speed, or go faster and faster. Because you are moving, you have kinetic energy—the energy of motion. Where does that energy come from? When you pedal the bike or push the skateboard, you are the source of the kinetic energy. But where does the kinetic energy come from when you roll down a hill without making any effort? In this lab, you will find out where such kinetic energy comes from.

OBJECTIVES

Form a hypothesis about where kinetic energy comes from. B.1.3.1 AA, B.1.3.2

Test your hypothesis by collecting and analyzing data.

MATERIALS

- balance, metric
- board, wood
- books (2 or 3)
- cart, rolling
- meterstick
- stopwatch
- tape, masking

 B.1.3.1 AA identifies forms of energy and explains that they can be measured and compared.

 B.1.3.2 knows that energy cannot be created or destroyed, but only changed from one form to another.

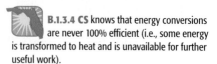 **B.1.3.4 CS** knows that energy conversions are never 100% efficient (i.e., some energy is transformed to heat and is unavailable for further useful work).

Ask a Question

① Where does the kinetic energy come from when you roll down a hill?

Form a Hypothesis

② Write a hypothesis that is a possible answer to the question above. Explain your reasoning.

Test the Hypothesis

③ Copy the Data Collection Table shown below.

Data Collection Table							
Height of ramp (m)	Length of ramp (m)	Mass of cart (kg)	Weight of cart (N)	Time of trial (s)			Average time (s)
				1	2	3	

DO NOT WRITE IN BOOK

4 Use your books and board to make a ramp.

5 Use masking tape to mark a starting line at the top of the ramp. Be sure the starting line is far enough down from the top of the ramp to allow the cart to be placed behind the line.

6 Use masking tape to mark a finish line at the bottom of the ramp.

7 Find the height of the ramp by measuring the height of the starting line and subtracting the height of the finish line. Record the height of the ramp in your Data Collection Table.

8 Measure the distance in meters between the starting line and the finish line. In the Data Collection Table, record this distance as the length of the ramp.

9 Use the balance to find the mass of the cart in grams. Convert this measurement to kilograms by dividing it by 1,000. In your Data Collection Table, record the mass in kilograms.

10 Multiply the mass by 10 to find the weight of the cart in newtons. Record this weight in your Data Collection Table.

11 Set the cart behind the starting line, and release it. Use a stopwatch to time how long the cart takes to reach the finish line. Record the time in your Data Collection Table.

12 Repeat step 11 twice more, and average the results. Record the average time in your Data Collection Table.

Analyze the Results

1 Organizing Data Copy the Calculations Table shown at right onto a separate sheet of paper.

2 Analyzing Data Calculate and record the quantities for the cart in the Calculations Table by using your data and the four equations that follow.

Calculations Table			
Average speed (m/s)	Final speed (m/s)	Kinetic energy at bottom (J)	Gravitational potential energy at top (J)
DO NOT WRITE IN BOOK			

$$average\ speed = \frac{length\ of\ ramp}{average\ time}$$

Final speed = 2 × average speed
(This equation works because the cart accelerates smoothly from 0 m/s.)

$$kinetic\ energy = \frac{mass \times (final\ speed)^2}{2}$$

(1 kg • m²/s² = 1 J, the unit used to express energy)

Gravitational potential energy =
weight × height
(Note that 1 N = 1 kg • m/s², so 1 N × 1 m = 1 kg • m²/s² = 1 J.)

Draw Conclusions

3 Drawing Conclusions Compare the cart's gravitational potential energy at the top of the ramp with the cart's kinetic energy at the bottom. Does this result support your hypothesis? Explain your answer.

4 Evaluating Data You probably found that the gravitational potential energy of the cart at the top of the ramp was almost, but not exactly, equal to the kinetic energy of the cart at the bottom of the ramp. Explain this finding.

5 Applying Conclusions Suppose that while riding your bike, you coast down both a small hill and a large hill. Compare your final speed at the bottom of the small hill with your final speed at the bottom of the large hill. Explain your answer.

Chapter Review

USING KEY TERMS

Use a term from the chapter to complete each sentence below.

1 The energy of motion is called ___.
B.1.3.1 AA

2 The distance between two adjacent crests on a wave is one ___. B.1.3.6 AA

3 Chemical energy can be changed into kinetic energy during a(n) ___.

4 Energy transferred as electromagnetic waves is called ___.

5 The lowest point on a wave is a(n) ___.
B.1.3.6 AA

UNDERSTANDING KEY IDEAS

Multiple Choice

6 An electron is an example of a particle. Electrons in an atom move quickly around the nucleus. Light is an example of a wave. Light can travel long distances in a short amount of time. What is a property that is shared by particles and waves? A.2.3.1 CS *FCAT*

a. amplitude

b. mass

c. speed

d. volume

7 Gravitational potential energy depends on B.1.3.1 AA

a. mass and velocity.

b. weight and height.

c. mass and weight.

d. height and distance.

8 You can create waves in a tank of water by repeatedly dipping a wire into the water. How can you dip the wire to increase the wavelength of the waves?
B.1.3.6 AA *FCAT*

a. less frequently

b. more frequently

c. more forcefully

d. less forcefully

9 Which of the following sentences describes a conversion from chemical energy to thermal energy? B.1.3.2

a. Food is digested and used to regulate body temperature.

b. Charcoal is burned in a barbecue pit.

c. Coal is burned to produce steam.

d. All of the above

10 When energy changes from one form to another, some of the energy always changes into B.1.3.2

a. kinetic energy.

b. potential energy.

c. thermal energy.

d. mechanical energy.

Short Answer

11 What is the relationship between thermal energy and kinetic energy? B.1.3.1 AA

12 Explain what a closed system is and how energy is conserved within it. B.1.3.2

CRITICAL THINKING

Extended Response

13 Applying Concepts Describe what happens in terms of energy when you fill a balloon with air and release the balloon.

14 Analyzing Ideas Use the law of conservation of energy to explain why you will eventually come to a complete stop after you coast down a hill on your bike. **B.1.3.1 AA** *FCAT*

15 Applying Concepts The energy that supports life on Earth comes from the sun. Identify the forms of energy that reach Earth from the sun, and explain how the energy travels to Earth. **B.1.3.1 AA** *FCAT*

16 Analyzing Processes Look at the photo below. Beginning with the pole vaulter's breakfast, trace the energy transfers necessary for the event shown to take place. **B.2.3.1 AA**

17 Evaluating Data The table below shows the frequencies of five musical notes. Predict the frequency of the sixth note listed in the table. **B.1.3.6 AA** *FCAT*

Note	Frequency (Hz)
C	260
A	440
B	500
High C	520
High A	880
High B	?

Concept Mapping

18 Use the following terms to create a concept map: *kinetic energy, friction, potential energy, energy conversion, thermal energy,* and *roller coaster.*

INTERPRETING GRAPHICS

Use the graphic below to answer the questions that follow.

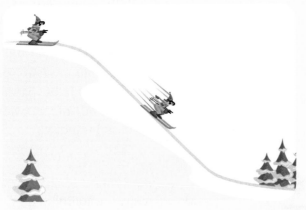

19 What kind of energy does the skier have at the top of the slope? **B.1.3.1 AA**

20 What happens to that energy after the skier races down the slope of the mountain? **B.1.3.2, B.1.3.1 AA**

For the following questions, write your answers on a separate sheet of paper.

1   Weather changes, nervous impulses in the human body, and moving cars all involve energy transfer. The image below shows how a car's engine works to turn the wheels of the car.

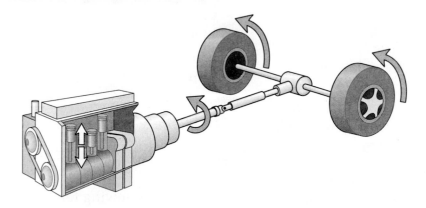

What type of energy transfer takes place in the automobile parts shown above?

A.   Light energy is converted into sound energy.

B.   Thermal energy is converted into kinetic energy.

C.   Kinetic energy is converted into potential energy.

D.   Chemical energy is converted into electrical energy.

2   A wave is a periodic motion that carries energy through matter and space. Matter is made up of particles, such as atoms and molecules. When a wave travels through matter, the wave causes the particles of the matter to vibrate. Waves and particles have different properties. Which of the following describes how waves and particles differ?

F.   Waves have volume, but not mass; particles have mass and volume.

G.   Waves have mass and volume; particles have neither mass nor volume.

H.   Particles have mass and volume; waves have neither mass nor volume.

I.   Particles have mass, but not volume; waves have volume, but not mass.

3   When a force causes an object to move in the direction of the force, scientists say that work has been done. Energy, the ability to do work, exists in many forms.

Part A   Explain the difference between potential energy and kinetic energy.

Part B   Identify and describe two forms of energy.

4 The relative amount of energy transferred by a wave depends on the properties of that wave. The properties of a wave include amplitude, wavelength, frequency, and wave speed. The image below shows a rope wave and its amplitude.

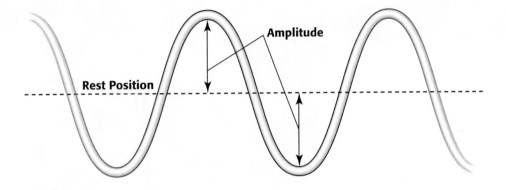

Part A   What is a wave's amplitude?

Part B   Explain how amplitude relates to the loudness of sound.

5 Wavelength is the distance from any point on a wave to an identical point on the next wave. For example, the wavelength of a transverse wave can be measured from one wave's crest or trough to the next wave's corresponding crest or trough. Electromagnetic waves have a wide range of wavelengths. What type of electromagnetic waves has the **shortest** wavelength?

A.   radio waves

B.   gamma rays

C.   ultraviolet light

D.   visible light waves

6 People use different forms of energy in many different ways. For example, light energy is often used to treat diseases, such as when gamma rays are used in the treatment of cancer. Light energy is also used when light from the sun is converted into electrical energy. How is thermal energy used in cooking?

F.   In a process called convection, thermal energy is transferred through direct contact.

G.   In a process called conduction, thermal energy is transferred through direct contact.

H.   In a process called convention, thermal energy is transferred through direct contact.

I.   In a process called conjunction, thermal energy is transferred through direct contact.

FCAT Preparation

Science in Action

Science, Technology, and Society

It's a Heat Wave

In 1946, Percy Spencer visited a laboratory belonging to Raytheon—the company for which he worked. When he stood near a device called a *magnetron,* he noticed that a candy bar in his pocket melted. Spencer hypothesized that the microwaves produced by the magnetron caused the candy bar to warm up and melt. To test his hypothesis, Spencer put a bag of popcorn kernels next to the magnetron. The microwaves heated the kernels and caused them to pop! Spencer's simple experiment showed that microwaves could heat foods quickly. Spencer's discovery eventually led to the development of the microwave oven—an appliance found in many kitchens today.

FOCUS ON FLORIDA

Place to Visit

The Great Gravity Clock

At the Museum of Discovery and Science in Fort Lauderdale, you can see the largest kinetic energy sculpture in Florida. The sculpture is called the *Great Gravity Clock* and is almost 16 m tall! Located in the museum's Grand Atrium, this enormous clock is only one of three in the entire world.

The Great Gravity Clock uses potential energy and kinetic energy to keep time. Balls at the top of the clock store potential energy. As time passes, these balls roll down the rails below the clock face. As a ball rolls down, the potential energy of that ball is converted into kinetic energy. The next time you are in Fort Lauderdale, be sure to visit the museum to watch the Great Gravity Clock in action!

Math ACTiViTY

Popcorn pops when the inside of the kernel reaches a temperature of about 175°C. Use the equation
°F = (9/5 × °C) + 32
to convert 175°C to degrees Fahrenheit.

Social Studies ACTiViTY

The water clock was one of the earliest kinds of timekeeping devices. Water clocks use gravitational potential energy to help keep time. Research water clocks, and build a model of a simple water clock.

Cheryl Mele

Power-Plant Manager Cheryl Mele is the manager of the Decker Power Plant in Austin, Texas, where she is in charge of almost 1 billion watts of electric power generation. Most of the electric power is generated by a steam-driven turbine system that uses natural gas as fuel. Gas turbines are also used. Together, the systems make enough electrical energy for many homes and businesses.

Cheryl Mele says that her job as plant manager is to do "anything that needs doing." Her training as a mechanical engineer allows her to run tests and to find problems in the plant. Previously, Mele had a job helping design more-efficient gas turbines. That job helped prepare her for the job of plant manager.

Mele believes that engineering and power-plant management are interesting jobs because they allow you to work with many new technologies. Mele thinks that young people should pursue what interests them. "Be sure to connect the math you learn to the science you are doing," she says. "This will help you to understand both."

Language Arts ACTiViTY

Look up the word *energy* in a dictionary. Compare the different definitions you find with the definition given in this chapter.

go.hrw.com

To learn more about these Science in Action topics, visit go.hrw.com and type in the keyword **HT6FEGFF**.

Current Science

Check out Current Science® articles related to this chapter by visiting go.hrw.com. Just type in the keyword **HP5CS09**.

20

Energy Resources

The Big Idea Using all energy sources wisely helps preserve the supply of nonrenewable resources.

About the PHOTO

Would you believe that this house is made from empty soda cans and old tires? Well, it is! *The Castle,* named by its designer, architect Mike Reynolds, and located in Taos, New Mexico, not only uses recycled materials but also saves Earth's energy resources. All of the energy used to run this house comes directly from the sun, and the water used for household activities is rainwater.

PRE-READING ACTIVITY

Graphic Organizer

Comparison Table Before you read the chapter, create the graphic organizer entitled "Comparison Table" described in the **Study Skills** section of the Appendix. Label the columns with an energy resource from the chapter. Label the rows with "Pros" and "Cons." As you read the chapter, fill in the table with details about the pros and cons of each energy resource.

START-UP ACTIVITY

What Is the Sun's Favorite Color?

Try the following activity to see which colors best absorb the sun's energy. **B.1.3.3**

Procedure

1. Obtain **at least five balloons** that are different colors but the same size and shape. One of the balloons should be white, and one should be black. Do not inflate the balloons.

2. Place **several small ice cubes** in each balloon. Each balloon should contain the same amount of ice.

3. Line up the balloons on a flat, uniformly colored surface that receives direct sunlight. Make sure that all of the balloons receive the same amount of sunlight and that the openings in the balloons are not facing directly toward the sun.

4. Record the time that it takes the ice to melt completely in each of the balloons. You can tell how much ice has melted in each balloon by pinching the balloons open and then gently squeezing the balloon.

Analysis

1. In which balloon did the ice melt first? Why?

2. What color would you paint a device used to collect solar energy? Explain your answer.

Natural Resources

What do the water that you drink, the paper that you write on, the gasoline used in the cars that you ride in, and the air that you breathe have in common?

Water, trees used to make paper, crude oil used to make gasoline, and air are just a few examples of Earth's resources. Can you think of other examples of Earth's resources?

Earth's Resources

Earth provides almost everything needed for life. For example, Earth's atmosphere provides the air that you breathe, maintains air temperatures, and produces rain. The oceans and other waters of Earth give you food and needed water. The solid part of Earth gives nutrients, such as potassium, to the plants that you eat. The resources that Earth provides for you are called natural resources.

A **natural resource** is any natural material that is used by humans. Examples of natural resources are water, petroleum, minerals, forests, and animals. Most resources are processed and made into products that make people's lives more comfortable and convenient, as shown in **Figure 1.** The energy that we get from many of these resources, such as gasoline and wind, ultimately comes from the sun's energy.

Figure 1 Natural Resources

This pile of lumber is made of wood, which comes from trees.

The gasoline in this can is made from oil that was pumped from Earth's crust.

Electrical energy generated by these wind turbines ultimately comes from the sun's energy.

Renewable Resources

Some natural resources can be renewed. A **renewable resource** is a natural resource that can be replaced at the same rate at which the resource is used. **Figure 2** shows two examples of renewable resources. Although many resources are renewable, they still can be used up before they can be renewed. Trees, for example, are renewable. However, some forests are being cut down faster than new forests can grow to replace them.

Figure 2 *Trees and fresh water are just a few of the renewable resources available on Earth.*

Nonrenewable Resources

Not all of Earth's natural resources are renewable resources. A **nonrenewable resource** is a resource that forms at a rate that is much slower than the rate at which the resource is consumed. Coal, shown in **Figure 3,** is an example of a nonrenewable resource. It takes millions of years for coal to form. Once coal is used up, no new coal will replace it. Petroleum and natural gas are other examples of nonrenewable resources. When these resources become scarce, humans will have to find new resources to replace the old.

natural resource any natural material that is used by humans, such as water, petroleum, minerals, forests, and animals

renewable resource a natural resource that can be replaced at the same rate at which the resource is consumed

nonrenewable resource a resource that forms at a rate that is much slower than the rate at which the resource is consumed

Benchmark Check How does a nonrenewable resource differ from a renewable resource? **G.2.3.1 CS**

 G.2.3.1 CS knows that some resources are renewable and others are nonrenewable.

Figure 3 *The coal used in the industrial process shown here is not quickly replaced by natural processes.*

Conserving Natural Resources

A natural resource—renewable or nonrenewable—should not be used wastefully. To conserve natural resources, you should use only as much of them as you need. For example, running the water while brushing your teeth wastes water. If you run the water only to rinse your brush and mouth, you save water. By saving water, you not only make water available for other uses but also reduce the amount of energy used to treat water for your household. Also, saving water reduces the water bill!

Conserving resources means conserving all natural resources, not only those that you use. So, keeping all lakes, rivers, and other water resources free of pollution is important. Plants and animals, including humans, depend on these water resources for survival. Polluted water harms these organisms.

Energy Conservation

Natural resources provide energy that we use to heat homes, drive cars, and run computers. Each day, ways that we choose to use energy affect resource availability. Most energy-providing natural resources are nonrenewable. We must make wise energy-use choices today to conserve resources for future use.

Energy conservation is needed to make sure that natural resources stay available. One way to conserve energy is to turn off lights that are not in use. Another way is to wash a full load of clothes, as shown in **Figure 4,** when you use the washing machine. A car uses more energy resources per person than walking, riding a bike, or taking a bus does. So, you conserve energy when you travel by these methods instead of by car.

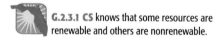 **Benchmark Check**) Are most of the energy resources that humans use renewable or nonrenewable? G.2.3.1 CS

Benchmark Activity

Is It Renewable?

With a parent or guardian, find five products in your home that were made from natural resources. List the resource or resources from which each product was made. Label each resource as renewable or nonrenewable. What can you do to help conserve the resources that you listed? In your **science journal,** describe a personal action plan to conserve some of the resources that you rely on every day.

G.2.3.1 CS

G.2.3.1 CS knows that some resources are renewable and others are nonrenewable.

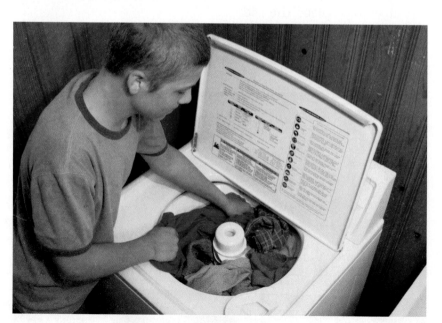

Figure 4 *Making sure that the washing machine is full before you run it is one way that you can avoid wasting natural resources.*

Reduce, Reuse, Recycle

Another way to conserve natural resources is to recycle, as shown in **Figure 5. Recycling** is the process of reusing materials from waste or scrap. Recycling reduces the amount of natural resources that must be obtained from Earth. For example, recycling paper reduces the number of trees that must be cut down to make new paper products. Recycling also conserves energy. Although energy is required to recycle materials, recycling an aluminum can takes less energy than making a new one does!

Newspaper, aluminum cans, most plastic containers, and cardboard boxes can be recycled. Most plastic containers have a recycle code number on them. This number indicates the type of plastic that the item is made of. Plastic products with the numbers 1 and 2 can be recycled in most communities. Check with your local recycling center to see what kinds of materials the center recycles.

recycling the process of recovering valuable or useful materials from waste or scrap; the process of reusing some items

Figure 5 *You can recycle many household items to help conserve natural resources.*

✓ **Reading Check** What are some kinds of products that can be recycled?

SECTION Review

Summary

● We use natural resources such as water, wood, and petroleum to make our lives more comfortable and convenient.

● Renewable resources can be replaced within a relatively short period of time, but nonrenewable resources may take thousands or even millions of years to form. **G.2.3.1 CS**

● Natural resources can be conserved by using only what is needed, taking care of resources, and recycling.

Understanding Key Ideas

1. How do humans use most natural resources?

2. Which of the following is a renewable resource? **G.2.3.1 CS**
   a. oil
   b. water
   c. coal
   d. natural gas

3. Describe three ways to conserve natural resources.

Critical Thinking

4. **Making Inferences** How does human activity affect Earth's renewable and nonrenewable resources? **G.2.3.1 CS**

5. **Making Inferences** Why is the availability of some renewable resources of more concern now than it was 100 years ago? **G.2.3.1 CS**

FCAT Preparation

6. Earth provides many natural resources that humans use to live. Which of the following is a nonrenewable resource? **G.2.3.1 CS**
   A. water
   B. wind
   C. sunlight
   D. natural gas

SCi**LINKS**®

NSTA
Developed and maintained by the National Science Teachers Association

For a variety of links related to this chapter, go to www.scilinks.org

Topic: Natural Resources
SciLinks code: HSM1015

Fossil Fuels

How do the dinosaurs, plants, and sunny days 200 million years ago relate to your life today?

If you traveled to school today or used a product made of plastic, chances are that you used some of the energy from sunlight that fell on Earth several hundred million years ago. Without the fuels or products formed from plants and animals that lived alongside the dinosaurs, your life would be very different from life as you know it today.

Energy Resources

The fuels that we use to run cars, ships, planes, and factories and to generate electrical energy, shown in **Figure 1,** are energy resources. *Energy resources* are natural resources that humans use to generate energy. Most of the energy that we use comes from a group of natural resources called fossil fuels. A **fossil fuel** is a nonrenewable energy resource formed from the remains of plants and animals that lived long ago. Examples of fossil fuels include petroleum, coal, and natural gas.

When fossil fuels are burned, they release energy. For example, power plants burn coal to release energy that is used to produce electrical energy. However, because fossil fuels are a nonrenewable resource, once they are burned, they are gone. Therefore, like other resources, fossil fuels need to be conserved. In the 21st century, societies will keep trying to develop fuels that are alternatives to fossil fuels. But societies will also continue to develop more-efficient ways to use fossil fuels.

READING WARM-UP

Objectives

- Describe what energy resources are.
- Identify three different forms of fossil fuels. B.2.3.2
- Explain how fossil fuels form. B.2.3.2, D.1.3.4. AA
- Describe how fossil fuels are found and obtained.
- Identify four problems with fossil fuels.

Terms to Learn

fossil fuel *FCAT VOCAB*
petroleum
natural gas
coal
acid precipitation
smog

READING STRATEGY

Brainstorming The key idea of this section is fossil fuels. Brainstorm words and phrases related to fossil fuels.

fossil fuel a nonrenewable energy resource formed from the remains of organisms that lived long ago; examples include oil, coal, and natural gas *FCAT VOCAB*

Figure 1 *Light produced from electrical energy can be seen in this satellite image taken from space.*

Figure 2 *Some refineries use a process called* distillation *to separate petroleum into various types of petroleum products.*

Types of Fossil Fuels

All living things are made up of the element carbon. Because fossil fuels are formed from the remains of plants and animals, all fossil fuels are made of carbon, too. Most of the carbon in fossil fuels exists as hydrogen-carbon compounds called *hydrocarbons*. But different fossil fuels have different forms. Fossil fuels may exist as liquids, gases, or solids.

Liquid Fossil Fuels: Petroleum

A liquid mixture of complex hydrocarbon compounds is called **petroleum.** Petroleum is also commonly known as *crude oil.* Petroleum is separated into several kinds of products in refineries, such as the one shown in **Figure 2.** Examples of fossil fuels separated from petroleum are gasoline, jet fuel, kerosene, diesel fuel, and fuel oil.

More than 40% of the world's energy comes from petroleum products. Petroleum products are the main fuel for forms of transportation, such as airplanes, trains, boats, and ships. Crude oil is so valuable that it is often called *black gold.*

Benchmark Check What percentage of the world's energy comes from petroleum products? **B.2.3.2**

Gaseous Fossil Fuels: Natural Gas

A gaseous mixture of hydrocarbons is called **natural gas.** Most natural gas is used for heating, but some gas is used for generating electrical energy. Your kitchen stove may be powered by natural gas. Some motor vehicles, such as the van in **Figure 3,** use natural gas as fuel. An advantage of natural gas is that using it causes less air pollution than using oil does. However, natural gas is very flammable. Gas leaks can lead to fires or deadly explosions.

Methane, CH_4, is the main component of natural gas. But other components, such as butane and propane, can be separated from natural gas, too. Butane and propane are often used as fuel for camp stoves and outdoor grills.

petroleum a liquid mixture of complex hydrocarbon compounds; used widely as a fuel source

natural gas a mixture of gaseous hydrocarbons located under the surface of the Earth, often near petroleum deposits; used as a fuel

B.2.3.2 knows that most of the energy used today is derived from burning stored energy collected by organisms millions of years ago (i.e., nonrenewable fossil fuels).

G.2.3.1 CS knows that some resources are renewable and others are nonrenewable.

Figure 3 *Vehicles powered by natural gas are becoming more common.*

Figure 4 *This coal is being gathered so that it may be burned in the power plant shown in the background.*

Solid Fossil Fuels: Coal

coal a fossil fuel that forms underground from partially decomposed plant material

The solid fossil fuel that humans use most is coal. **Coal** is a fossil fuel that is formed underground from partially decomposed plant material. Coal was once the major source of energy in the United States. People burned coal in stoves to heat their homes. They also used coal in transportation. Many trains in the 1800s and early 1900s were powered by coal-burning steam locomotives.

As cleaner energy resources became available and coal became more difficult to mine, people reduced their use of coal. People also began to use coal less because burning coal produces large amounts of air pollution. Now, people use forms of transportation that use oil instead of coal as fuel. In the United States, coal is now rarely used as a fuel for heating. However, many power plants, such as the one shown in **Figure 4,** burn coal to generate electrical energy.

Benchmark Check What is coal commonly used for in the United States today? B.2.3.2

INTERNET ACTIVITY

Nonrenewable Resources
Write a persuasive paper that discusses the pros and cons of using a nonrenewable energy resource. Go to **go.hrw.com,** and type in the keyword **HZ5ENRW.**

B.2.3.2 knows that most of the energy used today is derived from burning stored energy collected by organisms millions of years ago (i.e., nonrenewable fossil fuels).

D.1.3.4 AA knows the ways in which plants and animals reshape the landscape (e.g., bacteria, fungi, worms, rodents, and other organisms add organic matter to the soil, increasing soil fertility, encouraging plant growth, and strengthening resistance to erosion).

CONNECTION TO Chemistry

Hydrocarbons Both petroleum and natural gas are made of hydrocarbons. A *hydrocarbon* is an organic compound that contains only carbon and hydrogen. A molecule of propane, C_3H_8, a gaseous fossil fuel, contains three carbon atoms and eight hydrogen atoms. Using a molecular model set, create a model of a propane molecule. (Hint: Each carbon atom should have four bonds, and each hydrogen atom should have one bond.)

ACTIVITY

How Do Fossil Fuels Form?

All fossil fuels form from the buried remains of ancient organisms. But the various kinds of fossil fuels form in different ways and from different kinds of organisms.

Petroleum and Natural Gas Formation

Petroleum and natural gas form mainly from the remains of microscopic sea organisms. When these organisms die, their remains settle on the ocean floor. There, the remains decay, are buried, and become part of the ocean sediment. Over time, the sediment slowly becomes rock, and the decayed remains become trapped. Through physical and chemical changes over millions of years, the remains become petroleum and gas. Under the pressure of overlying rocks and sediments, the fossil fuels can move through permeable rocks. *Permeable rocks* are rocks that allow fluids, such as petroleum and gas, to move through them. As shown in **Figure 5,** these permeable rocks become reservoirs that hold petroleum and natural gas.

The formation of petroleum and natural gas is an ongoing process. Part of the remains of today's sea life will become petroleum and natural gas millions of years from now.

Benchmark Check How did plants and animals contribute to the formation of petroleum and natural gas? D.1.3.4 AA

Rock Sponge

1. Place **samples of sandstone, limestone,** and **shale** in separate **Petri dishes.**
2. Place **five drops of light machine oil** on each rock sample.
3. Observe and record the time required for the oil to be absorbed by each of the rock samples.
4. Which rock sample absorbed the oil fastest? Why?
5. Based on your findings, describe a property that allows fossil fuels to be easily removed from reservoir rock.

Figure 5 Petroleum and Natural Gas Reservoirs

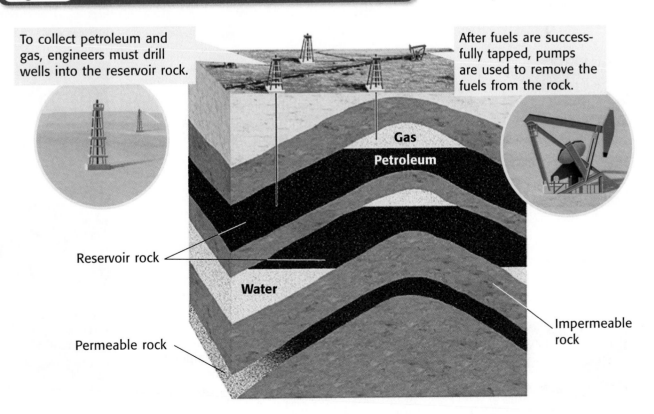

To collect petroleum and gas, engineers must drill wells into the reservoir rock.

After fuels are successfully tapped, pumps are used to remove the fuels from the rock.

Gas

Petroleum

Reservoir rock

Water

Permeable rock

Impermeable rock

Coal Formation

Coal forms differently from the way petroleum and natural gas form. Coal forms underground from decayed swamp plants over millions of years. When the plants die, they sink to the bottom of the swamp, and the process of coal formation begins.

The four types of coal are peat, lignite, bituminous coal, and anthracite, as shown in **Figure 6**. Peat is a form of coal in which the remains of plants are only partially decomposed by bacteria and fungi. Over time, the peat is buried under sediment. Water and gases are squeezed out of the peat. Pressure and high temperature then turn the peat into lignite. The process by which pressure and temperature increase because of the deposition of sediment creates the various forms of coal. The carbon content increases with each stage of coal formation. The higher the carbon content is, the more cleanly the material burns. However, when burned, all grades of coal pollute the air.

Benchmark Check Explain how decomposers, such as bacteria and fungi, are responsible for the formation of coal. B.2.3.2, D.1.3.4 AA

B.2.3.2 knows that most of the energy used today is derived from burning stored energy collected by organisms millions of years ago (i.e., nonrenewable fossil fuels).

D.1.3.4 AA knows the ways in which plants and animals reshape the landscape.

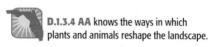
Figure 6 Coal Formation

Stage 1: Peat
Bacteria and fungi change sunken swamp plants into peat. Peat is about **60% carbon.**

Stage 2: Lignite
As sediment buries the peat, the pressure and temperature in the peat layer increase. The peat slowly changes into lignite, which is about **70% carbon.**

Stage 3: Bituminous Coal
As more sediment accumulates, the temperature and pressure continue to increase. Eventually, lignite turns into bituminous coal, which is about **80% carbon.**

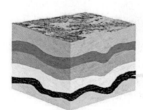 

Stage 4: Anthracite
As even more sediment accumulates, the temperature and pressure continue to increase. Bituminous coal turns into anthracite, which is about **90% carbon.**

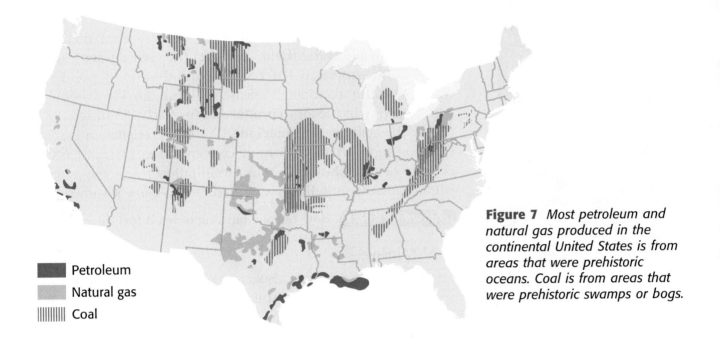

Petroleum
Natural gas
Coal

Figure 7 *Most petroleum and natural gas produced in the continental United States is from areas that were prehistoric oceans. Coal is from areas that were prehistoric swamps or bogs.*

Where Are Fossil Fuels Found?

Fossil fuels are found in many parts of the world. Some fossil fuels are found on land, while other fossil fuels are found beneath the ocean. As **Figure 7** shows, the United States has large reserves of petroleum, natural gas, and coal. Despite its large reserves of petroleum, the United States imports petroleum. In the United States, about one-half of the petroleum used is imported from the Middle East, South America, Africa, Canada, and Mexico.

How Do We Obtain Fossil Fuels?

Humans use several methods to remove fossil fuels from Earth's crust. The kind and location of the fuel determine the method that is used to remove the fuel. People remove petroleum and natural gas from Earth by drilling wells into rock that contains these resources. Oil wells exist on land and in the ocean. For offshore drilling, engineers mount drills on platforms that are secured to the ocean floor or that float at the ocean's surface. **Figure 8** shows an offshore oil rig.

People obtain coal either by mining deep beneath Earth's surface or by surface mining. Surface mining, also known as *strip mining,* is the process by which soil and rock are stripped from Earth's surface to expose the underlying coal that is to be mined.

✓ Reading Check How are natural gas and petroleum removed from Earth?

Figure 8 *Large oil rigs, some of which are more than 300 m tall, operate offshore in many places, such as the Gulf of Mexico and the North Sea.*

1994

1935

Figure 9 *Notice how this statue looked before the effects of acid precipitation.*

acid precipitation rain, sleet, or snow that contains a high concentration of acids

smog photochemical haze that forms when sunlight acts on industrial pollutants and burning fuels

Problems with Fossil Fuels

Although fossil fuels provide the energy that we need, methods of obtaining and using them can affect the environment negatively. For example, when coal is burned without pollution controls, sulfur dioxide is released. Sulfur dioxide combines with moisture in the air to produce sulfuric acid. Sulfuric acid is one of the acids in acid precipitation. **Acid precipitation** is rain, sleet, or snow that has a high concentration of acids, often because of air pollutants. Acid precipitation negatively affects wildlife, plants, buildings, and statues, as **Figure 9** shows.

✓ **Reading Check** How can the burning of fossil fuels affect rain?

Coal Mining

The mining of coal can also create environmental problems. Surface mining removes soil, which some plants need for growth and some animals need for shelter. If land is not properly restored afterward, surface mining can destroy wildlife habitats. Coal mining can also lower water tables and pollute water supplies. The potential for underground mines to collapse endangers the lives of miners.

Petroleum Problems

Producing, transporting, and using petroleum can cause environmental problems and can endanger wildlife. In June 2000, the carrier *Treasure* sank off the coast of South Africa and spilled more than 400 tons of oil. The toxic oil coated thousands of blackfooted penguins, as shown in **Figure 10.** The oil hindered the penguins' ability to swim and catch fish for food.

Smog

Burning petroleum products causes an environmental problem called smog. **Smog** is photochemical haze that forms when sunlight acts on industrial pollutants and burning fuels. Smog is particularly severe in cities such as Houston and Los Angeles because of millions of gasoline-burning automobiles that are used there. Also, mountains that surround Los Angeles prevent the wind from blowing pollutants away from the city.

Figure 10 *The oil spilled from the carrier* Treasure *endangered the lives of many animals, including blackfooted penguins.*

Summary

- Energy resources are resources that humans use to produce energy.
- Petroleum is a liquid fossil fuel that is made of hydrocarbon.
- Natural gas is a gaseous fossil fuel that is made of hydrocarbon.
- Coal is a solid fossil fuel that forms from decayed swamp plants. **B.2.3.2, D.1.3.4 AA**
- Petroleum and natural gas form from decayed sea life on the ocean floor. **B.2.3.2, D.1.3.4 AA**

- Fossil fuels are found worldwide. In the United States, half of the petroleum used is imported from the Middle East, South America, Africa, Canada, and Mexico.
- Fossil fuels are obtained from oil wells, mines below Earth's surface, and strip mines.
- Acid precipitation, smog, water pollution, and the destruction of wildlife habitat are some of the environmental problems that are created by the use of fossil fuels.

Using Key Terms

1. Use *fossil fuel, petroleum, natural gas, coal, acid precipitation,* and *smog* in separate sentences. **FCAT VOCAB**

Understanding Key Ideas

2. Which of the following types of coal has the highest carbon content?
   - **a.** lignite
   - **b.** anthracite
   - **c.** peat
   - **d.** bituminous coal

3. Name a solid fossil fuel, a liquid fossil fuel, and a gaseous fossil fuel.

4. Briefly describe how petroleum and natural gas form. **B.2.3.2, D.1.3.4 AA**

5. How do we obtain petroleum and natural gas?

6. Describe the advantages and disadvantages of using fossil fuels.

Critical Thinking

7. **Making Comparisons** How does the organic material from which coal forms differ from the organic material from which petroleum and natural gas form? **B.2.3.2, D.1.3.4 AA**

8. **Making Inferences** Why can't carpooling and using mass-transit systems eliminate the problems associated with fossil fuels?

FCAT Preparation

9. The formation of fossil fuels is an ongoing process. Fossil fuels that are used today formed from plants and animals that lived long ago. The decay of these plants and animals provided the raw materials for fossil fuels. Remains of today's plants and sea life may become fossil fuels in the future. Why are fossil fuels nonrenewable? **D.1.3.4 AA, G.2.3.1 CS**

   A. Fossil fuels cause pollution and other environmental problems.

   B. Fossil fuels must be obtained by drilling and mining.

   C. Fossil fuels form over millions of years, slower than the rate of their use.

   D. Most fossil fuels are from outside the United States.

SCiLINKS

NSTA
Developed and maintained by the
National Science Teachers Association

For a variety of links related to this chapter, go to www.scilinks.org

Topic: Fossil Fuels
SciLinks code: HSM0614

Alternative Resources

What would your life be like if you couldn't play video games, turn on lights, microwave your dinner, take a hot shower, or take the bus to school?

Most of your energy needs and the energy needs of others are met by the use of fossil fuels. Yet there are two main problems with fossil fuels. First, the availability of fossil fuels is limited. Fossil fuels are nonrenewable resources. Once fossil fuels are used up, new supplies won't be available for thousands—or even millions—of years.

Second, obtaining and using fossil fuels have environmental consequences. To continue to meet our energy needs and to eliminate pollution, we must find alternative sources of energy.

Splitting the Atom: Fission

The energy released by a fission or fusion reaction is called **nuclear energy.** *Fission* is a process in which the nuclei of radioactive atoms are split into two or more smaller nuclei, as shown in **Figure 1.** When fission takes place, a large amount of energy is released. This energy can be used to generate electrical energy. The SI unit for all forms of energy is the joule (J). However, electrical energy and nuclear energy are often measured in megawatts (MW).

Figure 1 **Fission**

A neutron from a uranium-235 atom splits the nucleus into two smaller nuclei called *fission products* and two or more neutrons.

Uranium-235

Neutron

Neutron

Barium-142

Energy

Krypton-91

Pros and Cons of Fission

Nuclear power plants provide alternative sources of energy that do not have the problems that fossil fuels do. So, instead of using fossil fuels, why don't we use nuclear energy more often? Nuclear power plants produce dangerous radioactive wastes. Radioactive wastes must be removed from the plant and stored until their radioactivity decreases to a harmless level. But many nuclear wastes remain dangerously radioactive for thousands of years. These wastes must be stored in an isolated place where the radiation that they emit cannot harm any living thing.

Another problem with nuclear power plants is the potential for accidental release of radiation into the environment. Cooling towers, such as the one shown in **Figure 2,** help regulate the temperature in a nuclear power plant. They also keep hot water from disrupting their local ecosystem. If a plant's cooling system stopped working, the plant would overheat. Then, its reactor would likely melt and release a large amount of radiation into the environment.

Figure 2 *Cooling towers are used to cool water leaving a nuclear power plant so that hot water is not released into the environment.*

Combining Atoms: Fusion

Another method of getting energy from nuclei is by fusion, shown in **Figure 3.** *Fusion* is the joining of two or more nuclei to form a larger nucleus. This process releases a large amount of energy and happens naturally in the sun.

The main advantage of fusion is that it produces few dangerous wastes. The main disadvantage of fusion is that very high temperatures are required for the fusion reaction to take place. No known material can withstand the high temperatures that fusion requires. So, the reaction must happen within a special environment, such as a magnetic field. Controlled fusion reactions have been limited to laboratory experiments.

nuclear energy the energy released by a fission or fusion reaction; the binding energy of the atomic nucleus

Benchmark Check How does the release of nuclear energy by fusion differ from the release of nuclear energy by fission? B.1.3.1 AA

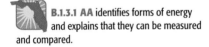 B.1.3.1 AA identifies forms of energy and explains that they can be measured and compared.

Figure 3 **Fusion**

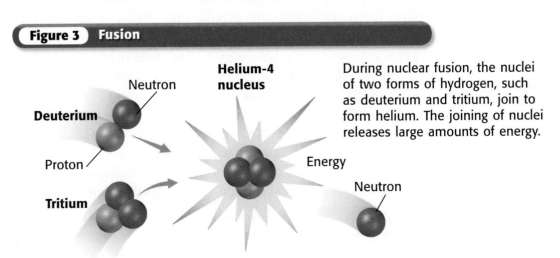

Helium-4 nucleus

Neutron

Deuterium

Proton

Tritium

Energy

Neutron

During nuclear fusion, the nuclei of two forms of hydrogen, such as deuterium and tritium, join to form helium. The joining of nuclei releases large amounts of energy.

Figure 4 *This image shows a prototype of a fuel-cell car. Power from fuel cells may be commonly used in the future.*

chemical energy the energy released when a chemical compound reacts to produce new compounds

solar energy the energy received by the Earth from the sun in the form of radiation

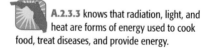 **A.2.3.3** knows that radiation, light, and heat are forms of energy used to cook food, treat diseases, and provide energy.

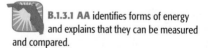 **B.1.3.1 AA** identifies forms of energy and explains that they can be measured and compared.

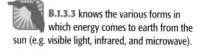 **B.1.3.3** knows the various forms in which energy comes to earth from the sun (e.g. visible light, infrared, and microwave).

G.2.3.1 CS knows that some resources are renewable and others are nonrenewable.

Chemical Energy

When you think of fuel for an automobile, you most likely think of gasoline. However, not all vehicles are fueled by gasoline. Some vehicles, such as the one shown in **Figure 4,** are powered by energy that is generated by fuel cells. Fuel cells power automobiles by converting **chemical energy** into electrical energy during a chemical reaction between hydrogen and oxygen. One advantage of using fuel cells as energy sources is that fuel cells do not generate pollution. The only byproduct of fuel cells is water. Fuel cells are also more efficient than internal combustion engines are.

The United States has used fuel cells in space travel since the 1960s. Fuel cells have provided space crews with electrical energy and drinking water. One day, fuel cells may generate electrical energy in buildings, ships, and submarines, too.

Solar Energy

Almost all forms of energy, including the energy of fossil fuels, come from the sun. The energy received by Earth from the sun in the form of radiation is **solar energy.** Earth receives more than enough solar energy to meet all of our energy needs. And because the Earth continuously receives solar energy, solar energy is a renewable resource. Solar energy can be used directly to heat buildings and to generate electrical energy. However, we do not yet have the technology to generate from solar energy alone all of the electrical energy that we need.

Sunlight can be changed into electrical energy by solar cells or photovoltaic cells. You may have used a calculator that is powered by solar cells. *Solar panels* are large panels that are made up of many solar cells wired together. Solar panels that are mounted on roofs of some homes and businesses provide a portion of the electrical energy that is used in the buildings.

Benchmark Check How is solar energy used, and why is it considered a renewable resource? **A.2.3.3, B.1.3.1 AA, B.1.3.3, G.2.3.1 CS**

Solar Heating

Solar energy is also used for direct heating through solar collectors. *Solar collectors* are dark-colored boxes that have glass or plastic tops. A common use of solar collectors is to heat water, as shown in **Figure 5.** More than 1 million solar water heaters have been installed in the United States. Solar water heaters are especially common in Florida and California.

Pros and Cons of Solar Energy

One of the best things about solar energy is that it doesn't produce pollution. Also, solar energy is renewable, because it comes from the sun. However, some climates don't have enough sunny days to benefit from solar energy. Also, although solar energy is free, solar cells and solar collectors are more expensive to make than other energy systems are. The cost of installing a complete solar-power system in a house can be up to one-third of the total cost of the house.

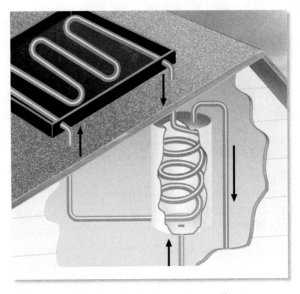

Figure 5 *The liquid in the solar collector is heated by the sun. Then, the liquid is pumped through tubes that run through a water heater, which causes the temperature of the water to increase.*

Wind Power

Wind is made indirectly by solar energy through the uneven heating of air. Energy can be harnessed from wind. **Wind power** is the use of a windmill to drive an electric generator. Clusters of wind turbines, such as the ones shown in **Figure 6,** can generate a significant amount of electrical energy. Wind energy is renewable and doesn't cause any pollution. However, in many areas, the wind isn't strong enough or frequent enough to create energy on a large scale.

wind power the use of a windmill to drive an electric generator

Figure 6 *Wind turbines take up only a small part of the ground's surface. As a result, the land on wind farms can be used for more than one purpose.*

Figure 7 *Falling water turns water wheels, which turn giant millstones that are used to grind grain into flour.*

hydroelectric energy electrical energy produced by the flow of water

 B.1.3.1 AA identifies forms of energy and explains that they can be measured and compared.

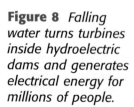 **G.2.3.1 CS** knows that some resources are renewable and others are nonrenewable.

Hydroelectric Energy

Humans have used the energy of falling water for thousands of years. Water wheels, such as the one shown in **Figure 7,** have been around since ancient times. In the early years of the Industrial Revolution, water wheels provided energy for many factories. Today, the energy of falling water is used to generate electrical energy. Electrical energy produced by falling water is called **hydroelectric energy.**

Pros and Cons of Hydroelectric Energy

After a dam is built, hydroelectric energy is inexpensive and causes little pollution. Hydroelectric energy is renewable because it depends on water, a renewable resource. But like wind energy, hydroelectric energy is not available everywhere. Hydroelectric energy can be produced only where large volumes of falling water can be harnessed. Huge dams, such as the one in **Figure 8,** must be built on major rivers to capture enough water to generate useful amounts of electrical energy.

Using more hydroelectric energy could reduce the use of fossil fuels, but there are trade-offs. Reducing the use of fossil fuels benefits the environment. But building the large dams needed for hydroelectric power often destroys resources, such as forests and wildlife habitats. For example, hydroelectric dams on the lower Snake and Columbia Rivers in Washington State disrupt the migratory paths of local populations of salmon and steelhead. Large numbers of these fish die each year because their migratory path is disrupted. Also, dams can decrease water quality and can cause erosion.

Benchmark Check Explain why hydroelectric energy is renewable. **B.1.3.1 AA, G.2.3.1 CS**

Figure 8 *Falling water turns turbines inside hydroelectric dams and generates electrical energy for millions of people.*

Power from Plants

Plants are similar to solar collectors. Both absorb energy from the sun and store it for later use. Leaves, wood, and other parts of plants contain the stored energy. Even the dung of plant-grazing animals is high in stored energy. These sources of energy are called biomass. **Biomass** is organic matter that can be a source of energy.

Burning Biomass

Biomass energy can be released in several ways. The most common way is to burn biomass. Approximately 70% of people living in developing countries, about half the world population, burn wood or charcoal to heat their homes and cook their food. In contrast, about 5% of the people in the United States heat and cook this way. Scientists estimate that the burning of wood and animal dung accounts for approximately 14% of the world's total energy use. **Figure 9** shows a woman who is preparing cow dung that will be dried and used for fuel.

Gasohol

Biomass material can also be changed into liquid fuel. Plants that contain sugar or starch can be made into alcohol. This alcohol can be burned as fuel. In addition, alcohol can be mixed with gasoline to make a fuel called **gasohol.** More than 1,000 L of alcohol can be made from 1 acre of corn. Although 1,000 L seems like a great deal of fuel, people in the United States use a large amount of fuel in cars.

Even though biomass is a renewable source of energy, the alcohol produced from about 40% of one corn harvest in the United States would provide only 10% of the fuel used in our cars! Also, the production of biomass requires land that could be used for growing food. The use of land to produce biomass for fuel must be balanced with the need to use land to grow food for an increasing human population.

biomass plant material, manure, or any other organic matter that is used as an energy source

gasohol a mixture of gasoline and alcohol that is used as a fuel

Miles per Acre

Imagine that you own a car that runs on alcohol made from corn that you grow. You drive your car about 15,000 mi per year, and you get 240 gal of alcohol from each acre of corn that you process. If your car has a gas mileage of 25 mi/gal, how many acres of corn must you process to fuel your car for a year?

Figure 9 *In many parts of the world where firewood is scarce, people burn animal dung for energy.*

geothermal energy the energy produced by heat within Earth

B.1.3.1 AA identifies forms of energy and explains that they can be measured and compared.

Energy from Within Earth

If you have ever seen a volcanic eruption, you know how powerful Earth can be. The energy produced by the heat within Earth is called **geothermal energy.**

Geothermal Energy

In some areas, groundwater is heated by *magma,* or melted rock. Often, the heated groundwater becomes steam. *Geysers* are natural vents that discharge this steam or water in a column into the air. The steam and hot water can also escape through wells drilled into the rock. From these wells, geothermal power plants can harness the energy from within Earth by pumping the steam and hot water, as shown in **Figure 10.** The world's largest geothermal power plant in California, called *The Geysers,* produces electrical energy for 1.7 million households.

Geothermal energy can also be used to heat buildings. In this process, hot water and steam are used to heat a fluid. Then, this fluid is pumped through a building in order to heat the building. Buildings in Iceland are heated from the country's many geothermal sites in this way.

Benchmark Check Describe how geothermal power plants obtain geothermal energy. B.1.3.1 AA

Figure 10 **Harnessing Geothermal Energy**

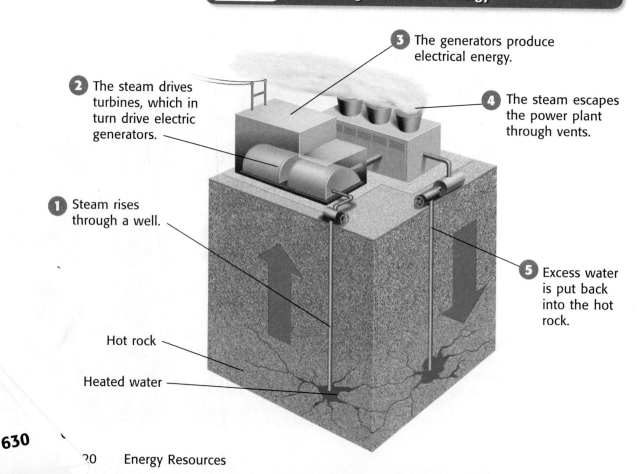

3 The generators produce electrical energy.

2 The steam drives turbines, which in turn drive electric generators.

4 The steam escapes the power plant through vents.

1 Steam rises through a well.

5 Excess water is put back into the hot rock.

Hot rock

Heated water

Summary

- Fission and fusion are processes that release nuclear energy. The byproduct of fission is radioactive waste. **B.1.3.1 AA**

- For fusion to take place, extremely high temperatures are required.

- Fuel cells combine hydrogen and oxygen to produce electrical energy. Fuel cells release water as a byproduct.

- Solar energy is a renewable resource that does not emit pollution. However, solar panels and solar collectors are expensive. **B.1.3.1 AA, G.2.3.1 CS**

- Wind power is a renewable resource that does not emit pollution. However, wind energy cannot be generated in all areas. **B.1.3.1 AA, G.2.3.1 CS**

- Hydroelectric energy is a cheap, renewable resource that causes little pollution. However, hydroelectric energy is available only in some areas. **B.1.3.1 AA, G.2.3.1 CS**

- Burning biomass and gasohol can release energy, but not enough to meet all of our energy needs. **B.1.3.1 AA**

- Geothermal energy comes from within Earth but is available only in certain areas. **B.1.3.1 AA**

Using Key Terms

1. Write an original definition for *nuclear energy, solar energy, hydroelectric energy,* and *geothermal energy.*

Understanding Key Ideas

2. Which of the following alternative resources requires hydrogen and oxygen to produce energy?
   a. fuel cells
   b. solar energy
   c. nuclear energy
   d. geothermal energy

3. Describe two ways of using solar energy. **A.2.3.3**

4. List two renewable and two nonrenewable alternatives to fossil fuels. **B.1.3.1 AA, G.2.3.1 CS**

5. From what source do almost all forms of energy on Earth ultimately come? **B.1.3.3**

Critical Thinking

6. **Analyzing Methods** If you were going to build a nuclear power plant, why would you not build it in the middle of a desert?

7. **Predicting Consequences** If an alternative, nonpolluting resource could successfully replace crude oil, how might the use of that resource affect the environment?

FCAT Preparation

8. Earth offers many energy resources that are alternatives to fossil fuels. Which of the following alternative energy sources is nonrenewable? **G.2.3.1 CS**
   A. nuclear fission
   B. solar energy
   C. wind power
   D. hydroelectric energy

9. Fuel cells can be used to power automobiles. What kind of energy conversion takes place in a fuel cell? **B.1.3.1 AA**
   F. nuclear energy into electrical energy
   G. water energy into hydroelectric energy
   H. chemical energy into electrical energy
   I. solar energy into electrical energy

SCiLINKS.

NSTA
Developed and maintained by the National Science Teachers Association

For a variety of links related to this chapter, go to www.scilinks.org

Topic: Renewable Resources
SciLinks code: HSM1291

Model-Making Lab

OBJECTIVES

Create a model of a water wheel. H.3.3.4 CS

Determine factors that influence the rate at which a water wheel lifts a weight. H.1.3.5 AA

MATERIALS

- bottle, soda, 2 L, water-filled
- card, index, 3 in. × 5 in.
- clay, modeling
- coin
- cork
- glue
- hole punch
- jug, milk, plastic
- marker, permanent, black
- meterstick
- safety razor (for teacher)
- scissors
- skewers, wooden (2)
- tape, transparent
- thread, 20 cm
- thumbtacks (5)
- watch or clock, shows seconds

SAFETY

H.1.3.5 AA knows that a change in one or more variables may alter the outcome of an investigation.

H.3.3.4 CS knows that technological design should require taking into account constraints such as natural laws, the properties of the materials used, and economic, political, social, ethical, and aesthetic values.

Make a Water Wheel

Lift Enterprises is planning to build a water wheel that will lift objects as a crane does. The president of the company has asked you to modify the basic water wheel design so that the water wheel will lift objects more quickly.

Ask a Question

1 What factors influence the rate at which a water wheel lifts a weight?

Form a Hypothesis

2 Change the question above into a statement to formulate a testable hypothesis.

Test the Hypothesis

3 Build a water wheel model. Measure and mark a 5 cm × 5 cm square on an index card. Cut the square out of the card. Fold the square in half to form a triangle.

4 Measure and mark a line 8 cm from the bottom of the plastic jug. Use scissors to cut along this line. (Your teacher may need to use a safety razor to start this cut for you.)

5 Use the paper triangle that you made in step 3 as a template. Use a permanent marker to trace four triangles onto the flat parts of the top section of the plastic jug. Cut the triangles out of the plastic to form four fins.

6 Use a thumbtack to attach one corner of each plastic fin to the round edge of the cork, as shown below. Make sure that the fins are equally spaced around the cork.

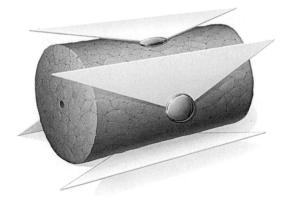

7 Press a thumbtack into one of the flat sides of the cork. Jiggle the thumbtack to widen the hole in the cork, and then remove the thumbtack. Repeat on the other side of the cork.

8 Place a drop of glue on one end of each skewer. Insert the first skewer into the hole in one end of the cork. Insert the second skewer into the hole in the other end of the cork.

9 Use a hole punch to punch one hole in each of two opposite sides of the jug's bottom section. Punch the two holes 1 cm below the top edge of the jug, directly opposite each other.

10 Suspend the cork in the center of the jug by carefully putting the free end of each skewer into a hole. Make two small, same-sized balls of clay. Attach one ball to the end of each skewer, outside the jug.

11 Tape one end of the thread to one skewer on the outside of the jug, next to the clay ball. Wrap the thread around the clay ball three times. (As the water wheel turns, the thread should wrap around the clay. The other ball of clay balances the weight and helps keep the water wheel turning smoothly.)

12 Tape the free end of the thread to a coin. Wrap the thread around the coin, and tape it again.

13 Slowly pour water from the 2 L bottle onto the fins so that the water wheel spins. What happens to the coin? Record your observations.

14 Lower the coin back to the starting position. Add more clay to the skewer to increase the diameter of the wheel. Repeat step 13. Did the coin rise faster or slower this time?

15 Lower the coin back to the starting position. Modify the shape of the clay ball, and repeat step 13. Does the shape of the ball affect how quickly the coin rises? Explain your answer.

16 What happens if you remove two of the fins from opposite sides? What happens if you add more fins?

17 Experiment with another fin shape. How does this shape affect the speed at which the coin rises?

Analyze the Results

1 **Examining Data** What factors influence how quickly you can lift the coin? Explain.

Draw Conclusions

2 **Drawing Conclusions** What recommendations for improving the water wheel would you make to the president of Lift Enterprises?

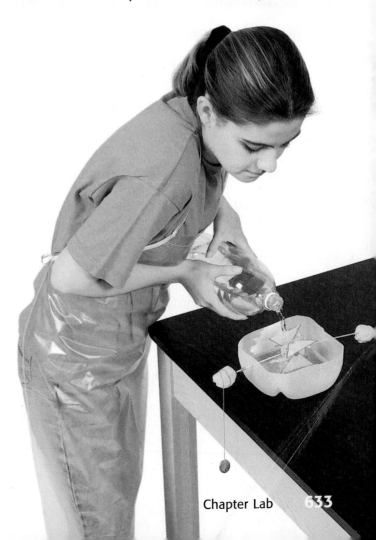

Chapter Review

USING KEY TERMS

Correct each statement by replacing the underlined term.

1 A liquid mixture of complex hydrocarbon compounds is called <u>natural gas</u>.

2 Energy that is released when a chemical compound reacts to produce a new compound is called <u>nuclear energy</u>.

For each pair of terms, explain how the meanings of the terms differ.

3 *solar energy* and *wind power*

4 *biomass* and *gasohol*

UNDERSTANDING KEY IDEAS

Multiple Choice

5 Resources are either renewable or nonrenewable. Which of the following resources is a renewable resource? **G.2.3.1 CS** *FCAT*

a. coal
c. oil
b. trees
d. natural gas

6 Which of the following fuels is NOT made from petroleum?

a. jet fuel
c. kerosene
b. lignite
d. fuel oil

7 Peat, lignite, and anthracite are forms of

a. petroleum.
b. natural gas.
c. coal.
d. gasohol.

8 Which of the following factors contributes to smog?

a. automobiles
b. sunlight
c. mountains surrounding urban areas
d. All of the above

9 Fusion releases a large amount of energy. Which of the following resources is produced by fusion? **B.1.3.1 AA** *FCAT*

a. solar energy
c. wind power
b. natural gas
d. petroleum

10 One alternative resource is nuclear energy. Which of the following processes do nuclear power plants use to produce energy? **B.1.3.1 AA** *FCAT*

a. fission
b. fusion
c. fractionation
d. coal formation

11 A solar-powered calculator uses

a. solar collectors.
b. solar panels.
c. solar mirrors.
d. solar cells.

Short Answer

12 How does acid precipitation form?

13 If sunlight is free, why is electrical energy from solar cells expensive?

14 Describe three ways that humans use natural resources.

15 Explain how fossil fuels are found and obtained.

CRITICAL THINKING

Extended Response

16 Predicting Consequences How would your life be different if fossil fuels were less widely available? B.2.3.2

17 Evaluating Assumptions Are fossil fuels nonrenewable? Explain. B.2.3.2

18 Evaluating Assumptions Why do we need to conserve renewable resources even though they can be replaced? G.2.3.1 CS

19 Identifying Relationships Explain why the energy that we get from many of our resources ultimately comes from the sun. B.1.3.1 AA *FCAT*

20 Applying Concepts Describe various ways that you can conserve natural resources at home.

21 Identifying Relationships Explain why coal usually does NOT form in locations where petroleum and natural gas form. B.2.3.2, D.1.3.4 AA

22 Applying Concepts Choose an alternative energy resource that you think should be developed more. Explain the reason for your choice.

Concept Mapping

23 Use the following terms to create a concept map: *fossil fuels, wind energy, energy resources, biomass, renewable resources, solar energy, nonrenewable resources, natural gas, gasohol, coal,* and *oil.*

INTERPRETING GRAPHICS

Use the graph below to answer the questions that follow.

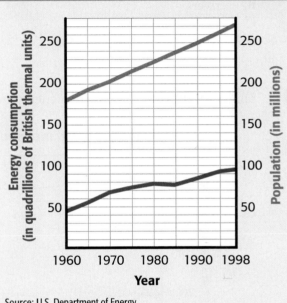

Energy Consumption and Population Growth in the United States

Source: U.S. Department of Energy.

24 How many British thermal units were consumed in 1970?

25 In what year was the most energy consumed?

26 Why do you think that energy consumption has not increased at the same rate at which the population has increased?

For the following questions, write your answers on a separate sheet of paper.

1 Some energy sources are not renewed rapidly enough for practical human purposes. Which of these is not renewable rapidly enough for practical human purposes?

A. coal

B. rivers

C. tides

D. wind

2 This chart shows a breakdown of energy usage in industrialized countries over twenty years.

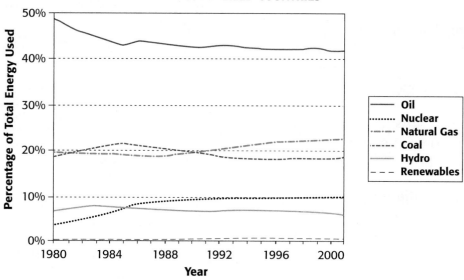

What is a source of **most** of the energy used during this period?

F. wind mills

G. fossil fuels

H. solar power

I. running water

3 Before the development of petroleum reserves, most engines were steam-powered. Some steam engines burned wood and others burned coal. When used as a fuel for steam-powered engines, what factor makes wood different from coal?

A. When burning wood, pollution is emitted.

B. When burning wood, most of the energy is wasted.

C. When burning wood, a renewable resource is being used.

D. When burning wood, thermal energy is transferred to form steam.

4 The chart below shows how coal is formed.

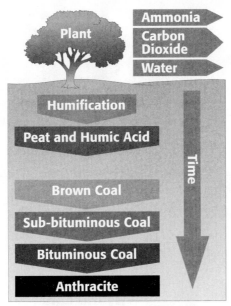

The Formation of Coal

What was the original source of energy that is stored within coal?

F. electrical energy from lightning
G. solar energy stored in organisms
H. wind energy from the atmosphere
I. potential energy from the water cycle

5 The Sahara Desert is known for its low humidity and rare rainfall. Beneath the Sahara Desert, there is a source of underground water left behind from thousands of years ago when climate conditions were different. Why would the water below the Sahara be classified as nonrenewable?

A. It is not replaced by natural processes.
B. It can be accessed by commercial wells.
C. It can be used to grow agricultural crops.
D. It is not stored in underground rock formations.

6 Natural gas is often considered to be a nonrenewable resource. What is the **best** source for renewable natural gas?

F. natural gas given off by bacteria
G. natural gas found with oil deposits
H. natural gas under the Gulf of Mexico
I. natural gas found with bituminous coal

Science in Action

FOCUS ON FLORIDA

Weird Science

Solar Energy Race

The Junior Solar Sprint is a solar-energy car race in Florida. The race is sponsored by the Florida Solar Energy Center at the University of Central Florida. Before the race, middle school students from all over the state design and build their own miniature cars. Each car entered in the race must use the same kind of solar cells and motor. But the students build other parts of their cars using a wide range of materials. Car bodies have been made of wood, rubber, and egg cartons. The wheels for some cars have even made out of old CDs! Of course, not everybody can win. But no matter how their cars perform, all of the students learn a lot about traction, torque, drag, and other scientific concepts.

Language Arts ACTIVITY

WRITING SKILL Find out more about another solar energy project. What do you think the best outcome would be? Create a fictional story that expresses this outcome.

Science, Technology, and Society

Hybrid Cars

One solution to the pollution problem caused by the burning of fossil fuels for transportation purposes is to develop cars that depend less on fossil fuels. One such car is a *hybrid*. Instead of using only gasoline for energy, a hybrid uses gasoline and electricity. Because a hybrid has special batteries, it uses less gasoline per mile than a car powered only by gasoline does. Some hybrids routinely get a gas mileage of as many as 45 mi/gal, or more than twice the mileage that many gasoline-only cars get! Several models of hybrids are on the market. Soon, you will likely see more hybrids on the roads.

Math ACTIVITY

Charlie's truck has a gas mileage of 17 mi/gal. Charlie drives his truck an average of 12,000 mi per year. Then, he sells the truck and buys a new hybrid car that has a gas mileage of 45 mi/gal. If gasoline costs $1.40 per gallon, how much money will Charlie save in a year by driving the hybrid car instead of driving his truck?

Fred Begay

Nuclear Physicist Generating energy by combining atoms is called *fusion*. This process is being developed by nuclear physicists, such as Fred Begay, at the Department of Energy's Los Alamos National Laboratory. Begay hopes to someday make fusion an alternative energy resource. Because fusion is the process that generates energy in the sun, Begay uses NASA satellites to study the sun. Begay explains that developing skills in abstract reasoning is necessary to the study of fusion. As a Navajo, Begay developed these skills while growing up at his Navajo home in Towaoc, Colorado, where his family taught him about nature. Today, Begay uses his skills not only to help develop a new energy resource but also to mentor Native American and other minority students. In 1999, Begay won the Distinguished Scientist Award from the Society for Advancement of Chicanos and Native Americans in Science.

Social Studies ACTIVITY

Research the lifestyle of Native Americans before 1900. Then, create a poster that compares resources that Native Americans used before 1900 with resources that many people use today.

go.hrw.com

To learn more about these Science in Action topics, visit **go.hrw.com** and type in the keyword **HT6FERFF**.

Current Science

Check out Current Science® articles related to this chapter by visiting **go.hrw.com**. Just type in the keyword **HZ5CS05**.

Contents

Skills Practice Lab

Go Fly a Bike!

Your friend Daniel just invented a bicycle that can fly! Trouble is, the bike can fly only when the wind speed is between 3 m/s and 10 m/s. If the wind is not blowing hard enough, the bike won't get enough lift to rise into the air, and if the wind is blowing too hard, the bike is difficult to control. Daniel needs to know if he can fly his bike today. Can you build a device that can estimate how fast the wind is blowing?

MATERIALS

- clay, modeling
- cups, paper, small (5)
- hole punch
- marker, colored
- pencil, sharp, with an eraser
- ruler, metric
- scissors
- stapler, small
- straws, straight plastic (2)
- tape, masking
- thumbtack
- watch (or clock) that indicates seconds

SAFETY

Ask a Question

1 How can I construct a device to measure wind speed?

Form a Hypothesis

2 Write a possible answer for the question above. Explain your reasoning.

Test the Hypothesis

3 Cut off the rolled edges of all five paper cups. They will then be lighter so that they can spin more easily.

4 Measure and place four equally spaced markings 1 cm below the rim of one of the paper cups.

5 Use the hole punch to punch a hole at each mark so that the cup has four equally spaced holes. Use the sharp pencil to carefully punch a hole in the center of the bottom of the cup.

6 Push a straw through two opposite holes in the side of the cup.

7 Repeat step 5 for the other two holes. The straws should form an X.

8 Measure 3 cm from the bottom of the remaining paper cups, and mark each spot with a dot.

9 At each dot, punch a hole in the paper cups with the hole punch.

10 Color the outside of one of the four cups.

11. Slide a cup on one of the straws by pushing the straw through the punched hole. Rotate the cup so that the bottom faces to the right.

12. Fold the end of the straw, and staple it to the inside of the cup directly across from the hole.

13. Repeat steps 11–12 for each of the remaining cups.

14. Push the tack through the intersection of the two straws.

15. Push the eraser end of a pencil through the bottom hole in the center cup. Push the tack as far as it will go into the end of the eraser.

16. Push the sharpened end of the pencil into some modeling clay to form a base. The device will then be able to stand up without being knocked over, as shown at right.

17. Blow into the cups so that they spin. Adjust the tack so that the cups can freely spin without wobbling or falling apart. Congratulations! You have just constructed an anemometer.

18. Find a suitable area outside to place the anemometer vertically on a surface away from objects that would obstruct the wind, such as buildings and trees.

19. Mark the surface at the base of the anemometer with masking tape. Label the tape "starting point."

20. Hold the colored cup over the starting point while your partner holds the watch.

21. Release the colored cup. At the same time, your partner should look at the watch or clock. As the cups spin, count the number of times the colored cup crosses the starting point in 10 s.

Analyze the Results

1. How many times did the colored cup cross the starting point in 10 s?

2. Divide your answer in step 21 by 10 to get the number of revolutions in 1 s.

3. Measure the diameter of your anemometer (the distance between the outside edges of two opposite cups) in centimeters. Multiply this number by 3.14 to get the circumference of the circle made by the cups of your anemometer.

4. Multiply your answer from step 3 by the number of revolutions per second (step 2). Divide that answer by 100 to get wind speed in meters per second.

5. Compare your results with those of your classmates. Did you get the same results? What could account for any slight differences in your results?

Draw Conclusions

6. Could Daniel fly his bicycle today? Why or why not?

Skills Practice Lab

Watching the Weather

Imagine that you own a private consulting firm that helps people plan for big occasions, such as weddings, parties, and celebrity events. One of your duties is making sure the weather doesn't put a damper on your clients' plans. In order to provide the best service possible, you have taken a crash course in reading weather maps. Will the celebrity golf match have to be delayed on account of rain? Will the wedding ceremony have to be moved inside so the blushing bride doesn't get soaked? It is your job to say yea or nay.

MATERIALS

• pencil

Procedure

1. Study the station model and legend shown on the next page. You will use the legend to interpret the weather map on the final page of this activity.

2. Weather data is represented on a weather map by a station model. A station model is a small circle that shows the location of the weather station along with a set of symbols and numbers around the circle that represent the data collected at the weather station. Study the table below.

Weather-Map Symbols					
Weather conditions		**Cloud cover**		**Wind speed (mph)**	
••	Light rain	◯	No clouds	◎	Calm
∴	Moderate rain	◖	One-eighth	⊙ 3–8	
∴•	Heavy rain	◖	Scattered	/ 9–14	
,	Drizzle	◗	Broken	// 15–20	
✳ ✳	Light snow	◑	Seven-eighths	// 21–25	
✳✳	Moderate snow	●	Overcast	/// 32–37	
⌐	Thunderstorm	⊗	Sky obscured	//// 44–48	
∿	Freezing rain	**Special Symbols**		◢ 55–60	
∞	Haze	▲▲▲▲	Cold front	◢ 66–71	
≡	Fog	●●●●	Warm front		
		H	High pressure		
		L	Low pressure		
		↩	Hurricane		

Station Model

Wind speed is represented by whole and half tails.

A line indicates the direction the wind is coming from.

Air temperature

A symbol represents the current weather conditions. If there is no symbol, there is no precipitation.

Dew point temperature

Shading indicates the cloud coverage.

234

77
73

Atmospheric pressure in millibars (mbar). This number has been shortened on the station model. To read the number properly you must follow a few simple rules.

- If the first number is greater than 5, place a 9 in front of the number and a decimal point between the last two digits.

- If the first number is less than or equal to 5, place a 10 in front of the number and a decimal point between the last two digits.

Interpreting Station Models

The station model below is for Boston, Massachusetts. The current temperature in Boston is 42°F, and the dew point is 39°F. The barometric pressure is 1011.0 mbar. The sky is overcast, and there is moderate rainfall. The wind is coming from the southwest at 15–20 mph.

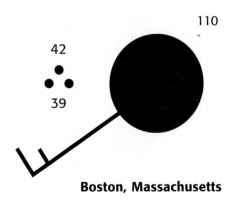

110

42
39

Boston, Massachusetts

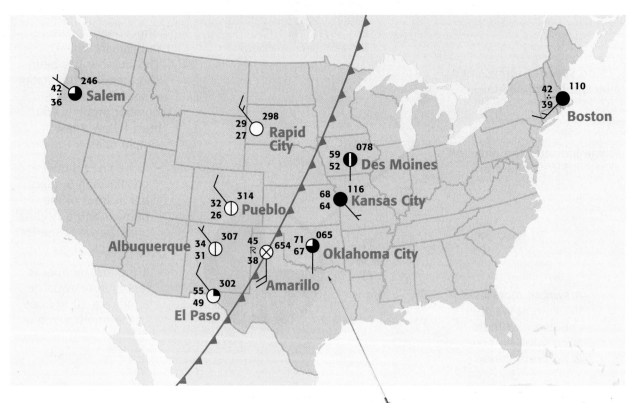

Analyze the Results

1 Based on the weather for the entire United States, what time of year is it? Explain your answer.

2 Interpret the station model for Salem, Oregon. What is the temperature, dew point, cloud coverage, wind direction, wind speed, and atmospheric pressure? Is there any precipitation? If so, what kind?

3 What is happening to wind direction, temperature, and pressure as the cold front approaches? as it passes?

Draw Conclusions

4 Interpret the station model for Amarillo, Texas.

Skills Practice Lab

Let It Snow!

Although 2 cm of rain might be good for your garden, 7 cm or 8 cm could cause an unwelcome flood. But what about snow? How much snow is too much? A blizzard might drop 40 cm of snow overnight. Sure it's up to your knees, but how does this much snow compare with rain? This activity will help you find out.

Procedure

1. Pour 50 mL of shaved ice into your beaker. Do not pack the ice into the beaker. This ice will represent your snowfall.

2. Use the ruler to measure the height of the snow in the beaker.

3. Turn on the hot plate to a low setting. **Caution:** Wear heat-resistant gloves and goggles when working with the hot plate.

4. Place the beaker on the hot plate, and leave it there until all of the snow melts.

5. Pour the water into the graduated cylinder, and record the height and volume of the water.

6. Repeat steps 1–5 two more times.

Analysis

1. What was the difference in height before and after the snow melted in each of your three trials? What was the average difference?

2. Why did the volume change after the ice melted?

3. What was the ratio of snow height to water height?

4. Use the ratio you found in step 3 of the Analysis to calculate how much water 50 cm of this snow would produce. Use the following equation to help.

$$\frac{\text{measured height of snow}}{\text{measured height of water}} = \frac{50 \text{ cm of snow}}{? \text{ cm of water}}$$

5. Why is it important to know the water content of a snowfall?

Applying Your Data

Shaved ice isn't really snow. Research to find out how much water real snow would produce. Does every snowfall produce the same ratio of snow height to water depth?

Model-Making Lab

Gone with the Wind

Pilots at the Fly Away Airport need your help—fast! Last night, lightning destroyed the orange windsock. This windsock helped pilots measure which direction the wind was blowing. But now the windsock is gone with the wind, and an incoming airplane needs to land. The pilot must know which direction the wind is blowing and is counting on you to make a device that can measure wind direction.

MATERIALS

- card, index
- compass, drawing
- compass, magnetic
- pencil, sharpened
- plate, paper
- protractor
- rock, small
- ruler, metric
- scissors
- stapler
- straw, straight plastic
- thumbtack (or pushpin)

SAFETY

Ask a Question

1 How can I measure wind direction?

Form a Hypothesis

2 Write a possible answer to the question above.

Test the Hypothesis

3 Find the center of the plate by tracing around its edge with a drawing compass. The pointed end of the compass should poke a small hole in the center of the plate.

4 Use a ruler to draw a line across the center of the plate.

5 Use a protractor to help you draw a second line through the center of the plate. This new line should be at a 90° angle to the line you drew in step 4.

6 Moving clockwise, label each line "N," "E," "S," and "W."

7 Use a protractor to help you draw two more lines through the center of the plate. These lines should be at a 45° angle to the lines you drew in steps 4 and 5.

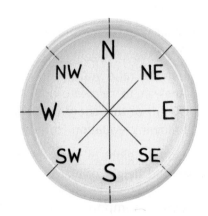

8. Moving clockwise from *N*, label these new lines "NE," "SE," "SW," and "NW." The plate now resembles the face of a magnetic compass. The plate will be the base of your wind-direction indicator. It will help you read the direction of the wind at a glance.

9. Measure and mark a 5 cm × 5 cm square on an index card, and cut out the square. Fold the square in half to form a triangle.

10. Staple an open edge of the triangle to the straw so that one point of the triangle touches the end of the straw.

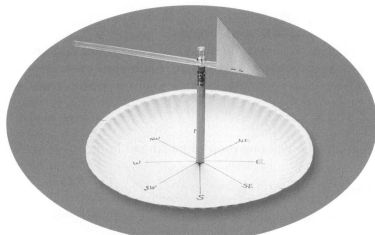

11. Hold the pencil at a 90° angle to the straw. The eraser should touch the balance point of the straw. Push a thumbtack or pushpin through the straw and into the eraser. The straw should spin without falling off.

12. Find a suitable area outside to measure the wind direction. The area should be clear of trees and buildings.

13. Press the sharpened end of the pencil through the center hole of the plate and into the ground. The labels on your paper plate should be facing the sky, as shown on this page.

14. Use a compass to find magnetic north. Rotate the plate so that the *N* on the plate points north. Place a small rock on top of the plate so that the plate does not turn.

15. Watch the straw as it rotates. The triangle will point in the direction the wind is blowing.

Analyze the Results

1. From which direction is the wind coming?

2. In which direction is the wind blowing?

Draw Conclusions

3. Would this be an effective way for pilots to measure wind direction? Why or why not?

4. What improvements would you suggest to Fly Away Airport to measure wind direction more accurately?

Applying Your Data

Use this tool to measure and record wind direction for several days. What changes in wind direction occur as a front approaches? as a front passes?

Review magnetic declination in the chapter entitled "Maps as Models of the Earth." How might magnetic declination affect your design for a tool to measure wind direction?

Investigating an Oil Spill

Have you ever wondered why it is important to recycle motor oil rather than pour it down the drain or sewer? Or have you ever wondered why a seemingly small oil spill can cause so much damage? The reason is that a little oil goes a long way.

Observing Oil and Water

Maybe you've heard the phrase "Oil and water don't mix." Oil dropped in water will spread out thinly over the surface of the water. In this activity, you'll learn how far a drop of oil can spread.

Ask a Question

1 How far will one drop of oil spread in a pan of water?

Form a Hypothesis

2 Write a hypothesis that could answer the question above.

Test the Hypothesis

3 Use a pipet to place one drop of oil into the middle of a pan of water. **Caution:** Machine oil is poisonous. Wear goggles and gloves. Keep materials that have contacted oil out of your mouth and eyes.

4 Observe what happens to the drop of oil for the next few seconds. Record your observations.

5 Using a metric ruler, measure the diameter of the oil slick to the nearest centimeter.

6 Determine the area of the oil slick in square centimeters. Use the formula below to find the area of a circle ($A = \pi r^2$). The radius (r) is equal to the diameter you measured in step 5 divided by 2. Multiply the radius by itself to get the square of the radius (r^2). Pi (π) is equal to 3.14. Record your answer.

> **Example**
>
> If your diameter is 10 cm,
>
> $r = 5$ cm, $r^2 = 25$ cm^2, $\pi = 3.14$
>
> $A = \pi r^2$
>
> $A = 3.14 \times 25$ cm^2
>
> $A = 78.5$ cm^2

MATERIALS

- calculator (optional)
- gloves, protective
- goggles
- graduated cylinder
- oil, light machine, 15 mL
- pan, large, at least 22 cm in diameter
- pipet
- ruler, metric
- water

SAFETY

Analyze the Results

1 What happened to the drop of oil when it came in contact with the water?

2 What total surface area was covered by the oil slick? (Show your calculations.)

Draw Conclusions

3 What can you conclude about the density of oil compared with the density of water?

Finding the Number of Drops in a Liter

"It's only a few drops," you may think as you spill something toxic on the ground. But those drops eventually add up. Just how many drops does it take to make a difference? In this activity, you'll learn just what an impact a few drops can have.

Procedure

1 Using a clean pipet, count the number of water drops it takes to fill the graduated cylinder to 10 mL. Be sure to add the drops slowly so you get an accurate count.

2 Since there are 1,000 mL in a liter, multiply the number of drops in 10 mL by 100. The result is the number of drops in a liter.

Analyze the Results

1 How many drops of water from your pipet did it take to fill a 1 L container?

2 What would happen if someone spilled 4 L of oil into a lake?

Applying Your Data

Can you devise a way to clean the oil from the water? Get permission from your teacher before testing your cleaning method.

Do you think oil behaves the same way in ocean water? Devise an experiment to test your hypothesis.

Skills Practice Lab

Great Ice Escape

Did you know that ice acts as a natural wrecking ball? Even rocks don't stand a chance against the power of ice. When water trapped in rock freezes, a process called *ice wedging* occurs. The water volume increases, and the rock cracks to "get out of the way." This expansion can fragment a rock into several pieces. In this exercise, you will see how this natural wrecker works, and you will try to stop the great ice escape.

Ask a Question

1 If a plastic jar is filled with water, is there a way to prevent the jar from breaking when the water freezes?

Form a Hypothesis

2 Write a hypothesis that is a possible answer to the question above. Explain your reasoning.

Test the Hypothesis

3 Fill three identical jars to overflowing with water, and close two of them securely.

4 Measure the height of the water in the unsealed container. Record the height.

5 Tightly wrap one of the closed jars with tape, string, or other items to reinforce the jar. These items must be removable.

6 Place all three jars in resealable sandwich bags, and leave them in the freezer overnight. (Make sure the open jar does not spill.)

7 Remove the jars from the freezer, and carefully remove the wrapping from the reinforced jar.

8 Did your reinforced jar crack? Why or why not?

9 What does each jar look like? Record your observations.

10 Record the height of the ice in the unsealed jar. How does the new height compare with the height you measured in step 4?

Analyze the Results

1 Do you think it is possible to stop the ice from breaking the sealed jars? Why or why not?

2 How could ice wedging affect soil formation?

- bags, sandwich resealable (3)
- freezer
- jars, hard plastic with screw-on lids, such as spice containers (3)
- ruler, metric
- tape, strings, rubber bands, and other items to bind or reinforce the jars
- water

SAFETY

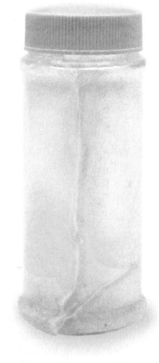

Model-Making Lab

Oh, the Pressure!

When scientists want to understand natural processes, such as mountain formation, they often make models to help them. Models are useful in studying how rocks react to the forces of plate tectonics. A model can demonstrate in a short amount of time geological processes that take millions of years. Do the following activity to find out how folding and faulting occur in the Earth's crust.

MATERIALS

- can, soup (or rolling pin)
- clay, modeling, 4 colors
- knife, plastic
- newspaper
- pencils, colored
- poster board, 5 cm × 5 cm squares (2)
- poster board, 5 cm × 15 cm strip

SAFETY

Ask a Question

1. How do synclines, anticlines, and faults form?

Form a Hypothesis

2. On a separate piece of paper, write a hypothesis that is a possible answer to the question above. Explain your reasoning.

Test the Hypothesis

3. Use modeling clay of one color to form a long cylinder, and place the cylinder in the center of the glossy side of the poster-board strip.

4. Mold the clay to the strip. Try to make the clay layer the same thickness all along the strip; you can use the soup can or rolling pin to even it out. Pinch the sides of the clay so that the clay is the same width and length as the strip. Your strip should be at least 15 cm long and 5 cm wide.

5 Flip the strip over on the newspaper your teacher has placed across your desk. Carefully peel the strip from the modeling clay.

6 Repeat steps 3–5 with the other colors of modeling clay. Each person should have a turn molding the clay. Each time you flip the strip over, stack the new clay layer on top of the previous one. When you are finished, you should have a block of clay made of four layers.

7 Lift the block of clay, and hold it parallel to and just above the tabletop. Push gently on the block from opposite sides, as shown below.

8 Use the colored pencils to draw the results of step 6. Use the terms *syncline* and *anticline* to label your diagram. Draw arrows to show the direction that each edge of the clay was pushed.

9 Repeat steps 3–6 to form a second block of clay.

10 Cut the second block of clay in two at a 45° angle as seen from the side of the block.

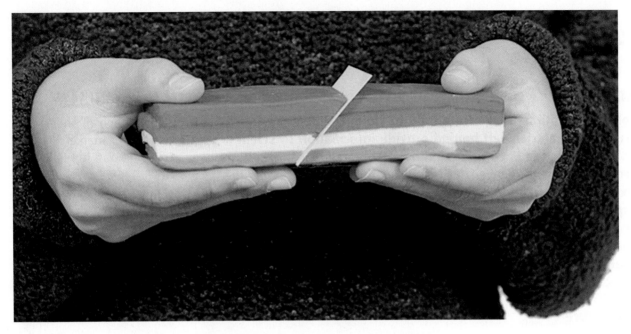

11. Press one poster-board square on the angled end of each of the block's two pieces. The poster board represents a fault. The two angled ends represent a hanging wall and a footwall. The model should resemble the one in the photograph above.

12. Keeping the angled edges together, lift the blocks, and hold them parallel to and just above the tabletop. Push gently on the two blocks until they move. Record your observations.

13. Now, hold the two pieces of the clay block in their original position, and slowly pull them apart, allowing the hanging wall to move downward. Record your observations.

Analyze the Results

1. What happened to the first block of clay in step 7? What kind of force did you apply to the block of clay?

2. What happened to the pieces of the second block of clay in step 12? What kind of force did you apply to them?

3. What happened to the pieces of the second block of clay in step 13? Describe the forces that acted on the block and the way the pieces of the block reacted.

Draw Conclusions

4. Summarize how the forces you applied to the blocks of clay relate to the way tectonic forces affect rock layers. Be sure to use the terms *fold, fault, anticline, syncline, hanging wall, footwall, tension,* and *compression* in your summary.

Skills Practice Lab

Some Go "Pop," Some Do Not

Volcanic eruptions range from mild to violent. When volcanoes erupt, the materials left behind provide information to scientists studying the Earth's crust. Mild, or nonexplosive, eruptions produce thin, runny lava that is low in silica. During nonexplosive eruptions, lava simply flows down the side of the volcano. Explosive eruptions, on the other hand, do not produce much lava. Instead, the explosions hurl ash and debris into the air. The materials left behind are light in color and high in silica. These materials help geologists determine the composition of the crust underneath the volcanoes.

Procedure

1. Copy the map below onto graph paper. Take care to line the grid up properly.

2. Locate each volcano from the list on the next page by drawing a circle with a diameter of about 2 mm in the proper location on your copy of the map. Use the latitude and longitude grids to help you.

3. Review all the eruptions for each volcano. For each explosive eruption, color the circle red. For each quiet volcano, color the circle yellow. For volcanoes that have erupted in both ways, color the circle orange.

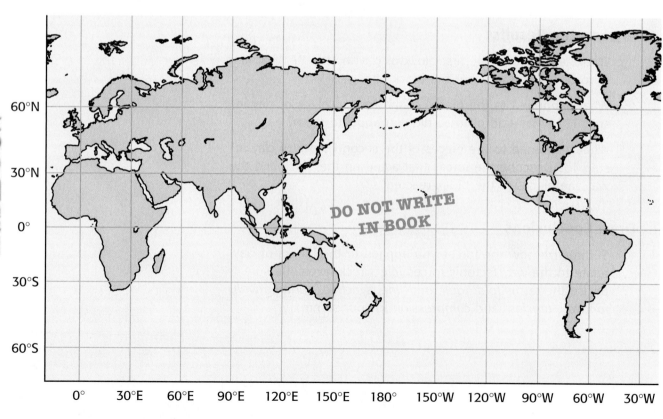

DO NOT WRITE IN BOOK

Volcanic Activity Chart		
Volcano name	**Location**	**Description**
Mount St. Helens	46°N 122°W	An explosive eruption blew the top off the mountain. Light-colored ash covered thousands of square kilometers. Another eruption sent a lava flow down the southeast side of the mountain.
Kilauea	19°N 155°W	One small eruption sent a lava flow along 12 km of highway.
Rabaul caldera	4°S 152°E	Explosive eruptions have caused tsunamis and have left 1–2 m of ash on nearby buildings.
Popocatépetl	19°N 98°W	During one explosion, Mexico City closed the airport for 14 hours because huge columns of ash made it too difficult for pilots to see. Eruptions from this volcano have also caused damaging avalanches.
Soufriere Hills	16°N 62°W	Small eruptions have sent lava flows down the hills. Other explosive eruptions have sent large columns of ash into the air.
Long Valley caldera	37°N 119°W	Explosive eruptions have sent ash into the air.
Okmok	53°N 168°W	Recently, there have been slow lava flows from this volcano. Twenty-five hundred years ago, ash and debris exploded from the top of this volcano.
Pavlof	55°N 161°W	Eruption clouds have been sent 200 m above the summit. Eruptions have sent ash columns 10 km into the air. Occasionally, small eruptions have caused lava flows.
Fernandina	42°N 12°E	Eruptions have ejected large blocks of rock from this volcano.
Mount Pinatubo	15°N 120°E	Ash and debris from an explosive eruption destroyed homes, crops, and roads within 52,000 km^2 around the volcano.

Analyze the Results

1. According to your map, where are volcanoes that always have nonexplosive eruptions located?

2. Where are volcanoes that always erupt explosively located?

3. Where are volcanoes that erupt in both ways located?

4. If volcanoes get their magma from the crust below them, what can you say about the silica content of Earth's crust under the oceans?

5. What is the composition of the crust under the continents? How do we know?

Draw Conclusions

6. What is the source of materials for volcanoes that erupt in both ways? How do you know?

7. Do the locations of volcanoes that erupt in both ways make sense, based on your answers to questions 4 and 5? Explain.

Applying Your Data

Volcanoes are present on other planets. If a planet had only nonexplosive volcanoes on its surface, what would we be able to infer about the planet? If a planet had volcanoes that ranged from nonexplosive to explosive, what might that tell us about the planet?

Skills Practice Lab

The Best-Bread Bakery Dilemma

The chief baker at the Best-Bread Bakery thinks that the yeast the bakery received may be dead. Yeast is a central ingredient in bread. Yeast is a living organism, a member of the kingdom Fungi, and it undergoes the same life processes as other living organisms. When yeast grows in the presence of oxygen and other nutrients, yeast produces carbon dioxide. The gas forms bubbles that cause bread dough to rise. Thousands of dollars may be lost if the yeast is dead.

The Best-Bread Bakery has requested that you test the yeast. The bakery has furnished samples of live yeast and some samples of the yeast in question.

Procedure

1. Make a data table similar to the one below. Leave plenty of room to write your observations.

2. Examine each yeast sample with a magnifying lens. You may want to sniff the samples to determine the presence of an odor. (Your teacher will demonstrate the appropriate way to detect odors in this lab.) Record your observations in the data table.

3. Label three test tubes or plastic cups "Live Yeast," "Sample A Yeast," and "Sample B Yeast."

4. Fill a beaker with 125 mL of water, and place the beaker on a hot plate. Use a thermometer to be sure the water does not get warmer than 32°C. Attach the thermometer to the side of the beaker with a clip so the thermometer doesn't touch the bottom of the beaker. Turn off the hot plate when the water temperature reaches 32°C.

MATERIALS

- beaker, 250 mL
- flour
- gloves, heat-resistant
- graduated cylinder
- hot plate
- magnifying lens
- scoopula (or small spoon)
- stirring sticks, wooden (3)
- sugar
- test-tube rack
- test tubes (3) (or clear plastic cups)
- thermometer, Celsius, with clip
- water, 125 mL
- yeast samples (live, A, and B)

SAFETY

Yeast sample	Observations	0 min	5 min	10 min	15 min	20 min	25 min	Dead or alive?
Live								
Sample A								
Sample B								

DO NOT WRITE IN BOOK

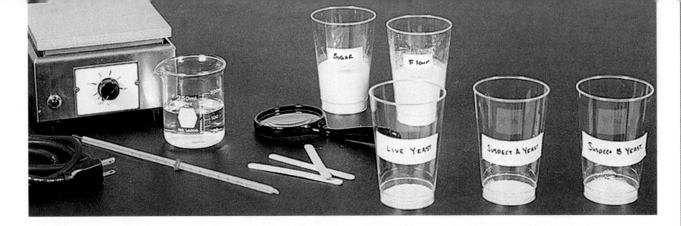

5. Add a small scoop (about 1/2 tsp) of each yeast sample to the correctly labeled container. Add a small scoop of sugar to each container.

6. Add 10 mL of the warm water to each container, and stir.

7. Add a small scoop of flour to each container, and stir again. The flour will help make the process more visible but is not necessary as food for the yeast.

8. Observe the samples carefully. Look for bubbles. Make observations at 5 min intervals. Write your observations in the data table.

9. In the last column of the data table, write "alive" or "dead" based on your observations during the experiment.

Analyze the Results

1. Describe any differences in the yeast samples before the experiment.

2. Describe the appearance of the yeast samples at the conclusion of the experiment.

3. Why was a sample of live yeast included in the experiment?

4. Why was sugar added to the samples?

5. Based on your observations, is either Sample A or Sample B alive?

Draw Conclusions

6. Write a letter to the Best-Bread Bakery stating your recommendation to use or not use the yeast samples. Give reasons for your recommendation.

Applying Your Data

Based on your observations of the nutrient requirements of yeast, design an experiment to determine the ideal combination of nutrients. Vary the amount of nutrients, or examine different energy sources.

Skills Practice Lab

Voyage of the USS *Adventure*

You are a crew member on the USS *Adventure*. The *Adventure* has been on a 5-year mission to collect life-forms from outside the solar system. On the voyage back to Earth, your ship went through a meteor shower, which ruined several of the compartments containing the extraterrestrial life-forms. Now it is necessary to put more than one life-form in the same compartment.

You have only three undamaged compartments in your starship. You and your crewmates must stay in one compartment, and that compartment should be used for extraterrestrial life-forms only if absolutely necessary. You and your crewmates must decide which of the life-forms could be placed together. It is thought that similar life-forms will have similar needs. You can use only observable characteristics to group the life-forms.

Life-form 1

Life-form 2

Life-form 3

Life-form 4

Procedure

1 Make a data table similar to the one below. Label each column with as many characteristics of the various life-forms as possible. Leave enough space in each square to write your observations. The life-forms are pictured on this page.

Life-form Characteristics				
	Color	**Shape**	**Legs**	**Eyes**
Life-form 1				
Life-form 2				
Life-form 3		*DO NOT WRITE IN BOOK*		
Life-form 4				

2 Describe each characteristic as completely as you can. Based on your observations, determine which of the life-forms are most alike.

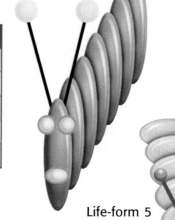
Life-form 5

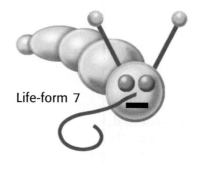
Life-form 7

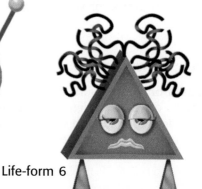
Life-form 6

③ Make a data table like the one below. Fill in the table according to the decisions you made in step 2. State your reasons for the way you have grouped your life-forms.

Life-form Room Assignments		
Compartment	**Life-forms**	**Reasons**
1		
2		*DO NOT WRITE IN BOOK*
3		

④ The USS *Adventure* has to make one more stop before returning home. On planet X437 you discover the most interesting life-form ever found outside of Earth—the CC9, shown at right. Make a decision, based on your previous grouping of life-forms, about whether you can safely include CC9 in one of the compartments for the trip to Earth.

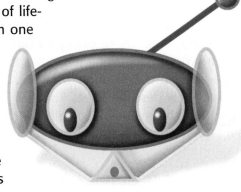

CC9

Analyze the Results

① Describe the life-forms in compartment 1. How are they similar? How are they different?

② Describe the life-forms in compartment 2. How are they similar? How do they differ from the life-forms in compartment 1?

③ Are there any life-forms in compartment 3? If so, describe their similarities. In which compartment will you and your crewmates remain for the journey home?

Draw Conclusions

④ Are you able to transport life-form CC9 safely back to Earth? If so, in which compartment will it be placed? How did you decide?

Applying Your Data

In 1831, Charles Darwin sailed from England on a ship called the HMS *Beagle*. You have studied the finches that Darwin observed on the Galápagos Islands. What were some of the other unusual organisms he found there? For example, find out about the Galápagos tortoise.

Skills Practice Lab

Leaf Me Alone!

Imagine you are a naturalist all alone on an expedition in a rain forest. You have found several plants that you think have never been seen before. You must contact a botanist, a scientist who studies plants, to confirm your suspicion. Because there is no mail service in the rain forest, you must describe these species completely and accurately by radio. The botanist must be able to draw the leaves of the plants from your description. In this activity, you will carefully describe five plant specimens by using the examples and vocabulary lists in this lab.

Procedure

1. Examine the leaf characteristics illustrated on the next page. These examples can be found on the following page. You will notice that more than one term is needed to completely describe a leaf. The leaf shown at right has been labeled for you using the examples and vocabulary lists found in this lab.

2. On a sheet of paper, draw a diagram of a leaf from each plant specimen.

3. Next to each drawing, carefully describe the leaf. Include general characteristics, such as relative size and color. For each plant, identify the following: leaf shape, stem type, leaf arrangement, leaf edge, vein arrangement, and leaf-base shape. Use the terms and vocabulary lists provided to describe each leaf as accurately as possible and to label your drawings.

Compound Leaf

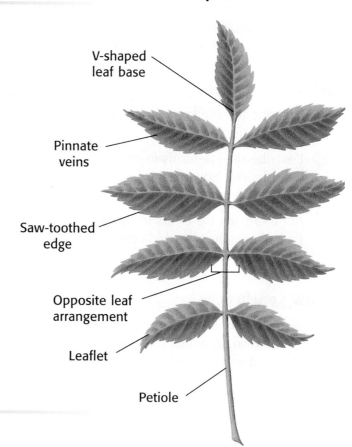

V-shaped leaf base

Pinnate veins

Saw-toothed edge

Opposite leaf arrangement

Leaflet

Petiole

Analyze the Results

1. What is the difference between a simple leaf and a compound leaf?

2. Describe two different vein arrangements in leaves.

3. Based on what you know about adaptation, explain why there are so many different leaf variations.

Communicating Your Data

Choose a partner. Using the keys and vocabulary in this lab, describe a leaf, and see if your partner can draw the leaf from your description. Switch roles, and see if you can draw a leaf from your partner's description.

Leaf Shapes Vocabulary List

cordate—heart shaped
lanceolate—sword shaped
lobate—lobed
oblong—rounded at the tip
orbicular—disk shaped
ovate—oval shaped, widest at base of leaf
peltate—shield shaped
reniform—kidney shaped
sagittate—arrow shaped

Stems Vocabulary List

herbaceous—green, nonwoody stems
woody—bark or barklike covering on stem

Leaf Arrangements Vocabulary List

alternate—alternating leaves or leaflets along stem or petiole
compound—leaf divided into segments, or several leaflets on a petiole
opposite—compound leaf with several leaflets arranged oppositely along a petiole
palmate—single leaf with veins arranged around a center point
palmate compound—several leaflets arranged around a center point
petiole—leaf stalk
pinnate—single leaf with veins arranged along a center vein
pinnate compound—several leaflets on either side of a petiole
simple—single leaf attached to stem by a petiole

Leaf Veins

Parallel   Palmate   Pinnate

Leaf Arrangement on the Stem

Opposite

Alternate

Leaf Division

Simple   Palmate compound   Pinnate compound

Shape of the Leaf Base

V-shaped
Rounded
Flat
Heart
Uneven

Variations in Leaf Edges

Smooth
Saw-toothed
Double saw-toothed
Lobed

Skills Practice Lab

Travelin' Seeds

You have learned from your study of plants that there are some very interesting and unusual plant adaptations. Some of the most interesting adaptations are modifications that allow plant seeds and fruits to be dispersed, or scattered, away from the parent plant. This dispersal enables the young seedlings to obtain the space, sun, and other resources they need without directly competing with the parent plant. In this activity, you will use your own creativity to disperse a seed.

MATERIALS

- bean seed
- seed-dispersal challenge card
- various household or recycled materials (examples: glue, tape, paper, paper clips, rubber bands, cloth, paper cups and plates, paper towels, and cardboard)

Procedure

1 Obtain a seed and a dispersal challenge card from your teacher. On a sheet of paper, record the type of challenge card you have been given.

2 Create a plan for using the available materials to disperse your seed, as described on the challenge card. Record your plan. Get your teacher's approval before proceeding.

3 With your teacher's permission, test your seed-dispersal method. Perform several trials. Make a data table, and record the results of your trials.

Analyze the Results

1 Were you able to complete the seed-dispersal challenge successfully? Explain.

2 Are there any modifications you could make to your method to improve the dispersal of your seed?

Draw Conclusions

3 Describe some plants that disperse their seeds in a way similar to your seed-dispersal method.

◀ Mangrove seed

◀ Cottonwood

Wild berry ▶

Grass bur ▶

Skills Practice Lab

Layering Liquids

You have learned that liquids form layers according to the densities of the liquids. In this lab, you'll discover whether it matters in which order you add the liquids.

Ask a Question

1 Does the order in which you add liquids of different densities to a container affect the order of the layers formed by those liquids?

Form a Hypothesis

2 Write a possible answer to the question above.

Test the Hypothesis

3 Using the graduated cylinders, add 10 mL of each liquid to the clear container. Remember to read the volume at the bottom of the meniscus, as shown below. Record the order in which you added the liquids.

4 Observe the liquids in the container. Sketch what you see. Be sure to label the layers and the colors.

5 Add 10 mL more of liquid C. Observe what happens, and record your observations.

6 Add 20 mL more of liquid A. Observe what happens, and record your observations.

4 Find out in what order your classmates added the liquids to the container. Compare your results with those of a classmate who added the liquids in a different order. Were your results different? Explain why or why not.

Draw Conclusions

5 Based on your results, evaluate your hypothesis from step 2.

Analyze the Results

1 Which of the liquids has the greatest density? Which has the least density? How can you tell?

2 Did the layers change position when you added more of liquid C? Explain your answer.

3 Did the layers change position when you added more of liquid A? Explain your answer.

Skills Practice Lab

Built for Speed

Imagine that you are an engineer at GoCarCo, a toy-vehicle company. GoCarCo is trying to beat the competition by building a new toy vehicle. Several new designs are being tested. Your boss has given you one of the new toy vehicles and instructed you to measure its speed as accurately as possible with the tools you have. Other engineers (your classmates) are testing the other designs. Your results could decide the fate of the company!

MATERIALS

- meterstick
- stopwatch
- tape, masking
- toy vehicle

SAFETY

Procedure

1. How will you accomplish your goal? Write a paragraph to describe your goal and your procedure for this experiment. Be sure that your procedure includes several trials.

2. Show your plan to your boss (teacher). Get his or her approval to carry out your procedure.

3. Perform your stated procedure. Record all data. Be sure to express all data in the correct units.

Analyze the Results

1. What was the average speed of your vehicle? How does your result compare with the results of the other engineers?

2. Compare your technique for determining the speed of your vehicle with the techniques of the other engineers. Which technique do you think is the most effective?

3. Was your toy vehicle the fastest? Explain why or why not.

Applying Your Data

Think of several conditions that could affect your vehicle's speed. Design an experiment to test your vehicle under one of those conditions. Write a paragraph to explain your procedure. Be sure to include an explanation of how that condition changes your vehicle's speed.

Energy of a Pendulum

A pendulum clock is a compound machine that uses stored energy to do work. A spring stores energy, and with each swing of the pendulum, some of that stored energy is used to move the hands of the clock. In this lab, you will take a close look at the energy conversions that occur as a pendulum swings.

Procedure

1. Make a pendulum by tying the string around the hook of the mass. Use the marker and the meterstick to mark points on the string that are 50 cm, 70 cm, and 90 cm away from the mass.

2. Hold the string at the 50 cm mark. Gently pull the mass to the side, and release it without pushing it. Observe at least 10 swings of the pendulum.

3. Record your observations. Be sure to note how fast and how high the pendulum swings.

4. Repeat steps 2 and 3 while holding the string at the 70 cm mark and again while holding the string at the 90 cm mark.

Analyze the Results

1. List similarities and differences in the motion of the pendulum during all three trials.

2. At which point (or points) of the swing was the pendulum moving the slowest? the fastest?

Draw Conclusions

3. In each trial, at which point (or points) of the swing did the pendulum have the greatest potential energy? the least potential energy? (Hint: Think about your answers to question 2.)

4. At which point (or points) of the swing did the pendulum have the greatest kinetic energy? the least kinetic energy? Explain your answers.

5. Describe the relationship between the pendulum's potential energy and its kinetic energy on its way down. Explain.

6. What improvements might reduce the amount of energy used to overcome friction so that the pendulum would swing for a longer period of time?

Skills Practice Lab

Power of the Sun

The sun radiates energy in every direction. Like the sun, the energy radiated by a light bulb spreads out in all directions. But how much energy an object receives depends on how close that object is to the source. As you move farther from the source, the amount of energy you receive decreases. For example, if you measure the amount of energy that reaches you from a light and then move three times farther away, you will discover that nine times less energy will reach you at your second position. Energy from the sun travels as light energy. When light energy is absorbed by an object it is converted into thermal energy. Power is the rate at which one form of energy is converted to another, and it is measured in watts. Because power is related to distance, nearby objects can be used to measure the power of far-away objects. In this lab you will calculate the power of the sun using an ordinary 100-watt light bulb.

Procedure

1. Gently shape the piece of aluminum around a pencil so that it holds on in the middle and has two wings, one on either side of the pencil.

2. Bend the wings outward so that they can catch as much sunlight as possible.

3. Use the marker to color both wings on one side of the aluminum strip black.

4. Remove the pencil and place the aluminum snugly around the thermometer near the bulb. **Caution:** Do not press too hard—you do not want to break the thermometer! Wear protective gloves when working with the thermometer and the aluminum.

5. Carefully slide the top of the thermometer through the hole in the lid. Place the lid on the jar so that the thermometer bulb is inside the jar, and screw down the cap.

6. Secure the thermometer to the jar lid by molding clay around the thermometer on the outside of the lid. The aluminum wings should be in the center of the jar.

7. Read the temperature on the thermometer. Record this as room temperature.

8. Place the jar on a windowsill in the sunlight. Turn the jar so that the black wings are angled toward the sun.

9. Watch the thermometer until the temperature reading stops rising. Record the temperature.

10. Remove the jar from direct sunlight, and allow it to return to room temperature.

11. Remove any shade or reflector from the lamp. Place the lamp at one end of a table.

12. Place the jar about 30 cm from the lamp. Turn the jar so that the wings are angled toward the lamp.

13 Turn on the lamp, and wait about 1 minute.

14 Move the jar a few centimeters toward the lamp until the temperature reading starts to rise. When the temperature stops rising, compare it with the reading you took in step 9.

15 Repeat step 14 until the temperature matches the temperature you recorded in step 9.

16 If the temperature reading rises too high, move the jar away from the lamp and allow it to cool. Once the reading has dropped to at least 5°C below the temperature you recorded in step 9, you may begin again at step 12.

17 When the temperature in the jar matches the temperature you recorded in step 9, record the distance between the center of the light bulb and the thermometer bulb.

Analyze the Results

1 The thermometer measured the same amount of energy absorbed by the jar at the distance you measured to the lamp. In other words, your jar absorbed as much energy from the sun at a distance of 150 million kilometers as it did from the 100 W light bulb at the distance you recorded in step 17.

2 Use the following formula to calculate the power of the sun (be sure to show your work):

$$\frac{\text{power of the sun}}{(\text{distance to the sun})^2} = \frac{\text{power of the lamp}}{(\text{distance to the lamp})^2}$$

Hint: $(\text{distance})^2$ means that you multiply the distance by itself. If you found that the lamp was 5 cm away from the jar, for example, the $(\text{distance})^2$ would be 25.

Hint: Convert 150,000,000 km to 15,000,000,000,000 cm.

3 Review the discussion of scientific notation in the Math Refresher found in the Appendix at the back of this book. You will need to understand this technique for writing large numbers in order to compare your calculation with the actual figure. For practice, convert the distance to the sun given above in step 2 of Analyze the Results to scientific notation.

15,000,000,000,000 cm = $1.5 \times 10^{?}$ cm

Draw Conclusions

4 The sun emits 3.7×10^{26} W of power. Compare your answer in step 2 with this value. Was this a good way to calculate the power of the sun? Explain.

Contents

FCAT Glossary

A

abiotic describes the nonliving part of the environment, including water, rocks, light, and temperature, that is not associated with the actions of organisms

acceleration the rate at which velocity changes over time; an object accelerates if its speed, direction, or both change; usually expressed in meters per second per second (m/s^2)

air resistance the force that opposes the motion of objects through air

allele one of the alternative forms of a gene that governs a characteristic, such as hair color

amplitude the maximum distance that the particles of a wave's medium vibrate from their rest position; the maximum variation of any periodic function

asexual reproduction reproduction that does not involve the union of sex cells, or gametes, and in which one parent produces offspring that are genetically identical to the parent

B

biodiversity the number and variety of organisms in a given area during a specific period of time

biotic describes living factors in the environment; related to, caused by, or produced by organisms

C

calorie the amount of energy needed to raise the temperature of 1 g of water 1°C at 1 standard atmosphere; the Calorie used to indicate the energy content of food is a kilocalorie; a unit of energy

chemical weathering the process by which rocks break down as a result of chemical reactions

circuit a complete path of an electric current formed from interconnected electrical elements

conduction the transfer of energy as heat through a material without movement of the material

conservation of energy the law that states that energy cannot be created or destroyed but can be changed from one form to another

convection the transfer of thermal energy by the circulation or movement of a liquid or gas

crest the highest point of a wave

crust the thin and solid outermost layer of the Earth above the mantle

D

dependent variable in an experiment, the factor that changes as a result of manipulation of one or more other factors (the independent variables)

deposition the process in which material is laid down after being carried by wind, rain, or water

diffraction a change in the direction of a wave when the wave finds an obstacle or an edge, such as an opening

dominance the tendency of certain (dominant) alleles to mask the expression of their corresponding (recessive) alleles

E

ecosystem a community of organisms and their abiotic, or nonliving, environment

efficiency a quantity, usually expressed as a percentage, that measures the ratio of work output to work input; used to describe the relative effectiveness of a system or device

electromagnetic radiation the radiation associated with an electric and magnetic field; it varies periodically and travels at the speed of light; includes radio waves, visible light, ultraviolet light, microwaves, X rays, and gamma rays

electron a subatomic particle that has a negative charge; found around the nucleus

entropy a measure of the randomness or disorder of a system

erosion the process by which wind, water, ice, or gravity transports soil and sediment from one location to another

F

fossil fuel a nonrenewable energy resource formed from the remains of organisms that lived long ago; includes natural gas, oil, and coal

frequency the number of waves produced in a given amount of time

G

gene one set of instructions for an inherited trait; in a DNA sequence or as a part of a chromosome

H

heterozygous describes an individual that has two different alleles for a trait

homozygous describes an individual that has identical alleles for a trait on both homologous chromosomes

I

independent variable in an experiment, the factor that is deliberately manipulated in order to examine how the dependent variable is affected

inertia the tendency of an object, as a result of its mass, to resist being moved or, if the object is moving, to resist a change in speed or direction until an outside force acts on the object

M

magnetic field a region where a magnetic force can be detected near electric currents or magnets

mass a measure of the amount of matter in an object

meiosis a process in cell division during which the number of chromosomes decreases to half the original number by two divisions of the nucleus, which results in the production of sex cells (gametes or spores)

mitosis in eukaryotic cells, a process of cell division that forms two new nuclei, each of which has the same number of chromosomes

N

neap tide a tide of minimum range that occurs during the first and third quarters of the moon; occurs when the positions of Earth, the moon, and the sun form a right angle

neutral lacking a net charge; can be applied to particles, objects, or systems

neutron a subatomic particle that has no charge and that is located in the nucleus of an atom

nucleus in physical science, an atom's central region, which is made up of protons and neutrons; also, in a eukaryotic cell, a membrane-bound organelle that contains the cell's DNA and that has a role in processes such as growth, metabolism, and reproduction

O

ocean basin the area of Earth that is covered by oceans

P

plate tectonics the theory that explains how large pieces of the Earth's outermost layer, called tectonic plates, move and change shape which results in seismic activity where the plates meet

potential energy the energy that an object has because of the position, shape, or condition of the object

pressure the amount of force exerted per unit area of a surface

prism in optics, a system that consists of two or more plane surfaces of a transparent solid at an angle with each other; used to separates white light into its colors

proton a subatomic particle that has a positive charge and that is located in the nucleus of an atom; the number of protons of the nucleus is the atomic number, which determines the identity of an element

Punnett square a graphic used to predict the results of a genetic cross

R

radiation the transfer of energy as electromagnetic waves

recessive describes an allele that will be masked unless the organism is homozygous for the trait

S

screw a simple machine that consists of an inclined plane wrapped around a cylinder

sexual reproduction reproduction in which the sex cells, or gametes, from two parents unite to produce offspring that share traits from both parents

spectroscope an instrument that splits white light into a band of colors

speed the distance traveled divided by the time interval during which the motion occurred; also, the rate at which a process occurs

spring tide a tide of increased range that occurs two times a month, at the new and full moons

T

thermal energy the kinetic energy of a substance's atoms

tropism growth of all or part of an organism in response to an external stimulus, such as light

trough the lowest point of a wave

V

variable a factor that changes in an experiment in order to test a hypothesis

velocity the speed of an object in a particular direction; found by dividing displacement by time

vibration a repetitive, back-and-forth motion of an object around its rest, or equilibrium, position

virus a microscopic particle that gets inside a cell and often destroys the cell; it replicates using its host's genetic material and often causes disease

W

wavelength the distance from any point on a wave to an identical point on the next wave (for example, from one crest to the next crest)

wedge a simple machine that is made up of two inclined planes and that moves; often used for cutting

wheel and axle a simple machine consisting of two circular objects of different sizes; the wheel is the larger of the two circular objects; the mechanical advantage is the ratio of the wheel's radius to the axle's radius

 **Science Reference Sheet**

Acceleration

Average **acceleration** is the rate at which velocity changes over time. An object accelerates if its speed, its direction, or both change.

$$\textit{average acceleration} = \frac{\textit{change in velocity (m/s)}}{\textit{time it takes to change velocity (s)}} = \frac{\textit{final velocity} - \textit{starting velocity}}{\textit{time it takes to change velocity}}$$

Example: Calculate the average acceleration of an Olympic 100 m dash sprinter who reaches a velocity of 20 m/s south at the finish line. The race was in a straight line and lasted 10 s.

$$\textit{average acceleration} = \frac{20 \text{ m/s} - 0 \text{ m/s}}{10 \text{ s}} = 2 \text{ m/s}^2$$

The sprinter's average acceleration is 2 m/s² south.

Average Speed

Most of the time, objects do not travel at a constant speed. So, it is useful to calculate average speed. **Average speed** is the total distance traveled divided by the total time interval during which the motion occurred.

$$\textit{average speed} = \frac{\textit{total distance}}{\textit{total time}}$$

Example: A bicycle messenger traveled a distance of 136 km in 8 h. What was the messenger's average speed?

$$\textit{average speed} = \frac{136 \text{ km}}{8 \text{ h}} = 17 \text{ km/h}$$

The messenger's average speed was 17 km/h.

Density

The ratio of the mass of a substance to the volume of the substance is **density.** An object's density is a measurement of the amount of matter packed in a given volume.

$$\textit{density} = \frac{\textit{mass (g)}}{\textit{volume (cm}^3)}$$

Example: Calculate the density of a sponge that has a mass of 10 g and a volume of 40 cm³.

$$\textit{density} = \frac{10 \text{ g}}{40 \text{ cm}^3} = 0.25 \text{ g/cm}^3$$

The density of the sponge is 0.25 g/cm³.

Percent Efficiency

The **percent efficiency** is found by dividing the work output by the work input and then multiplying the answer by 100. Percent efficiency is also known as *mechanical efficiency.* Percent efficiency tells you what percentage of the work input is converted to work output.

$$\textit{percent efficiency} = \frac{\textit{work out (J)}}{\textit{work in (J)}} \times 100$$

Example: A hand-crank drill requires 3,540 J to complete 2,480 J of work. What is the efficiency of the drill?

$$\textit{percent efficiency} = \frac{2,480\ J}{3,540\ J} \times 100 = 70.0\%$$

The hand-crank drill has a percent efficiency of 70.0%.

Force in Newtons

A **force** is a push or a pull in a particular direction. Force is calculated by multiplying the mass of the object being acted on and the acceleration of the object. The unit of force is the newton (N). One newton is equivalent to 1 kg•m/s^2.

$$\textit{force in newtons} = \textit{mass (kg)} \times \textit{acceleration (m/s}^2)$$

Example: A toy car whose mass is 0.03 kg has an acceleration of 0.5 m/s^2. Calculate the force that is acting on the toy car.

$$\textit{force in newtons} = \textbf{0.03 kg} \times \textbf{0.5 m/s}^2 = \textbf{0.15 kg} \times \textbf{m/s}^2 = \textbf{0.15 N}$$

The force acting on the toy car is 0.15 N.

Frequency in Hertz

The number of events produced in a given amount of time is the **frequency.** Frequency (f) is usually expressed in hertz (Hz). For waves, one hertz equals one wave per second.

$$\textit{frequency in hertz} = \frac{\textit{number of events}}{\textit{time (s)}}$$

Example: Joseph is floating in a wave pool. He observes two waves pass by a stationary point in 10 s. What is the frequency of the waves in Joseph's pool?

$$\textit{frequency in hertz} = \frac{\textbf{2 waves}}{\textbf{10 s}} = \textbf{0.2 waves per second} = \textbf{0.2 Hz}$$

The frequency of the waves is 0.2 Hz.

Momentum

The **momentum (ρ)** of an object depends on the object's mass and velocity. The more momentum an object has, the harder it is to stop the object or change its direction. Momentum is calculated by multiplying an object's mass by its velocity.

$$momentum = mass \text{ (kg)} \times velocity \text{ (m/s)}$$

Example: What is the momentum of a 6 kg bowling ball that is moving at 10 m/s down the alley toward the pins?

$$momentum = 6 \text{ kg} \times 10 \text{ m/s} = 60 \text{ kg} \times \text{m/s}$$

The momentum of the bowling ball is 60 kg × m/s.

Pressure

The amount of force exerted on a given surface area is called **pressure (p).** Pressure can be calculated by dividing the force acting on the surface by the area of the surface being acted on. The unit that scientists use to express pressure is the pascal (Pa). One pascal is equal to 1 N/m².

$$pressure = \frac{force \text{ (N)}}{area \text{ (m}^2)}$$

Example: A waterbed has an area of 3.75 m². If the waterbed is exerting a force of 1,025 N on the floor beneath, what pressure is the bed exerting on the floor?

$$pressure = \frac{1,025 \text{ N}}{3.75 \text{ m}^2} = 273 \text{ N/m}^2 = 273 \text{ Pa}$$

The pressure on the floor is 273 Pa.

Wavelength

A **wavelength (λ)** is the distance from any point on a wave to an identical point on the next wave. Wavelength can be calculated by dividing the velocity of the wave by the frequency of waves.

$$wavelength = \frac{velocity \text{ (m/s)}}{frequency \text{ (Hz)}}$$

Example: A wave has a frequency of 5 Hz and a wave speed of 18 m/s. What is its wavelength?

$$wavelength = \frac{18 \text{ m/s}}{5 \text{ Hz}} = 3.6 \text{ m/(s} \times \text{Hz)} = 3.6 \text{ m}$$

The wavelength is 3.6 m.

Work

Work is done by exerting a force through a distance. Work has units of joules (J), which are equivalent to newton-meters (N × m). Work is calculated by multiplying force by distance.

$$Work = force \text{ (N)} \times distance \text{ (m)}$$

Example: Calculate the amount of work done by a man who lifts a 100 N toddler 1.5 m off the floor.

$$Work = 100 \text{ N} \times 1.5 \text{ m} = 150 \text{ N} \times m = 150 \text{ J}$$

The work done by the man is 150 J.

Power

Power is the rate at which work is done. Power is measured in watts (W), which are equivalent to joules per second (J/s).

$$power = \frac{Work \text{ (J)}}{time \text{ (s)}}$$

Example: Calculate the power of a weightlifter who raises a 300 N barbell 2.1 m off the floor in 1.25 s.

$$power = \frac{(300 \text{ N} \times 2.1 \text{ m})}{1.25 \text{ s}} = 504 \text{ W}$$

The power of the weightlifter is 504 W.

Concentration

Concentration is a measure of the amount of a particular substance in a given quantity of a mixture, solution, or ore. One way to find concentration is by dividing the mass of the solute (the dissolved substance) by the volume of the solvent (the substance in which the solute dissolves).

$$concentration = \frac{mass \ of \ solute}{volume \ of \ solvent}$$

Example: Calculate the concentration of a solution in which 10 g of sugar is dissolved in 125 mL of water.

$$concentration = \frac{10 \text{ g of sugar}}{125 \text{ mL of water}} = 0.08 \text{ g/mL}$$

The concentration of sugar in the solution is 0.08 g/mL.

Net Force

There are many situations where multiple forces act on a single object. **Net force** is the combination of all forces acting on an object.

Forces in the Same Direction

When forces are in the same direction, add the forces together to determine net force.

net force = *force* + *force*

Example: Calculate the net force on a stalled car that is being pushed by two people. One person is pushing with a force of 13 N northwest, and the other person is pushing with a force of 8 N in the same direction.

net force = **13 N + 8 N = 21 N northwest**

The net force on the stalled car is 21 N northwest.

Forces in Opposite Directions

When forces are in opposite directions, subtract the smaller force from the larger force to determine the net force. The net force will be in the direction of the larger force.

net force = *larger force* − *smaller force*

Example: Calculate the net force on a rope that is being pulled on each end. One person is pulling on one end of the rope with a force of 12 N south. Another person is pulling on the opposite end of the rope with a force of 7 N north.

net force = **12 N − 7 N = 5 N south**

The net force on the rope is 5 N south.

The Periodic Table

Each square on the table includes an element's name, chemical symbol, atomic number, and atomic mass.

The color of the chemical symbol indicates the physical state at room temperature. Carbon is a solid.

6	Atomic number
C	Chemical symbol
Carbon	Element name
12.0	Atomic mass

The background color indicates the type of element. Carbon is a nonmetal.

Period 1

| 1 |
| **H** |
| Hydrogen |
| 1.0 |

	Group 1	Group 2
Period 2	3 **Li** Lithium 6.9	4 **Be** Beryllium 9.0
Period 3	11 **Na** Sodium 23.0	12 **Mg** Magnesium 24.3

	Group 1	Group 2	Group 3	Group 4	Group 5	Group 6	Group 7	Group 8	Group 9
Period 4	19 **K** Potassium 39.1	20 **Ca** Calcium 40.1	21 **Sc** Scandium 45.0	22 **Ti** Titanium 47.9	23 **V** Vanadium 50.9	24 **Cr** Chromium 52.0	25 **Mn** Manganese 54.9	26 **Fe** Iron 55.8	27 **Co** Cobalt 58.9
Period 5	37 **Rb** Rubidium 85.5	38 **Sr** Strontium 87.6	39 **Y** Yttrium 88.9	40 **Zr** Zirconium 91.2	41 **Nb** Niobium 92.9	42 **Mo** Molybdenum 95.9	43 **Tc** Technetium (98)	44 **Ru** Ruthenium 101.1	45 **Rh** Rhodium 102.9
Period 6	55 **Cs** Cesium 132.9	56 **Ba** Barium 137.3	57 **La** Lanthanum 138.9	72 **Hf** Hafnium 178.5	73 **Ta** Tantalum 180.9	74 **W** Tungsten 183.8	75 **Re** Rhenium 186.2	76 **Os** Osmium 190.2	77 **Ir** Iridium 192.2
Period 7	87 **Fr** Francium (223)	88 **Ra** Radium (226)	89 **Ac** Actinium (227)	104 **Rf** Rutherfordium (261)	105 **Db** Dubnium (262)	106 **Sg** Seaborgium (263)	107 **Bh** Bohrium (264)	108 **Hs** Hassium (265)[†]	109 **Mt** Meitnerium (268)[†]

A row of elements is called a *period*.

A column of elements is called a *group* or *family*.

Values in parentheses are the mass numbers of those radioactive elements' most stable or most common isotopes.

† Estimated from currently available IUPAC data.

These elements are placed below the table to allow the table to be narrower.

Lanthanides	58 **Ce** Cerium 140.1	59 **Pr** Praseodymium 140.9	60 **Nd** Neodymium 144.2	61 **Pm** Promethium (145)	62 **Sm** Samarium 150.4
Actinides	90 **Th** Thorium 232.0	91 **Pa** Protactinium 231.0	92 **U** Uranium 238.0	93 **Np** Neptunium (237)	94 **Pu** Plutonium (244)

Background

Metals	
Metalloids	
Nonmetals	

Chemical symbol

Solid	
Liquid	
Gas	

Topic: **Periodic Table**
Go To: **go.hrw.com**
Keyword: **HN0 PERIODIC**
Visit the HRW Web site for updates on the periodic table.

This zigzag line reminds you where the metals, nonmetals, and metalloids are.

			Group 13	Group 14	Group 15	Group 16	Group 17	Group 18
								2 **He** Helium 4.0
			5 **B** Boron 10.8	6 **C** Carbon 12.0	7 **N** Nitrogen 14.0	8 **O** Oxygen 16.0	9 **F** Fluorine 19.0	10 **Ne** Neon 20.2
Group 10	Group 11	Group 12	13 **Al** Aluminum 27.0	14 **Si** Silicon 28.1	15 **P** Phosphorus 31.0	16 **S** Sulfur 32.1	17 **Cl** Chlorine 35.5	18 **Ar** Argon 39.9
28 **Ni** Nickel 58.7	29 **Cu** Copper 63.5	30 **Zn** Zinc 65.4	31 **Ga** Gallium 69.7	32 **Ge** Germanium 72.6	33 **As** Arsenic 74.9	34 **Se** Selenium 79.0	35 **Br** Bromine 79.9	36 **Kr** Krypton 83.8
46 **Pd** Palladium 106.4	47 **Ag** Silver 107.9	48 **Cd** Cadmium 112.4	49 **In** Indium 114.8	50 **Sn** Tin 118.7	51 **Sb** Antimony 121.8	52 **Te** Tellurium 127.6	53 **I** Iodine 126.9	54 **Xe** Xenon 131.3
78 **Pt** Platinum 195.1	79 **Au** Gold 197.0	80 **Hg** Mercury 200.6	81 **Tl** Thallium 204.4	82 **Pb** Lead 207.2	83 **Bi** Bismuth 209.0	84 **Po** Polonium (209)	85 **At** Astatine (210)	86 **Rn** Radon (222)
110 **Ds** Darmstadtium (269)[†]	111 **Uuu** Unununium (272)[†]	112 **Uub** Ununbium (277)[†]		114 **Uuq** Ununquadium (285)[†]				

The names and three-letter symbols of elements are temporary. They are based on the atomic numbers of the elements. Official names and symbols will be approved by an international committee of scientists.

63 **Eu** Europium 152.0	64 **Gd** Gadolinium 157.2	65 **Tb** Terbium 158.9	66 **Dy** Dysprosium 162.5	67 **Ho** Holmium 164.9	68 **Er** Erbium 167.3	69 **Tm** Thulium 168.9	70 **Yb** Ytterbium 173.0	71 **Lu** Lutetium 175.0
95 **Am** Americium (243)	96 **Cm** Curium (247)	97 **Bk** Berkelium (247)	98 **Cf** Californium (251)	99 **Es** Einsteinium (252)	100 **Fm** Fermium (257)	101 **Md** Mendelevium (258)	102 **No** Nobelium (259)	103 **Lr** Lawrencium (262)

FCAT Study Guide

Annually Assessed Benchmark Focus

Benchmark

 A.1.3.1 The student identifies various ways in which substances differ (e.g., mass, volume, shape, density, texture, and reaction to temperature and light).

Tutorial

All objects are made up of one or more substances and have properties such as mass, shape, and volume. Substances have properties such as density and texture. Properties of substances are determined by gathering data from experiments. Properties of objects can usually be measured directly. The tables below show some of the properties of objects and substances.

PROPERTIES OF OBJECTS

Property	Description
Shape	Form of an object
Volume	Amount of space an object takes up
Weight	A measure of the pull of gravity on an object
Mass	A measure of the amount of matter in an object

PROPERTIES OF SUBSTANCES

Property	Description
Density	The ratio of the mass of a substance to the volume of the substance
Response to heat	The increased movement of particles when temperature is increased
Response to light	Whether light passes through a substance
Texture	The quality of the surface of a substance

Sample Problem

1. Hernando is finding the weight of a package in ounces (oz). He tests what happens when he tips the scale about 25°. The figures below show the results.

A

B

Why does Figure B show a different reading?

A. The mass of the package increased.

B. More gravitational pull was detected.

C. The volume of the package increased.

D. More magnetic attraction was detected.

Answer

Answer B is the correct choice. The mass and volume of the package are the same in both figures. Magnetic attraction does not affect weight. Because Hernando tipped the scale, only part of the pull of gravity is detected by the scale in Figure A. If you had difficulty with this question, review gravity.

FCAT Study Guide

Mini-Assessment

1. The sketch below shows the dimensions in centimeters (cm) of a piece of bronze whose mass is 534 grams (g).

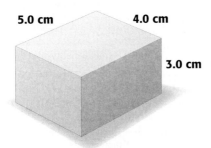

5.0 cm   **4.0 cm**

3.0 cm

Cube of Casting Bronze

Calculate the density of the bronze in grams per cubic centimeter (g/cm³).

2. Gravity on Earth is 2.65 times as great as gravity on Mercury. If Beatrice weighs 450.5 newtons (N) on Earth, calculate her weight in newtons on Mercury.

Enrichment

Making shadow puppets is a popular hobby. The sketch below shows how puppeteers create shadow puppets by using a cutout shape to cast a shadow onto a screen. The audience sees the shadow, not the puppet.

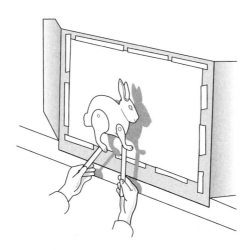

Try making shadow puppets of your own from different materials, such as cardboard or clear plastic. Identify the properties of the materials used to make the puppets. Explain how the different materials respond to light.

Benchmark

B.1.3.1 The student identifies forms of energy and explains that they can be measured and compared.

Tutorial

Energy is neither created nor destroyed. It is simply converted from one form to another. Some forms of energy are described in the table at right. Two main forms of energy are kinetic energy and potential energy. Kinetic energy is the energy of motion. The kinetic energy of an object can be measured using the object's mass and speed. An object's kinetic energy increases as the object's mass, speed, or both increase. Potential energy is the energy that an object has because of its position. Gravitational potential energy of an object can be measured by using the object's weight and height above a surface. An object's gravitational potential energy increases as the object's weight, height, or both increase. Although kinetic energy and potential energy are different forms of energy, they can be converted into one another. When an object is in motion, you can compare its kinetic energy and potential energy at different time intervals. Often, you will see that one form of energy increases as the other form decreases.

Chemical energy and nuclear energy are examples of potential energy. Electrical energy, electromagnetic energy, sound energy, and thermal energy are examples of kinetic energy.

DESCRIPTION OF SOME FORMS OF ENERGY

Energy	Description and Example
Chemical energy	Chemical bonds; natural gas
Electrical energy	Moving charges; circuits
Gravitational potential energy	Objects at a height; car parked on a hill
Kinetic energy	Moving objects; rolling car
Electromagnetic energy	Vibrating electric and magnetic fields; visible light, microwaves, X rays
Nuclear energy	Changes in atomic nuclei; fission in a nuclear power plant
Sound energy	Vibrating matter; music
Thermal energy	Random particle motion; air in a hot oven

Sample Problem

1. The picture below shows a lit candle.

What conversion of energy takes place after the candle is lit?

A. the conversion from thermal energy into kinetic energy and electromagnetic energy

B. the conversion of electromagnetic energy into kinetic energy and chemical energy

C. the conversion of chemical energy into thermal energy and electromagnetic energy

D. the conversion of kinetic energy into thermal energy and chemical energy

Answer

Answer C is the correct answer. The wax stores chemical energy, which is released as heat (thermal energy) and visible light (electromagnetic energy) when the candle is lit. If you had difficulty with this question, review energy conversions.

Mini-Assessment

1. The picture below shows the inside of a music box. By turning the crank, you wind a spring inside the box, which rotates a barrel. Protruding pins on the barrel strike a comb that has tuned teeth, and a tune is played.

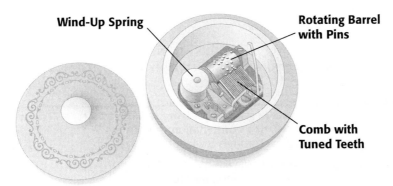

Wind-Up Spring

Rotating Barrel with Pins

Comb with Tuned Teeth

Inside of a Music Box

What type of energy conversion takes place when a music box plays?

A. the conversion of potential energy into kinetic energy

B. the conversion of chemical energy into thermal energy

C. the conversion of kinetic energy into electromagnetic energy

D. the conversion of electromagnetic energy into chemical energy

2. Humans generate heat even when they are sitting still. In fact, they generate so much heat that busy places, such as movie theaters, often turn on cooling systems to compensate for crowded conditions. From which form of energy is heat converted in the human body?

F. kinetic energy

G. chemical energy

H. gravitational energy

I. electromagnetic energy

Enrichment

Put some loose tea in a clear glass mug. If you have only tea bags available, simply open one and empty the contents into the mug. Make tea by pouring hot water into the mug over the loose tea. **Caution:** Be careful when handling hot water because it can cause burns. Observe how the tea leaves move in the mug as you add the water. Why do the leaves move in this way? Make a sketch of the entire system, including the materials that you used to heat the water, and trace the conversions of energy from the original heat source to the final product.

Benchmark

B.1.3.6 The student knows the properties of waves (e.g., frequency, wavelength, and amplitude), that each wave consists of a number of crests and troughs, and the effects of different media on waves.

Tutorial

A *wave* is any disturbance that transmits energy through matter or empty space. There are two main types of waves:

- **Mechanical Waves** Mechanical waves are waves, such as sound, water, and seismic waves, that must pass through a medium (a gas, a liquid, or a solid). Mechanical waves can be transverse, longitudinal, or a combination of both (as surface waves are). Mechanical waves cannot pass through a vacuum.

- **Electromagnetic Waves** Electromagnetic waves are waves that pass through both empty space and media. Examples include visible light, infrared light, and microwaves. Electromagnetic waves consist of changing electric and magnetic fields. Electromagnetic waves are transverse waves.

Transverse waves consist of crests and troughs. The height of the wave is related to the amplitude of the wave. Amplitude is the maximum distance that the particles of the medium through which a wave is passing move. All waves have a velocity, a wavelength, and a frequency. The following equation can be used to solve for any of these three variables:

$$Wavelength = \frac{Velocity}{Frequency}$$

Waves behave differently in different media. A wave can bounce off a barrier (reflection), bend as it passes from one medium into another (refraction), or bend around a barrier or through an opening (diffraction).

Sample Problems

1. The picture below shows an ultrasound image of a pancreas. This image was made by a machine that emits high-frequency sound waves.

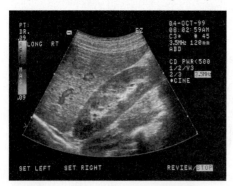

Which of the following statements **best** describes the property of sound waves that is most important to ultrasound imaging?

A. Sound waves reflect off a barrier.

B. Sound waves are longitudinal waves.

C. Sound waves travel slower than light waves.

D. Sound waves do not travel through a vacuum.

Answer

Answer A is the correct choice. By reflecting or refracting at medium boundaries, sound waves can create images of internal organs. The characteristics described in Answers B, C, and D do not aid in making images of internal organs. If you found this question difficult, review the definitions of *refraction, reflection,* and *diffraction.*

2. Middle C is a musical note. It has a frequency of 262 waves per second (Hz). If a pianist strikes middle C in a room where the speed of sound is 340.6 meters per second (m/s), what is the wavelength of the sound waves in meters (m)?

Mini-Assessment

1. Trains sound their horns at road intersections. A driver waiting for a train to pass notices that the horn's pitch gets lower as the train passes her car. What is the reason for this change in pitch?

A. The amplitude of the sound waves increases.

B. The wavelength of the sound waves decreases.

C. The vibration source moves closer to the driver.

D. The frequency of the vibration source increases.

Enrichment

The photos below show two satellite views of Baton Rouge, Louisiana, taken with different cameras. The image on the left shows reflected visible light, and the image on the right shows reflected infrared radiation.

Identify the differences between visible light and infrared radiation shown in these images, and explain how each form of radiation reacts when it reaches a medium.

Benchmark

B.2.3.1 The student knows that most events in the universe (e.g., weather changes, moving cars, and the transfer of a nervous impulse in the human body) involve some form of energy transfer and that these changes almost always increase the total disorder of the system and its surroundings, reducing the amount of useful energy.

Tutorial

Energy drives all systems. Every time that energy is transferred or converted, the amount of useful energy is reduced. Therefore, the energy output of any energy conversion is less than the input of energy. Efficiency is the ratio of energy output to energy input. Use the equation shown to the right to solve for efficiency, energy output, or energy input.

The law of conservation of energy states that energy is neither created nor destroyed. Useful energy, however, is always reduced in transfers and conversions. A decrease in useful energy results in an increase in the disorder of the system. Energy that is lost during a conversion is often in the form of heat that radiates into space.

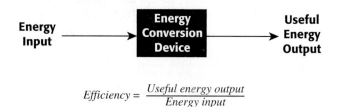

$$Efficiency = \frac{Useful\ energy\ output}{Energy\ input}$$

Sample Problem

1. The table below shows the energy input and light output of incandescent and compact fluorescent light bulbs.

ENERGY IN DIFFERENT LIGHT BULBS

Bulb Type	Energy Used Per Hour in Kilojoules (kJ)	Light Output Per Hour in Kilojoules (kJ)
Incandescent	216	4.3
Fluorescent	54	4.8

Which of the following statements **best** explains why the incandescent light bulb uses more energy and produces less light than a fluorescent light bulb does?

A. The incandescent bulb generates more heat.

B. The fluorescent bulb glows in the dark more.

C. The incandescent bulb produces more electricity.

D. The fluorescent bulb absorbs more ultraviolet rays.

Answer

Answer A is correct. Heat is a byproduct of inefficient energy conversions. The incandescent bulb requires more energy because so much energy is wasted as heat. Answers B and D are incorrect. While fluorescent bulbs can glow in the dark and absorb ultraviolet radiation, these characteristics do not affect efficiency. Answer C is incorrect. Incandescent bulbs do not produce electricity. If you had difficulty with this question, review the loss of heat during energy conversions.

Mini-Assessment

1. The sketch below shows how the amount of available energy changes as energy moves through an ecosystem.

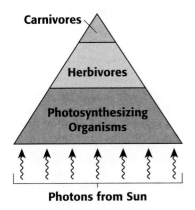

Movement of Energy Through an Ecosystem

Which of the following statements explains why less energy is available at the top of the pyramid than at the bottom?

A. Energy that exists in one form cannot be converted into other forms.

B. Every time that energy is converted, some of the energy is destroyed.

C. Every time that energy is converted, the amount of useful energy is reduced.

D. Energy that exists in one form cannot be transferred from one organism to another.

Enrichment

The sketches below illustrate how energy is used in an electric stove, a microwave oven, and a gas stove.

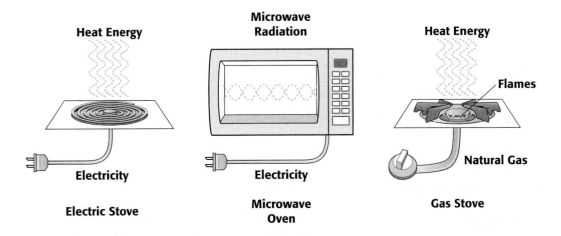

For each device, identify any energy conversions that occur, trace the energy from its original source to the food, and discuss where useful energy is reduced.

Benchmark

C.2.3.6 The student explains and shows the ways in which a net force (i.e., the sum of all acting forces) can act on an object (e.g., speeding up an object traveling in the same direction as the net force, slowing down an object traveling in the direction opposite of the net force).

Tutorial

When an unbalanced force acts on an object, the object will accelerate in the direction in which the force is being exerted. More than one force can act on an object at one time. The net force on an object is the combination of all of the forces acting on the object and is the force that causes objects to accelerate.

Gravitational force causes objects on Earth to accelerate toward the ground. A motionless object exerts a downward force on the ground. At the same time, the ground exerts an upward force of equal magnitude. As a result, the net force on the object is 0.

A falling object accelerates as it moves toward the ground. Resistance in the air (drag) slows the object down until the upward force of the air cancels the downward force of gravity. The object has then reached its terminal velocity.

Touching objects exert contact forces on one another. These forces include friction, tension, air resistance, buoyancy, and applied force. Objects can exert many contact forces at one time.

Sample Problem

1. The image below shows a soccer player preparing to kick a ball.

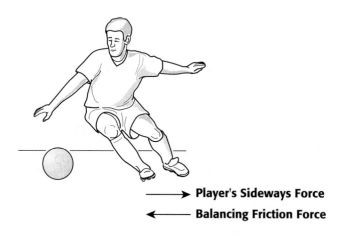

→ **Player's Sideways Force**

← **Balancing Friction Force**

What will happen to the player if the friction force of his foot is less than his sideways force?

A. He will slide forward.

B. He will fall backward.

C. He will move to the left.

D. He will slide to the right.

> **Answer**
>
> **Answer D** is correct. If the force of friction is less than the player's sideways force, the two forces will not balance each other and the player will slide to the right. Answers A and B are incorrect. Because the two forces are acting to the left and to the right, the player will move left or right if the forces do not balance. The player will move to the left if his sideways force is less than the force of friction, so Answer C is incorrect. If you had difficulty with this question, practice calculating net force.

Mini-Assessment

1. The image below shows a car with a mass of 2000 kilograms (kg) parked on a hill. A strong wind exerts a force of 240 newtons (N) downhill on the car.

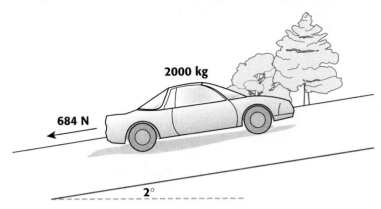

2000 kg

684 N

2°

Car Parked on a Hill

How much force in newtons (N) will the parking brake need to exert uphill to keep the car from rolling down the hill?

Enrichment

1. The sketch below shows a fishing trawler dragging nets through the water.

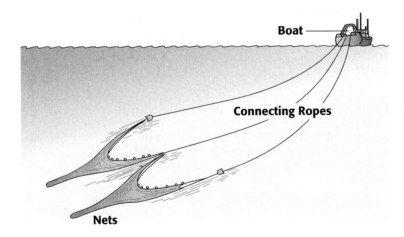

Boat

Connecting Ropes

Nets

Identify the primary forces acting on the ropes, including the direction in which each force acts.

2. Friction prevents cars from using all of the energy that they generate. Friction acts on most moving parts, including the engine and wheels, and thus decreases efficiency. Identify one way to reduce friction in a car.

Benchmark

D.1.3.4 The student knows the ways in which plants and animals reshape the landscape (e.g., bacteria, fungi, worms, rodents, and other organisms add organic matter to the soil, increasing soil fertility, encouraging plant growth, and strengthening resistance to erosion).

Tutorial

Every organism exchanges materials with its ecosystem. When an organism dies, for example, its body is broken down into molecules that either are used by other organisms or are incorporated into the rocks, water, and air. If this material is added to the soil, the fertility of the soil increases and plant growth is encouraged.

The image below shows how carbon cycles through Earth's systems. Every living thing is part of these recycling processes. For example, fungi return nutrients to the soil.

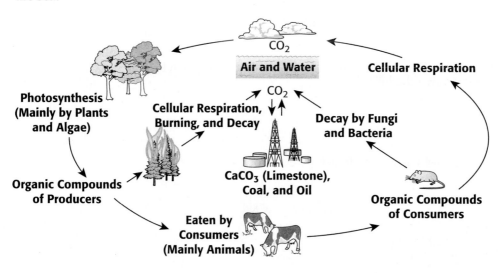

Plants and animals are also important agents of weathering. The roots of plants can expand cracks in rocks and eventually may break the rocks apart. The roots of plants may also anchor soil in place and prevent erosion. The digging activities of burrowing animals also cause weathering of rock and soil by moving rock material and by mixing soil with water and air. Animal activities and plants can dramatically affect the landscape over a long period of time.

Sample Problem

1. Debris from the tides collects in mudflat communities along the coast. People often dig for clams in these communities. Clams are organisms that have two shells and dig through the sand. Which of the following resources does the mudflat ecosystem get from clams' activities?

   A. bacteria and soil

   B. water and sediment

   C. oxygen and organic material

   D. inorganic minerals and erosion prevention

Answer

Answer C is correct. As clams dig through the sand, holes form. These holes can become filled with air, which allows oxygen to enter the ground. The clams provide organic materials in the form of wastes. In addition, dead clams provide organic material that other organisms consume. If you had difficulty with this question, review the carbon cycle.

Mini-Assessment

1. Corals are organisms that use calcium from ocean water to build a hard skeleton. The picture below shows corals living together.

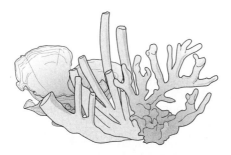

Which of the following statements **best** describes how corals reshape the ocean floor?

A. They remove minerals from the water.

B. They move sand to the ocean's surface.

C. They convert ocean minerals into structures.

D. They make minerals available to other organisms.

Enrichment

The picture below shows a beaver dam.

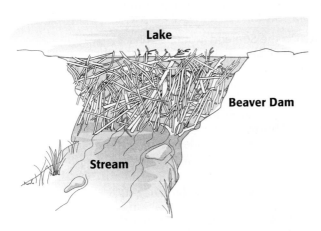

Explain how the dam affects the soil, water table, stream flow, and surrounding terrain. Describe how plant and animal life may have been affected by the near-elimination of beavers in the early 1900s.

Benchmark

E.1.3.1 The student understands the vast size of our solar system and the relationship of the planets and their satellites.

Tutorial

Our solar system is very large. If you made a scale model of the solar system in which Earth was the size of a peppercorn, your model would be 1 kilometer long! Even though the solar system includes the Sun, nine planets, and various smaller bodies, the solar system is made up mostly of empty space.

The Sun is a huge ball of hot gas that consists primarily of hydrogen and helium. The Sun and planets formed billions of years ago from a cloud of dust and gas. Because the Sun's gravity pulls on the planets, they orbit the Sun. The time that a planet takes to complete its orbit depends on the planet's distance from the Sun.

The solar system includes the inner planets and the outer planets. The inner planets—Mercury, Venus, Earth, and Mars—are closest to the Sun. The outer planets, which are farthest from the Sun, are Jupiter, Saturn, Uranus, Neptune, and Pluto. Rocky bodies called *asteroids* also orbit the Sun. Most of these asteroids orbit between Mars and Jupiter in an area called the *asteroid belt*. Comets, which are small bodies of rock and ice, also orbit the Sun. Comets come from the Oort cloud, which surrounds the solar system, and from the Kuiper belt, which lies outside the orbit of Neptune. In addition, nearly every planet in the solar system is orbited by one or more smaller bodies. These natural satellites are called *moons*.

Because everything in the solar system is constantly moving, eclipses sometimes occur. Solar eclipses occur when the Moon comes between Earth and the Sun and the shadow, or umbra, of the Moon falls on part of Earth. During a total solar eclipse, the Moon blocks the entire disk of the Sun in the areas of the world onto which the umbra falls, but the Sun's corona is still visible. People living farther away from the umbra and are in the penumbra and will see a partial eclipse.

Lunar eclipses occur when Earth passes between the Sun and Moon. During a lunar eclipse, sunlight is bent around Earth through Earth's atmosphere. Blue light is filtered out by particles in the atmosphere, causing mainly red light to reach the Moon. As a result, the Moon appears red. Lunar eclipses are more common than solar eclipses are.

The Moon controls Earth's tides. Its gravitational pull causes the oceans to bulge on the side of Earth that is nearest to the Moon. This bulge also occurs on the opposite side of Earth. These bulges are called *high tides*. Low tides occur in the areas where water is drawn away between the bulges. There are two high tides and two low tides each day.

The Sun also contributes to tides. However, because the Sun is so far away, its influence on tides is less powerful than the Moon's influence. When the Sun, Earth, and Moon are aligned, a spring tide occurs. A spring tide has the largest tidal range of all tides. When the Sun, Earth, and Moon form a 90° angle, a neap tide occurs. Neap tides are tides that have the smallest daily range.

Sample Problem

1. Early scientists believed that the Sun revolved around Earth instead of the other way around. What evidence in the night sky contributed to the idea that Earth revolves around the Sun?

Answer

Early scientists noticed that the constellations seemed to move across the sky as the seasons changed. They also noticed that some constellations were visible only during certain times of the year. Scientists recorded the apparent movement of the stars and found an orderly pattern. From the pattern, the scientists concluded that Earth changed positions relative to the stars and therefore was revolving around the Sun. If Earth did not revolve, the stars would always remain in the same positions.

Mini-Assessment

1. The Moon, like Earth, has gravity. While Earth's gravity keeps the Moon in orbit, the Moon's gravity pulls on Earth and causes the water in Earth's oceans to move, as shown in the illustration below. High tides and low tides are the result of this gravitational pull; they occur around the same time every day.

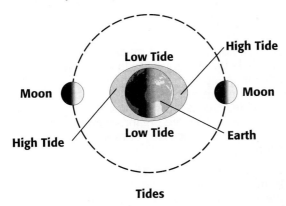

Tides

What two characteristics of Earth and the Moon are responsible for the regularity of the tides?

Enrichment

Study the diagram of a solar eclipse below.

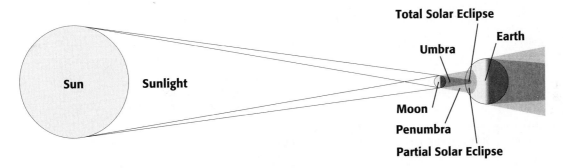

Solar Eclipse

Create a poster or model that illustrates the positions of the Sun, the Moon, and Earth during a lunar eclipse, and summarize how the orbits of the Moon and Earth allow both solar and lunar eclipses to occur.

Benchmark

F.1.3.1 The student understands that living things are composed of major systems that function in reproduction, growth, maintenance, and regulation.

Tutorial

All living organisms are made up of cells. Some organisms are made up of one cell, while other organisms are made up of many cells. In a single-celled organism, one cell must function in reproduction, growth, maintenance, and regulation. In multicellular organisms, a single cell is not required to perform all of these functions. Instead, cells are specialized for a specific function. Cells are organized into tissues, which are organized into organs. Organs are organized into organ systems, in which two or more organs work together to perform a function.

Like most other multicellular organisms, the human body is made up of specialized cells that work together to form tissues, organs, and organ systems. Use the table below to study the 11 human organ systems, their organs, and their major functions.

BODY SYSTEMS

Organ System	Major Organs	General Functions
Cardiovascular system	Heart, veins, arteries, capillaries, and blood	Carries oxygen and nutrients to cells, removes wastes, and helps fight infection
Digestive system	Salivary glands, esophagus, stomach, gallbladder, liver, pancreas, small intestine, and large intestine	Breaks down food into nutrients that can be used by cells
Endocrine system	Glands, includes the pituitary gland	Controls growth, helps maintain homeostasis and other body functions, and plays a role in reproduction
Integumentary system	Skin, hair, and nails	Protects the body, allows for sense of touch, regulates body temperature, and removes some wastes
Lymphatic system	Spleen, lymph nodes, thymus, and tonsils	Fights infection and returns leaked fluids to blood vessels
Muscular system	Muscles and tendons	Allows movement
Nervous system	Brain, spinal cord, and nerves	Senses internal and external environment, sends electrical signals throughout the body, and controls responses to stimuli
Reproductive system	Male: penis, testes, epididymis, vas deferens, and prostate gland Female: vagina, cervix, uterus, fallopian tubes, and ovaries	Male: produces and delivers sperm Female: produces eggs and nourishes and protects the fetus
Respiratory system	Lungs, bronchus, pharynx, larynx, trachea, and diaphragm	Absorbs oxygen from the air and expels carbon dioxide wastes
Skeletal system	Bones, cartilage, and ligaments	Supports and protects the body, allows movement, stores minerals, and produces blood cells
Urinary system	Kidneys, ureters, and urinary bladder	Removes wastes from body and regulates body fluids

Sample Problem

1. Shara is studying cells under a microscope. She knows that the shape of a cell helps determine the function of the cell. A diagram of the cell that Shara is examining appears below.

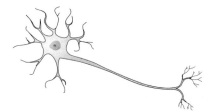

What type of cell is Shara studying?

A. a nerve cell

B. a muscle cell

C. a red blood cell

D. an epithelial cell

Answer

Answer A is correct. Shara is looking at a nerve cell. Nerve cells have long branches that allow the cells to receive information and send messages. Muscle cells are long, thin cells that form strands, which enable movement, so Answer B is incorrect. Answer C is incorrect. Because red blood cells are disk shaped, they can carry oxygen to other body cells. Answer D is incorrect because epithelial cells are compact cells that form a protective layer. If you had difficulty with this question, review the four kinds of tissues.

Mini-Assessment

1. The human digestive system breaks down the food that people eat into molecules that cells in the body can use. The image below shows the human digestive system.

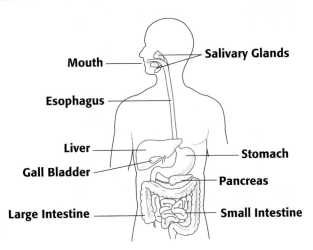

Which organ of the digestive system stores nutrients for future use? What other important function does this organ perform?

Enrichment

1. Several organs in the human body are part of more than one organ system. Identify one such organ. Describe its function in each of the organ systems of which it is a part.

2. Research how skin wounds, such as cuts and scrapes, heal. Make a timeline that shows all of the steps in the healing process, and describe which organ systems are involved in each step.

Benchmark

 F.2.3.2 The student knows that the variation in each species is due to the exchange and interaction of genetic information as it is passed from parent to offspring.

Tutorial

Sexual reproduction happens in many species in both plants and animals. In plants, the male and female reproductive systems often are on the same plant. Sometimes, this characteristic results in offspring that have traits that are identical to the parent if the parent plant self-pollinates. Two parent plants, or cross-pollinating plants, produce offspring that have traits from both parents.

Traits and characteristics are passed from parents to offspring through genes. Each individual has two *alleles*, or forms of the same gene. One allele comes from each parent. The combination of these two alleles is the organism's *genotype*. Genotype determines an organism's appearance, or *phenotype*. Often, alleles are either dominant or recessive. A dominant allele is expressed in the offspring's phenotype. Recessive alleles determine the phenotype of offspring if both parents contribute the recessive allele.

In humans, an egg and a sperm, each of which carries 23 chromosomes, join during sexual reproduction to form a zygote that has 23 pairs of chromosomes, or 46 chromosomes. Body cells also contain 46 chromosomes. Sex cells, or eggs and sperm, contain only 23 chromosomes as a result of division by meiosis, which produces cells that carry one-half of each pair of chromosomes.

Populations adapt over time to better survive in an environment. These adaptations are passed on to offspring and may eventually result in new species. In speciation, a population changes over time until the individuals in that population can no longer reproduce with individuals from the original species.

Sample Problem

1. The table below shows the number of bear cubs born to a pair of adult bears over a period of four years. The table lists whether the cubs had brown fur or white fur. Brown fur (*B*) is the dominant trait, and white fur (*b*) is the recessive trait.

BEAR CUB BIRTHS OVER FOUR YEARS

Year	Total Cubs Born	Cubs with Brown Fur	Cubs with White Fur
1	2	2	0
2	3	3	0
3	1	1	0
4	2	2	0

If both parents have brown fur, what genotype must at least one parent have to produce these offspring?

A. *bb*

B. *bB*

C. *Bb*

D. *BB*

> **Answer**
>
> **Answer D** is correct. At least one parent would have to carry two dominant alleles (*BB*) for fur color to produce only brown-furred cubs. Answers A, B, and C are incorrect. One parent can have the recessive allele (*Bb* or *bb*), but if both parents carry the recessive gene, some of the cubs will have white fur. In addition, the problem states that both parents have brown fur; a parent with *bb* genotype will have white fur. If you had difficulty with this question, use Punnett squares to examine different crosses.

Mini-Assessment

1. The table below shows some characteristics of three lizard species. The climate of an ecosystem has changed over time. The ecosystem was once very wet, but it is now very dry and resembles a desert biome.

CHARACTERISTICS OF THREE LIZARDS

	Characteristics
Lizard A	Stores fat in its tail, has coloring that indicates that it is poisonous, often feeds at night
Lizard B	Loses its tail when trapped by predators, has suckers on its toes for climbing, feeds mostly on insects
Lizard C	Changes color to blend in with the environment, has independently movable eyes, uses long tongue to capture insects

Which of these lizard species could survive and continue to reproduce in the new ecosystem? What adaptations would be passed along to future offspring?

Enrichment

Sometimes, offspring lack a sex chromosome, have an incomplete sex chromosome, or have extra sex chromosomes. These abnormalities can cause severe physical and emotional problems as a person grows and develops. The table below shows normal sex chromosomes and some sex chromosome abnormalities.

SEX CHROMOSOMES AND ABNORMALITIES

Description	Chromosomes
Normal female	XX
Normal male	XY
Turner's Syndrome	X chromosome with an incomplete or missing second X chromosome
Klinefelter's Syndrome	XXY, XXXY, XXXXY, XXYY, XXXYY
XYY Syndrome	XYY
Triple-X Syndrome	XXX

Choose one sex chromosome abnormality from the table to research. Identify the cause of the abnormality and the gender affected by the abnormality. Describe some of the physical and emotional characteristics of people who have the abnormality, and present your findings in a table or in an outline.

Benchmark

G.1.3.4 The student knows that the interactions of organisms with each other and with the nonliving parts of their environments result in the flow of energy and the cycling of matter throughout the system.

Tutorial

Energy is neither created nor destroyed. In an ecosystem, energy is transferred from one organism to another. This cycle begins with producers. Producers, such as plants, convert light energy into chemical energy during photosynthesis. Other organisms—the consumers—obtain this chemical energy by eating plants or by eating organisms that have eaten plants. Food chains and food webs show how energy is transferred through an ecosystem. Any energy that is not used for an organism's life functions or lost as heat is stored in the organism's body tissue. This stored energy is transferred to the organism that eats the organism. Consequently, less energy is available farther up the food chain.

If a species is removed from a food web, the rest of the ecosystem may be affected. The number of consumers in an ecosystem depends on the amount of energy that is available. Over time, organisms must evolve and adapt to better compete for this limited supply of energy.

Like energy, nonliving matter cycles through an ecosystem. For example, matter, such as nitrogen, can move from the atmosphere into the soil and from organism to organism until the matter returns to the atmosphere to begin the cycle again. Water, carbon, nitrogen, and oxygen are the most commonly cycled materials on Earth.

Sample Problem

1. The food web below shows some of the interactions between the organisms in an ecosystem.

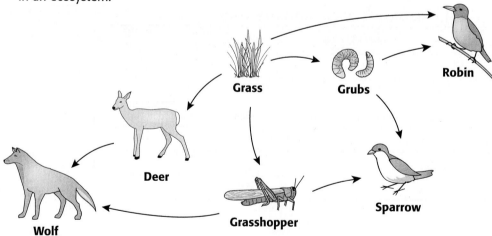

What is the **best** way to increase the total amount of energy available in this ecosystem?

A. eliminate the wolf population

B. increase the number of grubs

C. increase the sheep population

D. decrease the number of grasshoppers

Answer

Answer D is correct. Decreasing the number of grasshoppers would increase the amount of grass (and energy) in the system. Increasing the number of consumers of grass would decrease the amount of energy in the system. Eliminating wolves would increase populations of consumers that eat grass. If you had difficulty with this question, review food webs and energy pyramids.

Mini-Assessment

1. Many nonliving materials are cycled through ecosystems. Among these materials are carbon and nitrogen. Study the diagrams of the carbon and nitrogen cycles shown below.

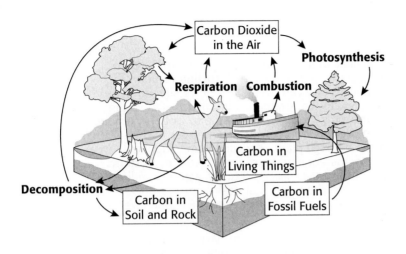

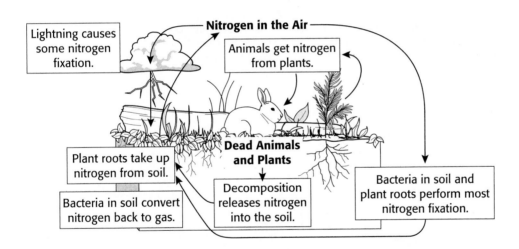

What role do decomposers play in these cycles? What function do bacteria serve in the nitrogen cycle?

Enrichment

1. Many parasites, such as ringworm and tapeworms, attack both humans and animals. Research a parasite that can live in both human and animal hosts. Create a graphic that shows the way in which the parasite infects the host and the type of damage that the parasite can produce.

2. Acid rain can develop when certain chemicals enter the water cycle. Make a flowchart that shows the process in which these chemicals form acid rain and the damage that they can cause in an environment.

Benchmark

G.2.3.4 The student understands that humans are a part of an ecosystem and their activities may deliberately or inadvertently alter the equilibrium in ecosystems.

Tutorial

Human activities affect other organisms in the environment. Sometimes, these activities are deliberate. For example, clearing land for construction can directly damage the habitats of other organisms and can decrease biodiversity. Humans may also harm the environment indirectly. For example, burning fossil fuels can increase carbon dioxide levels in the air, which may contribute to global warming. The burning of fossil fuels can also produce smog, which contributes to the formation of acid rain. Acid rain can damage plants, soil, and water supplies. When these resources are damaged, the equilibrium of the affected ecosystems may be altered. Another example of the ways in which human activities indirectly affect Earth systems is the use of certain chemicals that destroy ozone. The destruction of ozone in the upper atmosphere has weakened the ozone layer that protects Earth from harmful ultraviolet radiation.

Often, humans can have a positive effect on an ecosystem. Many natural areas are set aside and protected. Humans also restore some habitats and protect endangered organisms. Through these deliberate actions, people hope to restore equilibrium in an area. For example, scientists have been working to restore wetlands by flooding areas that have been drained. Scientists have also reintroduced wolves into several areas around the United States. By restoring these predators, scientists hope to restore the natural food web of an area.

Sample Problem

1. Scientists can make predictions about air quality in certain areas. Study the map of an air-quality forecast shown below.

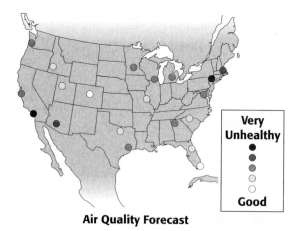

Air Quality Forecast

What is being measured to determine air quality?

A. ozone

B. pollen

C. humidity

D. barometric pressure

Mini-Assessment

1. Humans rely on power plants to provide electricity. However, power plants can have a negative effect on the environment. Study the illustration of a power plant shown below.

Describe some of the ways that a power plant can pollute an ecosystem. What are two ways to decrease the amount of pollution that a power plant generates?

Enrichment

Many people confuse global warming with the destruction of the ozone layer. Create a table that summarizes each process clearly. What factors contribute to each process? What are the effects of each process?

Benchmark

 H.1.3.1 The student knows that scientific knowledge is subject to modification as new information challenges prevailing theories and as a new theory leads to looking at old theories in a new way.

Tutorial

All scientific inquiry begins with asking questions, recording observations, and conducting research. Often, scientists examine what other scientists have studied and learned. By studying the work of other scientists, people can develop new theories and test these theories by using scientific methods.

Many early astronomers developed their theories about Earth's movements based on the conclusions of previous astronomers. For example, even though Ptolemy's theory that Earth was the center of the solar system was incorrect, his mathematical observations helped future astronomers develop accurate descriptions of planetary motion.

The current theory of plate tectonics was developed in the same way. Alfred Wegener theorized that all of the continents were once one mass and drifted apart over many years. Many scientists did not believe Wegener's theory. As scientists collected new evidence, they discovered that Wegener was partly right. Several of his ideas now form the basis of the current theory of plate tectonics.

The ideas of Gregor Mendel and Charles Darwin have had a great influence on the modern study of heredity and evolution. Gregor Mendel used pea plants to develop hypotheses about genetics and trait inheritance. However, Mendel's ideas were not accepted until long after his death. Charles Darwin, on the other hand, modified his theory of evolution several times throughout his lifetime and incorporated the influences and ideas of other scientists into his theories.

The development of increasingly powerful tools is another way that scientists can use old theories to help explain new observations. Isaac Newton's study of gravity and the attraction of planets, for example, explained previous astronomers' observations of the sky. Now, with tools such as satellites, telescopes, and robotics, who knows what future scientists may discover and which theories they may disprove!

Sample Problem

1. Imagine that you are a scientist investigating hair loss. Your theory currently states that men are more prone to hair loss than women are. Your next step is to research new developments in the field. While conducting your research, you discover that women who have high levels of testosterone experience more hair loss than men do. How should you treat this new information? Explain how you would reexamine your own research and possibly rethink your theory.

Answer

Science is always building on new discoveries. The discovery that women who have high levels of testosterone experience more hair loss than men do indicates that gender may not determine hair loss. So, a scientist would likely examine the results of his or her research to see whether testosterone levels, rather than gender, are the primary factor in hair loss.

Mini-Assessment

1. Hibiscus plants are flowering plants that thrive in Florida but are not known to survive where temperatures drop below freezing. The table below shows the average low temperatures in degrees Celsius (°C) of cities where hibiscus plants are grown. Two of these cities have below-freezing temperatures.

AVERAGE LOW TEMPERATURES FOR FOUR CITIES

City	Average Low Temperature (°C)
Atlanta, Georgia	0
Little Rock, Arkansas	−1.61
Nashville, Tennessee	−3.05
Santa Barbara, California	−4.5

How should a scientist react to this information?

A. A scientist should disregard this information.

B. A scientist should believe that the new information is true.

C. A scientist should decide that the new information is false.

D. A scientist should conduct additional research by using other sources.

Enrichment

1. For years, scientists have researched a number of serious diseases. These diseases include cancer, AIDS, Alzheimer's disease, tuberculosis, and Parkinson's disease. Choose a specific disease, and chart how theories about the cause of the disease have developed through history. Present your findings in a timeline.

2. Scientists often use the work of other scientists to help them develop new theories. Doing so allows scientists to look at problems in a new way. Choose a scientific problem that interests you, and describe how you would use the work of other scientists to help you conduct your own research.

Benchmark

 H.1.3.4 The student knows that accurate record keeping, openness, and replication are essential to maintaining an investigator's credibility with other scientists and society.

Tutorial

Science begins with direct observations of the world around us. When conducting research, scientists must use standard tools to measure and record data. Doing so allows scientists from different countries or different fields of science to share and compare data.

Scientists must keep accurate and detailed records of their observations and procedures. All observations, procedures, and data must be made available for other scientists to review. This practice allows other scientists to replicate an investigation and confirm or deny the results of any experiment. Other scientists should be able to repeat an investigation in the same way that the original investigation was conducted. Experiments that explore theories and laws in science must be replicated by other scientists several times before the results can be accepted.

When scientists repeat an investigation and obtain different results, they should thoroughly examine the reasons for the differences in the results. Scientists must determine whether the procedures of the experiment are flawed. They also must determine if they made an incorrect measurement or procedural error. If an error has not occurred, scientists must determine if the differences in the data are great enough to suggest another explanation for the results.

Sample Problem

1. Zach has a hypothesis about the commercials that are shown on TV during Saturday morning cartoons. He thinks that most of the commercials advertise cereals and trendy toys. Zach decides to watch some commercials to test his hypothesis. When should Zach conduct his experiment? How should he record his observations? Keep in mind that Zach must provide enough information for someone else to be able to repeat the experiment.

Answer

Zach should watch commercials at different times of the day and night as well as on different days. He should record the times that he watches TV. He should also record the number of commercials and the products that the commercials advertise during each time period. After Zach makes his observations, he should compare commercials shown on Saturday mornings with commercials shown at other times and then draw conclusions.

Mini-Assessment

1. Sheila surveyed two eighth-grade classes to determine whether eighth-grade students like pizza, hamburgers, or tacos best. Her results are shown in the table below.

FAVORITE FOODS FOR TWO CLASSES OF EIGHTH GRADERS

	Students in Class A	Students in Class B
Pizza	15	16
Hamburgers	5	10
Tacos	8	5

What should Sheila do to ensure that her results are reliable?

A. She should publish her results.

B. She should repeat her survey in another class.

C. She should interview a local restaurant owner.

D. She should research food choices in the library.

Enrichment

Antonio's class is studying the characteristics of different animals. The students recorded the environmental temperature in an area and the body temperatures of two different animals in the area during different times of the year. Their results are shown in degrees Celsius (°C) in the table below.

BODY TEMPERATURES OF TWO ANIMALS AT DIFFERENT TIMES OF THE YEAR

Outdoor Temperature (°C)	Body Temperature (°C) of Animal A	Body Temperature (°C) of Animal B
−5.0	−3.0	38.1
4.5	4.0	38.3
37.8	39.0	38.6
15.5	14.5	39.1

What information is missing from the collected data? What additional information about the experiment or the data should people interested in replicating the experiment know?

Benchmark

H.1.3.5 The student knows that a change in one or more variables may alter the outcome of an investigation.

Tutorial

When scientists begin an investigation, they start by using reputable and reliable sources to research what is known about their subject. When their research is complete, scientists can make predictions and form hypotheses for their own experiments. Hypotheses are tested through scientific methods, which can include recording observations and making measurements. To test hypotheses, scientists design experiments that have variables that are related to the subject being investigated. They look at how differences in these variables affect the outcome.

Scientists use controlled experiments, or experiments in which only one variable is tested at a time, to test their hypotheses. They set up both experimental groups and a control group. A control group is a group that serves as a standard of comparison with experimental groups. The control group is identical to the experimental groups except for one factor—the variable. The variable that scientists purposefully change is known as the *independent variable*. Changes in the independent variable may cause changes in another variable. The *dependent variable* is a variable that changes as a result of a change in the independent variable. For example, in an experiment in which a scientist is studying how different concentrations of a chemical affect plant height, the chemical concentration would be the independent variable and plant height would be the dependent variable.

When scientists design an experiment, they try to test as many subjects as they can. They do so to make sure that any differences in the results between the control group and the experimental groups are caused by the independent variable and not by another factor. Scientists often replicate their experiments to verify their results. After concluding their experiments, they analyze the results and draw conclusions. They also must decide whether the results support the hypothesis.

Sample Problem

1. Sheri has prepared three pitchers of iced tea to find out which recipe makes the sweetest drink. The volume of tea in milliliters (ml) and the mass of sugar in grams (g) that she put in each pitcher are recorded in the table below.

COMPARISON OF TEA MIXTURES

	Tea (ml)	Sugar (g)
Pitcher A	250	62
Pitcher B	450	62
Pitcher C	650	62

Which pitcher has the sweetest tea? How will the results change if Sheri doubles the amount of sugar in Pitcher B? What does this result reveal about the investigation?

> **Answer**
>
> **Pitcher A** has the sweetest tea. It has the highest concentration of sugar per volume. If Sheri doubles the amount of sugar in Pitcher B, the tea in Pitcher B will be the sweetest because it will have the greatest concentration of sugar. This investigation shows that changing one variable in a study affects the outcome of the study.

Mini-Assessment

1. Jorge wants to grow corn to sell at the farmer's market. He thinks that coffee grounds would be a good fertilizer, so he designs an experiment to test his hypothesis. First, Jorge plants one corn plant in each of two pots. He then adds coffee grounds to one of the pots. He measures the height of each plant in centimeters (cm). His results are recorded in the table below.

EFFECT OF COFFEE GROUNDS ON CORN PLANT GROWTH

Week	Height of Plant with No Fertilizer (cm)	Height of Plant with Coffee Grounds (cm)
0	10	10
1	11	20
2	15	26
3	21	34
4	26	42

What is the independent variable in this experiment? What is the dependent variable in this experiment? How does the dependent variable change in the presence of the independent variable?

Enrichment

Dr. Vet is developing new puppy-food formulas. She performs an experiment to see which of her three formulas causes the greatest increase in mass. She feeds a different formula to each of three puppies. Each puppy receives the same amount of food. Each puppy's mass in grams (g) at the end of each week are recorded in the table below.

MASS IN GRAMS OF FOUR PUPPIES OVER FIVE WEEKS

Week	Mass of Puppy A (g)	Mass of Puppy B (g)	Mass of Puppy C (g)
1	454	454	454
2	681	772	863
3	772	908	999
4	863	999	1226
5	954	1090	1544

Identify the independent and dependent variables. According to the data in Dr. Vet's table, which formula causes the greatest increase in mass? What changes in the design of this experiment would have made the experiment better?

Contents

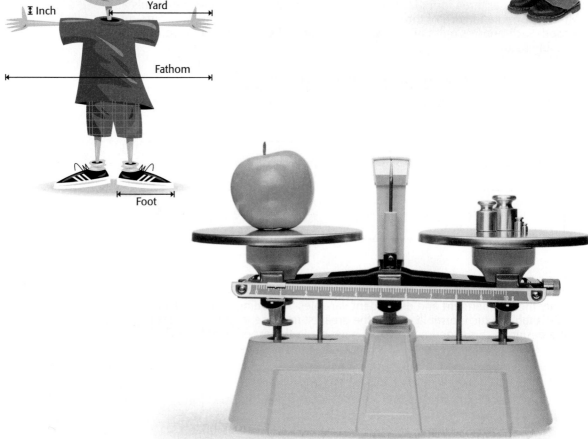

Study Skills

FoldNote Instructions

Have you ever tried to study for a test or quiz but didn't know where to start? Or have you read a chapter and found that you can remember only a few ideas? Well, FoldNotes are a fun and exciting way to help you learn and remember the ideas you encounter as you learn science!

FoldNotes are tools that you can use to organize concepts. By focusing on a few main concepts, FoldNotes help you learn and remember how the concepts fit together. They can help you see the "big picture." Below you will find instructions for building 10 different FoldNotes.

Pyramid

1. Place a sheet of paper in front of you. Fold the lower left-hand corner of the paper diagonally to the opposite edge of the paper.

2. Cut off the tab of paper created by the fold (at the top).

3. Open the paper so that it is a square. Fold the lower right-hand corner of the paper diagonally to the opposite corner to form a triangle.

4. Open the paper. The creases of the two folds will have created an X.

5. Using scissors, cut along one of the creases. Start from any corner, and stop at the center point to create two flaps. Use tape or glue to attach one of the flaps on top of the other flap.

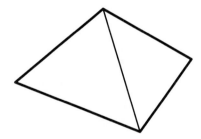

Double Door

1. Fold a sheet of paper in half from the top to the bottom. Then, unfold the paper.

2. Fold the top and bottom edges of the paper to the crease.

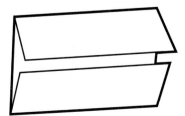

Booklet

1. Fold a sheet of paper in half from left to right. Then, unfold the paper.

2. Fold the sheet of paper in half again from the top to the bottom. Then, unfold the paper.

3. Refold the sheet of paper in half from left to right.

4. Fold the top and bottom edges to the center crease.

5. Completely unfold the paper.

6. Refold the paper from top to bottom.

7. Using scissors, cut a slit along the center crease of the sheet from the folded edge to the creases made in step 4. Do not cut the entire sheet in half.

8. Fold the sheet of paper in half from left to right. While holding the bottom and top edges of the paper, push the bottom and top edges together so that the center collapses at the center slit. Fold the four flaps to form a four-page book.

Layered Book

1. Lay one sheet of paper on top of another sheet. Slide the top sheet up so that 2 cm of the bottom sheet is showing.

2. Hold the two sheets together, fold down the top of the two sheets so that you see four 2 cm tabs along the bottom.

3. Using a stapler, staple the top of the FoldNote.

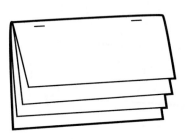

Key-Term Fold

1. Fold a sheet of lined notebook paper in half from left to right.

2. Using scissors, cut along every third line from the right edge of the paper to the center fold to make tabs.

Four-Corner Fold

1. Fold a sheet of paper in half from left to right. Then, unfold the paper.

2. Fold each side of the paper to the crease in the center of the paper.

3. Fold the paper in half from the top to the bottom. Then, unfold the paper.

4. Using scissors, cut the top flap creases made in step 3 to form four flaps.

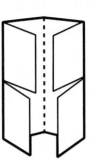

Three-Panel Flip Chart

1. Fold a piece of paper in half from the top to the bottom.

2. Fold the paper in thirds from side to side. Then, unfold the paper so that you can see the three sections.

3. From the top of the paper, cut along each of the vertical fold lines to the fold in the middle of the paper. You will now have three flaps.

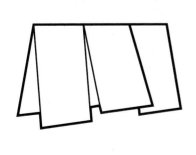

Table Fold

1. Fold a piece of paper in half from the top to the bottom. Then, fold the paper in half again.

2. Fold the paper in thirds from side to side.

3. Unfold the paper completely. Carefully trace the fold lines by using a pen or pencil.

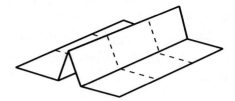

Two-Panel Flip Chart

1. Fold a piece of paper in half from the top to the bottom.

2. Fold the paper in half from side to side. Then, unfold the paper so that you can see the two sections.

3. From the top of the paper, cut along the vertical fold line to the fold in the middle of the paper. You will now have two flaps.

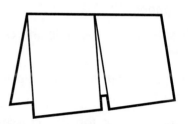

Tri-Fold

1. Fold a piece a paper in thirds from the top to the bottom.

2. Unfold the paper so that you can see the three sections. Then, turn the paper sideways so that the three sections form vertical columns.

3. Trace the fold lines by using a pen or pencil. Label the columns "Know," "Want," and "Learn."

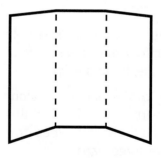

Graphic Organizer Instructions

Have you ever wished that you could "draw out" the many concepts you learn in your science class? Sometimes, being able to *see* how concepts are related really helps you remember what you've learned. Graphic Organizers do just that! They give you a way to draw or map out concepts.

All you need to make a Graphic Organizer is a piece of paper and a pencil. Below you will find instructions for four different Graphic Organizers designed to help you organize the concepts you'll learn in this book.

Spider Map

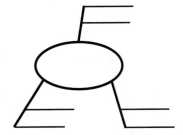

1. Draw a diagram like the one shown. In the circle, write the main topic.

2. From the circle, draw legs to represent different categories of the main topic. You can have as many categories as you want.

3. From the category legs, draw horizontal lines. As you read the chapter, write details about each category on the horizontal lines.

Comparison Table

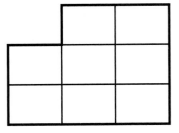

1. Draw a chart like the one shown. Your chart can have as many columns and rows as you want.

2. In the top row, write the topics that you want to compare.

3. In the left column, write characteristics of the topics that you want to compare. As you read the chapter, fill in the characteristics for each topic in the appropriate boxes.

Chain-of-Events-Chart

1. Draw a box. In the box, write the first step of a process or the first event of a timeline.

2. Under the box, draw another box, and use an arrow to connect the two boxes. In the second box, write the next step of the process or the next event in the timeline.

3. Continue adding boxes until the process or timeline is finished.

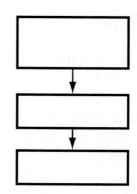

Concept Map

1. Draw a circle in the center of a piece of paper. Write the main idea of the chapter in the center of the circle.

2. From the circle, draw other circles. In those circles, write characteristics of the main idea. Draw arrows from the center circle to the circles that contain the characteristics.

3. From each circle that contains a characteristic, draw other circles. In those circles, write specific details about the characteristic. Draw arrows from each circle that contains a characteristic to the circles that contain specific details. You may draw as many circles as you want.

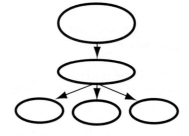

Appendix

Math Refresher

Science requires an understanding of many math concepts. The following pages will help you review some important math skills.

Averages

An **average**, or **mean**, simplifies a set of numbers into a single number that *approximates* the value of the set.

Example: Find the average of the following set of numbers: 5, 4, 7, and 8.

Step 1: Find the sum.
$$5 + 4 + 7 + 8 = 24$$

Step 2: Divide the sum by the number of numbers in your set. Because there are four numbers in this example, divide the sum by 4.
$$\frac{24}{4} = 6$$

The average, or mean, is **6.**

Ratios

A **ratio** is a comparison between numbers, and it is usually written as a fraction.

Example: Find the ratio of thermometers to students if you have 36 thermometers and 48 students in your class.

Step 1: Make the ratio.
$$\frac{36 \text{ thermometers}}{48 \text{ students}}$$

Step 2: Reduce the fraction to its simplest form.
$$\frac{36}{48} = \frac{36 \div 12}{48 \div 12} = \frac{3}{4}$$

The ratio of thermometers to students is **3 to 4,** or $\frac{3}{4}$. The ratio may also be written in the form 3:4.

Proportions

A **proportion** is an equation that states that two ratios are equal.
$$\frac{3}{1} = \frac{12}{4}$$

To solve a proportion, first multiply across the equal sign. This is called *cross-multiplication*. If you know three of the quantities in a proportion, you can use cross-multiplication to find the fourth.

Example: Imagine that you are making a scale model of the solar system for your science project. The diameter of Jupiter is 11.2 times the diameter of the Earth. If you are using a plastic-foam ball that has a diameter of 2 cm to represent the Earth, what must the diameter of the ball representing Jupiter be?
$$\frac{11.2}{1} = \frac{x}{2 \text{ cm}}$$

Step 1: Cross-multiply.
$$\frac{11.2}{1} \diagtimes \frac{x}{2}$$
$$11.2 \times 2 = x \times 1$$

Step 2: Multiply.
$$22.4 = x \times 1$$

Step 3: Isolate the variable by dividing both sides by 1.
$$x = \frac{22.4}{1}$$
$$x = 22.4 \text{ cm}$$

You will need to use a ball that has a diameter of **22.4** cm to represent Jupiter.

Percentages

A **percentage** is a ratio of a given number to 100.

> **Example:** What is 85% of 40?

Step 1: Rewrite the percentage by moving the decimal point two places to the left.

$$0.85$$

Step 2: Multiply the decimal by the number that you are calculating the percentage of.

$$0.85 \times 40 = 34$$

85% of 40 is **34.**

Decimals

To **add** or **subtract decimals,** line up the digits vertically so that the decimal points line up. Then, add or subtract the columns from right to left. Carry or borrow numbers as necessary.

> **Example:** Add the following numbers: 3.1415 and 2.96.

Step 1: Line up the digits vertically so that the decimal points line up.

$$\begin{array}{r} 3.1415 \\ + \ 2.96 \\ \hline \end{array}$$

Step 2: Add the columns from right to left, and carry when necessary.

$$\begin{array}{r} {\scriptstyle 1\ 1} \\ 3.1415 \\ + \ 2.96 \\ \hline 6.1015 \end{array}$$

The sum is **6.1015.**

Fractions

Numbers tell you how many; **fractions** tell you *how much of a whole*.

> **Example:** Your class has 24 plants. Your teacher instructs you to put 5 plants in a shady spot. What fraction of the plants in your class will you put in a shady spot?

Step 1: In the denominator, write the total number of parts in the whole.

$$\frac{?}{24}$$

Step 2: In the numerator, write the number of parts of the whole that are being considered.

$$\frac{5}{24}$$

So, $\frac{5}{24}$ of the plants will be in the shade.

Reducing Fractions

It is usually best to express a fraction in its simplest form. Expressing a fraction in its simplest form is called *reducing* a fraction.

> **Example:** Reduce the fraction $\frac{30}{45}$ to its simplest form.

Step 1: Find the largest whole number that will divide evenly into both the numerator and denominator. This number is called the *greatest common factor* (GCF).

Factors of the numerator 30:

> 1, 2, 3, 5, 6, 10, **15,** 30

Factors of the denominator 45:

> 1, 3, 5, 9, **15,** 45

Step 2: Divide both the numerator and the denominator by the GCF, which in this case is 15.

$$\frac{30}{45} = \frac{30 \div 15}{45 \div 15} = \frac{2}{3}$$

Thus, $\frac{30}{45}$ reduced to its simplest form is $\frac{2}{3}$.

Adding and Subtracting Fractions

To **add** or **subtract fractions** that have the **same denominator,** simply add or subtract the numerators.

Examples:

$$\frac{3}{5} + \frac{1}{5} = ? \quad \text{and} \quad \frac{3}{4} - \frac{1}{4} = ?$$

Step 1: Add or subtract the numerators.

$$\frac{3}{5} + \frac{1}{5} = \frac{4}{\ } \quad \text{and} \quad \frac{3}{4} - \frac{1}{4} = \frac{2}{\ }$$

Step 2: Write the sum or difference over the denominator.

$$\frac{3}{5} + \frac{1}{5} = \frac{4}{5} \quad \text{and} \quad \frac{3}{4} - \frac{1}{4} = \frac{2}{4}$$

Step 3: If necessary, reduce the fraction to its simplest form.

$\frac{4}{5}$ cannot be reduced, and $\frac{2}{4} = \frac{1}{2}$.

To **add** or **subtract fractions** that have **different denominators,** first find the least common denominator (LCD).

Examples:

$$\frac{1}{2} + \frac{1}{6} = ? \quad \text{and} \quad \frac{3}{4} - \frac{2}{3} = ?$$

Step 1: Write the equivalent fractions that have a common denominator.

$$\frac{3}{6} + \frac{1}{6} = ? \quad \text{and} \quad \frac{9}{12} - \frac{8}{12} = ?$$

Step 2: Add or subtract the fractions.

$$\frac{3}{6} + \frac{1}{6} = \frac{4}{6} \quad \text{and} \quad \frac{9}{12} - \frac{8}{12} = \frac{1}{12}$$

Step 3: If necessary, reduce the fraction to its simplest form.

The fraction $\frac{4}{6} = \frac{2}{3}$, and $\frac{1}{12}$ cannot be reduced.

Multiplying Fractions

To **multiply fractions,** multiply the numerators and the denominators together, and then reduce the fraction to its simplest form.

Example:

$$\frac{5}{9} \times \frac{7}{10} = ?$$

Step 1: Multiply the numerators and denominators.

$$\frac{5}{9} \times \frac{7}{10} = \frac{5 \times 7}{9 \times 10} = \frac{35}{90}$$

Step 2: Reduce the fraction.

$$\frac{35}{90} = \frac{35 \div 5}{90 \div 5} = \frac{7}{18}$$

Dividing Fractions

To **divide fractions,** first rewrite the divisor (the number you divide by) upside down. This number is called the *reciprocal* of the divisor. Then multiply and reduce if necessary.

Example:

$$\frac{5}{8} \div \frac{3}{2} = ?$$

Step 1: Rewrite the divisor as its reciprocal.

$$\frac{3}{2} \rightarrow \frac{2}{3}$$

Step 2: Multiply the fractions.

$$\frac{5}{8} \times \frac{2}{3} = \frac{5 \times 2}{8 \times 3} = \frac{10}{24}$$

Step 3: Reduce the fraction.

$$\frac{10}{24} = \frac{10 \div 2}{24 \div 2} = \frac{5}{12}$$

Appendix

Scientific Notation

Scientific notation is a short way of representing very large and very small numbers without writing all of the place-holding zeros.

Example: Write 653,000,000 in scientific notation.

Step 1: Write the number without the place-holding zeros.

653

Step 2: Place the decimal point after the first digit.

6.53

Step 3: Find the exponent by counting the number of places that you moved the decimal point.

6.53000000

The decimal point was moved eight places to the left. Therefore, the exponent of 10 is positive 8. If you had moved the decimal point to the right, the exponent would be negative.

Step 4: Write the number in scientific notation.

$$6.53 \times 10^8$$

Area

Area is the number of square units needed to cover the surface of an object.

Formulas:

area of a square = side × side
area of a rectangle = length × width
area of a triangle = $\frac{1}{2}$ × base × height

Examples: Find the areas.

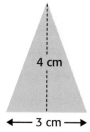

Triangle

area = $\frac{1}{2}$ × base × height
area = $\frac{1}{2}$ × 3 cm × 4 cm
area = **6 cm²**

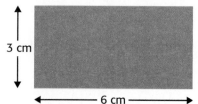

Rectangle

area = length × width
area = 6 cm × 3 cm
area = **18 cm²**

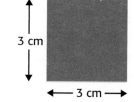

Square

area = side × side
area = 3 cm × 3 cm
area = **9 cm²**

Volume

Volume is the amount of space that something occupies.

Formulas:

volume of a cube =
side × side × side

volume of a prism =
area of base × height

Examples:

Find the volume of the solids.

Cube

volume = side × side × side
volume = 4 cm × 4 cm × 4 cm
volume = **64 cm³**

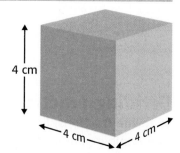

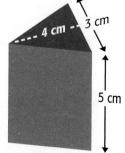

Prism

volume = area of base × height
volume = (area of triangle) × height
volume = ($\frac{1}{2}$ × 3 cm × 4 cm) × 5 cm
volume = 6 cm² × 5 cm
volume = **30 cm³**

Making Charts and Graphs

Pie Charts

A pie chart shows how each group of data relates to all of the data. Each part of the circle forming the chart represents a category of the data. The entire circle represents all of the data. For example, a biologist studying a hardwood forest in Wisconsin found that there were five different types of trees. The data table at right summarizes the biologist's findings.

Wisconsin Hardwood Trees	
Type of tree	**Number found**
Oak	600
Maple	750
Beech	300
Birch	1,200
Hickory	150
Total	3,000

How to Make a Pie Chart

1 To make a pie chart of these data, first find the percentage of each type of tree. Divide the number of trees of each type by the total number of trees, and multiply by 100.

$$\frac{600 \text{ oak}}{3,000 \text{ trees}} \times 100 = 20\%$$

$$\frac{750 \text{ maple}}{3,000 \text{ trees}} \times 100 = 25\%$$

$$\frac{300 \text{ beech}}{3,000 \text{ trees}} \times 100 = 10\%$$

$$\frac{1,200 \text{ birch}}{3,000 \text{ trees}} \times 100 = 40\%$$

$$\frac{150 \text{ hickory}}{3,000 \text{ trees}} \times 100 = 5\%$$

2 Now, determine the size of the wedges that make up the pie chart. Multiply each percentage by 360°. Remember that a circle contains 360°.

$20\% \times 360° = 72°$ $25\% \times 360° = 90°$

$10\% \times 360° = 36°$ $40\% \times 360° = 144°$

$5\% \times 360° = 18°$

3 Check that the sum of the percentages is 100 and the sum of the degrees is 360.

$20\% + 25\% + 10\% + 40\% + 5\% = 100\%$

$72° + 90° + 36° + 144° + 18° = 360°$

4 Use a compass to draw a circle and mark the center of the circle.

5 Then, use a protractor to draw angles of 72°, 90°, 36°, 144°, and 18° in the circle.

6 Finally, label each part of the chart, and choose an appropriate title.

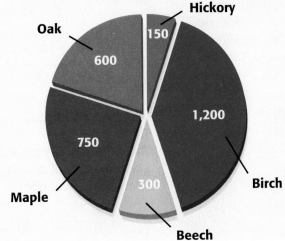

A Community of Wisconsin Hardwood Trees

Line Graphs

Line graphs are most often used to demonstrate continuous change. For example, Mr. Smith's students analyzed the population records for their hometown, Appleton, between 1900 and 2000. Examine the data at right.

Because the year and the population change, they are the *variables*. The population is determined by, or dependent on, the year. Therefore, the population is called the **dependent variable,** and the year is called the **independent variable.** Each set of data is called a **data pair.** To prepare a line graph, you must first organize data pairs into a table like the one at right.

Population of Appleton, 1900–2000	
Year	Population
1900	1,800
1920	2,500
1940	3,200
1960	3,900
1980	4,600
2000	5,300

How to Make a Line Graph

1 Place the independent variable along the horizontal (*x*) axis. Place the dependent variable along the vertical (*y*) axis.

2 Label the *x*-axis "Year" and the *y*-axis "Population." Look at your largest and smallest values for the population. For the *y*-axis, determine a scale that will provide enough space to show these values. You must use the same scale for the entire length of the axis. Next, find an appropriate scale for the *x*-axis.

3 Choose reasonable starting points for each axis.

4 Plot the data pairs as accurately as possible.

5 Choose a title that accurately represents the data.

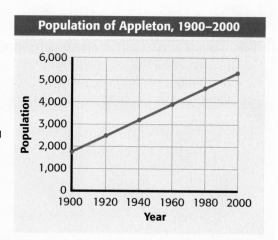

Population of Appleton, 1900–2000

How to Determine Slope

Slope is the ratio of the change in the *y*-value to the change in the *x*-value, or "rise over run."

1 Choose two points on the line graph. For example, the population of Appleton in 2000 was 5,300 people. Therefore, you can define point *a* as (2000, 5,300). In 1900, the population was 1,800 people. You can define point *b* as (1900, 1,800).

2 Find the change in the *y*-value. (*y* at point *a*) − (*y* at point *b*) = 5,300 people − 1,800 people = 3,500 people

3 Find the change in the *x*-value. (*x* at point *a*) − (*x* at point *b*) = 2000 − 1900 = 100 years

4 Calculate the slope of the graph by dividing the change in *y* by the change in *x*.

$$slope = \frac{change\ in\ y}{change\ in\ x}$$

$$slope = \frac{3,500\ people}{100\ years}$$

$$slope = 35\ people\ per\ year$$

In this example, the population in Appleton increased by a fixed amount each year. The graph of these data is a straight line. Therefore, the relationship is **linear.** When the graph of a set of data is not a straight line, the relationship is **nonlinear.**

Using Algebra to Determine Slope

The equation in step 4 may also be arranged to be

$$y = kx$$

where *y* represents the change in the *y*-value, *k* represents the slope, and *x* represents the change in the *x*-value.

$$slope = \frac{change\ in\ y}{change\ in\ x}$$

$$k = \frac{y}{x}$$

$$k \times x = \frac{y \times x}{x}$$

$$kx = y$$

Bar Graphs

Bar graphs are used to demonstrate change that is not continuous. These graphs can be used to indicate trends when the data cover a long period of time. A meteorologist gathered the precipitation data shown here for Hartford, Connecticut, for April 1–15, 1996, and used a bar graph to represent the data.

Precipitation in Hartford, Connecticut April 1–15, 1996			
Date	Precipitation (cm)	Date	Precipitation (cm)
April 1	0.5	April 9	0.25
April 2	1.25	April 10	0.0
April 3	0.0	April 11	1.0
April 4	0.0	April 12	0.0
April 5	0.0	April 13	0.25
April 6	0.0	April 14	0.0
April 7	0.0	April 15	6.50
April 8	1.75		

How to Make a Bar Graph

1 Use an appropriate scale and a reasonable starting point for each axis.

2 Label the axes, and plot the data.

3 Choose a title that accurately represents the data.

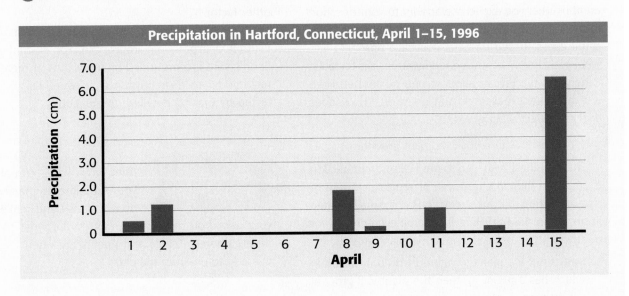

Appendix

Scientific Methods

The ways in which scientists answer questions and solve problems are called **scientific methods.** The same steps are often used by scientists as they look for answers. However, there is more than one way to use these steps. Scientists may use all of the steps or just some of the steps during an investigation. They may even repeat some of the steps. The goal of using scientific methods is to come up with reliable answers and solutions.

Six Steps of Scientific Methods

1 Ask a Question

Good questions come from careful **observations.** You make observations by using your senses to gather information. Sometimes, you may use instruments, such as microscopes and telescopes, to extend the range of your senses. As you observe the natural world, you will discover that you have many more questions than answers. These questions drive investigations.

Questions beginning with *what, why, how,* and *when* are important in focusing an investigation. Here is an example of a question that could lead to an investigation.

Question: How does acid rain affect plant growth?

2 Form a Hypothesis

After you ask a question, you need to form a **hypothesis.** A hypothesis is a clear statement of what you expect the answer to your question to be. Your hypothesis will represent your best "educated guess" based on what you have observed and what you already know. A good hypothesis is testable. Otherwise, the investigation can go no further. Here is a hypothesis based on the question, "How does acid rain affect plant growth?"

Hypothesis: Acid rain slows plant growth.

The hypothesis can lead to predictions. A prediction is what you think the outcome of your experiment or data collection will be. Predictions are usually stated in an if-then format. Here is a sample prediction for the hypothesis that acid rain slows plant growth.

Prediction: If a plant is watered with only acid rain (which has a pH of 4), then the plant will grow at half its normal rate.

3 Test the Hypothesis

After you have formed a hypothesis and made a prediction, your hypothesis should be tested. One way to test a hypothesis is with a controlled experiment. A **controlled experiment** tests only one factor at a time. In an experiment to test the effect of acid rain on plant growth, the **control group** would be watered with normal rain water. The **experimental group** would be watered with acid rain. All of the plants should receive the same amount of sunlight and water each day. The air temperature should be the same for all groups. However, the acidity of the water will be a variable. In fact, any factor that is different from one group to another is a **variable.** If your hypothesis is correct, then the acidity of the water and plant growth are *dependant variables.* The amount a plant grows is dependent on the acidity of the water. However, the amount of water each plant receives and the amount of sunlight each plant receives are *independent variables.* Either of these factors could change without affecting the other factor.

Sometimes, the nature of an investigation makes a controlled experiment impossible. For example, the Earth's core is surrounded by thousands of meters of rock. Under such circumstances, a hypothesis may be tested by making detailed observations.

4 Analyze the Results

After you have completed your experiments, made your observations, and collected your data, you must analyze all the information you have gathered. Tables and graphs are often used in this step to organize the data.

5 **Draw Conclusions** After analyzing your data, you can determine if your results support your hypothesis. If your hypothesis is supported, you (or others) might want to repeat the observations or experiments to verify your results. If your hypothesis is not supported by the data, you may have to check your procedure for errors. You may even have to reject your hypothesis and make a new one. If you cannot draw a conclusion from your results, you may have to try the investigation again or carry out further observations or experiments.

6 **Communicate Results** After any scientific investigation, you should report your results. By preparing a written or oral report, you let others know what you have learned. They may repeat your investigation to see if they get the same results. Your report may even lead to another question and then to another investigation.

Scientific Methods in Action

Scientific methods contain loops in which several steps may be repeated over and over again. In some cases, certain steps are unnecessary. Thus, there is not a "straight line" of steps. For example, sometimes scientists find that testing one hypothesis raises new questions and new hypotheses to be tested. And sometimes, testing the hypothesis leads directly to a conclusion. Furthermore, the steps in scientific methods are not always used in the same order. Follow the steps in the diagram, and see how many different directions scientific methods can take you.

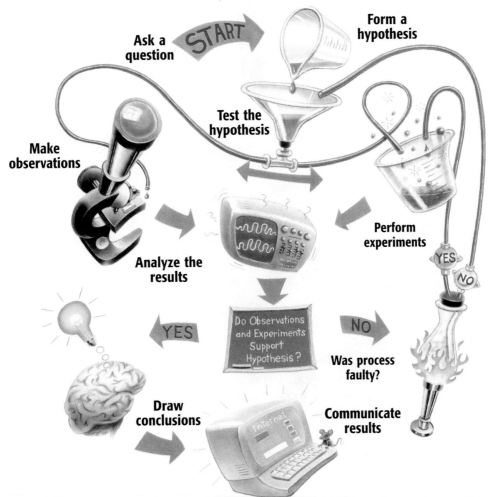

Using the Microscope

Parts of the Compound Light Microscope

- The **ocular lens** magnifies the image 10×.
- The **low-power objective** magnifies the image 10×.
- The **high-power objective** magnifies the image either 40× or 43×.
- The **revolving nosepiece** holds the objectives and can be turned to change from one magnification to the other.
- The **body tube** maintains the correct distance between the ocular lens and objectives.
- The **coarse-adjustment knob** moves the body tube up and down to allow focusing of the image.

- The **stage** supports a slide.
- **Stage clips** hold the slide in place for viewing.
- The **diaphragm** controls the amount of light coming through the stage.
- The light source provides a **light** for viewing the slide.
- The **arm** supports the body tube.
- The **base** supports the microscope.

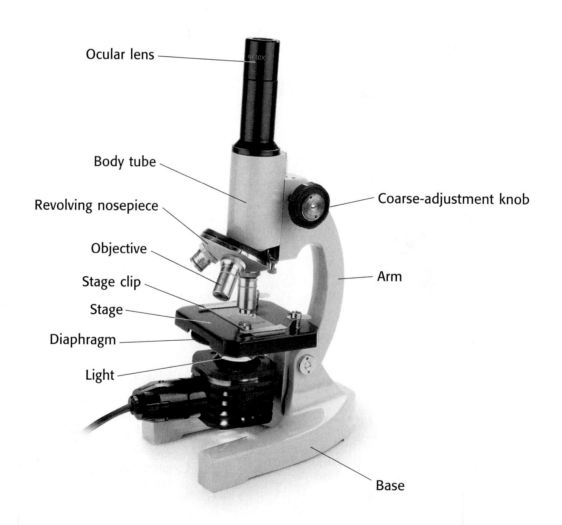

Ocular lens

Body tube

Coarse-adjustment knob

Revolving nosepiece

Objective

Arm

Stage clip

Stage

Diaphragm

Light

Base

Proper Use of the Compound Light Microscope

1. Use both hands to carry the microscope to your lab table. Place one hand beneath the base, and use the other hand to hold the arm of the microscope. Hold the microscope close to your body while carrying it to your lab table.

2. Place the microscope on the lab table at least 5 cm from the edge of the table.

3. Check to see what type of light source is used by your microscope. If the microscope has a lamp, plug it in and make sure that the cord is out of the way. If the microscope has a mirror, adjust the mirror to reflect light through the hole in the stage. **Caution:** If your microscope has a mirror, do not use direct sunlight as a light source. Direct sunlight can damage your eyes.

4. Always begin work with the low-power objective in line with the body tube. Adjust the revolving nosepiece.

5. Place a prepared slide over the hole in the stage. Secure the slide with the stage clips.

6. Look through the ocular lens. Move the diaphragm to adjust the amount of light coming through the stage.

7. Look at the stage from eye level. Slowly turn the coarse adjustment to lower the objective until the objective almost touches the slide. Do not allow the objective to touch the slide.

8. Look through the ocular lens. Turn the coarse adjustment to raise the low-power objective until the image is in focus. Always focus by raising the objective away from the slide. Never focus the objective downward. Use the fine adjustment to sharpen the focus. Keep both eyes open while viewing a slide.

9. Make sure that the image is exactly in the center of your field of vision. Then, switch to the high-power objective. Focus the image by using only the fine adjustment. Never use the coarse adjustment at high power.

10. When you are finished using the microscope, remove the slide. Clean the ocular lens and objectives with lens paper. Return the microscope to its storage area. Remember to use both hands when carrying the microscope.

Making a Wet Mount

1. Use lens paper to clean a glass slide and a coverslip.

2. Place the specimen that you wish to observe in the center of the slide.

3. Using a medicine dropper, place one drop of water on the specimen.

4. Hold the coverslip at the edge of the water and at a 45° angle to the slide. Make sure that the water runs along the edge of the coverslip.

5. Lower the coverslip slowly to avoid trapping air bubbles.

6. Water might evaporate from the slide as you work. Add more water to keep the specimen fresh. Place the tip of the medicine dropper next to the edge of the coverslip. Add a drop of water. (You can also use this method to add stain or solutions to a wet mount.) Remove excess water from the slide by using the corner of a paper towel as a blotter. Do not lift the coverslip to add or remove water.

Properties of Common Minerals

Mineral	Color	Luster	Streak	Hardness
Silicate Minerals				
Beryl	deep green, pink, white, bluish green, or yellow	vitreous	white	7.5–8
Chlorite	green	vitreous to pearly	pale green	2–2.5
Garnet	green, red, brown, black	vitreous	white	6.5–7.5
Hornblende	dark green, brown, or black	vitreous	none	5–6
Muscovite	colorless, silvery white, or brown	vitreous or pearly	white	2–2.5
Olivine	olive green, yellow	vitreous	white or none	6.5–7
Orthoclase	colorless, white, pink, or other colors	vitreous	white or none	6
Plagioclase	colorless, white, yellow, pink, green	vitreous	white	6
Quartz	colorless or white; any color when not pure	vitreous or waxy	white or none	7
Native Elements				
Copper	copper-red	metallic	copper-red	2.5–3
Diamond	pale yellow or colorless	adamantine	none	10
Graphite	black to gray	submetallic	black	1–2
Carbonates				
Aragonite	colorless, white, or pale yellow	vitreous	white	3.5–4
Calcite	colorless or white to tan	vitreous	white	3
Halides				
Fluorite	light green, yellow, purple, bluish green, or other colors	vitreous	none	4
Halite	white	vitreous	white	2.0–2.5
Oxides				
Hematite	reddish brown to black	metallic to earthy	dark red to red-brown	5.6–6.5
Magnetite	iron-black	metallic	black	5.5–6.5
Sulfates				
Anhydrite	colorless, bluish, or violet	vitreous to pearly	white	3–3.5
Gypsum	white, pink, gray, or colorless	vitreous, pearly, or silky	white	2.0
Sulfides				
Galena	lead-gray	metallic	lead-gray to black	2.5–2.8
Pyrite	brassy yellow	metallic	greenish, brownish, or black	6–6.5

Silicate Minerals / *Nonsilicate Minerals* / *Appendix*

Density (g/cm³)	Cleavage, Fracture, Special Properties	Common Uses
2.6–2.8	1 cleavage direction; irregular fracture; some varieties fluoresce in ultraviolet light	gemstones, ore of the metal beryllium
2.6–3.3	1 cleavage direction; irregular fracture	
4.2	no cleavage; conchoidal to splintery fracture	gemstones, abrasives
3.0–3.4	2 cleavage directions; hackly to splintery fracture	
2.7–3	1 cleavage direction; irregular fracture	electrical insulation, wallpaper, fireproofing material, lubricant
3.2–3.3	no cleavage; conchoidal fracture	gemstones, casting
2.6	2 cleavage directions; irregular fracture	porcelain
2.6–2.7	2 cleavage directions; irregular fracture	ceramics
2.6	no cleavage; conchoidal fracture	gemstones, concrete, glass, porcelain, sandpaper, lenses
8.9	no cleavage; hackly fracture	wiring, brass, bronze, coins
3.5	4 cleavage directions; irregular to conchoidal fracture	gemstones, drilling
2.3	1 cleavage direction; irregular fracture	pencils, paints, lubricants, batteries
2.95	2 cleavage directions; irregular fracture; reacts with hydrochloric acid	no important industrial uses
2.7	3 cleavage directions; irregular fracture; reacts with weak acid; double refraction	cements, soil conditioner, whitewash, construction materials
3.0–3.3	4 cleavage directions; irregular fracture; some varieties fluoresce	hydrofluoric acid, steel, glass, fiberglass, pottery, enamel
2.1–2.2	3 cleavage directions; splintery to conchoidal fracture; salty taste	tanning hides, salting icy roads, food preservation
5.2–5.3	no cleavage; splintery fracture; magnetic when heated	iron ore for steel, pigments
5.2	no cleavage; splintery fracture; magnetic	iron ore
3.0	3 cleavage directions; conchoidal to splintery fracture	soil conditioner, sulfuric acid
2.3	3 cleavage directions; conchoidal to splintery fracture	plaster of Paris, wallboard, soil conditioner
7.4–7.6	3 cleavage directions; irregular fracture	batteries, paints
5	no cleavage; conchoidal to splintery fracture	sulfuric acid

SI Measurement

The International System of Units, or SI, is the standard system of measurement used by many scientists. Using the same standards of measurement makes it easier for scientists to communicate with one another.

SI works by combining prefixes and base units. Each base unit can be used with different prefixes to define smaller and larger quantities. The table below lists common SI prefixes.

SI Prefixes

Prefix	Symbol	Factor	Example
kilo-	k	1,000	kilogram, 1 kg = 1,000 g
hecto-	h	100	hectoliter, 1 hL = 100 L
deka-	da	10	dekameter, 1 dam = 10 m
		1	meter, liter, gram
deci-	d	0.1	decigram, 1 dg = 0.1 g
centi-	c	0.01	centimeter, 1 cm = 0.01 m
milli-	m	0.001	milliliter, 1 mL = 0.001 L
micro-	μ	0.000 001	micrometer, 1 μm = 0.000 001 m

SI Conversion Table

SI units	From SI to English	From English to SI
Length		
kilometer (km) = 1,000 m	1 km = 0.621 mi	1 mi = 1.609 km
meter (m) = 100 cm	1 m = 3.281 ft	1 ft = 0.305 m
centimeter (cm) = 0.01 m	1 cm = 0.394 in.	1 in. = 2.540 cm
millimeter (mm) = 0.001 m	1 mm = 0.039 in.	
micrometer (μm) = 0.000 001 m		
nanometer (nm) = 0.000 000 001 m		
Area		
square kilometer (km^2) = 100 hectares	1 km^2 = 0.386 mi^2	1 mi^2 = 2.590 km^2
hectare (ha) = 10,000 m^2	1 ha = 2.471 acres	1 acre = 0.405 ha
square meter (m^2) = 10,000 cm^2	1 m^2 = 10.764 ft^2	1 ft^2 = 0.093 m^2
square centimeter (cm^2) = 100 mm^2	1 cm^2 = 0.155 in.^{2}	1 in.^{2} = 6.452 cm^2
Volume		
liter (L) = 1,000 mL = 1 dm^3	1 L = 1.057 fl qt	1 fl qt = 0.946 L
milliliter (mL) = 0.001 L = 1 cm^3	1 mL = 0.034 fl oz	1 fl oz = 29.574 mL
microliter (μL) = 0.000 001 L		
Mass		
kilogram (kg) = 1,000 g	1 kg = 2.205 lb	1 lb = 0.454 kg
gram (g) = 1,000 mg	1 g = 0.035 oz	1 oz = 28.350 g
milligram (mg) = 0.001 g		
microgram (μg) = 0.000 001 g		

Measuring Skills

Using a Graduated Cylinder

When using a graduated cylinder to measure volume, keep the following procedures in mind:

1. Place the cylinder on a flat, level surface before measuring liquid.

2. Move your head so that your eye is level with the surface of the liquid.

3. Read the mark closest to the liquid level. On glass graduated cylinders, read the mark closest to the center of the curve in the liquid's surface.

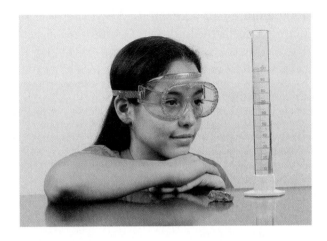

Using a Meterstick or Metric Ruler

When using a meterstick or metric ruler to measure length, keep the following procedures in mind:

1. Place the ruler firmly against the object that you are measuring.

2. Align one edge of the object exactly with the 0 end of the ruler.

3. Look at the other edge of the object to see which of the marks on the ruler is closest to that edge. (Note: Each small slash between the centimeters represents a millimeter, which is one-tenth of a centimeter.)

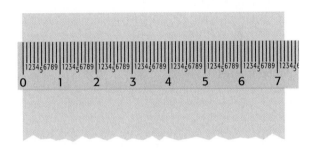

Using a Triple-Beam Balance

When using a triple-beam balance to measure mass, keep the following procedures in mind:

1. Make sure the balance is on a level surface.

2. Place all of the countermasses at 0. Adjust the balancing knob until the pointer rests at 0.

3. Place the object you wish to measure on the pan. **Caution:** Do not place hot objects or chemicals directly on the balance pan.

4. Move the largest countermass along the beam to the right until it is at the last notch that does not tip the balance. Follow the same procedure with the next-largest countermass. Then, move the smallest countermass until the pointer rests at 0.

5. Add the readings from the three beams together to determine the mass of the object.

6. When determining the mass of crystals or powders, first find the mass of a piece of filter paper. Then, add the crystals or powder to the paper, and remeasure. The actual mass of the crystals or powder is the total mass minus the mass of the paper. When finding the mass of liquids, first find the mass of the empty container. Then, find the combined mass of the liquid and container. The mass of the liquid is the total mass minus the mass of the container.

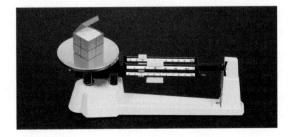

Temperature Scales

Temperature can be expressed by using three different scales: Fahrenheit, Celsius, and Kelvin. The SI unit for temperature is the kelvin (K).

Although 0 K is much colder than 0°C, a change of 1 K is equal to a change of 1°C.

Three Temperature Scales

	Fahrenheit	Celsius	Kelvin
Water boils	212°	100°	373
Body temperature	98.6°	37°	310
Room temperature	68°	20°	293
Water freezes	32°	0°	273

Temperature Conversions Table

To convert	Use this equation:	Example
Celsius to Fahrenheit °C → °F	$°F = \left(\dfrac{9}{5} \times °C \right) + 32$	Convert 45°C to °F. $°F = \left(\dfrac{9}{5} \times 45°C \right) + 32 = 113°F$
Fahrenheit to Celsius °F → °C	$°C = \dfrac{5}{9} \times (°F - 32)$	Convert 68°F to °C. $°C = \dfrac{5}{9} \times (68°F - 32) = 20°C$
Celsius to Kelvin °C → K	$K = °C + 273$	Convert 45°C to K. $K = 45°C + 273 = 318 \text{ K}$
Kelvin to Celsius K → °C	$°C = K - 273$	Convert 32 K to °C. $°C = 32K - 273 = -241°C$

Glossary

A

abiotic describes the nonliving part of the environment, including water, rocks, light, and temperature (486) **FCAT** *VOCAB*

abrasion the grinding and wearing away of rock surfaces through the mechanical action of other rock or sand particles (227)

abyssal plain a large, flat, almost level area of the deep-ocean basin (166)

acceleration the rate at which velocity changes over time; an object accelerates if its speed, direction, or both change (553) **FCAT** *VOCAB*

acid precipitation rain, sleet, or snow that contains a high concentration of acids (95, 229, 622)

air mass a large body of air throughout which temperature and moisture content are similar (128)

air pollution the contamination of the atmosphere by the introduction of pollutants from human and natural sources (92)

air pressure the measure of the force with which air molecules push on a surface (77)

amplitude the maximum distance that the particles of a wave's medium vibrate from their rest position (586) **FCAT** *VOCAB*

anemometer an instrument used to measure wind speed (143)

angiosperm a flowering plant that produces seeds within a fruit (456)

Animalia a kingdom made up of complex, multicellular organisms that lack cell walls, can usually move around, and quickly respond to their environment (442)

anticyclone the rotation of air around a high-pressure center in the direction opposite to Earth's rotation (132)

Archaea in a modern taxonomic system, a domain made up of prokaryotes (most of which are known to live in extreme environments) that are distinguished from other prokaryotes by differences in their genetics and in the makeup of their cell wall; this domain aligns with the traditional kingdom Archaebacteria (439)

area a measure of the size of a surface or a region (23)

asexual reproduction reproduction that does not involve the union of sex cells and in which one parent produces offspring that are genetically identical to the parent (382) **FCAT** *VOCAB*

asteroid a small, rocky object that orbits the sun; most asteroids are located in a band between the orbits of Mars and Jupiter (340)

asthenosphere the soft layer of the mantle on which the tectonic plates move (262)

atmosphere a mixture of gases that surrounds a planet or moon (76)

atom the smallest unit of an element that maintains the properties of that element (518)

ATP adenosine triphosphate, a molecule that acts as the main energy source for cell processes (388)

B

Bacteria in a modern taxonomic system, a domain made up of prokaryotes that usually have a cell wall and that usually reproduce by cell division; this domain aligns with the traditional kingdom Eubacteria (439)

barometer an instrument that measures atmospheric pressure (143)

bedrock the layer of rock beneath soil (236)

benthic environment the region near the bottom of a pond, lake, or ocean (171)

benthos organisms that live at the bottom of oceans or bodies of fresh water (170)

biomass plant material, manure, or any other organic matter that is used as an energy source (629)

biome a large region characterized by a specific type of climate and certain types of plant and animal communities (118)

biosphere the part of Earth where life exists (487)

biotic describes living factors in the environment (486) **FCAT** *VOCAB*

C

caldera a large, circular depression that forms when the magma chamber below a volcano partially empties and causes the ground above to sink (308)

carbohydrate a class of energy-giving nutrients that includes sugars, starches, and fiber; contains carbon, hydrogen, and oxygen (387)

carnivore an organism that eats animals (491)

cell in biology, the smallest unit that can perform all life processes; cells are covered by a membrane and contain DNA and cytoplasm (380, 400)

change of state the change of a substance from one physical state to another (527)

chemical change a change that occurs when one or more substances change into entirely new substances with different properties (536)

chemical energy the energy released when a chemical compound reacts to produce new compounds (626)

chemical property a property of matter that describes a substance's ability to participate in chemical reactions (530)

chemical weathering the process by which rocks break down as a result of chemical reactions (229) *FCAT* *VOCAB*

classification the division of organisms into groups, or classes, based on specific characteristics (432)

climate the average weather conditions in an area over a long period of time (112)

cloud a collection of small water droplets or ice crystals suspended in the air, which forms when the air is cooled and condensation occurs (124)

coal a fossil fuel that forms underground from partially decomposed plant material (618)

comet a small body of ice, rock, and cosmic dust that follows an elliptical orbit around the sun and that gives off gas and dust in the form of a tail as it passes close to the sun (339)

community all of the populations of species that live in the same habitat and interact with each other (487)

composition the chemical makeup of a rock; describes either the minerals or other materials in the rock (201)

compression stress that occurs when forces act to squeeze an object (276)

condensation the change of state from a gas to a liquid (123, 497)

conduction the transfer of energy as heat through a material (83) *FCAT* *VOCAB*

consumer an organism that eats other organisms or organic matter (385, 490)

continental drift the hypothesis that states that the continents once formed a single landmass, broke up, and drifted to their present locations (268)

continental rise the gently sloping section of the continental margin located between the continental slope and the abyssal plain (166)

continental shelf the gently sloping section of the continental margin located between the shoreline and the continental slope (166)

continental slope the steeply inclined section of the continental margin located between the continental rise and the continental shelf (166)

convection the transfer of thermal energy by the circulation or movement of a liquid or gas (83) *FCAT* *VOCAB*

core the central part of the Earth below the mantle (261)

Coriolis effect the curving of the path of a moving object from an otherwise straight path due to the Earth's rotation (88)

crater a bowl-shaped depression that forms on the surface of an object when a falling body strikes the object's surface or when an explosion occurs (308)

crest the highest point of a wave (584) *FCAT* *VOCAB*

crust the thin and solid outermost layer of the Earth above the mantle (260) *FCAT* *VOCAB*

cyclone an area in the atmosphere that has lower pressure than the surrounding areas and has winds that spiral toward the center (132)

D

data any pieces of information acquired through observation or experimentation (15)

day the time required for Earth to rotate once on its axis (356)

decomposer an organism that gets energy by breaking down the remains of dead organisms or animal wastes and consuming or absorbing the nutrients (385)

deformation the bending, tilting, and breaking of Earth's crust; the change in the shape of rock in response to stress (285)

density the ratio of the mass of a substance to the volume of the substance (517)

deposition the process in which material is laid down (210) *FCAT VOCAB*

desalination a process of removing salt from ocean water (179)

dichotomous key an aid that is used to identify organisms and that consists of the answers to a series of questions (436)

differential weathering the process by which softer, less weather resistant rocks wear away at a faster rate than harder, more weather resistant rocks do (232)

divergent boundary the boundary between two tectonic plates that are moving away from each other (273)

E

eclipse an event in which the shadow of one celestial body falls on another (362)

ecology the study of the interactions of living organisms with one another and with their environment (486)

ecosystem a community of organisms and their abiotic, or nonliving, environment (487) *FCAT VOCAB*

elastic rebound the sudden return of elastically deformed rock to its undeformed shape (285)

electron a subatomic particle that has a negative charge (519) *FCAT VOCAB*

element a substance that cannot be separated or broken down into simpler substances by chemical means (518)

elevation the height of an object above sea level (116)

energy the capacity to do work (578)

energy conversion a change from one form of energy to another (590)

energy pyramid a triangular diagram that shows an ecosystem's loss of energy, which results as energy passes through the ecosystem's food chain (493)

engineering the application of science and mathematics to solve real-life problems (57)

equinox the moment when the sun appears to cross the celestial equator (358)

erosion the process by which wind, water, ice, or gravity transports soil and sediment from one location to another (210, 246) *FCAT VOCAB*

Eukarya in a modern taxonomic system, a domain made up of all eukaryotes; this domain aligns with the traditional kingdoms Protista, Fungi, Plantae, and Animalia (440)

eukaryote an organism made up of cells that have a nucleus enclosed by a membrane; eukaryotes include protists, animals, plants, and fungi but not archaea or bacteria (401)

evaporation the change of state from a liquid to a gas (497)

F

fault a break in a body of rock along which one block slides relative to another (278)

first aid emergency medical care for someone who has been hurt or who is sick (30)

folding the bending of rock layers due to stress (277)

food chain the pathway of energy transfer through various stages as a result of the feeding patterns of a series of organisms (493)

food web a diagram that shows the feeding relationships between organisms in an ecosystem (493)

force a push or a pull exerted on an object in order to change the motion of the object; force has size and direction (556)

fossil fuel a nonrenewable energy resource formed from the remains of organisms that lived long ago (616) *FCAT VOCAB*

frequency the number of waves produced in a given amount of time (588) *FCAT VOCAB*

friction a force that opposes motion between two surfaces that are in contact (560, 593)

front the boundary between air masses of different densities and usually different temperatures (130)

function the special, normal, or proper activity of an organ or part (410)

Fungi a kingdom made up of nongreen, eukaryotic organisms that have no means of movement, reproduce by using spores, and get food by breaking down substances in their surroundings and absorbing the nutrients (440)

G

gas a form of matter that does not have a definite volume or shape (527)

gasohol a mixture of gasoline and alcohol that is used as a fuel (629)

geothermal energy the energy produced by heat within Earth (630)

global warming a gradual increase in average global temperature (85)

globular cluster a tight group of stars that looks like a ball and contains up to 1 million stars (333)

gravity a force of attraction between objects that is due to their masses (563)

greenhouse effect the warming of the surface and lower atmosphere of Earth that occurs when water vapor, carbon dioxide, and other gases absorb and reradiate thermal energy (84)

gymnosperm a woody, vascular seed plant whose seeds are not enclosed by an ovary or fruit (456)

H

herbivore an organism that eats only plants (491)

heredity the passing of genetic traits from parent to offspring (382)

homeostasis the maintenance of a constant internal state in a changing environment (381)

hot spot a volcanically active area of Earth's surface, commonly far from a tectonic plate boundary (314)

humidity the amount of water vapor in the air (121)

humus dark, organic material formed in soil from the decayed remains of plants and animals (238)

hurricane a severe storm that develops over tropical oceans and whose strong winds of more than 120 km/h spiral in toward the intensely low-pressure storm center (137)

hydroelectric energy electrical energy produced by the flow of water (628)

hypothesis a testable idea or explanation that leads to scientific investigation (14)

I

ion a charged particle that forms when an atom or group of atoms gains or loses one or more electrons (522)

K

kinetic energy the energy of an object that is due to the object's motion (579)

L

latitude the distance north or south from the equator; expressed in degrees (113)

law a descriptive statement or equation that reliably predicts events under certain conditions (53)

law of conservation of energy the law that states that energy cannot be created or destroyed but can be changed from one form to another (594) **FCAT** VOCAB

leaching the removal of substances that can be dissolved from rock, ore, or layers of soil due to the passing of water (238)

lightning an electric discharge that takes place between two oppositely charged surfaces, such as between a cloud and the ground, between two clouds, or between two parts of the same cloud (135)

light-year the distance that light travels in one year; about 9.46 trillion kilometers (330)

lipid a type of biochemical that does not dissolve in water; fats and steroids are lipids (388)

liquid the state of matter that has a definite volume but not a definite shape (526)

lithosphere the solid, outer layer of Earth that consists of the crust and the rigid upper part of the mantle (262)

M

magma chamber the body of molten rock that feeds a volcano (302)

mantle the layer of rock between the Earth's crust and core (261)

mass a measure of the amount of matter in an object (23, 514) **FCAT** VOCAB

matter anything that has mass and takes up space (514)

mechanical energy the amount of work an object can do because of the object's kinetic and potential energies (580)

mechanical weathering the process by which rocks break down into smaller pieces by physical means (226)

mesosphere the layer of the atmosphere between the stratosphere and the thermosphere and in which temperature decreases as altitude increases (79); *also* the strong, lower part of the mantle between the asthenosphere and the outer core (263)

metabolism the sum of all chemical processes that occur in an organism (382)

meteor a bright streak of light that results when a meteoroid burns up in Earth's atmosphere (340)

meteorite a meteoroid that reaches the Earth's surface without burning up completely (340)

meteoroid a relatively small, rocky body that travels through space (340)

meter the basic unit of length in the SI (symbol, m) (23)

mid-ocean ridge a long, undersea mountain chain that forms along the floor of the major oceans (167)

mineral a naturally formed, inorganic solid that has a definite chemical structure (200)

model a pattern, plan, representation, or description designed to show the structure or workings of an object, system, or concept (50)

motion an object's change in position relative to a reference point (550)

N

natural gas a mixture of gaseous hydrocarbons located under the surface of the Earth, often near petroleum deposits; used as a fuel (617)

natural resource any natural material that is used by humans, such as water, petroleum, minerals, forests, and animals (612)

neap tide a tide of minimum range that occurs during the first and third quarters of the moon (366) *FCAT VOCAB*

nebula a large cloud of gas and dust in interstellar space; a region in space where stars are born (331)

nekton all organisms that swim actively in open water, independent of currents (170)

net force the combination of all of the forces acting on an object (557)

neutron a subatomic particle that has no charge and that is located in the nucleus of an atom (519) *FCAT VOCAB*

newton the SI unit for force (symbol, N) (556)

nonpoint-source pollution pollution that comes from many sources rather than from a single, specific site (182)

nonrenewable resource a resource that forms at a rate that is much slower than the rate at which the resource is consumed (496, 613)

nonvascular plant a plant that lacks specialized conducting tissues and true roots, stems, and leaves (456)

nuclear energy the energy released by a fission or fusion reaction; the binding energy of the atomic nucleus (625)

nucleic acid a molecule made up of subunits called *nucleotides* (389)

nucleus in physical science, an atom's central region, which is made up of protons and neutrons (520) *FCAT VOCAB*

O

observation the process of obtaining information by using the senses (13)

ocean basin the area of Earth that is covered by oceans (167) *FCAT VOCAB*

omnivore an organism that eats both plants and animals (491)

open cluster a group of stars that are close together relative to surrounding stars (333)

orbit the path that a body follows as it travels around another body in space (352)

organ a collection of tissues that carry out a specialized function of the body (415)

organism a living thing; anything that can carry out life processes independently (400)

organ system a group of organs that work together to perform body functions (416)

P

parent rock a rock formation that is the source of soil (236)

pelagic environment in the ocean, the zone near the surface or at middle depths, beyond the sublittoral zone and above the abyssal zone (174)

petroleum a liquid mixture of complex hydrocarbon compounds; used widely as a fuel source (617)

phase the change in the sunlit area of one celestial body as seen from another celestial body (361)

phospholipid a lipid that contains phosphorus and that is a structural component in cell membranes (388)

physical change a change of matter from one form to another without a change in chemical properties (536)

physical property a characteristic of a substance that does not involve a chemical change, such as density, color, or hardness (530)

plankton the mass of mostly microscopic organisms that float or drift freely in freshwater and marine environments (170)

Plantae a kingdom made up of complex, multicellular organisms that are usually green, have cell walls made of cellulose, cannot move around, and use the sun's energy to make sugar by photosynthesis (441)

plate tectonics the theory that explains how large pieces of the Earth's outermost layer, called *tectonic plates,* move and change shape (272) *FCAT VOCAB*

platform an area of a continent that is composed of flat-lying layers of sedimentary rock (213)

point-source pollution pollution that comes from a specific site (183)

polar easterlies prevailing winds that blow from east to west between 60° and 90° latitude in both hemispheres (88)

population a group of organisms of the same species that live in a specific geographical area (487)

potential energy the energy that an object has because of the position, shape, or condition of the object (579) *FCAT VOCAB*

precipitation any form of water that falls to Earth's surface from the clouds (126, 497)

prevailing winds winds that blow mainly from one direction during a given period (115)

producer an organism that can make its own food by using energy from its surroundings (385, 490)

prokaryote a single-celled organism that does not have a nucleus or membrane-bound organelles; examples are archaea and bacteria (401)

protein a molecule that is made up of amino acids and that is needed to build and repair body structures and to regulate processes in the body (386)

Protista a kingdom of mostly one-celled eukaryotic organisms that are different from plants, animals, archaea, bacteria, and fungi (440)

proton a subatomic particle that has a positive charge and that is located in the nucleus of an atom; the number of protons in the nucleus is the atomic number, which determines the identity of an element (519) *FCAT VOCAB*

P wave a seismic wave that causes particles of rock to move in a back-and-forth direction (288)

R

radiation the transfer of energy as electromagnetic waves (82, 598) *FCAT VOCAB*

recycling the process of recovering valuable or useful materials from waste or scrap (615)

relative humidity the ratio of the amount of water vapor in the air to the amount of water vapor needed to reach saturation at a given temperature (121)

renewable resource a natural resource that can be replaced at the same rate at which the resource is consumed (496, 613)

revolution the motion of a body that travels around another body in space; one complete trip along an orbit (352)

rift valley a long, narrow valley that forms as tectonic plates separate (167)

rift zone an area of deep cracks that forms between two tectonic plates that are pulling away from each other (312)

rock a naturally occurring solid mixture of one or more minerals or organic matter (200)

rock cycle the series of processes in which rock forms, changes from one type to another, is destroyed, and forms again by geologic processes (206)

rotation the spin of a body on its axis (352)

S

salinity a measure of the amount of dissolved salts in a given amount of liquid (158)

salinization the accumulation of salts in soil (247)

science the knowledge obtained by observing natural events and conditions in order to discover facts and formulate laws or principles that can be verified or tested (6)

scientific literacy the understanding of the methods of scientific inquiry, the scope of scientific knowledge, and the role of science in society (47)

scientific methods a series of steps followed to solve problems (12)

sea-floor spreading the process by which new oceanic lithosphere (sea floor) forms as magma rises to Earth's surface and solidifies at a mid-ocean ridge (270)

seamount a submerged mountain on the ocean floor that is at least 1,000 m high and that has a volcanic origin (167)

Glossary

seismic wave a wave of energy that travels through the Earth and away from an earthquake in all directions (288)

seismology the study of earthquakes (284)

sexual reproduction reproduction in which the sex cells from two parents unite to produce offspring that share traits from both parents (382) **FCAT** *VOCAB*

skepticism a habit of mind in which a person questions the validity of accepted ideas (43)

smog photochemical haze that forms when sunlight acts on industrial pollutants and burning fuels (622)

soil a loose mixture of rock fragments, organic material, water, and air that can support the growth of vegetation (236)

soil conservation a method to maintain the fertility of the soil by protecting the soil from erosion and nutrient loss (244)

soil structure the arrangement of soil particles (237)

soil texture the soil quality that is based on the proportions of soil particles (237)

solar energy the energy received by Earth from the sun in the form of radiation (626)

solid the state of matter in which the volume and shape of a substance are fixed (525)

solstice the point at which the sun is as far north or as far south of the equator as possible (359)

spectroscope an instrument that splits white light into a band of colors (328) **FCAT** *VOCAB*

speed the distance traveled divided by the time interval during which the motion occurred (551) **FCAT** *VOCAB*

spring tide a tide of increased range that occurs two times a month, at the new and full moons (366) **FCAT** *VOCAB*

states of matter the physical forms of matter, which include solid, liquid, and gas (524)

stimulus anything that causes a reaction or change in an organism or any part of an organism (381)

stratosphere the layer of the atmosphere that is above the troposphere and in which temperature increases as altitude increases (79)

structure the arrangement of parts in an organism (410)

subsidence the sinking of regions of the Earth's crust to lower elevations (282)

surface current a horizontal movement of ocean water that is caused by wind and that occurs at or near the ocean's surface (117)

S wave a seismic wave that causes particles of rock to move in a side-to-side direction (288)

T

technology the application of science for practical purposes; the use of tools, machines, materials, and processes to meet human needs (56)

tectonic plate a block of lithosphere that consists of the crust and the rigid, outermost part of the mantle (264)

temperature a measure of how hot (or cold) something is; specifically, a measure of the average kinetic energy of the particles in an object (24)

tension stress that occurs when forces act to stretch an object (276)

texture the quality of a rock that is based on the sizes, shapes, and positions of the rock's grains (201)

theory a system of ideas that explains many related observations and is supported by a large body of evidence acquired through scientific investigation (53)

thermal energy the kinetic energy of a substance's atoms (580) **FCAT** *VOCAB*

thermometer an instrument that measures and indicates temperature (143)

thermosphere the uppermost layer of the atmosphere, in which temperature increases as altitude increases (80)

thunder the sound caused by the rapid expansion of air along an electrical strike (135)

thunderstorm a usually brief, heavy storm that consists of rain, strong winds, lightning, and thunder (134)

tidal range the difference in levels of ocean water at high tide and low tide (366)

tide the periodic rise and fall of the water level in the oceans and other large bodies of water (364)

tissue a group of similar cells that perform a common function (415)

tornado a destructive, rotating column of air that has very high wind speeds and that may be visible as a funnel-shaped cloud (136)

trade winds prevailing winds that blow from east to west from 30° latitude to the equator in both hemispheres (88)

transform boundary the boundary between tectonic plates that are sliding past each other horizontally (273)

tropism growth of all or part of an organism in response to an external stimulus, such as light (457) **FCAT** *VOCAB*

troposphere the lowest layer of the atmosphere, in which temperature decreases at a constant rate as altitude increases (79)

trough the lowest point of a wave (584) **FCAT** *VOCAB*

U

uplift the rising of regions of the Earth's crust to higher elevations (282)

V

vascular plant a plant that has specialized tissues that conduct materials from one part of the plant to another (456)

velocity the speed of an object in a particular direction (552) **FCAT** *VOCAB*

vent an opening at the surface of the Earth through which volcanic material passes (302)

volcano a vent or fissure in the Earth's surface through which magma and gases are expelled (300)

volume a measure of the size of a body or region in three-dimensional space (24, 514)

W

wave a periodic disturbance in a solid, liquid, or gas as energy is transmitted through a medium (582)

wavelength the distance from any point on a wave to an identical point on the next wave (587) **FCAT** *VOCAB*

weather the short-term state of the atmosphere, including temperature, humidity, precipitation, wind, and visibility (112)

weathering the natural process by which atmospheric and environmental agents, such as wind, rain, and temperature changes, disintegrate and decompose rocks (210, 226)

weight a measure of the gravitational force exerted on an object; its value can change with the location of the object in the universe (515)

westerlies prevailing winds that blow from west to east between 30° and 60° latitude in both hemispheres (88)

wind the movement of air caused by differences in air pressure (86)

wind power the use of a windmill to drive an electric generator (627)

Spanish Glossary

A

abiotic/abiótico término que describe la parte sin vida del ambiente, incluyendo el agua, las rocas, la luz y la temperatura (486) *FCAT VOCAB*

abrasion/abrasión proceso por el cual las superficies de las rocas se muelen o desgastan por medio de la acción mecánica de otras rocas y partículas de arena (227)

abyssal plain/llanura abisal un área amplia, llana y casi plana de la cuenca oceánica profunda (166)

acceleration/aceleración la tasa a la que la velocidad cambia con el tiempo; un objeto acelera si su rapidez cambia, si su dirección cambia, o si tanto su rapidez como su dirección cambian (553) *FCAT VOCAB*

acid precipitation/precipitación ácida lluvia, agua-nieve o nieve que contiene una alta concentración de ácidos (95, 229, 622)

air mass/masa de aire un gran volumen de aire, cuya temperatura y cuyo contenido de humedad son similares en toda su extensión (128)

air pollution/contaminación del aire la contaminación de la atmósfera debido a la introducción de contaminantes provenientes de fuentes humanas y naturales (92)

air pressure/presión del aire la medida de la fuerza con la que las moléculas del aire empujan contra una superficie (77)

amplitude/amplitud la distancia máxima a la que vibran las partículas del medio de una onda a partir de su posición de reposo (586) *FCAT VOCAB*

anemometer/anemómetro un instrumento que se usa para medir la rapidez del viento (143)

angiosperm/angiosperma una planta que da flores y que produce semillas dentro de la fruta (456)

Animalia/Animalia un reino formado por organismos pluricelulares complejos que no tienen pared celular, normalmente son capaces de moverse y reaccionan rápidamente a su ambiente (442)

anticyclone/anticiclón la rotación del aire alrededor de un centro de alta presión en dirección opuesta a la rotación de la Tierra (132)

Archaea/Archaea en un sistema taxonómico moderno, un dominio compuesto por procariotes (la mayoría de los cuales viven en ambientes extremos) que se distinguen de otros procariotes por diferencias genéticas y por la diferente composición de su pared celular; este dominio coincide con el reino tradicional Archaebacteria (439)

area/área una medida del tamaño de una superficie o región (23)

asexual reproduction/reproducción asexual reproducción que no involucra la unión de células sexuales, en la que un solo progenitor produce descendencia que es genéticamente igual al progenitor (382) *FCAT VOCAB*

asteroid/asteroide un objeto pequeño y rocoso que se encuentra en órbita alrededor del Sol; la mayoría de los asteroides se ubican en una banda entre las órbitas de Marte y Júpiter (340)

asthenosphere/astenosfera la capa blanda del manto sobre la que se mueven las placas tectónicas (262)

atmosphere/atmósfera una mezcla de gases que rodea un planeta o una luna (76)

atom/átomo la unidad más pequeña de un elemento que conserva las propiedades de ese elemento (518)

ATP/ATP adenosín trifosfato, una molécula orgánica que funciona como la fuente principal de energía para los procesos celulares (388)

B

Bacteria/Bacteria en un sistema taxonómico moderno, un dominio compuesto por procariotes que normalmente tienen pared celular y se reproducen por división celular; este dominio coincide con el reino tradicional Eubacteria (439)

barometer/barómetro un instrumento que mide la presión atmosférica (143)

bedrock/lecho de roca la capa de rocas que está debajo del suelo (236)

benthic environment/ambiente bentónico la región que se encuentra cerca del fondo de una laguna, lago u océano (171)

benthos/benthos organismos que viven en el fondo de los océanos o de las masas de agua dulce (170)

biomass/biomasa materia vegetal, estiércol o cualquier otra materia orgánica que se usa como fuente de energía (629)

biome/bioma una región extensa caracterizada por un tipo de clima específico y ciertos tipos de comunidades de plantas y animales (118)

biosphere/biosfera la parte de la Tierra donde existe la vida (487)

biotic/biótico término que describe los factores vivientes del ambiente (486) **FCAT**VOCAB

C

caldera/caldera una depresión grande y circular que se forma cuando se vacía parcialmente la cámara de magma que hay debajo de un volcán, lo cual hace que el suelo se hunda (308)

carbohydrate/carbohidrato una clase de nutrientes que proporcionan energía; incluye los azúcares, los almidones y las fibras; contiene carbono, hidrógeno y oxígeno (387)

carnivore/carnívoro un organismo que se alimenta de animales (491)

cell/célula en biología, la unidad más pequeña que puede realizar todos los procesos vitales; las células están cubiertas por una membrana y tienen ADN y citoplasma (380, 400)

change of state/cambio de estado el cambio de una sustancia de un estado físico a otro (527)

chemical change/cambio químico un cambio que ocurre cuando una o más sustancias se transforman en sustancias totalmente nuevas con propiedades diferentes (536)

chemical energy/energía química la energía que se libera cuando un compuesto químico reacciona para producir nuevos compuestos (626)

chemical property/propiedad química una propiedad de la materia que describe la capacidad de una sustancia de participar en reacciones químicas (530)

chemical weathering/desgaste químico el proceso por medio del cual las rocas se fragmentan como resultado de reacciones químicas (229) **FCAT**VOCAB

classification/clasificación la división de organismos en grupos, o clases, en función de características específicas (432)

climate/clima las condiciones promedio del tiempo en un área durante un largo período de tiempo (112)

cloud/nube un conjunto de pequeñas gotitas de agua o cristales de hielo suspendidos en el aire, que se forma cuando el aire se enfría y ocurre condensación (124)

coal/carbón un combustible fósil que se forma en el subsuelo a partir de materiales vegetales parcialmente descompuestos (618)

comet/cometa un cuerpo pequeño formado por hielo, roca y polvo cósmico que sigue una órbita elíptica alrededor del Sol y que libera gas y polvo, los cuales forman una cola al pasar cerca del Sol (339)

community/comunidad todas las poblaciones de especies que viven en el mismo hábitat e interactúan entre sí (487)

composition/composición la constitución química de una roca; describe los minerales u otros materiales presentes en ella (201)

compression/compresión estrés que se produce cuando distintas fuerzas actúan para estrechar un objeto (276)

condensation/condensación el cambio de estado de gas a líquido (123, 497)

conduction/conducción la transferencia de energía en forma de calor a través de un material (83) **FCAT**VOCAB

consumer/consumidor un organismo que se alimenta de otros organismos o de materia orgánica (385, 490)

continental drift/deriva continental la hipótesis que establece que alguna vez los continentes formaron una sola masa de tierra, se dividieron y se fueron a la deriva hasta terminar en sus ubicaciones actuales (268)

continental rise/elevación continental la sección del margen continental que tiene un ligero declive, ubicada entre el talud continental y la llanura abisal (166)

continental shelf/plataforma continental la sección del margen continental que tiene un ligero declive, ubicada entre la costa y el talud continental (166)

continental slope/talud continental la sección del margen continental que tiene una gran inclinación, ubicada entre la elevación continental y la plataforma continental (166)

convection/convección la transferencia de energía térmica mediante la circulación o el movimiento de un líquido o gas (83) **FCAT**VOCAB

core/núcleo la parte central de la Tierra, debajo del manto (261)

Coriolis effect/efecto de Coriolis la desviación de la trayectoria recta que experimentan los objetos en movimiento debido a la rotación de la Tierra (88)

crater/cráter una depresión con forma de tazón, que se forma sobre la superficie de un objeto cuando un cuerpo en caída impacta sobre ésta o cuando se produce una explosión (308)

crest/cresta el punto más alto de una onda (584)
FCAT VOCAB

crust/corteza la capa externa, delgada y sólida de la Tierra, que se encuentra sobre el manto (260)
FCAT VOCAB

cyclone/ciclón un área de la atmósfera que tiene una presión menor que la de las áreas circundantes y que tiene vientos que giran en espiral hacia el centro (132)

D

data/datos cualquier parte de la información que se adquiere por medio de la observación o experimentación (15)

day/día el tiempo que se requiere para que la Tierra rote una vez sobre su eje (356)

decomposer/descomponedor un organismo que, para obtener energía, desintegra los restos de organismos muertos o los desechos de animales y consume o absorbe los nutrientes (385)

deformation/deformación el proceso de doblar, inclinar y romper la corteza de la Tierra; el cambio en la forma de una roca en respuesta a la tensión (285)

density/densidad la relación entre la masa de una sustancia y su volumen (517)

deposition/deposición el proceso por medio del cual un material se deposita (210) *FCAT VOCAB*

desalination/desalación (o desalinización) un proceso de remoción de sal del agua del océano (179)

dichotomous key/clave dicotómica una ayuda para identificar organismos, que consiste en las respuestas a una serie de preguntas (436)

differential weathering/desgaste diferencial el proceso por medio cual las rocas más blandas y menos resistentes al clima se desgastan a una tasa más rápida que las rocas más duras y resistentes al clima (232)

divergent boundary/límite divergente el límite entre dos placas tectónicas que se están separando una de la otra (273)

E

eclipse/eclipse un suceso en el que la sombra de un cuerpo celeste cubre otro cuerpo celeste (362)

ecology/ecología el estudio de las interacciones de los seres vivos entre sí mismos y entre sí mismos y su ambiente (486)

ecosystem/ecosistema una comunidad de organismos y su ambiente abiótico o no vivo (487)
FCAT VOCAB

elastic rebound/rebote elástico ocurre cuando una roca deformada elásticamente vuelve súbitamente a su forma no deformada (285)

electron/electrón una partícula subatómica que tiene carga negativa (519) *FCAT VOCAB*

element/elemento una sustancia que no se puede separar o descomponer en sustancias más simples por medio de métodos químicos (518)

elevation/elevación la altura de un objeto sobre el nivel del mar (116)

energy/energía la capacidad de realizar un trabajo (578)

energy conversion/transformación de energía un cambio de un tipo de energía a otro (590)

energy pyramid/pirámide de energía un diagrama triangular que muestra la pérdida de energía en un ecosistema, producida a medida que la energía pasa a través de la cadena alimenticia del ecosistema (493)

engineering/ingeniería la aplicación de las ciencias y las matemáticas para resolver problemas de la vida diaria (57)

equinox/equinoccio el momento en que el Sol parece cruzar el ecuador celeste (358)

erosion/erosión el proceso por medio del cual el viento, el agua, el hielo o la gravedad transporta tierra y sedimentos de un lugar a otro (210, 246)
FCAT VOCAB

Eukarya/Eukarya en un sistema taxonómico moderno, un dominio compuesto por todos los eucariotes; este dominio coincide con los reinos tradicionales Protista, Fungi, Plantae y Animalia (440)

eukaryote/eucariote un organismo cuyas células tienen un núcleo contenido en una membrana; entre los eucariotes se encuentran protistas, animales, plantas y hongos, pero no arqueas ni bacterias (401)

evaporation/evaporación el cambio de estado de líquido a gas (497)

F

fault/falla una grieta en un cuerpo rocoso a lo largo de la cual un bloque se desliza respecto a otro (278)

first aid/ primeros auxilios atención médica de emergencia para una persona que se lastimó o está enferma (30)

folding/plegamiento fenómeno que ocurre cuando las capas de roca se doblan debido a la compresión (277)

food chain/cadena alimenticia la vía de transferencia de energía través de varias etapas, que ocurre como resultado de los patrones de alimentación de una serie de organismos (493)

food web/red alimenticia un diagrama que muestra las relaciones de alimentación entre los organismos de un ecosistema (493)

force/fuerza una acción de empuje o atracción que se ejerce sobre un objeto con el fin de cambiar su movimiento; la fuerza tiene magnitud y dirección (556)

fossil fuel/combustible fósil un recurso energético no renovable formado a partir de los restos de organismos que vivieron hace mucho tiempo (616) **FCAT**VOCAB

frequency/frecuencia el número de ondas producidas en una cantidad de tiempo determinada (588) **FCAT**VOCAB

friction/fricción una fuerza que se opone al movimiento entre dos superficies que están en contacto (560, 593)

front/frente el límite entre masas de aire de diferentes densidades y, normalmente, diferentes temperaturas (130)

function/función la actividad especial, normal o adecuada de un órgano o parte (410)

Fungi/Fungi un reino formado por organismos eucarióticos no verdes que no tienen capacidad de movimiento, se reproducen por esporas y obtienen alimento al descomponer sustancias de su entorno y absorber los nutrientes (440)

G

gas/gas un estado de la materia que no tiene volumen ni forma definidos (527)

gasohol/gasohol una mezcla de gasolina y alcohol que se usa como combustible (629)

geothermal energy/energía geotérmica la energía producida por el calor del interior de la Tierra (630)

global warming/calentamiento global un aumento gradual de la temperatura global promedio (85)

globular cluster/cúmulo globular un grupo compacto de estrellas que parece una bola y contiene hasta un millón de estrellas (333)

gravity/gravedad una fuerza de atracción entre dos objetos debido a sus masas (563)

greenhouse effect/efecto invernadero el calentamiento de la superficie y de la parte más baja de la atmósfera, el cual se produce cuando el vapor de agua, el dióxido de carbono y otros gases absorben y vuelven a irradiar la energía térmica (84)

gymnosperm/gimnosperma una planta leñosa vascular que produce semillas que no están contenidas en un ovario o fruto (456)

H

herbivore/herbívoro un organismo que sólo come plantas (491)

heredity/herencia la transmisión de caracteres genéticos de padres a hijos (382)

homeostasis/homeostasis la capacidad de mantener un estado interno constante en un ambiente en cambio (381)

hot spot/mancha caliente un área volcánicamente activa de la superficie de la Tierra que comúnmente se encuentra lejos de un límite entre placas tectónicas (314)

humidity/humedad la cantidad de vapor de agua que hay en el aire (121)

humus/humus material orgánico obscuro que se forma en la tierra a partir de restos de plantas y animales en descomposición (238)

hurricane/huracán tormenta severa que se desarrolla sobre océanos tropicales, con vientos fuertes que soplan a más de 120 km/h y que se mueven en espiral hacia el centro de presión extremadamente baja de la tormenta (137)

hydroelectric energy/energía hidroeléctrica energía eléctrica producida por el flujo del agua (628)

hypothesis/hipótesis una idea o explicación que conlleva a la investigación científica y que se puede probar (14)

I

ion/ion una partícula cargada que se forma cuando un átomo o grupo de átomos gana o pierde uno o más electrones (522)

K

kinetic energy/energía cinética a energía de un objeto debido al movimiento del objeto (579)

L

latitude/latitud a distancia hacia el norte o hacia el sur del ecuador; se expresa en grados (113)

law/ley una ecuación o afirmación descriptiva que predice sucesos de manera confiable en determinadas condiciones (53)

law of conservation of energy/ley de la conservación de la energía la ley que establece que la energía ni se crea ni se destruye, sólo se transforma de una forma a otra (594) **FCAT VOCAB**

leaching/lixiviación la remoción de sustancias que pueden disolverse de rocas, menas o capas de suelo debido al paso del agua (238)

lightning/relámpago una descarga eléctrica que ocurre entre dos superficies que tienen carga opuesta, como por ejemplo, entre una nube y el suelo, entre dos nubes o entres dos partes de la misma nube (135)

light-year/año luz la distancia que viaja la luz en un año; aproximadamente 9.46 trillones de kilómetros (330)

lipid/lípido un tipo de sustancia bioquímica que no se disuelve en agua; las grasas y los esteroides son lípidos (388)

liquid/líquido el estado de la materia que tiene un volumen definido, pero no una forma definida (526)

lithosphere/litosfera la capa externa y sólida de la Tierra que está formada por la corteza y la parte superior y rígida del manto (262)

M

magma chamber/cámara de magma la masa de roca fundida que alimenta un volcán (302)

mantle/manto a capa de roca que se encuentra entre la corteza terrestre y el núcleo (261)

mass/masa una medida de la cantidad de materia que tiene un objeto (23, 514) **FCAT VOCAB**

matter/materia cualquier cosa que tiene masa y ocupa un lugar en el espacio (514)

mechanical energy/energía mecánica la cantidad de trabajo que un objeto realiza debido a las energías cinética y potencial del objeto (580)

mechanical weathering/desgaste mecánico el proceso por medio del cual las rocas se rompen en pedazos más pequeños mediante medios físicos (226)

mesosphere/mesosfera la capa de la atmósfera que se encuentra entre la estratosfera y la termosfera, en la cual la temperatura disminuye al aumentar la altitud (79); *también,* la parte fuerte e inferior del manto que se encuentra entre la astenosfera y el núcleo externo (263)

metabolism/metabolismo la suma de todos los procesos químicos que ocurren en un organismo (382)

meteor/meteoro un rayo de luz brillante que se produce cuando un meteoroide se quema en la atmósfera de la Tierra (340)

meteorite/meteorito un meteoroide que llega a la superficie de la Tierra sin quemarse por completo (340)

meteoroid/meteoroide un cuerpo rocoso relativamente pequeño que viaja en el espacio (340)

meter/metro la unidad fundamental de longitud en el sistema internacional de unidades (símbolo: m) (23)

mid-ocean ridge/dorsal oceánica una larga cadena submarina de montañas que se forma en el suelo de los principales océanos (167)

mineral/mineral un sólido natural e inorgánico que tiene una estructura química definida (200)

model/modelo un diseño, plan, representación o descripción cuyo objetivo es mostrar la estructura o funcionamiento de un objeto, sistema o concepto (50)

motion/movimiento el cambio en la posición de un objeto respecto a un punto de referencia (550)

N

natural gas/gas natural una mezcla de hidrocarburos gaseosos que se encuentran debajo de la superficie de la Tierra, normalmente cerca de los depósitos de petróleo, y los cuales se usan como combustible (617)

natural resource/recurso natural cualquier material natural que es utilizado por los seres humanos, como agua, petróleo, minerales, bosques y animales (612)

neap tide/marea muerta una marea que tiene un rango mínimo, la cual ocurre durante el primer y el tercer cuartos de la Luna (366) **FCAT VOCAB**

nebula/nebulosa una nube grande de gas y polvo en el espacio interestelar; una región en el espacio donde las estrellas nacen (331)

nekton/necton todos los organismos que nadan activamente en las aguas abiertas, de manera independiente de las corrientes (170)

net force/fuerza neta la combinación de todas las fuerzas que actúan sobre un objeto (557)

neutron/neutrón una partícula subatómica que no tiene carga y que está ubicada en el núcleo de un átomo (519) **FCAT**VOCAB

newton/newton a unidad de fuerza del sistema internacional de unidades (símbolo: N) (556)

nonpoint-source pollution/contaminación no puntual contaminación que proviene de muchas fuentes, en lugar de provenir de un solo sitio específico (182)

nonrenewable resource/recurso no renovable un recurso que se forma a una tasa que es mucho más lenta que la tasa a la que se consume (496, 613)

nonvascular plant/planta no vascular una planta que carece de tejidos transportadores y de raíces, tallos y hojas verdaderos (456)

nuclear energy/energía nuclear la energía liberada por una reacción de fisión o fusión; la energía de enlace del núcleo atómico (625)

nucleic acid/ácido nucleico una molécula formada por subunidades llamadas *nucleótidos* (389)

nucleus/núcleo en ciencias físicas, la región central de un átomo, la cual está constituida por protones y neutrones (520) **FCAT**VOCAB

O

observation/observación el proceso de obtener información por medio de los sentidos (13)

ocean basin/cuenca oceánica el área de la Tierra que está cubierta por océanos (167) **FCAT**VOCAB

omnivore/omnívoro un organismo que come tanto plantas como animales (491)

open cluster/conglomerado abierto un grupo de estrellas que se encuentran juntas respecto a las estrellas que las rodean (333)

orbit/órbita la trayectoria que sigue un cuerpo al desplazarse alrededor de otro cuerpo en el espacio (352)

organ/órgano un conjunto de tejidos que desempeñan una función especializada en el cuerpo (415)

organism/organismo un ser vivo; cualquier cosa que pueda llevar a cabo procesos vitales independientemente (400)

organ system/aparato (o sistema) de órganos un grupo de órganos que trabajan en conjunto para desempeñar funciones corporales (416)

P

parent rock/roca precursora una formación rocosa que es la fuente a partir de la cual se origina el suelo (236)

pelagic environment/ambiente pelágico en el océano, la zona ubicada cerca de la superficie o en profundidades medias, más allá de la zona sublitoral y por encima de la zona abisal (174)

petroleum/petróleo una mezcla líquida de compuestos hidrocarburos complejos; se usa ampliamente como una fuente de combustible (617)

phase/fase el cambio en el área iluminada de un cuerpo celeste según se ve desde otro cuerpo celeste (361)

phospholipid/fosfolípido un lípido que contiene fósforo y que es un componente estructural de la membrana celular (388)

physical change/cambio físico un cambio de materia de una forma a otra sin que ocurra un cambio en sus propiedades químicas (536)

physical property/propiedad física una característica de una sustancia que no implica un cambio químico, tal como la densidad, el color o la dureza (530)

plankton/plancton la masa de organismos en su mayoría microscópicos que flotan o se encuentran a la deriva en ambientes de agua dulce o marina (170)

Plantae/Plantae un reino formado por organismos pluricelulares complejos que normalmente son verdes, tienen una pared celular de celulosa, no tienen capacidad de movimiento y utilizan la energía del Sol para producir azúcar mediante la fotosíntesis (441)

plate tectonics/tectónica de placas la teoría que explica cómo se mueven y cambian de forma las placas tectónicas, que son grandes porciones de la capa más externa de la Tierra (272) **FCAT**VOCAB

platform/plataforma área de un continente compuesta por capas planas de rocas sedimentarias (213)

point-source pollution/contaminación puntual contaminación que proviene de un lugar específico (183)

polar easterlies/vientos polares del este vientos preponderantes que soplan de este a oeste entre los 60° y los 90° de latitud en ambos hemisferios (88)

population/población un grupo de organismos de la misma especie que viven en un área geográfica específica (487)

potential energy/energía potencial la energía que tiene un objeto debido a su posición, forma o condición (579) *FCAT VOCAB*

precipitation/precipitación cualquier forma de agua que cae de las nubes a la superficie de la Tierra (126, 497)

prevailing winds/vientos prevalecientes vientos que soplan principalmente de una dirección durante un período de tiempo determinado (115)

producer/productor un organismo que puede elaborar sus propios alimentos utilizando la energía de su entorno (385, 490)

prokaryote/procariote un organismo unicelular que no tiene núcleo ni organelos cubiertos por una membrana, por ejemplo, las arqueas y las bacterias (401)

protein/proteína una molécula formada por aminoácidos que es necesaria para construir y reparar estructuras corporales y para regular procesos del cuerpo (386)

Protista/Protista un reino compuesto principalmente por organismo eucarióticos unicelulares que son diferentes de las plantas, animales, bacterias y hongos (440)

proton/protón una partícula subatómica que tiene una carga positiva y que está ubicada en el núcleo de un átomo; el número de protones que hay en el núcleo es el número atómico, y éste determina la identidad del elemento (519) *FCAT VOCAB*

P wave/onda P una onda sísmica que hace que las partículas de roca se muevan en una dirección de atrás hacia delante (288)

R

radiation/radiación la transferencia de energía en forma de ondas electromagnéticas (82, 598) *FCAT VOCAB*

recycling/reciclar el proceso de recuperar materiales valiosos o útiles de los desechos o de la basura (615)

relative humidity/humedad relativa la proporción de la cantidad de vapor de agua que hay en el aire respecto a la cantidad de vapor de agua necesaria para alcanzar la saturación a una temperatura dada (121)

renewable resource/recurso renovable un recurso natural que puede reemplazarse a la misma tasa a la que se consume (496, 613)

revolution/revolución el movimiento de un cuerpo que viaja alrededor de otro cuerpo en el espacio; un viaje completo a lo largo de una órbita (352)

rift valley/valle de rift un valle largo y estrecho que se forma cuando se separan las placas tectónicas (167)

rift zone/zona de rift un área de grietas profundas que se forma entre dos placas tectónicas que se están alejando una de la otra (312)

rock/roca una mezcla sólida de uno o más minerales o de materia orgánica que se produce de forma natural (200)

rock cycle/ciclo de las rocas la serie de procesos por medio de los cuales una roca se forma, cambia de un tipo a otro, se destruye y se forma nuevamente por procesos geológicos (206)

rotation/rotación el giro de un cuerpo alrededor de su eje (352)

S

salinity/salinidad una medida de la cantidad de sales disueltas en una cantidad determinada de líquido (158)

salinization/salinización la acumulación de sales en el suelo (247)

science/ciencia el conocimiento que se obtiene por medio de la observación natural de acontecimientos y condiciones con el fin de descubrir hechos y formular leyes o principios que puedan ser verificados o probados (6)

scientific literacy/cultura científica la comprensión de los métodos de la investigación científica, el alcance del conocimiento científico y el papel de las ciencias en la sociedad (47)

scientific methods/métodos científicos una serie de pasos que se siguen para solucionar problemas (12)

sea-floor spreading/expansión del suelo marino el proceso por medio del cual se forma nueva litosfera oceánica (suelo marino) a medida que el magma se eleva a la superficie de la Tierra y se solidifica en una dorsal oceánica (270)

seamount/montaña submarina una montaña sumergida que se encuentra en el fondo del océano, la cual tiene por lo menos 1,000 m de altura y cuyo origen es volcánico (167)

seismic wave/onda sísmica una onda de energía que viaja a través de la Tierra y se aleja de un terremoto en todas direcciones (288)

seismology/sismología el estudio de los terremotos (284)

sexual reproduction/reproducción sexual reproducción en la que se unen las células sexuales de los dos progenitores para producir descendencia que comparte caracteres de ambos progenitores (382) **FCAT**VOCAB

skepticism/escepticismo mentalidad que lleva a una persona a cuestionar la validez de ideas aceptadas (43)

smog/esmog bruma fotoquímica que se forma cuando la luz solar actúa sobre contaminantes industriales y combustibles (622)

soil/suelo una mezcla suelta de fragmentos de roca, material orgánico, agua y aire en la que puede crecer vegetación (236)

soil conservation/conservación del suelo un método para mantener la fertilidad del suelo protegiéndolo de la erosión y la pérdida de nutrientes (244)

soil structure/estructura del suelo la organización de las partículas del suelo (237)

soil texture/textura del suelo la cualidad del suelo que se basa en las proporciones de sus partículas (237)

solar energy/energía solar la energía que la Tierra recibe del Sol en forma de radiación (626)

solid/sólido el estado de la materia en el cual el volumen y la forma de una sustancia están fijos (525)

solstice/solsticio el punto en el que el Sol está tan lejos del ecuador como es posible, ya sea hacia el norte o hacia el sur (359)

spectroscope/espectroscopio un instrumento que separa la luz blanca en una banda de colores (328) **FCAT**VOCAB

speed/rapidez la distancia que un objeto se desplaza dividida entre el intervalo de tiempo durante el cual ocurrió el movimiento (551) **FCAT**VOCAB

spring tide/marea viva una marea de mayor rango que ocurre dos veces al mes, durante la luna nueva y la luna llena (366) **FCAT**VOCAB

states of matter/estados de la materia las formas físicas de la materia, que son sólida, líquida y gaseosa (524)

stimulus/estímulo cualquier cosa que causa una reacción o cambio en un organismo o cualquier parte de un organismo (381)

stratosphere/estratosfera la capa de la atmósfera que se encuentra encima de la troposfera y en la que la temperatura aumenta al aumentar la altitud (79)

structure/estructura el orden y distribución de las partes de un organismo (410)

subsidence/hundimiento del terreno el hundimiento de regiones de la corteza terrestre a elevaciones más bajas (282)

surface current/corriente superficial un movimiento horizontal del agua del océano que es producido por el viento y que ocurre en la superficie del océano o cerca de ella (117)

S wave/onda S una onda sísmica que hace que las partículas de roca se muevan en una dirección de lado a lado (288)

T

technology/tecnología la aplicación de la ciencia con fines prácticos; el uso de herramientas, máquinas, materiales y procesos para satisfacer las necesidades de los seres humanos (56)

tectonic plate/placa tectónica un bloque de litosfera formado por la corteza y la parte rígida y más externa del manto (264)

temperature/temperatura una medida de qué tan caliente (o frío) está algo; específicamente, una medida de la energía cinética promedio de las partículas de un objeto (24)

tension/tensión estrés que se produce cuando distintas fuerzas actúan para estirar un objeto (276)

texture/textura la cualidad de una roca que se basa en el tamaño, la forma y la posición de los granos que la forman (201)

theory/teoría un sistema de ideas que explica muchas observaciones relacionadas y que está respaldado por una gran cantidad de pruebas obtenidas mediante la investigación científica (53)

thermal energy/energía térmica la energía cinética de los átomos de una sustancia (580) **FCAT**VOCAB

thermometer/termómetro un instrumento que mide e indica la temperatura (143)**thermosphere/termosfera** la capa más alta de la atmósfera, en la cual la temperatura aumenta a medida que la altitud aumenta (80)

thunder/trueno el sonido producido por la expansión rápida del aire a lo largo de una descarga eléctrica (135)

thunderstorm/tormenta eléctrica una tormenta fuerte y normalmente breve que consiste en lluvia, vientos fuertes, relámpagos y truenos (134)

tidal range/rango de marea la diferencia en los niveles del agua del océano entre la marea alta y la marea baja (366)

tide/marea el ascenso y descenso periódico del nivel del agua en los océanos y otras masas grandes de agua (364)

tissue/tejido un grupo de células similares que llevan a cabo una función común (415)

tornado/tornado una columna destructiva de aire en rotación cuyos vientos se mueven a velocidades muy altas y que puede verse como una nube con forma de embudo (136)

trade winds/vientos alisios vientos prevalecientes que soplan de este a oeste desde los 30° de latitud hacia el ecuador en ambos hemisferios (88)

transform boundary/límite de transformación el límite entre placas tectónicas que se están deslizando horizontalmente una sobre otra (273)

tropism/tropismo el crecimiento de un organismo o de una parte de él en respuesta a un estímulo externo, como por ejemplo, la luz (457) *FCAT VOCAB*

troposphere/troposfera la capa inferior de la atmósfera, en la que la temperatura disminuye a una tasa constante a medida que la altitud aumenta (79)

trough/seno el punto más bajo de una onda (584) *FCAT VOCAB*

U

uplift/levantamiento la elevación de regiones de la corteza terrestre a elevaciones más altas (282)

V

vascular plant/planta vascular una planta que tiene tejidos especializados que transportan materiales de una parte de la planta a otra (456)

velocity/velocidad la rapidez de un objeto en una dirección dada (552) *FCAT VOCAB*

vent/chimenea una abertura en la superficie de la Tierra a través de la cual pasa material volcánico (302)

volcano/volcán una chimenea o fisura en la superficie de la Tierra a través de la cual se expulsan magma y gases (300)

volume/volumen una medida del tamaño de un cuerpo o región en un espacio de tres dimensiones (24, 514)

W

wave/onda una perturbación periódica en un sólido, líquido o gas que se transmite a través de un medio en forma de energía (582)

wavelength/longitud de onda la distancia entre cualquier punto de una onda y un punto idéntico en la onda siguiente (587) *FCAT VOCAB*

weather/tiempo el estado de la atmósfera a corto plazo que incluye la temperatura, la humedad, la precipitación, el viento y la visibilidad (112)

weathering/meteorización el proceso natural por medio del cual los agentes atmosféricos o ambientales, como el viento, la lluvia y los cambios de temperatura, desintegran y descomponen las rocas (210, 226)

weight/peso una medida de la fuerza gravitacional ejercida sobre un objeto; su valor puede cambiar en función de la ubicación del objeto en el universo (515)

westerlies/vientos del oeste vientos preponderantes que soplan de oeste a este entre 30° y 60° de latitud en ambos hemisferios (88)

wind/viento el movimiento de aire producido por diferencias en la presión barométrica (86)

wind power/potencia eólica el uso de un molino de viento para hacer funcionar un generador eléctrico (627)

Index

Index

Index

Index

Index

Index

Index

Index

Index

Index

X

Y

Z

Acknowledgments *continued from page ii*

Florida Teacher Consultants *continued*

Barbara Rapoza
President, Florida Association of Science Teachers
New River Middle School
Fort Lauderdale, Florida

Cary B. Rosillo
Science Teacher
Independence Middle School
Jupiter, Florida

Patricia Soto
Science Department Chair
George Washington Carver Middle School
Coral Gables, Florida

ZoEllen Warren
Science Teacher
Oak View Middle School
Archer, Florida

Angie Williams
Science Teacher
Riversprings Middle School
Crawfordville, Florida

Inclusion and Special Needs Consultants

Karen Clay
Inclusion Consultant
Boston, Massachusetts

Ellen McPeek Glisan
Special Needs Consultant
San Antonio, Texas

Safety Reviewer

Jack Gerlovich, Ph.D.
Associate Professor
School of Education
Drake University
Des Moines, Iowa

Academic Reviewers

Glenn Adelson, Ph.D.
Instructor
Department of Organismic and Evolutionary Biology
Harvard University
Cambridge, Massachusetts

David M. Armstrong, Ph.D.
Professor
Ecology and Evolutionary Biology
University of Colorado
Boulder, Colorado

Carl Beaver, Ph.D.
Research Scientist
Florida Fish and Wildlife Commission
St. Petersburg, Florida

Paulette Bond
Professional Geologist
Florida Geological Survey
Tallahassee, Florida

Kenneth H. Brink, Ph.D.
Senior Scientist and Physical Oceanography Director
Coastal Ocean Institute and Rinehart Coastal Research Center
Woods Hole Oceanographic Institution
Woods Hole, Massachusetts

John Brockhaus, Ph.D.
Director of Geospatial Science Information Program
Department of Geography and Environmental Engineering
United States Military Academy
West Point, New York

Howard L. Brooks, Ph.D.
Professor of Physics & Astronomy
DePauw University
Greencastle, Indiana

Dan Bruton, Ph.D.
Associate Professor
Department of Physics and Astronomy
Stephen F. Austin State University
Nacogdoches, Texas

Wesley N. Colley, Ph.D.
Lecturer
Department of Astronomy
University of Virginia
Charlottesville, Virginia

Joe W. Crim, Ph.D.
Professor and Head of Cellular Biology
Department of Cellular Biology
University of Georgia
Athens, Georgia

Scott Darveau, Ph.D.
Assistant Professor of Chemistry
Chemistry Department
University of Nebraska at Kearney,
Kearney, Nebraska

Cassandra Eagle, Ph.D.
Professor of Inorganic Chemistry
Chemistry Department
Appalachian State University
Boone, North Carolina

Simonetta Frittelli, Ph.D.
Associate Professor
Department of Physics
Duquesne University
Pittsburgh, Pennsylvania

Linda K. Gaul, Ph.D., MPH
Epidemiologist
Texas Department of State Health Services
Austin, Texas

P. Shiv Halasyamani, Ph.D.
Associate Professor of Chemistry
Department of Chemistry
University of Houston
Houston, Texas

Deborah Hanley, Ph.D.
Meteorologist
State of Florida Department of Agriculture and Consumer Services
Division of Forestry
Tallahassee, Florida

David Hershey, Ph.D.
Education Consultant
Hyattsville, Maryland

Richard N. Hey, Ph.D.
Professor of Geophysics
Department of Geophysics and Planetology
University of Hawaii
Honolulu, Hawaii

Ken Hon, Ph.D.
Associate Professor of Volcanology
Geology Department
University of Hawaii at Hilo
Hilo, Hawaii

Susan Hough, Ph.D.
U.S. Geological Survey
Pasadena, California

William H. Ingham, Ph.D.
Professor of Physics
James Madison University
Harrisonburg, Virginia

Steven A. Jennings, Ph.D.
Associate Professor
Department of Geography & Environmental Studies
University of Colorado
Colorado Springs, Colorado

Ping H. Johnson, M.D., Ph.D., CHES
Assistant Professor of Health Education
Department of Health, Physical Education and Sport Science
Kennesaw State University
Kennesaw, Georgia

Daniela Kohen, Ph.D.
Assistant Professor of Chemistry
Chemistry Department
Carleton College
Northfield, Minnesota

David Lamp, Ph.D.
Associate Professor of Physics
Physics Department
Texas Tech University
Lubbock, Texas

Joel S. Leventhal, Ph.D.
Emeritus Scientist, Geochemistry
U.S. Geological Survey
Denver, Colorado

Academic Reviewers

continued

Mark Mattson, Ph.D.
Director, College of Science and Mathematics Learning Center
James Madison University
Harrisonburg, Virginia

Nancy L. McQueen, Ph.D.
Professor of Microbiology
Department of Biological Sciences
California State University, Los Angeles
Los Angeles, California

Madeline Micceri Mignone, Ph.D.
Assistant Professor
Natural Science
Dominican College
Orangeburg, New York

Richard F. Niedziela, Ph.D.
Assistant Professor of Chemistry
Department of Chemistry
DePaul University
Chicago, Illinois

John Oliver, Ph.D.
Associate Chair, Department of Astronomy
University of Florida
Gainesville, Florida

Michael H. Renfroe, Ph.D.
Professor of Biology
Department of Biology
James Madison University
Harrisonburg, Virginia

Kenneth H. Rubin, Ph.D.
Associate Professor
Department of Geology and Geophysics
University of Hawaii
Honolulu, Hawaii

Dork Sahagian, Ph.D.
Research Professor
Department of Earth Sciences
Institute for the Study of Earth, Oceans, and Space
University of New Hampshire
Durham, New Hampshire

Walter Schmidt, Ph.D.
State Geologist
Chief of Florida Geological Survey
Tallahassee, Florida

Daniel Z. Sui, Ph.D.
Professor
Department of Geography
Texas A&M University
College Station, Texas

Vatche P. Tchakerian, Ph.D.
Professor
Department of Geology and Geography
Texas A&M University
College Station, Texas

Richard P. Vari, Ph.D.
Research Scientist and Curator
Department of Vertebrate Zoology
National Museum of Natural History
Washington, D.C.

Kim Withers, Ph.D.
Research Scientist
Center for Coastal Studies
Texas A&M University at Corpus Christi
Corpus Christi, Texas

Teacher Reviewers

Laura Buchanan
Science Teacher and Department Chair
Corkran Middle School
Glen Burnie, Maryland

Sarah Carver
Science Teacher
Jackson Creek Middle School
Bloomington, Indiana

Robin K. Clanton
Science Department Head
Berrien Middle School
Nashville, Georgia

Randy Dye, M.S.
Science Department Head
Wood Middle School
Fort Leonard Wood, Missouri

Meredith Hanson
Science Teacher
Westside Middle School
Rocky Face, Georgia

Denise Hulette
Science Teacher
Conway Middle School
Orlando, Florida

James Kerr
Oklahoma Teacher of the Year 2002-2003
Union Public Schools
Tulsa, Oklahoma

Janet Keskinen
Science Teacher
Green Cove Springs Junior High School
Green Cove Springs, Florida

M. R. Penny Kisiah
Science Teacher and Department Chair
Fairview Middle School
Tallahassee, Florida

Laura Kitselman
Science Teacher and Coordinator
Loudoun Country Day School
Leesburg, Virginia

Debra S. Kogelman, MAed.
Science Teacher
University of Chicago Laboratory Schools
Chicago, Illinois

Deborah L. Kronsteiner
Science Teacher
Spring Grove Area Middle School
Spring Grove, Pennsylvania

Jennifer L. Lamkie
Science Teacher
Thomas Jefferson Middle School
Edison, New Jersey

Rebecca Larsen
Science Teacher
Fernandina Beach Middle School
Fernandina Beach, Florida

Sally M. Lesley
ESL Science Teacher
Burnet Middle School
Austin, Texas

Bill Martin
Science Teacher
Southeast Middle School
Kernersville, North Carolina

Magdalena F. Molledo
Science Department Chair
DeLaura Middle School
Satellite Beach, Florida

Nancy Poage-Nixon
Science Teacher
Covington Middle School
Austin, Texas

Susan H. Robinson
Science Teacher
Oglethorpe County Middle School
Lexington, Georgia

Cary B. Rosillo
Science Teacher
Independence Middle School
Jupiter, Florida

Elizabeth J. Rustad
Science Department Chair
Coronado Elementary
Gilbert, Arizona

Helen P. Schiller
Instructional Coach
The School District of Greenville County
Greenville, South Carolina

Marci L. Stadiem
Science Department Head
Cascade Middle School
Seattle, Washington

Martha B. Trisler
Science Teacher
Rising Starr Middle School
Fayetteville, Georgia

Angie Williams
Science Teacher
Riversprings Middle School
Crawfordville, Florida

Roberta Young
Science Teacher
Gunn Junior High School
Arlington, Texas

Lab Testing

Daniel L. Bugenhagen
*Science Teacher and
    Department Chair*
Yutan Junior & Senior High
    School
Yutan, Nebraska

Gladys Cherniak
Science Teacher
St. Paul's Episcopal School
Mobile, Alabama

Georgiann Delgadillo
Science Teacher
Continuous Curriculum
    School
Spokane, Washington

Rebecca Ferguson
Science Teacher
North Ridge Middle School
North Richland Hills, Texas

Susan Gorman
Science Teacher
North Ridge Middle School
North Richland Hills, Texas

C. John Graves
Science Teacher
Monforton Middle School
Bozeman, Montana

Tracy Jahn
Science Teacher
Berkshire Junior-Senior
    High School
Canaan, New York

Kerry A. Johnson
Science Teacher
Isbell Middle School
Santa Paula, California

M. R. Penny Kisiah
*Science Teacher and
    Department Chair*
Fairview Middle School
Tallahassee, Florida

Jane M. Lemons
Science Teacher
Western Rockingham
    Middle School
Madison, North Carolina

Maurine O. Marchani
*Science Teacher and
    Department Chair*
Raymond Park Middle
    School
Indianapolis, Indiana

Edith McAlanis
*Science Teacher and
    Department Chair*
Socorro Middle School
El Paso, Texas

Kathy Mckee
Science Teacher
Hoyt Middle School
Des Moines, Iowa

Alyson Mike
Science Teacher
East Valley Middle School
East Helena, Montana

Jan Nelson
Science Teacher
East Valley Middle School
East Helena, Montana

Terry J. Rakes
Science Teacher
Elmwood Junior High
    School
Rogers, Arkansas

Helen P. Schiller
Instructional Coach
The School District of
    Greenville County
Greenville, South Carolina

David M. Sparks
Science Teacher
Redwater Junior High
    School
Redwater, Texas

Larry Tackett
*Science Teacher and
    Department Chair*
Andrew Jackson Middle
    School
Cross Lanes, West Virginia

Elsie Waynes
Science Teacher
Terrell Junior High School
Washington, D.C.

Walter Woolbaugh
Science Teacher
Manhattan Junior High
    School
Manhattan, Montana

Gordon Zibelman
Science Teacher
Drexel Hill Middle School
Drexel Hill, Pennsylvania

Contributing Writers

Karin Akre
William J. Barlow
Bill Burnside
David Gilbert
Eric Kincaid
Eileen Nehme
Catherine Podeszwa
Marjorie Rouché
Daniel Sharp
Larry Ward
Molly Frohlich
    Wetterschneider

Answer Checking

Marie Amato
Bronx, New York

Alyson Mike
East Helena, Montana

Staff Credits

Editorial

Leigh Ann García,
  Executive Editor
Kelly Rizk, *Senior Editor*
David Westerberg,
  Senior Editor
Laura Zapanta, *Senior Editor*

Editorial Development Team

Monica Brown
Jen Driscoll
Michael Mazza
Kristen McCardel
Laura Prescott
Bill Rader
Jim Ratcliffe
Betsy Roll
Roshan Strong
Tam Voynick
David Wisnieski

Copyeditors

Dawn Marie Spinozza,
  Copyediting Manager
Simon Key
Jane A. Kirschman
Kira J. Watkins

Editorial Support Staff

Debbie Starr,
  Managing Editor
Soojinn Choi

Online Products

Bob Tucek, *Executive Editor*
Wesley M. Bain

Design

Book Design

Kay Selke
Peter Reid
Sally Bess
Sonya Mendeke
Mercedes Newman
Holly Whittaker
Lisa Woods

Media Design

Richard Metzger
Chris Smith

Ancillary Design

Jeff Robinson

Image Acquisitions

Curtis Riker
Jeannie Taylor
Angela Boehm
Andy Christiansen
Michelle Dike

Cover Design

Kay Selke

Graphic Services

Cathy Murphy
Nanda Patel

Publishing Services

Technology Services

Juan Baquera
Sarah Buller
Laura Likon
Margaret Sanchez
Patty Zepeda

eMedia

Melanie Baccus
Lydia Doty
Cathy Kuhles
Marsh Flournoy
Tara F. Ross
Ed Blake
Kimberly Cammerata
Michael Rinella

Production

Eddie Dawson,
  Senior Production Manager
Sherry Sprague,
  Project Manager
Dustin Ognowski,
  Production Assistant

Credits

Abbreviations used: (t) top, (c) center, (b) bottom, (l) left, (r) right, (bkgd) background

PHOTOGRAPHY